Slurry Walls as
Structural Systems

Slurry Walls as Structural Systems

Petros P. Xanthakos
Consulting Engineer
Great Falls, Virginia

Second Edition

McGraw-Hill, Inc.

New York   San Francisco   Washington, D.C.   Auckland   Bogotá
Caracas   Lisbon   London   Madrid   Mexico City   Milan
Montreal   New Delhi   San Juan   Singapore
Sydney   Tokyo   Toronto

Library of Congress Cataloging-in-Publication Data

Xanthakos, Petros P.
  Slurry walls as structural systems / Petros P. Xanthakos.
    p.   cm.

  Includes index.
  ISBN 0-07-072216-1 (alk. paper)
  1. Slurry trench construction. 2. Diaphragm walls—Design and
construction. 3. Concrete walls—Design and construction.
I. Title.
TA775.X38   1994
624.1'5—dc20   93-31724
                                                          CIP

The first edition of this book was published in 1979 under the title
Slurry Walls.

1 2 3 4 5 6 7 8 9 0 DOC/DOC 9 9 8 7 6 5 4 3

ISBN 0-07-072216-1

*The sponsoring editor for this book was Larry S. Hager, the editing
supervisor was Paul R. Sobel, and the production supervisor was
Suzanne W. Babeuf. It was set in Century Schoolbook by Techna Type,
Inc.*

Printed and bound by R. R. Donnelley & Sons Company.

This book is printed on acid-free paper.

To Eleni

Contents

Preface   xiii

Chapter 1. Wall Systems   1

   1-1   General Method of Construction   1
   1-2   Conventional Diaphragm Walls   4
   1-3   Anchored Walls   8
   1-4   Posttensioned Diaphragm Walls   10
   1-5   Prefabricated Diaphragm Walls   19
   1-6   Bored Pile Walls   28
   1-7   Composite Walls   35
   1-8   Examples of Structure Combinations   39
   1-9   Circular and Polygonal Enclosures   43
   1-10 Buttressed Walls, Cells, and Arched (Quays) Structures   47
   1-11 Rigid Cutoff Walls   55
   1-12 Soil-Cement Structural Walls   56
         References   61

Chapter 2. Construction Fundamentals   63

   2-1   Site Conditions and Effect on Construction Methods   63
   2-2   General Construction Requirements   69
   2-3   Guide Walls   72
   2-4   Construction Accuracy and Tolerance   74
   2-5   Watertightness of Diaphragm Walls   78
   2-6   Problems Related to Underground Structures and Utilities   81
   2-7   Problems Caused by Boulders and Obstructions   84
   2-8   Introduction to Excavating Systems   85
   2-9   Excavation with Clamshells   88
   2-10 Special Systems   91
   2-11 Excavation with Rotary Drilling Equipment   94
   2-12 Tools and Equipment for Hard Ground and Boulders   109
         References   117

Chapter 3. Geotechnical Considerations   119

3-1   Introduction   119
3-2   Geotechnical Parameters Relevant to Structural Performance   121
3-3   Stability of Unsupported Trenches   123
3-4   Stability of Slurry-Filled Trenches in Clay   126
3-5   Special Considerations for Excavations in Clay   133
3-6   Stability of Slurry-Filled Trenches in Sand   136
3-7   Special Considerations for Excavations in Sand   140
3-8   Further Topics on Trench Stability   147
3-9   Effect of Gel Strength of Slurry on Stability   154
3-10 Stability under Dynamic Loading   155
3-11 The Cylindrical Surface Method   160
3-12 Trenches with Horizontal Curvature, Case Study   162
3-13 Performance Monitoring   165
3-14 Soil-Slurry Interaction   175
      References   192

Chapter 4. Analysis and Design Considerations   195

4-1   Ground Response in Supported Excavations   195
4-2   Heave in Narrow Excavations Supported by Diaphragm Walls   201
4-3   Wall Bracing Systems   209
4-4   Prediction and Control of Movement   217
4-5   Special Problems in Excavations   250
4-6   General Stability of the Ground-Anchor-Wall System   254
4-7   Lateral Earth Stresses   263
4-8   Further Topics on Earth Pressures   279
4-9   Measured Lateral Earth Stresses on Diaphragm Walls   291
4-10 Refined Methods of Analysis   303
4-11 Other Loads   320
4-12 Design Methodologies   324
4-13 Safety, Loads, and Performance Factors   329
4-14 Design Examples   340
4-15 Further Topics for Analysis in Soil with Cohesion   348
      References   353

Chapter 5. Load-Bearing Panels and Foundation Elements   361

5-1   The Use of Slurries in Drilled Shafts   361
5-2   The Use of Slurries in Prismatic and Linear Elements   363
5-3   Construction Problems and Repairs   366
5-4   Basic Concepts of Load Transfer   368
5-5   Design Considerations   373
5-6   Load Tests and Experimental Data   376
5-7   General Guidelines for the Selection of Load-Bearing Elements   384
5-8   Design for Axial Loading, Limit State   387
5-9   Design Procedure, Working Stress Method   398

5-10   Settlement Considerations   399
5-11   Design Example 1   400
5-12   Examples from Applications   402
5-13   Negative Skin Friction and Uplift   406
5-14   Design Example 2   409
5-15   Design Example 3   412
5-16   Design for Lateral Loading   415
5-17   Load-Bearing Capacity of Prefabricated Panels   418
5-18   Case Studies from U.S. Practice   419
5-19   Design Example 4   425
       References   429

Chapter 6. Concrete Technology and Design   433

6-1   Factors Influencing Mix Design   433
6-2   Proportioning Concrete Mixes   434
6-3   Strength Considerations of Reinforced Concrete for Diaphragm Walls 438
6-4   Concrete Placement   441
6-5   Flow Motion of Tremied Concrete   444
6-6   Attainable Concrete Strength   450
6-7   Bond Strength and Bond Stress   459
6-8   Flexural Analysis and Compression Failure   468
6-9   Assembly and Details of Reinforcement   472
6-10   Common Vertical Construction Joints   478
6-11   Special Construction Joints   483
6-12   Efficiency of Construction Joints   490
6-13   Structural Capacity of Joints and Connections   495
6-14   Design Examples   512
6-15   Watertight Joints   517
       References   520

Chapter 7. Design Principles of Wall-Structure Systems   523

7-1   Two-Way Wall Systems   523
7-2   Posttensioned Diaphragm Walls   538
7-3   Prefabricated Diaphragm Walls   561
7-4   Composite Walls   570
7-5   Bored Pile Groups and Walls   578
7-6   Single Walls, Built-Up Walls, and Composite Sections   592
7-7   Walls Used as Underpinning   614
7-8   Structural Combinations   619
       References   627

Chapter 8. Underground Transportation Systems   629

8-1   General Construction Requirements   629
8-2   Basic Procedures for Subway Tunnels   632
8-3   Subway Stations   643

8-4   Examples of Subway Construction   648
8-5   Underground Roadways and Traffic Underpasses   660
8-6   Design Concepts, Subway Sections   667
8-7   Parametric Studies, Subway Stations   673
8-8   Design Considerations   682
8-9   Design Fundamentals   688
8-10 Design Example 1, Stage Construction   696
8-11 Design Example 2, Subway Station   699
8-12 Design Example 3, Traffic Underpass   704
8-13 Design Example 4, Soil-Cement Walls   711
      References   714

Chapter 9. Buildings and Deep Basements   715

9-1   Assessment of Deep Basements   715
9-2   Superstructure-Substructure Interaction   717
9-3   Comparative Evaluation of Ground Support Methods   720
9-4   Plan Area, Shape, and Completion Time   722
9-5   Protection in Water-Bearing Ground   724
9-6   Bracing   727
9-7   Diaphragm Walls with Compensated Foundations   729
9-8   Requirements during Construction   732
9-9   Soil-Structure Interaction   735
9-10 Loads and Load Groups   751
9-11 Design Example 1, Economic Analysis of Deep Basement   756
9-12 Design Example 2, Resistance to Earthquake and Wind   756
9-13 The Downward Construction Methods in Buildings   759
      References   762

Chapter 10. Other Uses and Applications   765

10-1   Utility Tunnels   765
10-2   Underground Parking   770
10-3   Industrial and Service Installations   774
10-4   Design Considerations, Deep Shafts   778
10-5   Design Considerations, Circular Enclosures   784
10-6   Selection Criteria of Waterfront Installations   791
10-7   Loads for Waterfront Structures   793
10-8   Design Considerations of Buttressed (T) Walls   797
10-9   Design Considerations of Arch (Quay) Walls   800
10-10 Design Considerations of Diaphragm Wall Cells   803
10-11 Walls Built to Protect Dykes, Reservoirs, River Banks, and Dams   808
10-12 Special Uses   813
10-13 Design Example 1, Quay Wall along River   816
10-14 Design Example 2, Circular Enclosure   820
10-15 Design Example 3, T-Quay Wall   822
       References   826

Chapter 11. Economic and Legal Considerations   827

    11-1   Factors Affecting Cost   827
    11-2   Legal Considerations   831

Appendix A. Technology, Preparation, and Control of Slurries   835

Appendix B. Specifications   843

    Index   847

Preface

The 1979 edition of *Slurry Walls* dealt with the process inherent in this method of construction, and presented the associated technology and related applications. The present edition maintains the same basic approach necessary for a clear understanding of the slurry wall system, but it makes also a definite departure from the subject with emphasis on the structural aspects of slurry walls. The terms *diaphragm walls* and *slurry walls* are likewise used interchangeably and are intended to mean the same thing, i.e., an underground reinforced concrete structural wall inserted by the slurry trench process.

During the past ten to fifteen years the state of the art has undergone a dramatic but decisive evolution in terms of analysis and design methodologies, evidenced also by an expansion of uses and applications and articulated by the extension of the deterministic approach to include limit states and strength design.

To bring matters to a focus and consistent with recent trends, the stage has been ready to combine the previously separate treatment of the structural and geotechnical capacity, in order to make it possible to explain and quantify ultimate capacity and strength in terms of the same parameters, criteria, and loading conditions.

The introduction of load factor (strength) design is thus a key feature of the text. Whereas it draws from completed research as well as from judgment, it also signifies new provisions and major areas of change. It addresses load and force models, load factors, nominal resistance and resistance factors, limit states, and the soil-structure system on a global basis. The underlying philosophy moves the design toward a more rational and probability-based procedure, although it does not exclude the application of the working stress method independently or as a supplement to the limit state approach. Within this framework the structural behavior of slurry walls can be understood under service conditions as well as at failure.

The text is developed to achieve the following major objectives: (*a*) present a systems study of walls and related elements; (*b*) develop explicit design criteria and methods of analysis; (c) articulate uses and applications in terms of specific classes of structure; and (d) give design examples to show how to obtain credible solutions.

Chapter 1 reviews wall types from the conventional diaphragm wall to the more complex configurations. The text emphasizes the explicit interdependence of the wall system, its design and details, and the field execution. This interdependence is far greater than routinely assumed in most types of construction. Promising wall systems are anchored, posttensioned, and composite walls as well as structural combinations thereof.

The construction fundamentals are reviewed in Chap. 2. An important point is that slurry walls are not excluded from difficult sites. On the contrary, they can be used in congested areas, and at sites with environmental restrictions or with difficult geotechnical conditions. A relevant conclusion is that slurry walls may be used in conjunction with ground control techniques. This convergence between ground support and ground controls is an essential phase of the design, and very often this combination provides a viable option in engineering an underground construction.

Chapter 3 deals with the geotechnical issues with reference to three distinct phases: trench excavation under slurry protection, general excavation with the wall acting as ground support, and during service when the wall interacts with other components of the structure. Among the topics discussed in this chapter are the geotechnical parameters necessary to predict the performance of a wall during service, and monitoring techniques.

Chapter 4 is one of the longest chapters, and covers analysis and design considerations. The prediction and control of movement still has a prominent place in the text because of the obvious effects on surroundings, especially in urban excavations. Movement of diaphragm walls is considered analytically and is documented from observed field performance under a variety of bracing conditions and excavation procedures. The formulation of the problem of predicting lateral earth pressures is equally important, especially with an explicit definition of appropriate boundary conditions. Analytical predictions of lateral earth pressures are supplemented with data from measured earth stresses. This chapter introduces the two design philosophies, namely allowable stress design and load factor design.

The use of diaphragm walls and related configurations as load bearing elements is discussed in Chap. 5. The basic concepts of load transfer are explained in terms of a division of load between shaft resistance and base bearing. In the usual range of working loads, the load transfer begins with the skin friction or side adhesion and is completed with base bearing. The latter is influenced by the depth and size of the element, the soil characteristics, and the disturbance of the base. Among the advantages associated with this foundation type are potential cost savings and the ability to install these elements where soil conditions inhibit the installation of other foundation systems. Among the disadvantages is the inability of a single shaft or prismatic element to provide the redundancy associated with a multiple path system. Analytical formulations are developed for load transfer estimates of shaft resistance and base bearing, and are supplemented with empirical procedures.

Chapter 6 deals with the considerations relevant to reinforced concrete produced in slurry trenches. The method of concrete placement, the attainable concrete strength, and the development of bond strength are examined explicitly and applicable criteria are established. The flexural analysis and compression failure of slurry walls are presented in the context of ultimate strength. In this context, provisions for ductility should be logically considered because of the extra concrete strength usually available with the generous wall thickness. Ductility is thus an important advantage of diaphragm walls subjected to flexure. The details and the structural capacity of joints and connections are examined in terms of applicable codes.

The design principles of wall systems are reviewed in Chap. 7. Among these are two-way walls, also referred to as flat plates, post-tensioned walls, prefabricated elements, composite units, bored pile groups, configurations with composite sections, walls used as underpinning, and structural combinations thereof.

Diaphragm walls for underground transportation systems are discussed in Chap. 8. The resulting structures are subway tunnels built in cut-and-cover, multiple level subway stations, and ground supports for traffic underpasses. This chapter presents studies of subway sections in which the section geometry is a design parameter, and articulates the influence of key factors on the selection of structural systems and the method of design. The feasibility of integral structures is examined in conjunction with traffic underpasses and the associated soil-structure interaction.

Chapter 9 deals with diaphragm walls used in deep building basements. The assessment of deep basements must take into account economic factors and the relationship of cost to the expected use. A comparative evaluation of ground support methods should cover soldier piles, sheet piles, bored piles, and diaphragm walls, used singly or in conjunction with ground controls. The soil-structure interaction (including compensated foundations) is particularly critical because the walls become part of the permanent structure and must resist, besides lateral earth stresses, considerable vertical loads. In addition, the dynamic interaction of a basement structure and the soil must be considered for blasts, wind effects, and seismic events. The text articulates the contribution of diaphragm walls in resisting these effects.

Chapter 10 reviews the design principles of diaphragm walls used in a variety of applications. These topics include utility tunnels, underground parking, deep shafts, circular enclosures, waterfront installations, reservoirs, dams, and special uses. The associated topics cover the overall stability, the geotechnical capacity, and the structural capacity.

Economic and legal considerations are briefly discussed in Chap. 11. The main factors affecting cost are the site conditions, the use of specialized equipment, the need to use experienced personnel, and the expansion of the service functions of the walls. Among the typical problems associated with the legal implementation of a slurry wall contract is the design responsibility. The slurry wall serves the two distinct functions, first as temporary ground support and then as an integral part of the permanent structure. Both the initial designer and the field contractor may contribute to the design or modification thereof. Hence, any question of legal responsibility for the design of the wall for the temporary and permanent functions must be explicitly addressed in the contract documents.

Many detailed examples appear in the text. Because this is a book on the basic philosophy, behavior, theory, and design of a structural system, these examples have been developed both as a teaching tool and as design aids to practicing engineers.

Petros P. Xanthakos

Slurry Walls as
Structural Systems

1

Wall Systems

1-1 General Method of Construction

The continuous diaphragm wall (also referred to as slurry wall) is a structure formed and cast in a slurry trench. It can be looked upon as a combined development from two related systems: the mud-filled borehole and the continuous bored pile wall. The complexity of the operation was to a great extent simplified with the use of conventional grabs for direct linear excavation while the slurry was used only for face support.

The construction sequence of a diaphragm wall using modern methods and equipment is shown in Fig. 1-1, and involves the following steps:

1. Excavate a linear trench as shown in Fig. 1-1a using one or more equipment passes. As the trench is excavated, a suitable bentonite slurry (hence the term slurry walls) is inserted into the panel to provide trench stability.

2. On completion of the excavation, insert a round tube as shown in Fig. 1-1b to form the panel joint with the adjacent wall unit.

3. Insert a reinforcement cage (fabricated and assembled on the ground) as shown in Fig. 1-1c.

4. Pour fresh concrete into the panel using tremie pipes as shown in Fig. 1-1d. As the concrete rises, it displaces the slurry by its own gravity with the intent to fill the trench completely. The slurry is pumped into a storage area for reconditioning and reuse, and the round tube steel pipe is gradually withdrawn, producing a concrete element of a cross section as shown in Fig. 1-1d.

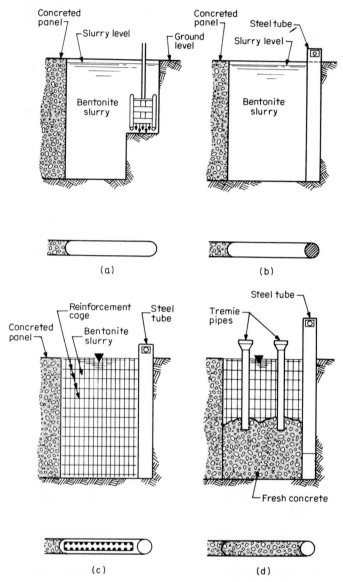

Figure 1-1 Typical construction sequence of a diaphragm wall, executed in four stages: (*a*) Excavation. (*b*) Insertion of steel tubing. (*c*) Placement of reinforcement cage. (*d*) Concrete placement.

Basic requirements. It follows from this simple presentation that a slurry wall is a structural system that can be used for ground support, as retaining wall, and as load-bearing element. Since the inception of the technique and the construction of the first continuous diaphragm wall in the 1950s, specialist engineers have emphasized the importance of the practical aspects of wall systems and their applicability or limitations before a detailed design is attempted. This is necessary if pitfalls and consequential substandard work are to be avoided.

The associated requirements bring engineers to an explicit interdependence of a wall system, its detail design, and field execution that is far greater than routinely assumed in most types of construction. This is particularly true since the work is generally carried under bentonite slurry and the face of the trench is the formwork for the fresh concrete, yet the wall must be functional and ready for structural use immediately after exposure.

Although this practice covers now a long period of development, the early practical problems associated with the interdependence of design and construction have not changed. The technique still requires previous experience and skills, and the state of the art remains a specialty among designers and contractors. The construction fundamentals, excavating techniques, slurry quality controls, methods of concrete placement, structural connections, waterproofing requirements, bracing systems, and other details must be addressed and dealt with in the planning and design stage. Among the problems commonly raised and questions that must be answered are the following:

1. The short- and long-term stability of a bentonite-filled trench, in both a static and dynamic state. This may involve the type and characteristics of the soil, the practical maximum panel length, arching effects, slurry density, impact from mechanical operations, the insertion of heavy steel cages, and vibratory effects from nearby activities.

2. The complete displacement of the bentonite slurry by the rising fresh concrete mix. This may involve the flow motion of tremie concrete, intermixing with bentonite, and pockets of soft material trapped in the volume.

3. The bond between reinforcing bars and concrete placed under slurry. This may relate to certain types of reinforcing bars, bar arrangement within a cage, density of slurry, and effect of mix design and concreting procedure.

4. The end bearing (base) and side resistance that can be developed at the concrete-soil interface of a partially or fully embedded wall or foundation panel cast under bentonite slurry. This may depend on the type of the soil and its characteristics, the properties of the bentonite slurry, the bottom-cleaning procedures, plan geometry of the element, the concreting operation, and the roughness of the interface.

5. The expected performance of the finished wall and its interaction with the overall structural system. This may relate to panel size and geometry, panel joints and structural connections, the level of watertightness actually achieved, possible weakening effects of boxouts and recesses, concrete cover and crack control, protrusion, deviations and imperfections beyond the specified tolerance, and procedures for checking and testing for adequacy.

These seeming areas of uncertainty can be answered qualitatively and quantitatively in the design stage by following proper criteria and quality controls, and by specifying the construction procedures. These topics are addressed in the following chapters in the context of design.

1-2   Conventional Diaphragm Walls

A conventional diaphragm wall is the structural system shown in Fig. 1-1. The factors dictating panel size and dimensions first depend on site conditions. A specified panel length sometimes cannot be provided in the field because of restrictions on availability of construction space and time.

Panel length.   In general, it is advantageous to have a wall constructed in longer units. This reduces the number of vertical construction joints, allows better control of wall alignment, and may result in less water seepage. Despite these obvious advantages, the panel length is also governed by the following factors.

Face stability and slurry loss.   Relatively short panels enhance overall trench stability through the arching effect. They are also preferred where there is danger of slurry loss through open cavities and very permeable formations. Short panels usually have a length of 1.2 to 2.4 m (4 to 8 ft) and are excavated with one equipment pass.

Concreting.   The concrete pour should be completed before any significant stiffening or setting of the fresh mix occurs, and in practice the pouring process should not exceed 4 h. For average panel lengths 3.5 to 4.5 m (11.5 to 15 ft) and for one tremie pipe the speed of rising concrete may be inferred by reference to Fig. 1-2, where the speed is plotted vs. the depth. Evidently lower speeds should be expected near the end of the pour. Extrapolating a mean average speed, a panel 21 m (70 ft) deep can be concreted in about 3 to 3½ h and will probably require 110 to 130 yd³ of concrete (84 to 100 m³). Longer panels may thus need more than one tremie pipe.

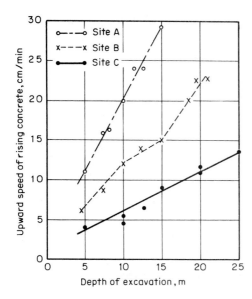

Figure 1-2 Relationship between depth of excavation and speed of rising concrete level; panel length from 3.5 to 4.5 m (11.5 to 15 ft), and one 8-in-diameter tremie pipe.

Reinforcing cage. This must be assembled and handled at the site, and if space is not available its size must be restricted. Its weight should not exceed the lifting and handling capability of the available equipment.

Location of bracing and anchorage. Panel lengths, and subsequently joint locations, should be coordinated with the design of bracing. If this includes the use of anchors and tiebacks, the panel length must be optimized in conjunction with anchor spacing and capacity.

Excavating equipment. A panel cannot be shorter than one equipment pass. For panels requiring more than one pass, the design must consider the compatibility discussed in other sections. Grabs work more efficiently if the load is symmetrically applied to the jaws, especially in dense ground, and this efficiency is further improved if the grab is assured of full bite.

Incidental factors. These include site and traffic conditions as they may affect the delivery and supply of fresh concrete, space for the preparation of slurries, storage facilities and materials handling, and water supply and plant facilities.

A tentative panel length is first selected to accommodate trench stability and concreting requirements, and then is compared with the range of excavating systems and checked for other considerations that may govern. It follows, therefore, that the design should not finalize the panel length unless the construction phase and sequence has been established.

Panel depth. For most jobs the panel depth is within the excavating range of clamshells and rotary drills. The wall depth is therefore determined by the design, and accommodates the project characteristics. A wall may be founded on rock or other firm material to transfer vertical load, it may be extended into an impervious layer to protect the excavation from water seepage, or it may be sufficiently embedded below excavation level for lateral stability and control of movement.

The elevation at the top of the wall is determined in conjunction with the details of the subgrade and superstructure, the location and level of adjacent footings, and the proximity of the new construction to existing or future utilities.

Panel width. This must be within the range of available equipment. For clamshells the usual range is from 45 cm to 1.5 m (18 in to 5 ft), and for rotary drilling from 40 cm to 1.2 m (16 in to 4 ft). A practical minimum width is 45 cm (18 in) to allow the passage of tremie pipes within the steel cage. Specialist contractors maintain heavy grabs for special projects. Excavating a wide panel by double digging is possible but is not recommended. A frequent wall thickness is 60 cm (24 in).

Interestingly, a thinner wall produces materials savings but is not necessarily the most economical design, especially if it is heavily reinforced. Furthermore, practical experience indicates that a narrow trench may retard the flow of fresh concrete. For a panel width less than 60 cm (24 in) the recommendation is to place the tremie pipes closer. Regarding the unavoidable tolerance in the width of the finished wall, the panel thickness should also be considered in relation to the tolerance factors during excavation, particularly in very deep walls (see also other sections).

Method of detailing. For wall panels with round joints the reinforcement should be detailed in relation to the stop ends. Some panels have no end tubes, most have one, and some have two. This variation can complicate the detailing of the reinforcement. Sliwinski and Fleming (1974) recommend the method of detailing shown in Fig. 1-3. For simplicity the stop end or ends are considered to lie outside the panel length as shown. If the cover to the main steel is 9 cm ($3\frac{1}{2}$ in) measured from the theoretical concrete face to the center of the bar, and if the tolerance in the verticality of stop ends is $L/80$, the relationship between wall thickness, panel length, reinforcing cage length, and equivalent panel length is as shown.

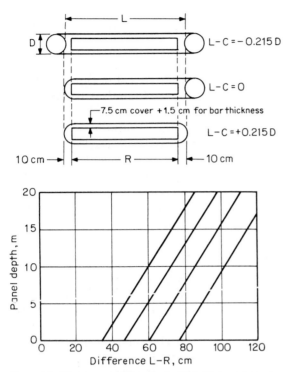

Figure 1-3 Recommended method of detailing and relationship between panel dimensions. Verticality tolerance for stop ends—1/80. L = panel length for detailing; R = standard cage length for detailing; C = mean concrete length; D = panel width. (*From Sliwinski and Fleming, 1974.*)

Effective wall thickness. Some codes and specifications recommend a certain reduction in the effective wall thickness to compensate for construction imperfections and to reflect a probable decrease in concrete strength near the face on account of intermixing with bentonite. For a load-bearing wall this reduction, usually 1 in, or 2.5 cm, may be applied to both faces, but for a wall subjected to bending it should be applied to the compressive side only. Alternatively, the design may reflect the usual overbreak and the resulting wall overwidth; hence a reduction in the wall thickness is not necessary.

Panel sequence and arrangement. For construction along streets traffic may dictate the panel sequence. For building construction the usual practice is to choose the first panel near the entrance and then work sequentially along the perimeter to complete the wall.

The panel sequence should allow free and unrestricted flow of traffic, accommodate a fixed location of the mud plant units, and allow

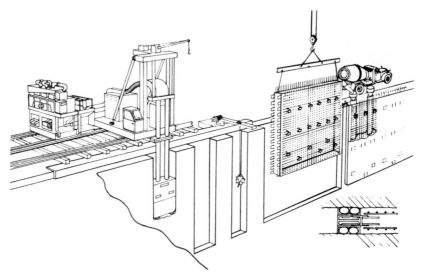

Figure 1-4 Typical panel installation and construction sequence.

the work to proceed simultaneously on three successive panels, as shown in Fig. 1-4. For example, as one panel is excavated, a second panel is prepared and a third is concreted. Alternatively, the sequence should not result in interference with panels already cast.

An example of panel sequence is shown in Fig. 1-5. In this case, the wall required several panel lengths and configurations as shown. Corner panels were detailed so that each side corresponds to one equipment pass. This arrangement allows the panel to be concreted with one pipe placed at the corner.

1-3 Anchored Walls

Anchored walls have become popular in braced excavations because of (1) the substantial progress in the anchoring techniques and the availability of dependable high-capacity anchors, and (2) the advantages of free excavation and the absence of interior obstructions that permit uninterrupted earth moving and thus improve the construction conditions of the underground portion of a building.

Vertical excavation walls are common in urban sites or other locations where demand for space is at a premium. In addition, the excavation is likely to involve underpinning and control of ground movement. The stiffness and rigidity of diaphragm walls enhance the range of solutions. Interestingly, anchor capacity necessary to secure the stability of the wall is nominal as long as there is no unusual lateral

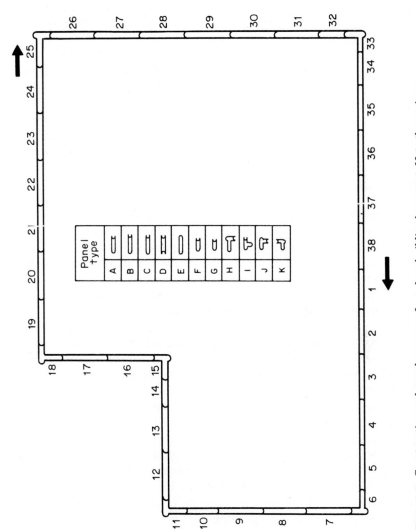

Figure 1-5 Construction and panel sequence for a deep building basement. Note the various panel configurations and types.

9

stress action against the support. Depending on anchor spacing and distance between rows, a typical anchor capacity range is between 200 and 1000 kN (45 and 225 kips).

In many instances anchors for deep basement excavations are temporary, and remain until the permanent framing is in place. In this case, the anchors must be of the extractable or restressable type. A typical problem is the vertical load component induced by the anchor force, and for 45° inclination this component is essentially the horizontal thrust. However, loads as high as 150 tons/m have been transferred to dense fine sand from diaphragm walls 80 cm thick. Walls 75 cm (30 in) thick have been used as load-bearing elements to carry a load of 25 kips/ft giving a bearing pressure 10 kips/ft^2, and at working loads this transfer occurs as side resistance (see also Chap. 5). In this context, anchors can safely be designed to induce vertical loads to diaphragm walls, and these can be adapted to carry loads from the superstructure after the anchors are distressed.

Construction requirements. Wall movement begins almost as soon as the excavation commences, implying that the uppermost anchor level should be determined accordingly. The sequence of excavation stages and bracing levels should likewise be decided from similar considerations. If the underground structure includes sections and members that are to be used to brace the walls and replace the anchors, the final interaction should be determined before construction. In most cases the permanent bracing is provided from the bottom up. If the introduction of load and transition from anchors to permanent members is not coordinated, it may interfere with the upper anchorages and cause uneven redistribution of loads (Xanthakos, 1991).

Anchors cannot be installed if major obstructions exist such as utility lines and incidental underground structures. In some instances there may be specific statutory requirements to be met, or the adjoining owner may have the right of support and refuse an easement. This problem becomes more serious in relatively deep cuts where the anchors must be installed under several properties. If the installation is permanent, it should be carried out under the implied guarantee that future activities will not impair, damage, or otherwise interfere with the system. An anchored diaphragm wall is shown in Fig. 1-6.

1-4 Posttensioned Diaphragm Walls

Background

The general principles of prestressing can be applied to diaphragm walls mainly to extend their effective (unbraced) structural depth. In

Figure 1-6 Diaphragm walls for the Sixty State Street Tower, Boston. (*Franki.*)

this common concept, internal stresses of a certain magnitude and distribution are introduced in the concrete that will partially or wholly counteract and balance the tensile stresses expected to occur in service from external loadings. This application visualizes prestressed walls as essentially concrete walls but with the process transforming the brittle concrete into an elastic member by the precompression applied to it. The concrete diaphragm wall is treated as a member that is weak in tension and strong in compression. From this principle the criterion of no tensile stresses becomes relevant, and the concept is expanded further to suggest that if there are no tensile stresses in the concrete there can be no cracks, and the concrete wall is no longer a brittle element but becomes an elastic support. Treating the wall in this manner articulates the interaction of the two systems of forces, the internal prestress and external load, with the former counteracting the latter. Similarly, if cracking of the wall due to load (external or prestress) is prevented or delayed, the stresses, strains, and deflections of the two systems of forces can be considered separately and superimposed if necessary.

A common procedure is to posttension high-strength steel wire strands, properly located in the panel, after the concrete has cured. An associated advantage in this case is the increase in the stiffness of the section and the subsequent decrease in the elastic deflection, with a corresponding extension of the unbraced excavation depth. For instance, a wall 75 to 90 cm thick (30 to 36 in) is likely to have a maximum unsupported cantilever height of about 7.5 m (25 ft), but with posttensioning this can be increased by more than 50 percent. This improvement becomes even more significant if a single bracing can be provided at the top so that the wall is laterally supported at its two ends. Braun (1972) designed a posttensioned diaphragm wall 80 cm (32 in) thick that supports an excavation 16 m (53 ft) deep without bracing other than a single row of anchors installed near the top and the wall embedment below excavation level.

The advantages of unbraced walls through posttensioning become obvious with certain classes of building construction where lateral support by intermediate floors cannot be provided in the service stage. Examples are certain underground garages requiring a continuous ventilation gap between the retaining walls and parking levels, and as access for pumping water and foam directly from ground level. In this case, the diaphragm walls are self-contained and must be self-supported; otherwise the construction is not feasible.

First tests.   The first fully instrumented test panel was probably constructed in 1969 to study the response of a diaphragm wall cast in the ground and subjected to posttensioning while still embedded in the soil (Fuchsberger, 1980). The underlying concept was that because of the embedment, bending or deformation of the concrete member resulting from the eccentricity of the applied prestress would be restrained by the stiffness of the surrounding soil.

The tests involved a wall panel 5 m long, 15 m deep, and 60 cm thick, subjected to a prestressing force up to 300 t with a maximum eccentricity of 20 cm, as shown in Fig. 1-7. The panel was monitored for a period of 4 months, with measurements taken periodically, and the results verified the original concept. No discernible deformations of the wall were observed, and no tensile stresses were measured in the five cross sections shown in Fig. 1-7 even when the cables were overstressed.

Construction and installation

Prestressed-concrete applications normally are under the provision of high-strength concrete that has low creep, shrinkage, and thermal response. In practice these requirements are under the influence of the construction technique. Because the wall is restrained by its confinement, the prestressing is applied under favorable conditions. The usually moist environment enhances the curing conditions and results in higher strength. Other favorable factors are the current availability of dependable steel strands, posttensioning equipment, and progress in the state of the art.

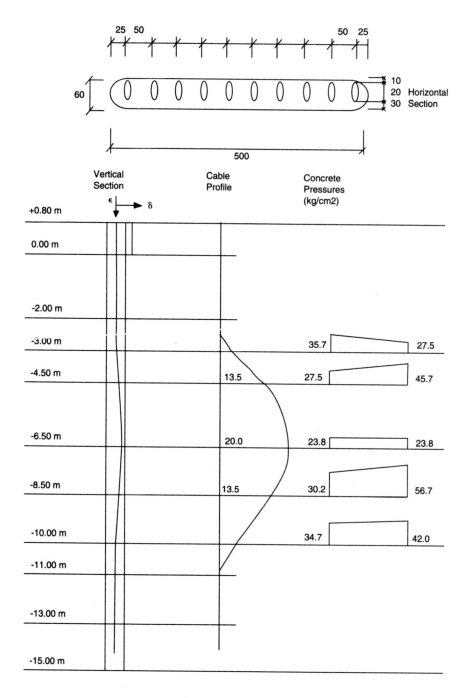

Figure 1-7 First posttensioned diaphragm wall test panel. (*From Fuchsberger, 1980.*)

13

Conversely, high-strength concrete (commonly used for prestressing) and high-slump concrete (typically required for slurry wall construction) have opposite requirements, the only common characteristic being the small size of the aggregate fraction. In spite of this conflict, concrete for posttensioned diaphragm walls can be provided in a strength range of 275 to 310 kg/cm^2 (4000 to 4500 lb/in^2) without reducing the slump.

Locating and stressing the tendons.   A typical arrangement of prestressing strands for a posttensioned panel is shown in Fig. 1-8. The assembly exemplifies the difficult handling of the cage by providing diagonal stiffeners to prevent its distortion. These attachments and tackling aids are reusable and devised according to the panel size to ensure that neither the prestressing strands nor the stressing heads will be displaced during handling and lowering of the cage.

The tendon loops are cased in metal ducts, and bottom anchorages are avoided by placing the cables in a U shape. The upper ends are tensioned and anchored using a suitable device. The method of looping the cables generates a tendency for stress concentration in the bottom zone of the anchorage, but in practice no loss of tension due to yielding of concrete has occurred. The cables are usually tensioned in one stage, and excessive deflection of the wall is prevented by its confinement in the soil.

For nominal panels two sets of metal ducts are sufficient, as shown in Fig. 1-8a. The ends together with the stressing heads are projected into a top capping beam and must be accurately located along the centerline of the wall. Similar accuracy must ensure the eccentricity of the ducts elsewhere in the panel, and spot welding the supporting rods maintains the exact fixing positions within the cage. The eccentricity can reach a maximum of 30 to 40 cm (12 to 16 in) within the panel where maximum moment is expected to occur during service.

When the wall is completed, a separate capping beam is constructed in conventional formwork using normal-slump concrete. When the concrete strength has reached at least 80 percent of its 28-day strength, the stressing is applied simultaneously by means of two jacks, one at each end of the loop as shown in Fig. 1-9. Where doubt exists about the stiffness and response of the soil, the stressing force should be applied sequentially. Stressing continues progressively by working along the anchorage of each capping beam. The operation is completed by injecting grout into one arm of the duct system until it emerges from the end of the opposite arm.

The advantage of the apparent rigidity of the panel in the ground can be used by allowing temporary overstress in the concrete. Gradually, self-adjustment will take place following a normal prestress loss

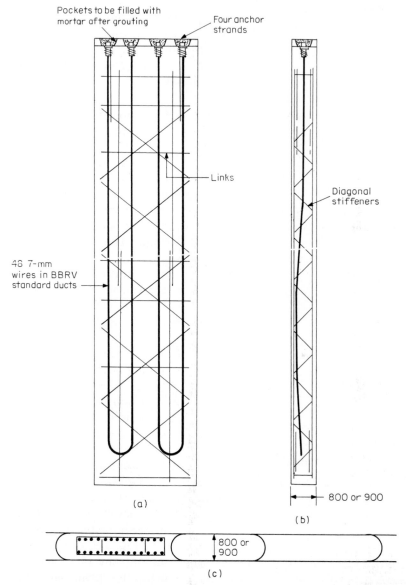

Pockets to be filled with
mortar after grouting

Four anchor
strands

Links

48 7-mm
wires in BBRV
standard ducts

(a)

Diagonal
stiffeners

800 or 900

(b)

800 or
900

(c)

Figure 1-8 Arrangement of strands in posttensioned diaphragm walls: (*a*) Elevation. (*b*) Vertical section. (*c*) Horizontal section. Plan of the German Embassy in London; dimensions in millimeters.

Figure 1-9 Posttensioning of diaphragm walls; construction of the German Embassy in London. (*ICOS, Great Britain.*)

and during the introduction of moment upon excavation. A promising development is the use of concentric tendons in conjunction with multianchored or multibraced diaphragm walls.

Example of posttensioned diaphragm wall

More than 70 percent of the retaining walls for the Irlams O' Th' Height underpass in Manchester (England) have been constructed as posttensioned diaphragm walls. This project is approximately 3600 ft long and carries a depressed roadway, as part of an extensive urban improvement scheme. These walls have been designed and built as free cantilevers, except at three crossings where they also serve as abutments and are therefore restrained at the top. The principal factor influencing this design was the site location within a built-up urban area, and the requirement to maintain traffic during construction.

The original design provided for conventional diaphragm walls as free cantilevers retaining an excavation 10 to 30 ft high. The cantilever concept implied considerable wall embedment below excavation level and required a heavily reinforced wall. As an alternative, over two-thirds of the depressed roadway was redesigned and constructed as posttensioned diaphragm walls 62 cm (24 in), 82 cm (33 in), and 100 cm (40 in) thick, with a minimum penetration depth of 21 m (68 ft) and a cantilever height of up to 29 ft.

The panels are 5.5 m (18 ft) long with semicircular ends and a nominal gap of 15 cm (6 in) between adjacent sections to accommodate drainage behind the wall by means of a PVC pipe. A typical wall panel and drainage detail are shown in Fig. 1-10.

The prestressing scheme consists of four U-shaped sheathed tendons for each panel. Each tendon was stressed to a level of 104 to 500 t based on the design requirements of cantilever height and wall penetration. The concrete for the diaphragm walls has a strength of 31.5 N/mm^2 (4500 lb/in^2) and a 7-in minimum slump. The concrete for the capping beam is a specially designed mix with strength of 52.5 N/mm^2 (7600 lb/in^2).

The abutments for the three bridges consist of a line of T-shaped panels, posttensioned in the stem by two pairs of U-shaped tendons. The tendons have a stressing load up to 200 t. The depth of these panels varies from 16.5 m (54 ft) to 22.10 m (72.5 ft) according to the soil conditions and the design load. After posttensioning a capping beam was placed on top of the panels to support the superstructure, consisting of precast prestressed I beams and a concrete deck, shown in Fig. 1-11. This construction was completed and the bridge was open to traffic before bulk excavation of the ground below was commenced.

Results of a test section indicated that the calculated and measured elastic modulus of the concrete compared as expected, and that the entire prestressing force was transferred to the panel, with the surrounding soil having no apparent influence on this transfer. Small tensile stresses were measured in the bottom anchoring zone, and only compressive stresses occurred elsewhere with a distinct trapezoidal distribution.

The monitoring and associated measurements after stress transfer but before excavation provided a good indication of stress losses due to creep. This factor was important in scheduling the bulk excavation, since not more than 50 percent of the total creep would be allowed to occur prior to bulk excavation in order to utilize the stressing steel effectively.

A main advantage of this design is that the main structures of the underpass (retaining walls and bridges) were completed prior to bulk excavation. The conversion from conventional diaphragm walls to posttensioned diaphragm walls resulted in a net reduction in the weight of the steel reinforcement from 2715 to 1090 t.

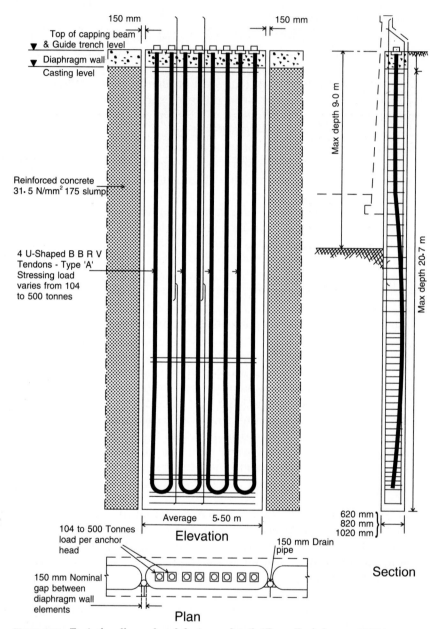

Figure 1-10 Typical wall panel and drainage detail. (*From Fuchsberger, 1980.*)

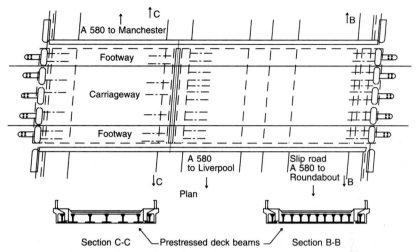

Figure 1-11 Plan and sections at bridge locations. (*From Fuchsberger, 1980.*)

1-5   Prefabricated Diaphragm Walls

Prefabricated-concrete panels inserted in slurry trenches to form structural retaining systems were introduced in the early 1970s. The process can be visualized as the combined result of two foundation types, the prefabricated interlocking pile and the sheet pile wall. Likewise, the trench is excavated under slurry, but the in situ tremie placement of concrete is replaced by the insertion of precast panels. Guide walls (discussed in other sections) are required and must be detailed considering the size and weight of the precast panels, since they must hold and support these sections until the wall becomes self-supported.

Grout systems

Invariably the process requires a more detailed interaction between the initial slurry and the wall in its final configuration. A grout system or slurry in the final position must ensure an effective sealing bond between panels, and this is best obtained by the use of special cement-bentonite mixes designed to delay premature stiffening.

Single grout.   This consists of water, bentonite, cement, and some additives included to control the process of conversion from a slurry to a final material. Initially the slurry is introduced for trench support, but since it must also be used as final grout it should not have excessive soil retention from the excavation. The slurry must therefore be checked and recycled if necessary to remove the soil fraction.

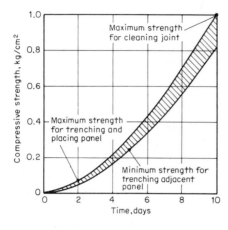

Figure 1-12 Increase in grout strength with time for installing prefabricated panels. (Some contractors have successfully cleaned the joints when the grout attained twice the maximum strength shown.)

The twofold junction implies conversion from a colloidal suspension into a self-hardening material. Such a slurry usually is referred to as "coulis." Figure 1-12 shows the development of strength of a typical coulis as a function of time after mixing. Evidently, the setting process must be controlled within a relatively narrow range (shaded area). The slurry must remain flowable until the precast panel is inserted and positioned, but it must rapidly gain strength thereafter and become stiff so that the next panel can be excavated. With time the grout is consolidated and blends with the panels at the construction joints.

It appears from this brief review that a successful installation depends on controls over the process so that the grout can progressively stiffen around the precast panels and finally set to a hardened material. Its strength is influenced primarily by the cement content and usually is in the range of 7 to 15 kg/cm^2 (100 to 200 lb/in^2). Its density, however, is only 25 to 30 percent higher than the density of water.

Displacement grout.   Introduced by Bachy in France, this requires two stages. Initially, bentonite slurry is used for trench stability and face support, and is replaced by a suitable bonding grout just before the precast sections are placed. The bonding grout has, therefore, properties and strength that depend mainly on its interaction with the finished wall.

The two-grout application has the following advantages: (1) it eliminates strict adherence to schedule and allows better timing; (2) it allows a suitable strength range; (3) it eliminates problems related to slurry contamination with materials from the excavation; and (4) it allows initial excavation under more stable conditions. The final substitution, however, is accomplished in a displacement process, and this requires special skills and previous experience.

Usually the grout is prepared from the initial bentonite slurry merely by adding cement and probably more bentonite. The final strength of the cement-bentonite grout should be determined taking into account the possibility of some soil inclusion from the trench. Low-strength grouts of this type are known to be anomalous systems with erratic variations in their properties, so that laboratory test results should be interpreted in conjunction with previous experience with this type of work.

Des Francs (1974) emphasizes the water-cement ratio as the most important factor. Next, it is necessary to recycle and recondition the slurry if the sand content is more than 8 percent, the specific gravity exceeds 1.10, and the cone viscosity is greater than 40 s. These adjustments are not necessary for strength control but are recommended because too dense or viscous slurries may not be displaced by the grout.

A trial grout sample is first prepared at the batching plant and checked for strength-time behavior under the effect of constituent materials. When a sufficient quantity is available in the field, the grout is pumped into the trench using a special spreader that is lowered near the bottom to initiate a displacement from the bottom up. When the substitution is complete, routine tests are necessary on the grout density. After the precast sections are in place, control tests are mandatory to monitor the development of grout strength.

Example of displacement grout. The displacement grout shown in Table 1-1 was sampled from a trial batch prepared using the following materials per cubic meter of grout: water, 870 kg; cement, 310 kg; and bentonite, 62 kg. The 90-day compressive strength of the laboratory sample was 2 MPa (about 285 lb/in^2), and this was considered adequate. The recycled slurry had a specific gravity of 1.08, sand content 2 percent, and a viscosity of 36 s before displacement. The grout at the site was prepared from another batch of recycled slurry (specific

TABLE 1-1   Properties of Grout Used with Prefabricated Wall Panels

		Location		
			With panels in place	
Property	Mixing plant	When pumped into trench	At surface	4 m from surface
Specific gravity	1.29	1.29 at bottom 1.27 at 2 m from bottom 1.25 at 4 m from bottom	1.25	1.25
Funnel viscosity, s	20			
Strength, lb/in^2:				
7-day	45	38 (at bottom)	31	34
28-day	305	272 (at bottom)	214	245
90-day	460	415 (at bottom)	355	385

Data from Des Francs, 1974.

gravity 1.10, sand content 3.4 percent, and cone viscosity 39 s) by adding cement until a cement-water ratio of 0.4 was obtained.

Panel types and configuration

Prefabricated panels are of conventional reinforced concrete. Prestressing has been tried, but its practicality is yet to be established. Conceivable variations are hollow panels or sections made with lightweight aggregate. A practical size limitation is imposed by crane and hoisting capabilities, and a usual maximum weight for a single panel is 20 t. A practical maximum panel length will accommodate a five-story basement.

There has been a tendency to standardize panel size and configurations to ensure uniform installation details. Figure 1-13 shows typical panels that slot together. This interlocking ensures rigidity and produces a smooth wall. A second type, shown in Fig. 1-14, has alternate beam and slab sections. The beams are usually twice as thick as the slab panels. A standard thickness is 50 cm (20 in) for beam sections and 25 cm (10 in) for slab panels.

Other configurations include hybrid construction where prefabricated sections of I shape are used as beams for cast-in-place panels, a system similar to soldier beams with lagging (Xanthakos, 1979). These should be considered in special conditions and under competent technical judgment.

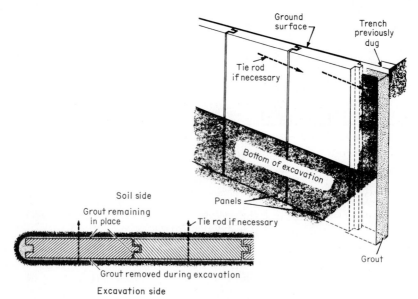

Figure 1-13 Prefabricated wall with identical panels.

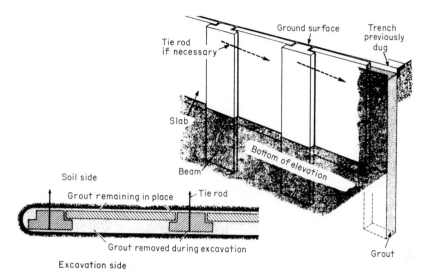

Figure 1-14 Prefabricated wall with beam-and-slab panels.

Uses. A prefabricated wall with identical panels such as the ones shown in Fig. 1-13 is suitable for ground consisting of stiff or dense layers below the base of excavation so that the wall can derive its lateral stability with minimum embedment, and most of its depth is utilized to enclose the basement levels. In loose or soft ground this embedment can be 20 to 40 percent of the overall wall depth, and this is a considerable reduction of usable wall height. In these conditions it may be more practical to build the wall with beam-and-slab panels of the type shown in Fig. 1-14.

Beam-and-slab walls are essentially similar to soldier piles with lagging. Since the beam sections are narrower than the slab panels, they can be made longer without exceeding the maximum weight for handling and lifting. Passive resistance is developed below excavation level in the beam sections that can also transfer vertical loads by side shear and base bearing. The slab sections resist active earth pressures only, and have only minimum embedment below excavation level, usually 0.5 to 1 m (1.5 to 3 ft). Thus, in elevation the wall appears as a series of T shapes or as a wall on stilts.

The installation follows the sequence shown in Fig. 1-15. Primary panels consisting of two beams and one slab section are inserted in alternate trenches numbered 1 and 2. The secondary panel numbered 3 is installed between panels 1 and 2 and consists of two slabs and one beam. The number of units in each panel is therefore three. The installation continues, repeating the sequence with panels 4 and 5, so

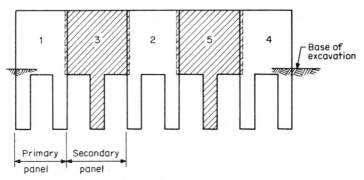

Figure 1-15 Installation of a prefabricated wall consisting of beam and slab sections: one primary panel = two beam sections and one slab section; one secondary panel = two slab sections and one beam section.

that the grout in any panel becomes self-standing as the next panel is excavated.

Where, besides the ground support, the design must also provide for groundwater control, the construction systems can be combined as shown in Fig. 1-16. The upper part of the wall consists of prefabricated structural panels and constitutes the ground support. The lower portion of the system is the initial self-hardening coulis that provides a

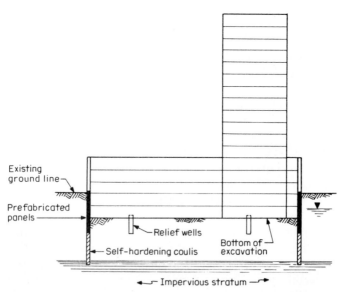

Figure 1-16 Use of prefabricated walls for ground support and protection of the excavation from groundwater.

barrier for groundwater seepage. Protection is afforded first by trenching down to the impervious substratum using a self-hardening grout, and then by placing prefabricated sections in the upper part where lateral support is needed.

Besides providing a seal, the coulis can also transfer vertical load by side shear and base bearing. This topic is discussed in Chap. 5.

Installation

A practical maximum panel length is 15 m (50 ft) for a panel width of 2 m (6.5 ft), but this is not necessarily a fixed limit. Standard details include fitting and lifting hooks for handling and positioning. The interior face is coated with a special compound to facilitate removal of any grout that may adhere to the concrete.

A casting yard usually must be provided at or near the construction site to accommodate at least the number of panels expected to be installed per day. If the sections must be transported to the site from a central plant, undue costs and delays will be incurred, particularly with long hauling distances and heavy traffic conditions. For average job sites, a usual practice is to schedule the installation of three panels per day using one excavating machine and one crane.

The panels are lifted and held vertically by cranes, and then they are lowered slowly into the trench, normally excavated wider. This overwidth allows the grout to surround the precast sections completely as shown in Fig. 1-17. The sections are checked for alignment, dis-

Figure 1-17 Setting a prefabricated section in place. Note that the trench is made wider than the concrete section.

engaged from the crane, and held in position by special devices bearing on guide walls. This support is maintained until the grout has hardened. Usually the tip of the sections is stopped above the bottom of the trench, allowing some grout to remain underneath for full contact and bearing.

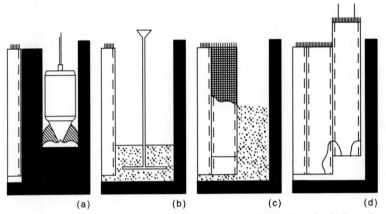

(a)   (b)   (c)   (d)

Figure 1-18 (*a*) Excavation under slurry using a self-guided grab. (*b*) Introduction of displacement grout through a spreader. (*c*) Setting the first panel in the sealing grout. (*d*) Placing the next panel.

A typical installation and staging sequence using a displacement grout is shown in Fig. 1-18, which is self-explanatory. A special locking device at the lower end serves to align two adjoining sections and keeps them together, as shown in Fig. 1-19. The hook at the bottom of the next panel engages in the locking bar of the previous panel.

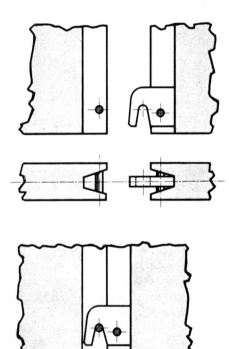

Figure 1-19 Special coupling device fitted at the bottom of prefabricated sections.

With the use of displacement grout it is sometimes expedient to graduate the strength characteristics of the bonding material. This transition and variation in grout composition and strength is feasible even at different levels within the same panel. For compatibility high-strength grout is required underneath the panel where heavy loads must be transferred, whereas a relatively weak but plastic sealer is suitable for the upper portion of the wall to deform without cracking.

End joints. Contractors usually suggest special joints developed and tested for prefabricated panels. A special joint suitable for rectangular sections is shown in Fig. 1-20. This is intended to improve watertightness by controlling differential movement between panels. The double recess is regrouted with the insertion of a water stop. The special hook of Fig. 1-19 prevents differential vertical movement between panels.

Another detail of the watertight joint used by Bachy in France is shown in Fig. 1-21, known as a WSI joint. The process is self-explanatory, and the joint has reportedly been tested in the vicinity of large main sewers.

Advantages and disadvantages

Prefabricated walls have the advantages inherent in precasting. The exposed wall has satisfactory appearance with smooth face, and further treatment is not necessary. The quality control available within precasting ensures the specified strength and allows better accuracy in positioning the reinforcement. The structure is built to finer tolerances, and openings and miscellaneous inserts for connections are more accurately positioned. In addition, the practical problems asso-

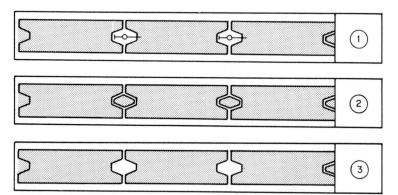

Figure 1-20 Use of slots to make a watertight joint: (1) Water-stop detail. (2) Reinforced-concrete key. (3) Sealing grout only.

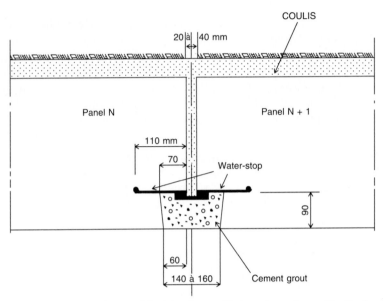

Figure 1-21 Detail of watertight joint for prefabricated panels used by Bachy.

ciated with cast-in-place walls and tremie placement of concrete are eliminated.

However, these favorable considerations must be balanced against the careful planning and strict adherence to schedule; the minimum job size necessary to offset certain fixed costs inherent in precasting; unfavorable soil conditions that may result in differential panel movement, forcing the grout to crack at the joints; and the lack of structural continuity across panels. A prefabricated wall is shown in Fig. 1-22.

1-6   Bored Pile Walls

Bored piles are used as conventional foundation elements (see also Chap. 5). Bored pile walls can be used as ground support. This installation can be completed in most sites and ground conditions. The presence of utilities or difficult soil offers a minor impediment to the construction operations. On congested sites the use of auger rigs and reverse circulation rotary drills for both small- and large-diameter piles ensures speed and construction flexibility. Bored pile walls can be capped with a top beam to distribute vertical loads.

Configuration and size

A bored pile wall can be built according to the following configurations: (1) as a contiguous wall, i.e., with the piles in contact or adjoining; (2) as an interlocking wall, also called secant piles, with the elements

Figure 1-22 A prefabricated diaphragm wall consisting of beam-and-slab sections shown after general excavation; the wall is laterally braced with tiebacks.

overlapping; and (3) as intermittent wall, with a spacing exceeding the pile diameter if the ground is fairly stable.

Contiguous bored pile walls have been in general use since the early 1950s, almost 30 years after the introduction of the bored pile system. This activity is probably associated with the rebuilding programs in large European cities after World War II. To this date, the system is frequently associated with deep and shallow excavations for deep basements and cofferdam work.

When it is practicable from the standpoint of hole stability, bored piles can be installed inclined to the vertical to increase resistance to overturning. For free-standing cantilever walls the excavation arm may be 8 m (26 ft), but at this depth it is advisable to brace the wall laterally to limit movement. If the bracing involves ground anchors, a waling beam is cast as the excavation is carried down.

The pile scheme and configuration are decided according to the loads, the ground conditions, and the proposed construction methods. Typical configurations of the three basic types are shown in Figs. 1-23 and 1-24. For the intermittent wall shown in Fig. 1-23, the ground support is completed with precut lagging placed as shown in *a* and *b* or with a face wall as shown in *c*.

In caving soil or in water-bearing formations contiguous walls usually have the configuration shown in Fig. 1-24*a* and *b*. The outer (primary) row is constructed first, with pile spacing less than two diameters. The piles of the secondary row are located as shown, and since

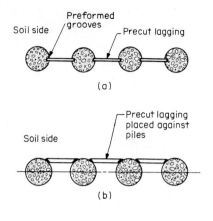

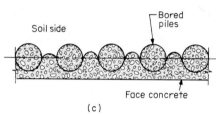

Figure 1-23 Various types of bored-pile walls: (*a*) Wall with lagging inserted in preformed grooves (made by positioning metal forms or foamed-plastic strips. (*b*) Wall with precut lagging placed against piles as the excavation is carried down. (*c*) Bored piles with a separate concrete-face wall.

all piles touch each other, the support is called also a "tangent wall." Face concrete or a separate concrete wall may be added as shown. The secant pile method shown in Fig. 1-24*c* and *d* is selected in unfavorable ground conditions or where complete watertightness must be provided.

Alternatively, it is common practice to construct contiguous bored pile walls by the hit-and-miss method when using auger rigs. Alternate or primary piles in a row are constructed, allowing the concrete time to harden before boring the intermediate piles.

Installation under slurry

Preboring with bentonite slurry can be used to facilitate the installation and extraction of temporary casing or as an independent method in conjunction with rotary drills and reverse circulation. Construction close to existing buildings or in dense sand and gravel may not be possible without the risk of some damage, or the ground may be too compact for driving and extracting casings. In this case preboring under slurry down to the bottom of the ground layer is necessary. A casing is then lowered through the slurry and sealed into the un-

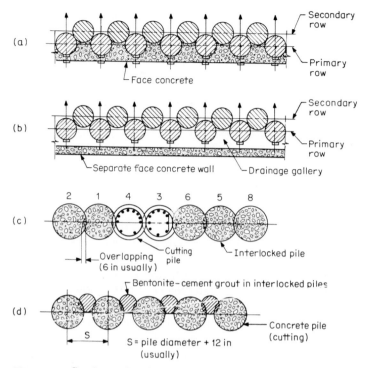

Figure 1-24 Contiguous bored-pile walls: (*a*) Tangent wall with a concrete face cast against the piles. (*b*) Tangent wall with a separate concrete facing for seepage and drainage control. (*c*) Secant wall formed with equal-diameter piles. (*d*) Secant piles of different materials.

derlying clay, the slurry is pumped out, and the excavation is continued in the dry. The concrete is pumped or lowered with buckets.

When the upper formations consist of clay, the hole is initially bored in the dry. Slurry is introduced as soon as troublesome layers and water-bearing formations are reached. In many instances, however, a temporary casing can provide a useful function in setting the correct spacing and line. This process involves the following steps: (1) prebore and insert collar casing; (2) drill with auger to the top of sand layer in the dry; (3) fill hole with bentonite slurry; (4) drill to foundation level using drilling and cleaning buckets, and (5) concrete the hole using tremie pipe. If the slurry is used for the entire depth, the use of machines equipped with reverse circulation facilitates materials handling.

Contractors summarize the following advantages for installation under slurry:

1. Even in clay formations a dry and stable hole is not guaranteed. Hole stability may be further jeopardized by delays in concreting.

2. The slurry keeps sand particles in suspension, limiting the volume of unconsolidated materials accumulated at the bottom.

3. A head of bentonite slurry can effectively oppose base heave.

4. The concrete can be tremied instead of lowered.

Other factors that can influence the decision to excavate under slurry are: the expected deviation from the true vertical line longitudinally and laterally; hole enlargement discussed in other sections; and slurry mud communications between adjoining holes in pervious ground.

Sealing of joints

Bored pile walls in water-bearing formations must have their joints sealed, usually by grouting techniques. Grouting, however, will not always provide an entirely watertight seal (North-Lewis and Lyons, 1974). Normally the sealing is adequate to the extent that it allows the general excavation to be completed free of major problems.

Grouting of joints is carried out behind the piles and prior to bulk excavation. Near the ground level the sealing may be less effective without additional cover or surcharge of soil. Better watertightness is accomplished by guniting or by raking and sealing the defective joints as a supplement to the initial operation and when the face is exposed. Specialist contractors use a 2½-in-thick (6.5 cm) facing of gunite to make bored pile walls watertight.

Other sealing techniques include the presetting of grout tubes in the shaft. Another method is to provide the wall with a continuous concrete membrane or face, but this can be used only in good cohesive strata.

Uses and limitations

Bored pile walls constructed with auger-type tools supplemented with casings are suitable in cohesive soils or where the upper ground layer consists of water-bearing formations of limited depth. Contiguous walls built in slurry holes have less dependence on the type and conditions of soil, and the most serious impediment to the application is the presence of hard rock and similar obstructions.

The system is flexible in terms of diameter, construction, and installation in restricted conditions close to buildings and services. The walls are further attractive because they are free from noise and vibration. They are equally feasible as retaining structures or as load-bearing elements. Permanent walls usually are provided with helical steel cages. If the piles are to serve temporarily, the reinforcing cage may be replaced by rolled steel joists recovered when the permanent construction is completed.

Certain limitations and disadvantages associated with the application include the following: (1) excessive overbreak can occur in unstable ground as the casing is withdrawn, and an oversized hole can result with the use of slurry, especially in granular soil; (2) seepage and leakage through the joints cannot always be stopped to the degree desired, expecially with high water table and in deep excavations; and (3) structural connections are more difficult, especially with members such as slabs and beams, and require complicated details.

In practice, the choice of bored pile walls is largely a matter of economics and ground conditions. An indication of the likely order of comparison for three different ground support systems is given by North-Lewis and Lyons (1974) for purely hypothetical examples based on two different soil and groundwater conditions, shown in Table 1-2. This comparison applies to the structural system only and excludes other costs such as underpinning, groundwater control, and permanent support. The contiguous bored piling under B cannot be expected to provide the same degree of watertightness (although some grouting has been allowed) as the diaphragm walls and the sheet piling. Also, the relative construction cost is subject to regional and market fluctuations.

Secant pile walls

Secant pile walls, shown in Fig. 1-24c, are regarded as the predecessors of diaphragm walls; the development of machines that can excavate linear slots made the conversion from interlocked holes to straight walls possible. Secant pile walls are used as ground support, but they exhibit the flexibility of bored piles without their undesirable characteristics.

The minimum practical wall thickness (hole diameter) is about 45 cm (18 in), but this depends on the overlapping dimension, usually 10 to 15 cm (4 to 6 in). The resulting interlocking ensures a nearly watertight wall provided out-of-plumb piles do not become unlapped.

Initially, alternate piles (numbered 1, 3, 5, etc.) are cast using conventional auger rigs, and are concreted with or without reinforcement. The cutting of the reinforced piles (marked 2, 4, 6, etc.) into piles 1, 3, 5, etc., usually is done 1 day later so that the concrete has set but is not too hard. This operation is carried out by means of a hydraulically actuated casing fitted with a special cutting edge. The casing is guided at two points on a heavy boring rig.

All piles in a secant wall resist the lateral loads simultaneously and equally; hence reinforcement should be provided in every pile. Some

TABLE 1-2 Cost Comparison between Contiguous Bored Pile Walls, Diaphragm Walls, and Sheet Pile Walls

Subsoil profile	Type of construction	Diameter, thickness or section	Depth to dredge level, m	Overall depth, m	Approximate material content per meter run of wall			Relative construction cost per meter run of wall (approx.)	Remarks
					Net concrete volume, m^3	Horizontal steel reinforcement, kg	Vertical steel reinforcement, kg		
A Stiff fissured clay	Contiguous piles	0.450 m	5	6	2.12	18.6	81.3	1.00	1 row of props
	Diaphragm wall	0.500 m	5	6	3.00	93	57	1.58	1 row of props
	Sheet piles	Frodingham 1A	5	7–8	—	—	—	1.37	1 row of props; alternate pairs of piles 7.0 and 8.0 m long
A Stiff fissured clay	Contiguous piles	0.600 m	10	13	6.6	198	827	1.00	2 rows of props
	Diaphragm wall	0.800 m	10	13	10.4	427	685	1.60	2 rows of props
	Sheet piles	Frodingham 2N	10	11.5–12	—	—	—	1.08	2 rows of props; alternate pairs of piles 11.5 and 12.0 m long
B Gravel and sand with water at 1 m below ground level	Contiguous piles	0.550 m	5	8	3.3	43	264	1.00	1 row of props; grout sealing treatment included
	Diaphragm wall	0.500 m	5	8	4.0	112	82	0.71	1 row of props
	Sheet piles	Frodingham 2N	5	8–9	—	—	—	0.62	1 row of props; alternate pairs of piles 8.0 and 9.0 m long

From North-Lewis and Lyons, 1974.
No restrictions due to access, working space, etc., have been taken into account, and the differences in establishment costs have been ignored on the basis that the volume
A factor has been included for walings to the sheet piling and bored piles. For the diaphragm wall extra reinforcement in place of walings has been included.
Cost factor for grouting to the bored pile walls included under B.
Cost of ground anchors and strutting not taken into account, being common to all systems.

objections to this practice relate to the difficulty of cutting into piles already cast, particularly if the time schedule cannot always be followed as desired. A practical solution is to arrange the bars of the cutting piles along a spiral, and the bars of the interlocked piles along square ties. Secant piles are generally more expensive than other types of bored pile walls.

A special equipment, developed and made for secant pile walls, is the Benoto rig, self-powered and capable of traveling up to 300 m (1000 ft).

1-7   Composite Walls

In general, these consist of concrete panels cast under slurry but combined with other structural elements to produce a composite ground support or foundation wall. Practical combinations are obtained with drilled piers or steel I beam sections. These variations are usually worked out to satisfy structural compatibility and construction methods, but they can also be the result of local customs and regional trends.

Steel-concrete panels

Soldier piles and concrete panels.   Two usual variations of this type are shown in Figs. 1-25 and 1-26, the difference being in the method of construction. In the United States this wall was developed regionally on the West Coast, with the first application on the BART system. The wall shown in Fig. 1-26 is processed in shorter excavation panels and is more suitable in difficult ground interbedded with soft bay muds, loose sand, recent rubble fill, abandoned timber piles, and miscella-

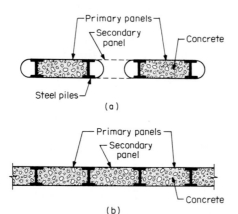

Figure 1-25 Typical composite wall: (*a*) Outline of excavated panels. (*b*) Finished wall.

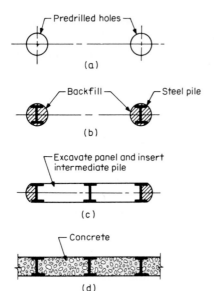

Figure 1-26 Alternate construction method of composite wall.

neous debris, all typical in the San Francisco Bay Area. The introduction of steel I beams is compatible with the structural system selected for the underground metro.

For the installation shown in Fig. 1-25, the entire trench is excavated under slurry in one operation. The primary panels have the steel piles and the reinforcing cage assembled and inserted as one piece. The primary panels are then concreted as shown in Fig. 1-25a. The reinforcing cage for the secondary panel is inserted next, and the wall is completed as shown in Fig. 1-25b.

For the composite wall shown in Fig. 1-26, the steel beams are set in predrilled holes as shown in a and b, and this usually is done by preboring under slurry support. After the beams are set the holes are filled with granular material to block escaping fresh concrete. The panels between beams are excavated with square-end clamshells, the intermediate beam is inserted as one assembly with the steel cage, and the panel is concreted.

The wall types shown in Figs. 1-25 and 1-26 are usually more expensive than all-concrete walls for the same loading, but in many cases the difference in direct cost is balanced by other considerations, such as feasibility of construction in difficult soil and compatibility with an all-steel structural framing for the underground portion of the facility.

Soldier piles and plain (unreinforced) concrete. This type has been used widely in Japan. It is built in a series of rectangular panels, each containing three or four H piles. The piles are spaced close enough so that reinforcement in the concrete is not necessary. An angle or flat bar is welded to the flanges of the end beams to stop the flow of leaking fresh concrete, and a spacer box is used at the end chamber in lieu of an interlocking pipe.

The excavation is carried out with any type of slurry trench equipment, including machines with round and square ends. Accuracy in verticality is quite important. The construction is staged according to the sequence shown in Fig. 1-27, and involves the following steps.

1. Excavate primary (alternate) panels as shown in Fig. 1-27a. The panel size is dictated by the maximum subsection length that is structurally adequate without reinforcement but depends also on excavation and concreting procedures.

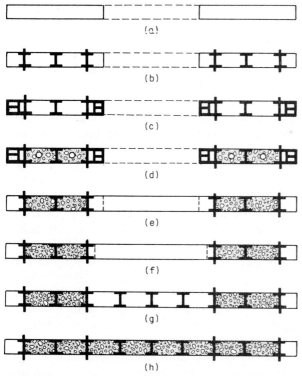

Figure 1-27 Construction sequence of steel and plain (unreinforced) concrete composite wall: (a) Excavation of primary (alternate) panels. (b) Installation of steel piles. (c) Installation of spacer boxes. (d) Placement of tremie concrete. (e) Excavation of secondary panel (f) Cleaning steel faces to remove residual material. (g) Installation of steel piles in secondary panel. (h) Completion of wall.

2. Install the necessary number of H piles. The intermediate piles are lowered, but the fin piles usually must be driven. The pile width matches the width of the trench.

3. Install spacer box, as shown in Fig. 1-27c.

4. Place concrete with the use of tremie pipes, as shown in Fig. 1-27d. Adjoining chambers in the same panel must be filled simultaneously to avoid distortion or distortion of intermediate piles from uneven pressure.

5. Excavate secondary panels, extract spacer boxes, and scrape steel face to remove residual material adhering to it, as shown in Fig. 1-27e and f.

6. Construct secondary panels, as shown in Fig. 1-27g and h. The piles are kept in exact position if they penetrate the soil below excavation level and if their tops are braced while the fresh concrete is tremied. The spacer boxes can be extracted any time after initial concrete setting.

For design purposes, the concrete section is assumed to act in bending; hence failure should be expected to occur when its tensile strength is exceeded. This analysis is presented in Chap. 7.

In Japan, this wall type is often found more economical than the conventional diaphragm wall or bored pile wall of the same flexural capacity. A favorable factor is the use of factory-produced steel I sections vs. the cost of on-site assembly of reinforcement.

Bored piles and concrete panels

Another example of composite walls is the diaphragm panel interlocked with large-diameter bored piles. The feasibility of this combination is obvious in the underground portion of tall buildings and basement enclosures that must receive and transfer large loads from the superstructure.

The bored piles are installed first. The pile spacing is dictated by the main features of the superstructure, such as columns and bays, but is also dependent on the maximum horizontal span of the diaphragm wall panel for the selected wall thickness.

For the construction shown in Fig. 1-28, a casing is used only for the excavation. The reinforcing cage of the bored piles is provided with a slot formed by a styrofoam filler. The casing is withdrawn as the hole is concreted. The linear panel is usually excavated with square-end clamshells, and suitable scraping tools must be used to remove the styrofoam and clean the concrete for good connection. The key remains intact and smooth provided the cage is positioned and cen-

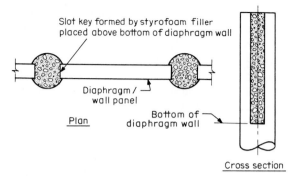

Figure 1-28 Diaphragm wall interlocking with drilled piers.

tered accurately. For the joint to be watertight, the residual material must be removed completely.

If the steel casing must be left in place, a mechanical connector can be provided by welding sections of a flat bar to the casing, as shown in Fig. 1-29. The bored hole must be large enough to receive the entire assembly; otherwise the casing must be driven. The annular space is then backfilled with fine gravel or granular material as shown. Panel excavation at the junction of the bored pile and diaphragm panel requires special chisels guided by a kelly to embrace and trim residual material around this attachment since this area cannot be reached by the main equipment. Interestingly, these construction details must be considered in the design since they influence the load-transfer characteristics of the wall.

1-8   Examples of Structure Combinations

Walls on stilts, piles, subpiers, and rock

The usual wall thickness (24 in or larger) imparts to the system an unusual capacity to resist compressive stresses, and thus enhances

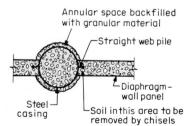

Figure 1-29 Connection detail of cased piers and diaphragm-wall panels.

the structural capacity of the wall. For example, a wall 24 in thick, and for a working concrete stress of 700 lb/in^2, has a structural capacity of 200 kips/ft (linear) in compression, or 300 t/m.

If the combined base bearing and side resistance for the selected tip elevation cannot accommodate the service loads on the wall, rather than extending the entire wall deeper, it may be more economical to support the wall in one of the following ways.

Support on stilts.   A wall on stilts is shown in Fig. 1-30. For each panel, the middle section (usually one equipment pass) is carried down to firm bearing (hardpan or rock), resulting in a wall tip considerably deeper than the excavation level. Usually one or two stilts are sufficient for each panel, depending on the panel dimensions and loads to be transferred. For a better interaction the panels should be provided with dowels to form shear joints. Other relevant considerations are the following: (1) the reinforcing cage should be assembled and installed in one section; (2) the average load transfer per stilt should be nearly uniform for all panels; (3) the stilt spacing should be compatible with the spacing of tremie pipes; and (4) the gross volume should accommodate the maximum continuous practicable pour.

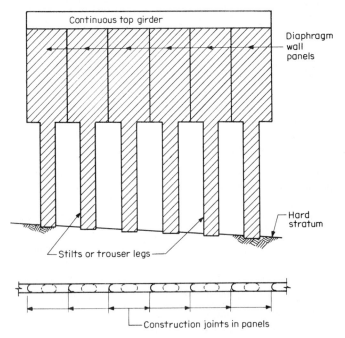

Figure 1-30   Example of a diaphragm wall supported on stilts.

The load-carrying capacity of a wall on stilts may be determined on a displacement compatibility basis. In this case, actual vertical deflections will determine the mechanism of load transfer and the division of load between base bearing and side resistance (see also Chap. 5).

Support on piles. In certain conditions diaphragm walls may be supported on load-bearing piles. Whether the wall is laterally braced at the bottom by sufficient embedment or by internal bracing is a matter of economics, lateral stability, and groundwater conditions.

Steel H piles may be driven through an excavated panel under slurry. Alternatively, steel casings can be installed and left in the panel so that the piles can be rammed after the wall is constructed.

Driving the piles through the open trench is preferred by many contractors and by the author. The operation is independent of the panel sequence and size, and is carried between the excavation phase and the concrete placement. The piles must project 1 m (3 ft) minimum into the concrete wall. A usual problem resulting from pile driving is some sloughing and peel-off because of vibrations and slurry disturbance, but this is not any worse than the effect of chiseling.

Driving the piles in preformed holes after the wall is constructed is better in terms of equipment use and labor. The difficulty is in arranging the pile casings, tremie pipes, and construction joints without blocking the flow of fresh concrete. An important advantage is the ability to extend the steel pile to ground level for direct connection with superstructure columns. In this respect, the installation is a derivative of the prefounded column method discussed in other sections.

Support on subpiers. In this arrangement, the wall is not interlocked with the subpiers but is directly supported on them. The two methods of installation are shown in Fig. 1-31a and b. For the wall shown in a the holes are bored from the ground level and are concreted to a level that is the base of the wall. The casing, if used, is withdrawn, and the hole is backfilled with granular material above the concreted section. The diaphragm wall is concreted as a separate structure arranged to have a vertical panel joint at each subpier location. Steel dowels from the concreted hole should extend into the wall.

The wall shown in Fig. 1-31b is cast as an integral unit between panel joints. The holes are excavated from the ground using drills or augers, and the panel excavation is completed with clamshells or slot-type machines. The reinforcing cage must be assembled and installed as one unit, and the concrete is placed through tremie pipes placed in the holes. This procedure eliminates the construction joint between subpiers and concrete panels.

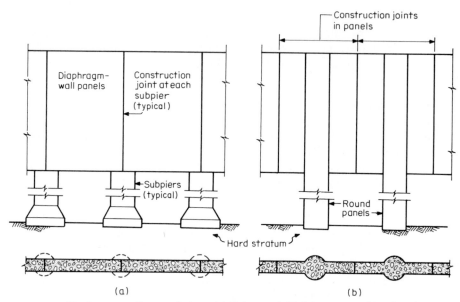

Figure 1-31 Diaphragm walls on subpiers. (*a*) Subpiers drilled from ground level and concreted to bottom of wall. (*b*) Round panels excavated simultaneously with wall panels.

Walls on hard stratum.   When rock exists at relatively shallow depths, the wall may be carried down to the same level if considerable loads must be carried. In this case, the transfer of load can be accomplished in two ways: (1) by terminating the wall at the top of the hard stratum using anchors at this level for lateral support or (2) by penetrating into the hard layer if this is more economical. In some instances, local building codes may require a rock socket for the load transfer.

Strip panels

Wall connections with intermediate floor slabs and beams require the design and detailing of suitable construction joints, discussed in other sections. This structural interaction can also be achieved with the use of pillars cast against the wall after it is exposed and as the excavation is carried down sequentially. This procedure is demonstrated in Fig. 1-32*a*. The pillars, or counterforts, are built in sections using starter bars where the intermediate floors are to serve as lateral bracing, or monolithically at the end of excavation if temporary bracing is used.

If the groundwater is not a factor and the ground is stable, strip panels can be executed as shown in Fig. 1-32*b*. The wall is a sequence of individual slot sections without end tubes or vertical construction joints. As the excavation is deepened, the intermediate tongue is filled in sections using again starter bars, and receives the connections from

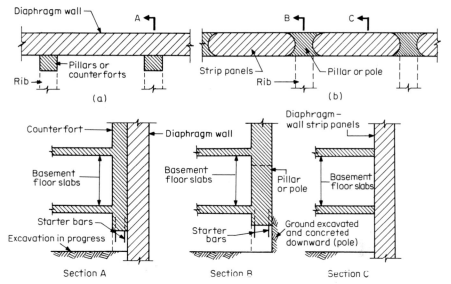

Figure 1-32 Construction of diaphragm walls: (*a*) Conventional method. (*b*) Strip-panel method.

floor slabs and frame ribs. The resulting economy relates to simplicity from the elimination of panel joints, and wall-to-beam or wall-to-slab connections.

An example of strip-panel wall for a different application is shown in Fig. 1-33. The strip panels provide the foundation structure for a continuous mat cast at ground level to support surface facilities and warehouses. Each strip panel was excavated and concreted on the same day. A solid earth tongue is left between strips as shown. The two subway tunnels were constructed in steel tubes using the shield process.

The strip panels serve as underpinning for the surface mat and as lateral support for the tunnel excavation. This design is therefore similar in many aspects to the foundation plan of Fig. 5-24. A more conventional scheme would have been to construct continuous diaphragm walls for the exterior bays, construct two concrete boxes for the subway, backfill, and cast the mat for the ground facilities. This project was planned, however, with private and public involvement, and included different contracts and construction schedules, and the cut-and-cover option was thus deterred.

1-9   Circular and Polygonal Enclosures

Circular enclosures can be built along guide walls that have a truly circular configuration. In this case the distance between guide walls

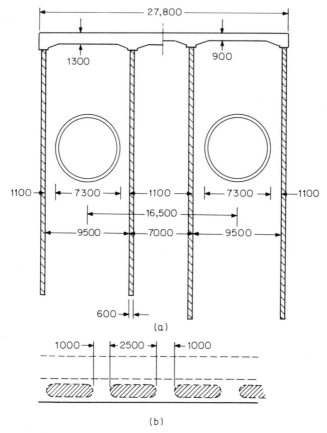

Figure 1-33 Use of strip panels for the construction of subway tunnels at Haneda Airport in Tokyo: (*a*) Typical section. (*b*) Partial plan; all dimensions in millimeters.

is increased to include, besides the normal tolerance, the chord deflection corresponding to one panel (usually one equipment pass). The resulting structure is not perfectly circular but is assumed to act as a circular ring resisting lateral stresses with axial thrusts. When the diameter is relatively small, the enclosure is built as a polygon.

There are two major structural advantages: (1) the elimination of interior lateral bracing under certain conditions and (2) the reduction or elimination of wall embedment below excavation level. Functionally, circular enclosures are suitable for deep construction and access shafts, underground storage tanks, hydraulic and power facilities, and underground parking where the conversion to a circular plan is not in conflict with the layout of the superstructure.

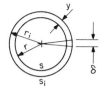

Figure 1-34 Movement of a circular wall toward the excavation caused by yielding at the construction joints.

For a given plan area a square structure requires 12 percent more perimeter than a circular shape of the same area. A circular wall resists lateral stresses by developing a corresponding axial thrust, and the inward radial movement is much smaller and often inconsequential. Yielding at the joints because of bentonite and impurities trapped between panels can be kept to a minimum by proper execution of the joints and proper concrete placement.

The lateral (inward) wall displacement due to yielding at panel joints can be estimated as follows: Let r_i be the initial mean radius, s_i the initial perimeter corresponding to r_i, and let n be the number of panels and joints. If each construction joint yields tangentially by an amount δ, the initial perimeter will shorten to a final value s corresponding to a radius r, as shown in Fig. 1-34. The following relations hold:

$$r_i = \frac{s_i}{2\pi} \qquad r = \frac{s}{2\pi} \qquad \text{and} \qquad s = s_i - n\delta$$

When we note that inward movement is $y = r_i - r$, it follows that

$$y = \frac{n\delta}{2\pi} \tag{1-1}$$

which shows that inward wall movement is independent of the radius and depends only on the number of joints and the compressibility of unconsolidated material left there. For example, a circular wall with 20 panels and a yield of ⅛ at the joints will have an inward movement (irrespective of its radius) $20(0.125)/6.28 = 0.4$ in.

Polygonal shapes. For underground openings of relatively small diameter (up to 10 m, or 35 ft) the shape can be converted into a polygonal configuration. Typical uses are as ventilation, access, drop, and mining shafts. The polygon is evolved as shown in Fig. 1-35. If the interior clear distance between faces and the tentative wall thickness are known, a basic inscribed circle is drawn as shown with a diameter

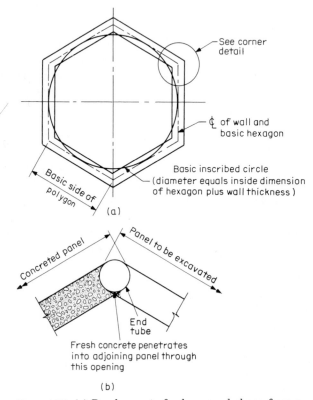

(a)

(b)

Figure 1-35 (*a*) Development of a hexagonal shape from a basic circle. (*b*) Corner detail.

equal to the sum of these two parameters. A suitable polygon is drawn next with sides tangents to the basic circle, and this is the polygon configuration along its centerline. The usual side length is 1.5 to 2.5 m (5 to 8 ft) and is excavated with one equipment pass.

For unreinforced-concrete polygonal shafts the excavation panel extends from corner to corner and may involve two or three sides. Tremie pipes are placed at the interior corners, and the construction joints are formed with end pipes as shown in Fig. 1-35. Unless a barrier is provided and the flow of fresh concrete is completely blocked, the fresh mix may flow or leak into the common area of the next panel as shown. This protrusion must be broken with chisels to permit a smooth excavation.

If the shafts must be reinforced, construction joints may be formed in two ways. One method is to place the joint away from the corners, preferably at the center of the side. The reinforcement is continuous horizontally, and one cage covers a concrete panel consisting of one or two full sides and two half sides. This detail was selected for the construction shafts of the Chicago underflow system (TARP); these shafts have an interior clear dimension of about 38 ft and are from 60 to 70 ft deep (Xanthakos, 1976). Another method is to use the I beams used for composite walls (Fig. 1-25) placed at the ends of panels. For excavation and concreting purposes the panels may consist of two or three sides. These details were used for the construction shafts of the Staten Island, New York, pumping station. These shafts have an interior diameter of 45 ft, and they are 165 ft deep. The walls were excavated in seven panels, each panel consisting of three polygon sides, with I beams inserted at each joint (Bruce et al., 1991).

Construction considerations.   The usual range of wall thickness is 60 to 75 cm (24 to 30 in). Certain construction requirements can influence the design: (1) the wall must have adequate bearing capacity at its base; (2) the ground must be stable against base heave; and (3) the resultant lateral forces should be essentially uniform around the structure to deter local distortions.

Where the wall is expected to perform as a compression ring and is designed accordingly, the construction joints must be detailed to ensure this behavior. Square-end joints are more effective in transferring compressive stresses, especially if the horizontal reinforcement is extended through. The actual yield of panels at the joints will depend on workmanship and execution. Processing the enclosure in longer units results in fewer joints but more tremie pipes per panel.

A cap beam usually is cast separately after the wall is completed and serves as an upper ring to tie the panels. More internal circular braces are provided, if necessary, in two forms: as either steel rings or cast-in-place concrete. Experience shows that circular enclosures of relatively large diameter (50 m, or 160 ft) are likely to undergo local distortion or excessive inward movement associated with nonuniform lateral thrust and geometric imperfections altering the ring response.

1-10   Buttressed Walls, Cells, and Arched (Quays) Structures

These structures are usually constructed in waterfront installations in lieu of cellular cofferdams, concrete monoliths, and open quays. Unlike conventional diaphragm walls that resist lateral earth stresses and vertical loads in one plane, the stability concept of these systems covers a broad range from essentially stiffened cantilevers to gravity-type walls.

Buttressed or T walls

The continuous series of T sections shown in Fig. 1-36 is usually analyzed as a stiffened cantilever and not necessarily as a gravity wall,

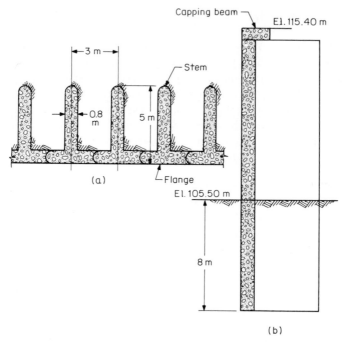

Figure 1-36 T-shaped diaphragm wall built as perimeter wall for the Harrow-on-the-Hill reservoir, England: (*a*) Sectional plan. (*b*) Cross section. (*From Fisher, 1974.*)

unless the height is small compared with the width. Although an important advantage is the extra rigidity allowing greater unbraced heights, the wall derives its stability by sufficient embedment below excavation level. With the wall oriented as shown, most of the flange of the T section and probably a portion of the stem are in compression, with tensile reinforcement placed at the end of the stem as in T beams.

The assumption of side shear (friction or adhesion) at the interface with the surrounding soil has considerable influence on the analysis of stability, since it means that a portion of the soil column between stems must be taken into consideration in calculating the forces resisting overturning. Where this is justified, it will result in smaller wall deflection.

With nominal stem and flange dimensions, one tremie pipe at their junction is sufficient for concrete placement in one T section. Construction joints are typically located in the flange and consist of simple round tubes. The T shape is better excavated with a relatively mobile equipment and is advantageous to have one leg completed in one pass. The reinforcement for one T panel is assembled and installed in a single cage.

An example of a T wall is the perimeter structure of the Harrow-on-the-Hill Reservoir (England). This structure retained 17 m (55 ft) of soil, including surcharge, during construction. The T wall was found suitable for these loads, and the soil was compatible with the diaphragm wall construction. The design finally evolved consists of a series of independent T sections forming a counterforted but baseless cantilever system. A total of 84 Ts are used to enclose the three sides of the reservoir. The design considered adhesion between the fin and the soil (Fisher, 1974).

Arch-type quay walls

An arch type of closed face wall is shown in Figs. 1-37 to 1-39. The upper deposits at the site are dense sand layers over a considerable bed of boulder clay overlying sandstone layers. For the geometric configuration shown this wall was designed as a gravity structure, so that

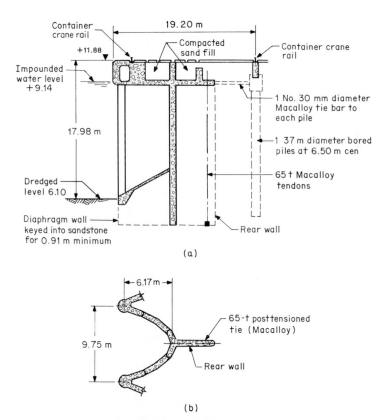

Figure 1-37 Details of Seaforth dock wall, Liverpool: (*a*) Typical cross section. (*b*) Plan. (*From Agar and Irwin-Childs, 1973.*)

Figure 1-38 Guide-wall construction for the arch wall of Seaforth dock, Liverpool.

Figure 1-39 View of Seaforth dock arch wall, Liverpool.

all lateral loads are converted into direct bearing at the base. For this reason the wall of Fig. 1-37 has front corners constructed as bored piles to increase the contact bearing area. The long back fin improves resistance to overturning by adding weight and by increasing the arm of the resisting moment. The fin wall increases resistance to failure by altering the failure mechanism: this section should have to be drawn and extracted like a tooth from the surrounding ground before the wall could rotate about its toe, and this behavior would engage a ground mass in resisting overturning. Rock anchors connecting the back fin to the ground resist further uplift at this location.

A typical postconstruction problem is sliding along the base. This condition can arise because of the absence of a base footing or mat supporting ground weight to generate frictional resistance. Interestingly, sliding may be initiated also at a deeper level if, for example, a thin seam of plastic clay exists at this level and is not detected. Failure of this type can occur without wall tilting.

The wall of Fig. 1-37 was given the arch shape to introduce progressive arching within the soil behind the completed structure and thus reduce the resultant lateral force. Resistance to overturning is increased by the heavy superstructure. The most severe loading condition was with the wall completed and the channel excavated but empty, as shown in Fig. 1-39.

An open quay wall is shown in Fig. 1-40, also part of the Seaforth Dock in Liverpool (shown in Fig. 1-37). On the western side of the dock the existing beach is 10 m (33 ft) below the final deck level. From the beach level a series of cross walls were constructed by the slurry wall technique and were extended to the deck soffit using conventional concrete walls. Between the cross walls on the dock face diaphragm wall panels were inserted to retain the ground between beach level and deck bottom, a height of 8 m (26 ft). The tops of these walls are integrated into capping beams spanning between the cross walls and retained by wedges with compressible packings inserted into slots left in the cross walls.

Diaphragm-wall cells

Closed cells. These can replace steel-sheet cellular cofferdams in poor soil conditions, where pile driving is difficult because of hard obstructions, and where the excavation is too deep for piles to be driven without distorting. Reinforced-concrete monoliths or open quays are good alternatives for waterfront installations, but in certain instances they will cost more.

The cellular construction is a series of diaphragm wall panels combined to form cells. An example is shown in Fig. 1-41. The principle

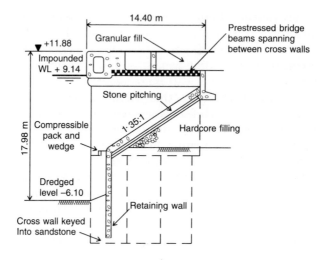

Typical cross-section

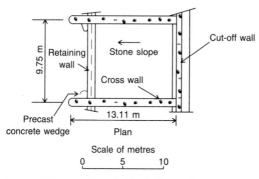

Plan

Scale of metres

0   5   10

Figure 1-40 Royal Seaforth dock; west quay wall. (*From Agar and Irwin-Childs, 1973.*)

of double-walled structures and cell-type cofferdams is applicable; two rows of diaphragm walls are built across from each other and connected by cross walls to form closed cells. With steel sheeting the arches are in tension, but with concrete diaphragms this is impracticable. Therefore, the first requirement in adapting the cell design to concrete is to reverse the front arches as shown so that both front and back walls are in compression. The simple diaphragm panels in the transverse walls act as buttresses for the rear arches but also take in tension the thrust of the front arches and therefore require doweled connections at the joints.

The absence of bracing is the main characteristic of this construction but requires each cell to be stable against overturning, sliding, and tension at the joints. Although each row acts separately, the cells must resist lateral earth stresses exerted by the interior earth volume and also overturning as one unit when one side is lowered or unwatered. A quick condition can be prevented by selecting the width of cells in relation to the height of the finished structure and the depth of penetration. If the construction is in clay, the stability analysis must also consider the safety against shearing rupture along a curved surface for the mass of soil behind the cells (deep-seated failure). Resistance to overturning is helped by side shear that also prevents laminar tilting and integrates the panels into one unit. The cross walls must also be analyzed for flexure when different resultant pressures are developed in adjoining cells.

The front arch is stiffened against bending after dredging by means of vertical ribs or T heads at suitable points. The structure is completed by the placement of a rigid top slab or by a series of peripheral beams. For good bearing the front arches and cross walls should rest on rock or penetrate a comparable stratum.

Panel connectors.   Since the cross walls must restrain the front arches, they must be prevented from laminar tilting. This means that axial forces and shears can be transferred across the half-round joints at any joint location. The connection device for the wall of Fig. 1-41 is based on the RPT joint discussed in other sections.

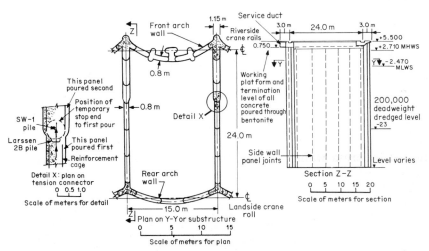

Figure 1-41   Diaphragm-wall cell details for Redcar ore terminal, England. (MHWS = mean high-water surface; MLWS = mean low-water surface) (*From Fisher, 1974.*)

Since more bearing area is required under the cross walls near the front arches, the wall thickness is increased accordingly. The transition is made as shown in the detail of Fig. 1-41; the thinner wall panel is built first, and the end round pipe is extracted as usual. When the thicker panel is excavated, the tool will not fit exactly into the narrower preformed end and some chiseling may be necessary to trim off residual soil.

Open cells.   Open cell construction is shown in Fig. 1-42. This structure consists of a single wall formed with steel sheet piles, and cross walls built as concrete diaphragms. The continuous transverse diaphragm panel shown in Fig. 1-42*a* is indicated in poor soil, whereas the intermittent panel shown in *b* can be used in firm soil or rock.

These bents form the legs of a continuous portal frame. Unlike stiffened cantilever walls, open-type cells derive their stability acting as gravity structures. Hence stability is improved if more load is transferred to the cells, such as a heavy deck, and if adequate bearing resistance is available at the base.

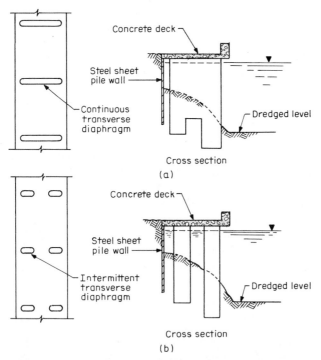

Figure 1-42 Open-cell construction for a dock in Bristol, England: (*a*) Construction in poor soil. (*b*) Construction in firm spoil or rock. (*From Fisher, 1974.*)

1-11 Rigid Cutoff Walls

In a broad context these systems encompass the entire range of earth, semirigid, and rigid structures built below grade for the control of groundwater. Only the latter type will be discussed here. Examples from these applications are cutoff walls built as seepage barriers beneath the main body of canal embankments and earth dams, impervious barriers for pollution control, systems constructed to deter landslips, and groundwater and aquifer recharge schemes.

Concrete diaphragm walls, either plain or reinforced, including the range of interlocking elements, are used when rigidity is the prime factor for the service conditions or where the cutoff is exceptionally deep. The wall is essentially needed for strength and durability but must also provide the required reduction in seepage. If concrete of high quality is available at the site and the construction details are planned and executed well, the structure can provide a cutoff of durable quality and satisfactory watertightness for the period of the expected services. A conventional concrete cutoff wall may also be indicated for very deep installations (up to 100 m or 330 ft), where the site and soil conditions restrict the method of excavation and where the wall must be structurally connected to other components.

Requirements. Full-scale field tests are mandatory and useful to confirm the feasibility of the construction, the effectiveness of the selected method over the entire depth range, the rate of progress and the probable construction time, and the relative cost.

The action of a rigid wall inserted in the ground must be predicted in terms of the overall project function. For example, in compressible soil, a diaphragm wall inserted beneath the central impervious core of an earth dam may punch the core as the dam begins to settle, and cause fissures and cracks at the base. Alternatively, downdrag forces (negative friction) at the concrete-soil interface can accelerate the effect of compressive loads and cause some form of structural damage. At best, a crack developed in this fashion may result in some small movement as the wall adjusts, and this may be sufficient to relieve the load in the sheared zone. This process may propagate to other zones and be repeated until most of the settlement is completed. These possible effects demonstrate the importance of suitable connection details at the top of the wall. These details should be designed and executed for the expected service conditions.

Types of rigid walls. A rigid cutoff wall usually is processed in a series of panels. It may consist of plain concrete, or it may be partly or fully reinforced. Cutoffs of these types are basically conventional diaphragm walls.

A rigid cutoff wall can also consist of two parallel walls made with interlocking piles or with interlocking primary and secondary elements for the deepest portion. Two parallel walls provide better control of ground movement and offer a better seal for seepage through the cutoff. If necessary, grouting of the intermediate area from a gallery located on top of the structure can be used to supplement the watertightness of the cutoff.

Usual problems.   For deep diaphragm walls, typical problems are associated with low excavation rates, limited ability to excavate bedrock, overbreak and panel irregularities, the presence of large hard boulders, and the handling and disposal of excavated materials and bentonite slurry.

Alternative technologies have been introduced to ensure verticality, joint contact, and concrete quality control. These options have, however, certain common operational disadvantages and often tend to compromise effectiveness.

Interlocking elements.   These are installed in hard ground or through formations strewn with boulders, and where the cutoff must reach considerable depth. Primary holes are first drilled using percussive tools or rotary drills with direct circulation of slurry to remove earth materials. The holes are reinforced and concreted using tremie pipes. A special hydraulically expandable chisel shaped to fit the primary holes excavates the intermediate tongue. These sections are likewise provided with steel reinforcement and concreted. More details on this method are given by Xanthakos (1979).

1-12   Soil-Cement Structural Walls

This system represents a relatively new concept developed independently in Japan (Taki and Yang, 1989). It consists of mixing in situ soils with cement grout using multiaxis augers and mixing paddles to construct overlapping soil-cement columns. The resulting applications are as cutoff walls for groundwater control and structural diaphragm walls for excavation supports.

The installation is feasible in a broad range of soils including soft to very stiff and low to highly plastic clays and silts; loose to dense sand, gravel, and cobble; and soft rock. During the process, soils are broken up by the cutting heads of the multiaxis auger and mixed with cement grout in situ, in a pugmill fashion by sections of auger flight and paddles mounted on the multiaxis auger shafts. Lightweight H piles are inserted into the columns before the hardening of the soil-cement for reinforcement. The resulting structural combination can resist lateral earth pressures, and when the wall is properly braced laterally it can support excavations of considerable depth.

Origin and development. The concept appears to have originated from the construction of mixing in-place single soil-cement piles, using single-axis earth augers, in 1954. Single piles often result in incomplete overlapping because of limitations of the single-axis equipment. The multiaxis machine has solved this problem and thus provides continuity in the soil-cement columns. The insertion of steel H piles imparts to the system a structural configuration.

Equipment. The equipment for this installation has the following operational characteristics (Taki and Yang, 1989):

1. The adjacent augers rotate in opposite directions.
2. Each auger shaft consists of sections of auger flights and mixing paddles for in situ soil mixing.
3. Auger flight and mixing paddles on adjacent auger shafts overlap during operation to give overlapping soil-cement columns.
4. Auger flights and mixing paddles are designed and detailed to accommodate various soil conditions.
5. The auger mixes soil with grout at its original depth uniformly and continuously but without the traditional auger that moves the soil upward.
6. Tie bands are used to maintain the rigidity of the auger shafts and the space between individual auger shafts for better operation and quality control.

Comparison with conventional slurry wall construction. In principle, the application is completely independent of stability requirements. There is no need to use slurry, and because most of the in situ soil is used as construction material, the volume of soil spoils for disposal is smaller than the by-products of slurry wall excavations. Likewise, the construction time is shorter, and the in situ conversion of natural soil into a construction system results in higher production rates. The process is also compatible with urban requirements and ideal for use in noise- and vibration-sensitive areas.

Mechanical characteristics. These depend essentially on the physical properties of the in situ soil materials, the soil-cement mixing rates, and the extent of mixing.

As in conventional cement technology, the strength of soil-cement is influenced by the method of sample preparation and testing conditions. The compressive strength of the soil-cement mix is used as the basic characteristic for design and quality control. According to tests, the curing period affects the development of strength, and increasing the curing period results in higher strength. The 28-day strength is almost twice the 7-day strength for either sand or clay, as shown in Fig. 1-43. Likewise, within the working stress range, the soil-cement

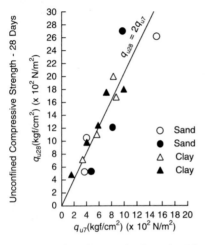

Figure 1-43 Relationship between unconfined compressive strengths with different curing times.

material is linearly elastic, as evidenced by Fig. 1-44 where the unconfined compressive strength is plotted vs. the modulus of elasticity. The tensile strength of the mix is low and generally ignored in structural computations.

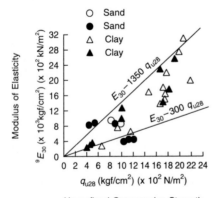

Figure 1-44 Relationship between modulus of elasticity and unconfined compressive strength.

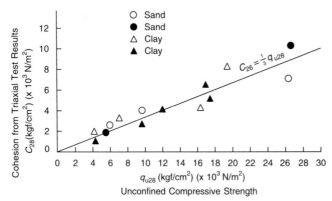

Figure 1-45 Relationship between cohesion and unconfined compressive strength.

The relationship between cohesion and unconfined compressive strength is shown in Fig. 1-45. The function of shear strength and unconfined compressive strength is shown in Fig. 1-46. It follows that for design purposes the shear strength of the soil-cement material can be taken as one-third the unconfined compressive strength.

Taki and Yang (1989) quote a coefficient of permeability in the range 1×10^{-6} to 1×10^{-7} cm/s, or practically a watertight wall for excavation purposes.

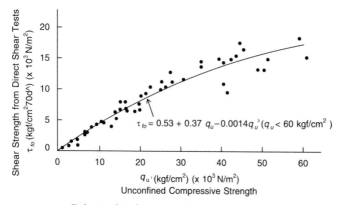

Figure 1-46 Relationship between shear strength and unconfined compressive strength.

Design considerations.   The design of soil-cement walls involves essentially two steps: (1) the design of reinforcing members (H piles or equivalent members) to resist moments, shears, etc., as in conventional soldier pile walls, and (2) the design of the soil-cement elements to resist and transfer horizontal earth stresses to the H members.

If the reinforcement member (H beam) is installed in every column as shown in Fig. 1-47a, it is only necessary to consider the punch-through shear force Q in calculating the shear stresses. Where the reinforcement member is not installed in every soil-cement column, the soil-cement element may be analyzed using the hypothetical model shown in Fig. 1-47b. In this case, in addition to the punch-through shear stresses, the analysis may consider compressive stresses along a hypothetical parabolic arch with a configuration formed as shown.

A strength test and a permeability test are commonly performed to obtain strength parameters and provide the basis for a semiempirical design. Prior to construction, tests may be performed on samples prepared in the laboratory using in situ soil mixed with cement. This test is indicated where previous data for the side conditions are not available or where the soil is known to contain constituents that may be deleterious to the soil-cement structure.

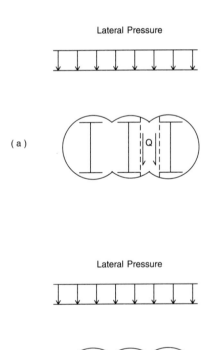

Figure 1-47 (a) Stress flow in soil cement wall, punch-through shear. (b) Stress analysis and compressive action of arching effects.

Field sampling is mandatory during the construction of the wall. Wet soil-cement samples are obtained routinely and cured in the laboratory for testing and quality control. After construction core samples should be obtained from the exposed wall according to a testing schedule to be determined by the site conditions during excavation.

Unconfined compressive strength tests, direct shear tests, and triaxial compression tests are suggested for strength assessment and evaluation of the finished cement-soil wall. For quality control purposes, the unconfined compressive strength test is adequate, and the results may be used as standard values.

References

Agar, M., and F. Irwin-Childs, 1973: "Seaforth Dock, Liverpool; Planning and Design," *Proc. Inst. Civ. Eng. London*, vol. 1, p. 54.

Architectural Institute of Japan, 1988 edition: Recommendations for the Design and Construction Practice of Earth Retaining Structures for Excavation.

Braun, W. M., 1972: "Post-tensioning Diaphragm Walls in Milan." *Ground Eng., London*. March.

Bruce, D. A., H. C. Chan, and G. J. Tamaro, 1991: "Design, Construction, and Performance of a Deep Circular Diaphragm Wall," *ASTM Intern. Symp.*, Atlantic City, N.J., June 27–28.

Des Francs, E. C., 1974: "Prefasif Prefabricated Diaphragm Walls," *Proc. Diaphragm Walls Anchorages, Inst. Civ. Eng. London*.

Fisher, F. A., 1974: "Diaphragm Wall Projects at Seaforth, Redcar, Bristol and Harrow," *Proc. Diaphragm Walls Anchorages, Inst. Civ. Eng. London*.

Fuchsberger, M., 1980: "The Posttensioned Diaphragm Wall," *Proc. Symp. Slurry Walls for Underground Transportation Facilities*, U.S. Department of Transportation, Cambridge, Mass., pp. 293–314.

Iima, H., K. Ujihara, and M. Uenaka, 1983: "S.M.W. Underground Continuous Earth Retaining Wall Method, Ikoma Tunnel West Section, East Osaka Line Project," *Found. Eng.*, July 1983.

Japan Material Society, 1987: Guidelines on Design and Construction of the Soil-Cement Mixing Wall (S.M.W.).

North-Lewis, J. P., and G. H. A. Lyons, 1974: "Contiguous Bored Piles," *Proc. Diaphragm Walls Anchorages, Inst. Civ. Eng. London*.

Sliwinski, Z., and W. G. K. Fleming, 1974: "Practical Considerations Affecting the Construction of Diaphragm Walls," *Proc. Diaphragm Wall Anchorages, Inst. Civ. Eng. London*.

Suzuki, S., M. Hirano, and H. Nozaki, 1987: "Large Scale Excavation in Water-Bearing Sand and Gravel Strata, Takamatsu Garage, Municipal Subway No. 12," *Tunnel and Underground*, October 1987.

Taki, O., and D. S. Yang, 1989: "Excavation Support and Groundwater Control Using Soil-Cement Mixing Wall for Subway Projects," *Proc. RETC*, Los Angeles, Calif., June 11–14.

Xanthakos, P. P., 1976: Construction Shafts for TARP, In house study.

Xanthakos, P. P., 1979: *Slurry Walls*, McGraw-Hill, New York.

Xanthakos, P. P., 1991: *Ground Anchors and Anchored Structures*, Wiley, New York.

Yoshinari, S., J. Mase, J. Shinkai, and T. Kunito, 1984: "Design and Construction of Soil-Cement Mixing Wall," Design and Construction of Foundations, General Civil Engineering Research Institute of Japan.

2

Construction Fundamentals

2-1 Site Conditions and Effect on Construction Methods

Slurry wall technology, applied on a global basis, may be used as an independent construction approach or in conjunction with ground control techniques, for the temporary support of deep excavations, and as a permanent solution where structural slurry walls are part of the permanent structure. Parameters affecting the choice are (1) site conditions such as environmental restrictions, hydrology, type of soil, and geotechnical factors; (2) the type of structure to be built (framing system, depth, etc.); and (3) nontechnical considerations such as real estate values, labor, and material cost.

The Rationale of Convergence

Figure 2-1 shows an excavation in noncohesive soils (mainly sandy-gravelly alluvia) supported by a diaphragm wall. At the raft level, the cut is almost 5 m (16.5 ft) below the average groundwater table. The feasibility of this construction requires (1) a suitable ground support, (2) control of groundwater so that it does not enter the excavation area, and (3) protection of the bottom raft against uplift. The artificial support is in this case supplemented by the use of grouting along a zone below the base, and by the installation of a bottom anchorage for holding the raft down.

This example demonstrates a situation where the artificial ground support is combined with ground improvement to produce a unified design. Problems arising from the choice of ground support and the

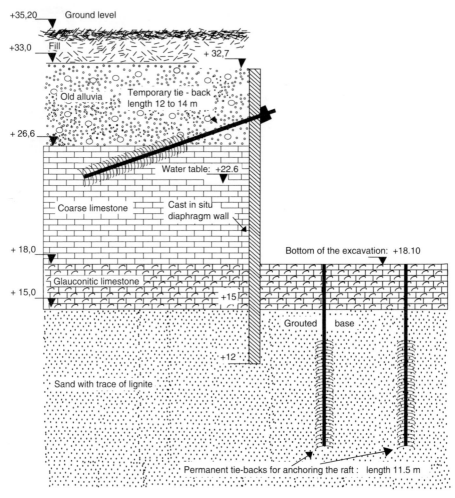

Figure 2-1 Cross section of an urban excavation showing the grouted base for groundwater control.

placement of foundations on poor soils often signify the absence of a global approach and may also indicate uncertainty in design criteria. Conversely, the application of ground controls and improvement techniques should be accepted as a formidable supplement that will balance the structural requirements of the supports by satisfying certain site conditions. Whether this contribution is intended to improve structural safety or enhance functional performance, it may be considered in quantitative terms and diagnosed as an independent remedy.

The convergence between support and control requirements must first recognize ground response to an externally applied action. This response may be specific and predictable, uncertain and random, rapid or slow, and temporary or permanent. A forecast of this response in engineering terms is the main factor that determines the need for ground controls or concludes reliance on the exclusive use of ground supports.

Ground response is also recognized in a quantitative analysis, usually in a time-dependent fashion, where it can supplement the total capacity of the support system; examples are situations where some ground deformation is encouraged and allowed to occur under controlled conditions to mobilize ground strength and thus reduce the requirements of the artificial support. This well-known ground-structure interaction clearly shows the effect of support and ground stiffness: the stiffer the support is relative to the ground, the greater will be the support load.

Permanent walls

The most common techniques used to support excavations are summarized in Fig. 2-2, and obviously the solution to be selected should be the least expensive appropriate to the project. Soldier piles with lagging and sheet pile walls represent time-tested systems used for temporary ground support. These systems have been treated comprehensively in the existing technical literature so that a review here is not considered necessary. Ground control and improvement technologies are discussed by Xanthakos et al. (1994).

Experience shows that slurry walls will in many cases be the most economical and structurally safest support if it is designed to function

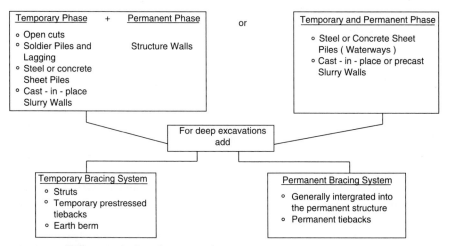

Figure 2-2 Different solutions for excavation supports.

for both the temporary and permanent phase, or if the following conditions exist: (1) deep excavations in soils, (2) construction in urban environment, and (3) construction in ground with high water table.

These articulated considerations suggest site and ground conditions and site situations that can lead to the selection of slurry walls.

Site situations. Environmental constraints in urban areas include densely populated neighborhoods, the high cost of land, the prevention of damage and construction effects on buildings and utilities, and typical forms of nuisances.

The associated advantages of slurry walls are: feasibility of deeper construction and increase in usable subsurface space, reduced and more controllable risk of disturbance and damage to buildings, absence of noise and vibrations, reduced disruption of surface activities and minimum surface restoration, and often fastest construction time.

Soil conditions. Adverse soil conditions that offer impediment to underground construction are high water table, layers of compressible soils, and running cohesionless material.

The use of slurry walls reduces and sometimes eliminates the need for dewatering, alleviates the risk of material running, provides better control of ground movement and associated settlement, and enhances confinement of construction effects to tolerable limits. The system usually is cheaper if it combines the temporary and permanent support.

The cut-and-cover example shown in Fig. 2-3 shows how the technique can be used to minimize surface disruption. The diaphragm walls (in this case precast panels) are inserted sequentially so that one lane is always open to traffic. As soon as the top slab is in place and the roadway is restored, the remaining work is practically carried out under cover.

Attractive uses of the system are also demonstrated in nonurban environments. The example shown in Fig. 2-4 required a massive excavation for the construction of a nuclear power station (Namy, 1979). The bearing stratum was below a mud layer 15 m (50 ft) deep, and the water table was consistently at ground level. The initial solution proposed a cutoff wall around the site and excavation of mud under stable slopes. This work would require the removal of 2,600,000 yd^3 of mud.

The solution finally selected was a cast-in-place anchored diaphragm wall forming both a retaining wall and a cutoff. The volume of mud removal was reduced to about 1,300,00 yd^3, or one-half the initial scheme. The use of panels with T section required only one row of anchors near the top. The excavation was carried out by dredging.

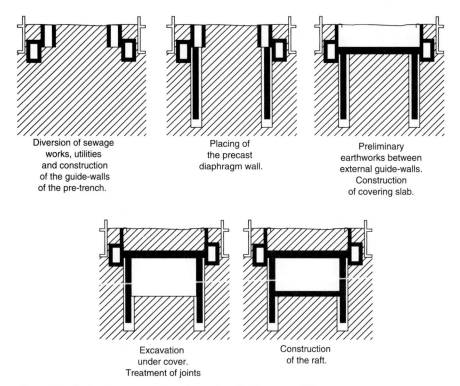

Diversion of sewage works, utilities and construction of the guide-walls of the pre-trench.

Placing of the precast diaphragm wall.

Preliminary earthworks between external guide-walls. Construction of covering slab.

Excavation under cover. Treatment of joints

Construction of the raft.

Figure 2-3 Cut-and-cover construction using diaphragm walls.

Other functions.   The choice becomes more attractive if, besides acting as ground support, the walls can perform other functions, for example: (1) transfer vertical loads for either temporary and permanent phase; (2) serve as lateral underpinning for adjacent buildings and foundations; and (3) resist uplift pressure on the bottom slab by side shear at the wall-soil interface. If a continuous dependable impervious soil layer exists below the planned excavation, the wall may be carried down to this level and penetrate the impervious stratum. This enclosure isolates the excavation from the groundwater environment and provides an effective cutoff during and after construction. A simple drainage layer just beneath the bottom slab will convey any seepage to a central sump and pumping unit and will relieve the bottom slab of any uplift pressures. This solution becomes even more attractive if the wall combines a structural unit in the upper part for stability, and a cement-bentonite in the lower part for watertightness.

Specific site conditions

Certain site conditions may impose specific construction requirements, and a usual situation is when the slurry walls must be combined with

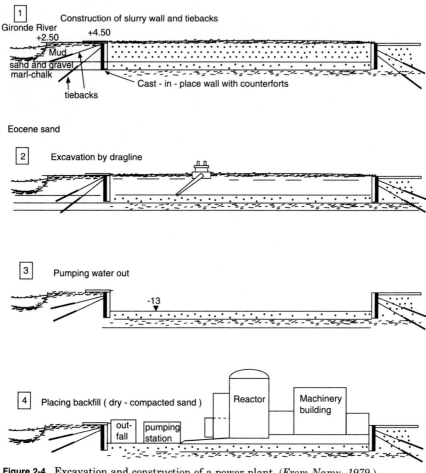

Figure 2-4 Excavation and construction of a power plant. (*From Namy, 1979.*)

other specialty techniques. A typical problem frequently encountered with deep excavations is the absence of an impervious layer into which the wall can be embedded economically. This problem is compounded if the lowering of the water table is not permitted outside the proposed excavation. The convergence approach discussed in the foregoing sections is feasible and may involve the following solutions.

1. Dewatering plus underpinning of the buildings that might be affected by the general dewatering. This is practical and feasible when this operation is limited in scope and involves only few buildings.

2. Dewatering inside the excavation, with realimentation of the water table outside the excavation boundaries, where soil conditions are favorable.

3. Creation of an impervious horizontal layer between the toes of the slurry wall by grouting, as shown in the example of Fig. 2-1.

4. When the excavation is through overburden and rock, providing a minimum embedment of the wall in rock may be cheaper. If necessary, the wall is extended down by an effective vertical grout cutoff.

In most cases the slurry walls are a part of the total substructure system. Because of their rigidity and their placement prior to any bulk excavation, however, they are the key element to minimize horizontal displacements (and consequently vertical settlement) during general excavation. In this context, the walls and the bracing must be designed and optimized as one system.

2-2   General Construction Requirements

The construction procedures stipulated in the contract specifications should normally reflect a design that is closely related to the site conditions. The main factors to be considered are:

1. Soil characteristics as they may require pretreatment and as they may affect trench stability and panel length.

2. Adjacent buildings and foundations as they may require protection and as they may dictate construction sequence.

3. Site layout and overall space availability since this may affect plant size and optimum daily operations. Site congestion and its effect on production.

4. Depth of slurry wall in conjunction with the nature of subsoils, since it may dictate a practicable allowable deviation from verticality.

5. Soil characteristics and aggressiveness of groundwater since these may affect the requirements of cement, slurry controls, and steel coverage.

6. Existing utilities that may have to be protected or relocated.

7. Requirements for traffic maintenance in public right-of-way because of the effect on construction phases and working schedules.

Site inspection and preparation

A complete site inspection in the predesign stage will help avoid later problems. This is essential because construction of this type usually is scheduled with regard to traffic maintenance, preservation or relocation of existing utilities, and frequent interaction with existing buildings. The objective and scope of this survey is not prescribed by mandatory guidelines but depends essentially on the project and its location. Although the site inspection focuses on the immediate construction area, a general survey of the surrounding neighborhood is often indicated. The program should typically include the following.

Environmental effects. Excessive noise is objectionable and the noise level is regulated by local ordinances. Alternatively the method of mud disposal and treatment of used slurries should be the subject of a preconceived program.

Space availability. This is examined in the context of construction. It can dictate the type of wall and influence the slurry plant layout, working space for assembling reinforcing cages, and incidental field work. Space availability can thus influence panel length and panel sequence. Where the construction encroaches on adjacent property or falls within the street right-of-way, an easement must be obtained.

Local traffic. This has a decisive effect on the construction schedule and field priorities. Traffic can dictate the pouring sequence but can also delay or disrupt a pour already started. In most instances, various operations must proceed simultaneously at different locations while traffic must move freely around and through the site.

Overhead structures and facilities. Fire escapes, canopies, and overhead attachments likely to interfere with the excavation and new construction should be removed temporarily or rearranged. Exceptional mobility of equipment is required under limited headroom and clearance to existing buildings, particularly for corner panels.

Underground utilities and structures. The critical construction phases depend on the time required for relocation of utilities and roads, and quite often the maximum panel length will vary according to the type, condition, and proximity of adjacent foundations. Excavation near existing storm sewers may be subject to leakage, causing slurry contamination. Near defective water mains the excavation may be subjected to dynamic groundwater flow changing the stability of trench, and near abandoned sewers sudden loss of slurry can occur with loss of stability.

In addition, abandoned underground utilities, tunnels, and incidental obstacles should be located and identified since they may require special methods and equipment for their removal.

Availability of utilities.   Fresh water and electricity are necessary for this work. If good water is not available or its supply is limited, special slurries must be used, requiring more elaborate preparation and controls.

Plant layout

Sites that are irregularly contoured or have sloping topography will require extensive preparatory work. Excavation in man-made fills or at the toe of a slope imposes certain stability requirements and may imply grade changes or adjustments that must be considered in the design. In general, trench excavation does not start until guide walls have been built at the ground level. These are discussed and detailed in subsequent sections.

The next step is to locate and set the mud circulation and preparation plant. This consists of slurry mixers, storage tanks, the mud plant separation units, and mud storage area. Adequate mixing facilities and mechanical separators must be provided for the job size and type of excavating equipment.

For rule-of-thumb estimates the average volume of slurry to be used for a given panel can be related to the type of soil; in fine soils of low permeability the slurry volume is about 1.5 times the trench volume; for excavations in gravel and relatively pervious ground, an extra supply of slurry, often 100 percent of the panel volume, should be available.

Plant facilities should be arranged and set in convenient locations where they will not interfere with construction operations such as panel excavation, assembly of reinforcing cages, or flow of traffic. If the construction is central and is carried along a perimeter, the plant units can be arranged at or near the center, where they remain until the work is completed. If the walls are built along a street, the mud plant is moved as needed. When reverse circulation systems are used, most assemblies should be within their optimum range.

Spoil containers and storage tanks can be set at any convenient location that is fairly accessible from any excavation point to receive and hold excavated soil and incidental materials. Since it is not possible to remove these materials immediately as they are excavated, extra storage capacity is necessary.

In regular and unrestricted sites the construction can be processed by simultaneously carrying out several phases (excavation, concreting, materials removal), and a site where these operations are possible at the same time is shown in Fig. 2-5. Conversely, work in a restricted site (for example, a narrow street) will require special rigs, and the resulting congestion will most certainly affect productivity and time

Figure 2-5 Construction of a traffic underpass in Brussels. The site conditions allow several phases of the work to be carried out simultaneously (excavation, concreting, materials handling, assembly of cages).

schedule. The many unknown factors related to underground conditions must be assessed, and this is typically one of the most important phases of the predesign task.

2-3   Guide Walls

Guide walls are reinforced-concrete sections of a suitable configuration built at grade and along the exact alignment of the trench. They are typically constructed ahead of the trenching operations. Since they serve only temporarily, at least one side is dismantled and removed when the structure is built. Guide walls provide several functions: (1) they control the line and grade of the trench and therefore guide the excavation and movement of equipment along the correct outline of the wall; (2) they allow excavation to start from a lower level when obstructions such as sewers and footings exist close to the ground; (3) they brace the guide trench against construction surcharge loads including the passage of equipment, especially with sudden lowering of the slurry level; (4) they protect the upper sections of the excavation face from turbulent action of up-and-down passage of equipment; (5) they support the prefabricated diaphragm sections where this method is used; and (6) they function together with the trench as reservoir for the slurry.

The distance face to face is usually 2 in (5 cm) wider than the equipment pass to facilitate its movement. After the panel is excavated and cleaned, the reinforcing cage is inserted and suspended at the guide walls. Normally, guide walls are internally braced with wood struts to keep them in place and stable against ground distortion. Construction joints should be structurally continuous.

With shallow utilities and footings the tip of guide walls is placed at the same level. Invariably, this base should rest on firm and compact soil to ensure the absence of protrusions that sometimes appear on the finished diaphragm wall just below the guide-wall base level, as shown in Fig. 2-6a. Likewise, in very soft or saturated soil the base level of the guide walls should be selected to prevent washout of soil resulting in bulges formed as shown in Fig. 2-6b.

If the upper ground layer consists of unstable soil (running granular material or soft saturated clay) the guide walls may be built deeper

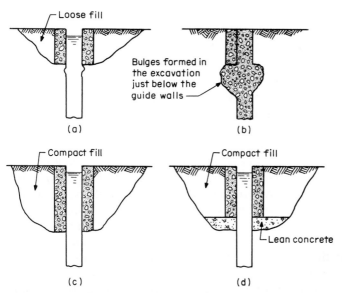

Figure 2-6 Specific guide-wall construction in soft or in caving soil: (a) Variation in slurry level induces flow in outside soft soil and creates cavities. (b) Shallow guide walls and loose fill behind high water table cause the formation of bulges. (c) Preventive action provided by deep guide walls and compact fill behind. (d) Preventive action provided by lean concrete at the base of guide walls and compact fill.

or with a solid base as shown in Fig. 2-6c and d, respectively, replacing also the unstable layer with compact fill.

In most cases a track is laid alongside the guide walls and serves to receive the moving derrick, except when the excavating machine is suspended from crane tractors. Since neither the weight nor the size of this assembly can be known ahead of the contract award, the practice is to detail the guide walls only after the excavating system has been selected. In firm and stable ground portable guide walls made of steel trench sheets, wood blocks, and reusable forms can be used in lieu of concrete guide walls.

Usual guide-wall configurations, shown in Fig. 2-7, cover most situations and ground conditions. The ground side is cast against the soil, whereas the inner face is formed. If a rail is used, the top should be finished smooth and truly horizontal. Certain details are worked out to accommodate the site and ground conditions rather than the excavating system; these details should be specified ahead of the main construction.

2-4 Construction Accuracy and Tolerance

Usual problems and remedies

A finished diaphragm wall may show three basic deviations from the specified accuracy. The first relates to the true vertical alignment; the second involves the wall alignment in plan; and the third involves irregularities and protrusions from the average wall face. The occurrence and extent of these deviations depend on several factors but mainly on the excavating equipment and the skills of its operator; the method of supporting and guiding the rig, including the guide-wall construction; and the type of soil encountered. In the field the construction control that is practicable and attainable should focus on early detection of any deviation. Control, however, is difficult to maintain in ground with boulders and erratic or sloping hard layers.

The horizontal accuracy is better maintained by building the guide walls to true line and by monitoring and checking their actual position during excavation and application of surcharge loads. Concrete bypassing the stop-end tube, either through an existing cavity or because of overexcavation, will obstruct the excavation of the adjacent panel. The result may be the angular distortion of the wall in plan, as shown in Fig. 2-8.

The usually accepted tolerance on verticality is between $\frac{1}{100}$ and $\frac{1}{200}$. For some excavating systems and in ideal ground conditions a tolerance of $\frac{1}{500}$ has been claimed, but in some instances the tolerance

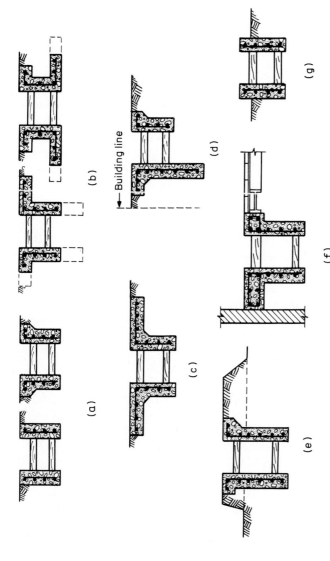

Figure 2-7 Guide-wall details: (*a*) Stable ground conditions and normal-weight excavating machines. (*b*) Unstable ground conditions or heavy-surcharge loads. (*c*) Guide walls for machines requiring a platform on one or on both sides. (*d*) Guide walls near existing buildings or structures. (*e*) Guide walls in man-made fills. (*f*) Guide walls built as part of the main bracing system. (*g*) Guide walls built above existing grade to raise the slurry level.

75

(a)

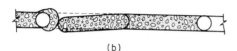

(b)

Figure 2-8 Angular deviation from true alignment caused by concrete penetrating beyond the stop-end tube: (a) Deviation from verticality. (b) Deviation shown in plan.

cannot be better than $\frac{1}{50}$. The FPS specification recommends a construction accuracy in the vertical alignment $\frac{1}{80}$, measured along the wall face at the ends of panels. These limits are, however, academic since in some instances they are unattainable. There is an observed tendency for the vertical construction accuracy to be better in cohesive than in granular soil. In any case, an actual deviation in verticality of more than $\frac{1}{80}$ might indicate a serious condition even when the panels are not continuous structurally. For example, excess deviation could result in construction joints where the adjoining panels are not interlocking but separated at some depth with a potential leakage path, or it could mean an eccentric application of vertical loads. If the vertical accuracy cannot be assured, the wall becomes nonfunctional below a certain depth, and it is better to limit its penetration.

Within the specified limits of vertical tolerance a finished panel may show an angular deviation at any level when viewed in plan. This condition becomes objectionable with respect to the exposed wall face even though the structural performance is not inhibited. Permitted tolerances for such angular deviations are not always necessary, except in special cases when they must be established according to panel length, position, and relation to site conditions.

Protrusions, wall finish, and wall thickness

For every project it is mandatory to specify the tolerance to be allowed for normal wall protrusions resulting from irregularities beyond the general concrete face as the trench is excavated. An overbreak of 3 in

(7.5 cm) has been allowed on many walls considering the functional requirements. The usual tolerance for protrusions on the finished walls is from 7½ to 10 cm (3 to 4 in), but this applies to homogeneous clays or to dense sands and gravel formations where face stability is better maintained. In badly fissured clays and in loose sands, or in the presence of underground obstructions and pockets of soft ground interbedded with hard formations, the tolerance should be increased accordingly. A distinction should be made between unavoidable protrusions and acceptable protrusions in the final wall service. Since some structures show a certain extension of irregularities beyond the average wall face, provisions should be made for trimming the wall when it is exposed. The general appearance of the wall may also be disrupted by various irregular sections that should be finished by chipping and grinding or by applying cement grout in order to make the final surface conform to the specified maximum variations.

The surface finish of a concrete wall cast against a vertical earth cut depends to a great extent on the nature and texture of soil. A filter cake formed along the face acts as a smooth plaster form and produces a relatively smooth face. The same effect is also noticed at the ends of panels where vinylon sheets are used to deter leakage of fresh concrete. In general the wall finish is influenced by the roughness of the soil worked through, and varies from good in clay to rough in gravel so that face treatment is sometimes necessary. The wall finish is improved by guniting, and where necessary face treatment may be specified to include masonry blocks or face brick, precast panels, and a separate inside decoration wall.

The actual wall thickness is greater than the design or theoretical width dimension, for three different reasons: (1) the excavation is likely to trim off soil beyond the theoretical lines as it moves up and down the trench; (2) individual soil grains may be lost by sloughing and peeling off until this process is stopped by the plastering effect of the filter cake; and (3) the lateral thrust of fresh concrete can displace soft silty soil inward. Practical experience shows a wall overbreak 3 to 6 percent in clay, 4 to 8 percent in sand, and 7 to 10 percent in gravel.

Top concrete layer

When the fresh concrete is poured to ground level, overpouring is mandatory to skim off intermixed slurry and concrete until clean mix emerges. When the wall must be terminated below the slurry level, the pour is usually finished at least 30 cm (1 ft) above the theoretical elevation. The extra concrete may be broken out and replaced with new concrete when the wall is exposed.

The flow motion of fresh concrete around a tremie pipe produces an alignment that is seldom level, and this complicates the desired top of wall finish. With a central tremie pipe position, the highest point of the rising surface is around the tremie pipe, and this surface slopes away from the pipe according to an angle of repose so that the more flowable and liquid the concrete the flatter the slope. The concrete around the tremie pipe is likely to emerge and reach the top first, with the concrete at the panel ends much lower; hence some tamping may be necessary to give the wall an even surface.

Walls terminated below guide walls

For walls that must be terminated below ground level, the end of the pour may require special handling. The top surface must be as level as possible, and this sometimes can be achieved only by ramming the fresh concrete with heavy flat-faced or grid-type tools. In addition, immersion vibrators can be inserted to consolidate the fresh mix around the tremie pipe and spread it evenly in the panel. Since this is done through the slurry and in the absence of visual contact, it can produce a reasonably smooth and level top but can also cause some mixing of fresh concrete with bentonite.

The construction must be modified when excavating a panel adjacent to a concreted panel for a wall terminated below ground level. In this case it may be necessary to backfill the previous panel with granular material above the concreted portion and use an end barrier to isolate this backfill from the adjacent new excavation. Another solution is to use a lean concrete mix as backfill above the top of the wall.

If the upper wall section must be used to support soldier piles with lagging, the top of the poured wall should be relatively level to ensure a uniform pile embedment. These details should be studied and worked out in the design stage since they require the inclusion of appropriate items in the specifications and in the bill of material, and also result in construction tolerances that must be compatible with the final arrangement. If the wall is to be terminated below ground level, the plans should indicate the lowest elevation for good, durable concrete.

2-5   Watertightness of Diaphragm Walls

Watertightness is particularly important for permanent walls used in building basements, subway construction, traffic underpasses, and applications where function is as essential as strength. The degree of watertightness that can be achieved with this type of construction depends primarily on the pore structure of set concrete and on the joint details and adequacy of execution. Invariably, the watertightness of the wall must be accomplished ignoring back-face treatment since this is not accessible except for some grouting operations.

Watertightness of concrete

For normal concrete the impermeability of the finished structure is improved with the quality of constituent materials. Factors influencing this characteristic are the degree of compaction actually attained, the lack of any special surface finish, and the subsequent treatment and exposure to favorable curing conditions.

Cement and water.   For workable mixes of the type used in diaphragm walls the permeability increases quite rapidly with the water-cement ratio provided the latter exceeds 0.6, or about 7 gal of water per sack of cement. For water-cement ratios up to 0.6 the permeability k_c of hardened concrete is of the order 10^{-11} cm/s but increases with wetter mixes, and for water-cement ratio close to 0.7 it approaches 10^{-10} cm/s (Powers et al., 1955, 1959).

Permeability decreases as the cement-voids ratio increases, and this is confirmed by several investigators (Troxell et al., 1968). On the other hand, greater fineness of the cement generally improves watertightness as it improves strength and durability.

Aggregate type and grade.   For a given water-cement ratio, the greater the maximum aggregate size the greater the flow because of the large water voids developed on the underside of the coarser particles (Valenta, 1968). The aggregate fraction should be of low porosity and permeability. As a means of comparison, a well-graded aggregate system is even more important from the standpoint of watertightness than in terms of flowability and strength since it produces denser concrete. For a dense mix with maximum aggregate size of 2 cm (¾ in) and a water-cement ratio of 0.6, the permeability will be of the order of 10^{-10} cm/s. These values have been established by testing samples from large-diameter piles installed under bentonite slurry (Sliwinski and Fleming, 1974).

Admixtures.   The use of the so-called waterproof cements or special admixtures to improve watertightness does not necessarily produce the desired result. Except for pozzolans, the use of extra cement is more effective. The presence of entrained air should not be expected to increase permeability provided the water-cement ratio is within the limits specified in the previous section. Entrained air can benefit watertightness by reducing bleeding and segregation. The risk of demixing during the long transport and placing time is reduced, and while in place the capillary system is inactivated because of the limited amount of air.

Placing and curing. The final watertightness is markedly influenced by minor construction defects and by the conditions of placement and curing. Serious leaks will result from cracks in the finished structure or from voids created in the concrete due to honeycombing or segregation. The lack of vibratory compaction should be compensated by a flowable mix and careful placement. Bentonite and mud trappings in the finished wall are critical in terms of strength but are practically impermeable. However, cavities and openings around inserts not reached by the fresh mix can be particularly harmful and potential sources of leakage.

Because of the humid curing conditions shrinkage cracks are almost eliminated. Since panel lengths are relatively short, long-term shrinkage is accommodated at the vertical joints so that intermediate cracks need not be developed. For the usual conditions of underground curing the continued hydration of cement can cause gel development that reduces the void size with a beneficial effect on watertightness.

Theoretical permeability. This can be expressed in terms of a coefficient k_c according to Darcy's law. For example, we consider a wall that is 60 cm (24 in) thick, has a porosity of 15 percent, and retains a hydraulic head of 10 m (33 ft); taking into account a suction pressure of 1 atm to assist water flow, the quantity of water percolating through the wall is close to 0.3 liter for 1000 m^2 of wall surface over a period of 24 h (Sliwinski and Fleming, 1974).

Watertightness of construction joints

The simple butt connection or the round-end tube joint cannot be considered waterproof since they cannot completely stop seepage. Significant leakage is rare, however, probably because of the presence of bentonite gel mixed with soil fraction behind and across the joint. Whenever some leakage has occurred, it has been attributed to differential deflection and movement between adjoining panels, and this situation is more likely to develop near corners. Typically differential movement is followed by a corresponding leakage at the construction joint.

The matter of deflection differentials between wall panels is essentially a structural problem, and depends on panel shape and plan, wall height, the use of anchors and preloading, excavation procedures, and the application of load. If the solution is structurally satisfactory, the construction joints should perform as expected. The use of shear transfer devices between panels merely to control differential deflection should be considered with caution since it may only shift the problem away from the joints.

The usual practice for dealing with damp joints is to allow the leak to appear and wait until the differential wall deflection has occurred. The problem is then remedied by grouting the back of the joint either vertically or horizontally depending on access. Alternatively, a steel or other suitable plate bedded on epoxy-resin mortar can be bolted to the concrete over the interior face of the joint.

In walls constructed with prefabricated panels the continuous layer of grout remaining on the soil side provides an added protection as long as the joint does not crack because of movement.

If a waterproof joint is specified, the water stop details shown in other sections can be used in conjunction with a round tube joint, and if necessary a special treatment may be applied to the joints. With prefabricated panels, a thin impervious lining can be placed on the soil side. Watertight joint details are discussed in Sec. 6-15.

Watertightness of finished structure

In many instances the waterproofing of underground structures where diaphragm walls are part of the permanent system is decided as a compromise between watertightness and economy after all merits and relative costs are known. The same principle is also used to determine the extent and location of areas to be waterproofed. Thus, if a dry roadway or a dry railroad is all that is required and lateral water infiltration is not significant, it usually is sufficient to waterproof the roof of the box section.

For building basements watertightness is improved by proper construction and execution of details. A common cause of leakage is panel separation. Good panel contact is therefore essential, and if necessary premolded water stops can be inserted across the joint to improve watertightness.

The leakage of tunnel structures usually is attributed to poor construction. The junction between the roof slab and the sidewalls is the most critical and should be detailed considering tunnel dimensions, shape, and anticipated shrinkage. At present there are two trends for waterproofing. One is to treat the roof of the section externally with hot bituminous materials and overlap the joint between tunnel walls and roof. By contrast the second method shows reliance of fully watertight concrete and joints, and is used with the conventional cut-and-cover construction.

2-6   Problems Related to Underground Structures and Utilities

As the case is with any form of underground construction, the design should address effects associated with utilities, sewers, water mains, existing subbasements, freight tunnels, and incidental underground openings. The severity of this problem often is ignored and often is exaggerated. From the construction standpoint it may require special work or combination of methods and the use of special equipment.

Sewers, water mains, and utilities. This problem can be particularly severe at crossings where these utilities occur as a dense network. The most usual effects are slurry contamination, trench instability because of broken mains, and slurry escaping to existing openings. Underground power and communication lines are commonly protected or relocated before trenching.

If sewers and water mains are at relatively shallow depth, the walls should be terminated below that level. If the ground support must be extended to ground level, a practical solution is to insert soldier piles and use lagging in the top part. Many city ordinances prohibit construction in the 10 ft below grade to ensure space for future utilities. If the utilities are still shallow but too many to deal with, it is better to pretrench to just below the utility line and carry the guide walls to the same level.

In the extreme case it may be necessary to combine the system with other ground techniques and special equipment, such as high-mobility backhoes as shown in Fig. 2-9. If isolated utilities exist at considerable depth (20 ft or more), the construction may be carried out by bypassing the utility as shown in Fig. 2-10 and by pregrouting the zone around the pipe before excavation. The wall portion left unfinished around and beneath the sewer is completed in sections after general excavation. If the utilities are too many and erratically located, the diaphragm wall can be combined with bored piles.

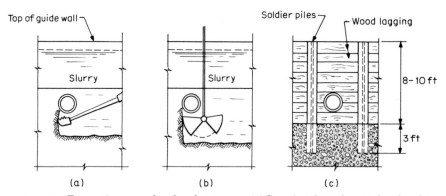

Figure 2-9 Excavation around and under a sewer: (*a*) Scraping the soil around and under the pipe using special tools attached to a backhoe. (*b*) Lowering a low-head bucket close to and under the pipe. (*c*) Setting soldier piles into fresh concrete and installing wood lagging.

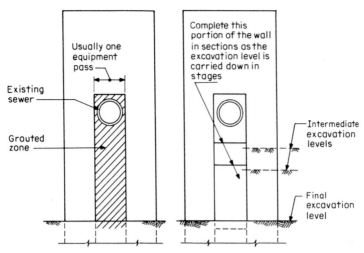

Figure 2-10 Construction around and under an existing sewer located at relatively great depth.

Subbasements. In this category are chambers, access holes, and small openings. Long subbasements along the trench alignment can serve as working platform and as guide walls, but more often they are an obstruction in the path of excavation interfering with new construction. In this case a closure wall will protect adjacent usable space, and the work is carried out as shown in Fig. 2-11.

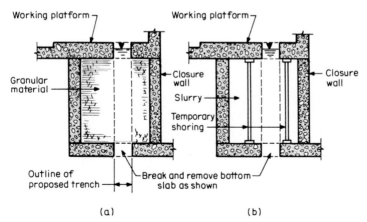

Figure 2-11 Construction through an existing subbasement: (*a*) Break slab as shown, backfill with granular material, and start trenching from the existing ground level. (*b*) Support subbasement temporarily as shown, fill with slurry if necessary, and pour wall to basement level.

Abandoned tunnels. In most urban areas these are the reality of the past, and unless they are identified, located, and dealt with, they may be the cause of various problems. If their configuration is similar to Fig. 2-11, the construction can proceed in the same manner. If the openings are in good condition and accessible from within, a common remedy is to plug the sections on either side of the proposed trench and then break and remove the portion that interfaces with the excavation.

2-7 Problems Caused by Boulders and Obstructions

Large boulders and man-made obstructions typically slow down excavation. If they are isolated and occur occasionally, they do not require conversion to percussive tools since they can be removed by conventional grabs or by special extractors. The decision as to how many obstructions per panel will justify the use of chisels and percussive tools is usually left with the contractor.

If large boulders exist at shallow depth and above the water table, they should be dug out, as shown in Fig. 2-12. The hole is backfilled to satisfactory compaction, the guide walls are rebuilt, and the excavation is repeated several days later.

If large boulders are encountered at considerable depth or below the water table, the construction can proceed as shown in Fig. 2-13. In this case the obstruction is bypassed and the concrete is poured to the top of the boulder. The wall is finished as shown in Fig. 2-13c and d.

In these cases the construction tolerance should be established with regard to boulder size, in terms of both attainable verticality and al-

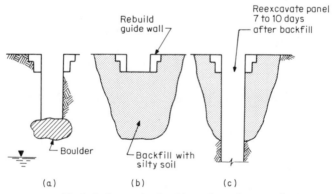

Figure 2-12 Method of removing boulders above the groundwater table: (a) Boulder is found at relatively shallow depth. (b) Obstruction is dug out and the area is backfilled. (c) Panel is reexcavated.

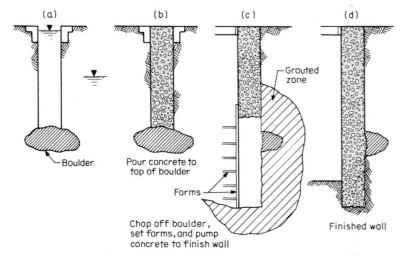

Figure 2-13 Method of removing boulders and finishing panels when boulders exist below the groundwater table or in deep strata.

lowable protrusions. These items are usually handled in the special provisions on a time and material basis.

2-8   Introduction to Excavating Systems

Although it is rather unorthodox to identify the method of excavation or the type of equipment when a project is in the design stage, it is expedient to know that in certain sites and soil conditions certain types of equipment may be more efficient than others; in this case the construction details should be planned and scheduled accordingly.

The ideal endeavor for any contractor is to use a process and equipment that will expedite the work in the shortest possible time and at the least possible cost. An important factor in planning the excavation is the direct cost and availability of equipment to the contractor, including initial investment, rental charges, and operating and maintenance charges. Any misconceptions with regard to these considerations should be resolved by a simple statement: For this type of work, only excavating systems developed for this purpose should be used.

Classification of excavating systems

Since only concrete diaphragm walls are discussed here, we consider machines and equipment developed for this purpose.

Bucket and grab types.   These machines must have a high weight-to-volume ratio to overcome drag and flotation effects of the slurry gel.

The grabs are usually round or egg-shaped to provide half-rounded joints at the ends. The excavation is carried out directly and the materials are discharged by the grab in a cyclic process. Examples are mechanical diggers, bucket excavators, shovels, and special trenching grabs and clamshells.

The last type is in broad use and popular among contractors. Cable-supported grabs are lighter and more maneuverable, but the digging action must be controlled by experienced operators. They give fast excavation speeds, but unless the ground is relatively soft, they require bouncing at the trench bottom to give sufficient bite. This problem is remedied by power-closing grabs, operated by either hydraulic or electric mechanisms. This allows higher operating speeds even in dense ground and improves efficiency.

Other improvements include the use of a kelly to which the main equipment is fixed. The kelly is guided above the ground and functions to position and control the equipment above the ground, guide the machine during lowering, and provide additional weight. Kelly bars are much heavier and suitable where restricted headroom, difficult perimeter, and weight limitations do not exist.

Percussive tools.   These are extra heavy and rigid, often of special design. They are typically used to break rock or loosen hard ground where other types of equipment are not effective. The excavation is slow and therefore the cost is higher. The cost factor should be carefully articulated when a determination is made to have the wall penetrate into rock or similar hard stratum either for bearing or for sealing the excavation. This requirement means conversion of the excavating system to percussive tools when the hard formation is reached.

Rotary drilling equipment.   Also referred to as hollow-stem large-diameter bit rigs, this equipment can perform either slot or circular excavations. The drilling bits loosen the soil through simultaneous action, helped by side cutters moving vertically to cut through soil not reached by the bits along the tangent line. The soil is consolidated into individual cuttings that are mixed with slurry and held in suspension, and then circulated upward through the drill stem and reverse-circulation hose for separation in screens and cyclones.

These machines are used primarily for structural diaphragm walls and load-bearing elements of linear, prismatic, and circular configurations. Continuous improvements include better controls and devices in the main system to monitor the various operations.

Reverse circulation.   This feature allows the direct removal of sand and clay cuttings through the drill stem and a hydraulic pipeline. Reverse

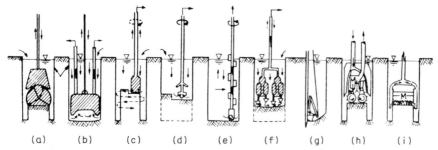

(a)   (b)   (c)   (d)   (e)   (f)   (g)   (h)   (i)

Figure 2-14 Equipment for slurry-trench excavation: (*a*) Clamshell bucket attached to a kelly. (*b*) Vertical percussive bit with reverse circulation. (*c*) Percussive benching bit. (*d*) Rotary benching bit. (*e*) Rotary bit with vertical cutter. (*f*) Rotary drilling machine with reverse circulation. (*g*) Bucket scraper. (*h*) Bell-mouth suction rotary cutter with direct circulation. (*i*) Horizontal auger machine.

circulation is thus a built-in process whereby the slurry suspends all excavated materials in its volume and through continuous circulation conveys them to the surface. The process is possible through suction or air lift forcing the slurry up through a reverse hose to the mechanical separation units. There the solid materials are intercepted and collected for disposal while the slurry is returned to the trench through the supply line. The slurry functions therefore in two ways: initially for face support and trench stability, and then as the transporting agent for the excavated materials. This dual function means compatibility between drilling and materials handling, and coordination of the supply and suction pumps.

Representative types of equipment are shown in Fig. 2-14.

Factors affecting selection of equipment

Consistent excavation rates, horizontal and vertical accuracy, and flexibility to deal with special site and soil conditions are the main criteria that dictate the choice of equipment. The selection must also be satisfied in terms of cost and maintainability; i.e., equipment is chosen because it can do the job at the least total cost. Caution is necessary, however, to distinguish between the cost of different types of equipment and the total cost of a job under various types of machines.

Purpose of construction. Structural diaphragm walls are built in relatively narrow trenches (24 to 30 in) that require better excavation accuracy, coordination in materials handling, and operational flexibility. This work requires more sophisticated equipment with better controls.

Type of soil. The soil at the site can vary from very soft to very hard, and often encompasses the entire range. Most clay and sand formations can be excavated with most machine types. A serious drop in efficiency should be expected in hard formations, dense gravel, bouldery ground, and bedrock. In these conditions percussive tools or rotary equipment are often the only method of excavation.

Operating difficulties and efficiency, penetrating rates, and drilling output are often critical from the viewpoint of construction scheduling and also in terms of design consistency. Contractors and equipment manufacturers usually provide data from actual field practice where the difficulty of excavation in hard strata is quantified in terms of time. These may be used as guidelines in the design stage but should not be the sole criterion for detailing a project.

Excavation depth. Most excavating systems have depth limitations, or at some point efficiency decreases to a level at which the equipment becomes inoperable.

Physical layout and special conditions. For urban construction, the selection may be limited or dictated by space availability, proximity to existing structures, headroom, size and weight limitations, mobility, accuracy of excavation, time restrictions, and constraints such as noise and vibrations.

Project specifications normally should dictate or define the final results, but occasionally it is necessary to identify certain processes to ensure the final structure, and this may restrict the choice of equipment. In addition, the engineer should check the commercial availability of equipment; some machines are developed on a proprietary basis, and others can be available through rental or purchase.

Operating skills. Mobile equipment for slurry trench excavation requires exceptional operating skills. Some machines have automatic control devices; others rely on hand controls, levers, and pedals. Thus the operation requires coordination of operator and equipment, and previous experience or training become mandatory. Relevant factors are also the local labor requirements and regulations.

2-9   Excavation with Clamshells

Cable-suspended clamshells. These have fairly simple structural details. Grabbing types of equipment operated on cables are easy to handle and popular because of their efficiency in bulk excavation for average soil conditions and the smooth shearing operation when cutting the soil.

Cable-suspended clamshells are flexible and maneuverable, and therefore suited to sites with physical constraints. They can work under limited headroom, and when crane-operated they do not require a fixed relationship between the excavating clam and the position of the crane. This mobility is important in congested sites and allows the crane to handle the excavating implement for trenching directly adjacent and close to buildings while positioned away from the trench, so that live load surcharge has little effect on trench stability.

In cable-suspended clamshells the verticality of the tool and therefore the accuracy of the excavation are primarily controlled by gravity action. In this context a heavy tool performs better than a light one, and the suspending mechanism from the winching rig is most effective if it utilizes the continuous effect of gravity. The cyclic process of lifting and lowering the tool under gravity has a rectifying effect on deviations from verticality (Fuchsberger, 1974). The penetration of the grab depends on its design and construction features but more specifically on the closing force and weight, as shown in Fig. 2-15.

Mechanical (or rope-operated) clamshells depend on their own weight to close the grab, but the effective weight is the actual minus the lifting force. To assist closing, pulleys are often used to bring the grabs together.

Hydraulic or power-operated clamshells have greater closing power, and this improves efficiency. Either hydraulic or electric motors may be self-contained in the main body. The choice depends on several factors, although hydraulic grabs tend to be favored because they are more flexible, less dependent on union and local regulations, and have

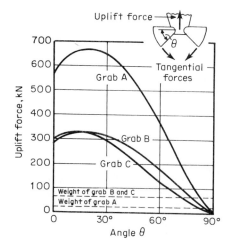

Figure 2-15 Uplift force on grab during closing cycle. (*From Sliwinski and Fleming, 1974.*)

their operating power readily available. Power-operated clamshells are better controlled because of unlimited power.

Obstructions, boulders, and difficult formations are handled more efficiently with cable-suspended grabs of extra heavy type. Where boulders are involved, mechanical clamshells are claimed to be more flexible (Ressi, 1974). Certain depth limitations may have to be accepted for all types, and in most instances these do not relate to the excavating capability but are imposed by the desired tolerance in the verticality of the wall.

Kelly bars. A hydraulic clamshell attached to a kelly bar is shown in Fig. 2-16. This attachment improves vertical control and introduces more weight for closing the grabs. The choice depends on preference and convenience but is often related to productivity. The excavation depth is also a limiting factor. Single-piece kelly bars will perform economically up to depths of 40 m (130 ft). Telescoping kelly bars have a usual depth range up to 60 m (200 ft). The structural details of kellys and extensions therefrom are designed to suit the general or special requirements of the excavation including resistance to buckling, abil-

Figure 2-16 Hydraulic clamshell attached to a kelly bar excavating slurry-trench panels for load-bearing elements. (*Frankl.*)

ity to withstand distortions, and the need to increase the downward force to close the grab for higher productivity.

2-10   Special Systems

With the current state of the art, diaphragm wall panels can be cast alternately or successively, as shown in Figs. 1-4 and 1-5. In the first case, the construction begins by excavating and concreting primary panels 1, 3, 5, ... Then the construction is completed by excavathing and concreting secondary panels 2, 4, 6, . . . between the primary panels. In the sequential construction successive panels are excavated and concreted one after another; i.e., panel $n + 1$ is cast against panel n.

The stop-end forms shown in Fig. 1-1 can have various sections, but the simplest is the round tube. Irrespective of their slope, they are used as sliding forms and must be pulled out lengthwise. They must therefore be extracted before the final setting of the concrete, but selecting the proper time for this extraction must be carefully controlled: the concrete should set but should not collapse into the hollow space created as the tube is withdrawn, and there should be no considerable adhesion that may prevent extraction. The extraction operation is shown in Fig. 2-17 in connection with concreting a panel and excavating the next panel. In this process the diaphragm wall is an assembly of primary independent panels placed side by side. Structural continuity is feasible and can be provided as shown in other sections.

Diaphragm wall with CWS joint.   Bachy (Dupeuble, 1985) has developed a joint detail that in many instances can provide a practical solution to the problems of discontinuous wall construction. With this detail the continuity of wall watertightness is restored by installing additional water barriers, and the mechanical continuity of the joint allows the transfer of forces between panels.

The CWS form is not extracted as a sliding form before excavating the adjacent panel, but it is extracted laterally after the adjacent panel has been excavated. This basic departure from the conventional ways of detailing joints allows the presence of an actual rail temporarily sealed in the concrete of the previous panel while the excavation is carried out. This rail is a guide for the excavating grab, and secures the geometric continuity of the wall.

The form is composed of a caisson beam made of high-strength steel. After the panel is excavated the CWS form is installed against the ground at the end of the panel, and remains there as the fresh concrete is set. When the excavation of the adjacent panel is completed, the form is pulled aside by the actual excavating machine, adapted to slide down the wings of the form, as shown in Fig. 2-18. The progression of

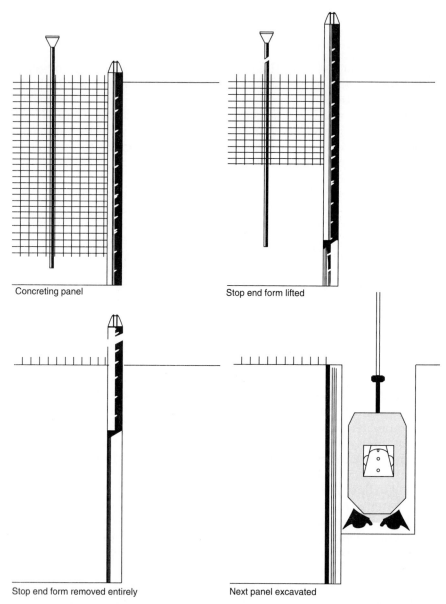

Concreting panel

Stop end form lifted

Stop end form removed entirely

Next panel excavated

Figure 2-17 Round tube form; extracting the stop-end form at the end of concreting and before excavating the next panel. (*From Dupeuble, 1985.*)

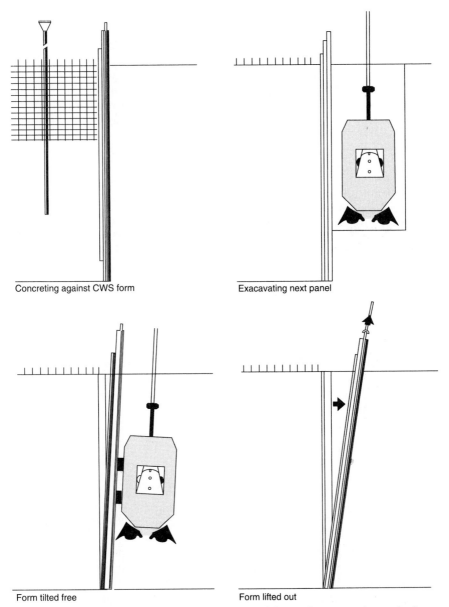

Concreting against CWS form

Exacavating next panel

Form tilted free

Form lifted out

Figure 2-18 CWS system; pulling aside the stop-end form after concreting and after excavating the next panel. (*From Dupeuble, 1985.*)

the blades pushed between metal and concrete from top to bottom of the panel secures the detachment of the form and the subsequent lifting out to be placed at the far end again.

The excavating tool is locked onto the form at regular intervals throughout the excavation process. Thus each excavation elementary sequence includes an excavation run, followed by a guidance run, that brings proper calibration of the panel as construction progresses. Any tendency toward deviation is corrected as soon as it appears. At the end of the excavation operation the form is essentially unrestrained and can be readily detached.

The waterproofing and structural connection across this joint are discussed in other sections.

2-11   Excavation with Rotary Drilling Equipment

Figure 2-14d to f and h shows commercially produced rotary drilling machines for slot excavation available in a variety of mountings and driving arrangements. The cutting elements are rotary drilling bits provided with hard teeth. The drilling is done either by cutting the soil or by crushing soft rock. The cuttings thus produced are suspended in the slurry volume and removed or flushed out of the trench. A sufficient number of cutters or bits are extended over the face of the machine to cover the entire area as the equipment is operated. The excavation is usually accompanied by reverse circulation, or suction and direct circulation. Examples of rotary drilling systems are presented in the following sections.

The BW system

The BW long drill, shown in Fig. 2-19, is a power-operated excavator with reverse circulation as standard feature. Developed in Japan, it has operational characteristics to accommodate urban construction conditions and requirements. Thus the machine is designed to have manageable size and overall height to work under limited overhead room and in confined space. The system has adjustable components and variable motor drill sizes to allow variations in panel width and length, and is free from noise and vibrations.

The motor drill usually is operated from the standard drilling rig shown in Fig. 2-19a and b, but for increased mobility around corners and irregular excavations the drill is mounted on crawler tractors. The submersible motor drill is available in three models. Figure 2-19c and d shows mechanical drawings for model BWN-5580. Specifications and dimensions are shown in Table 2-1.

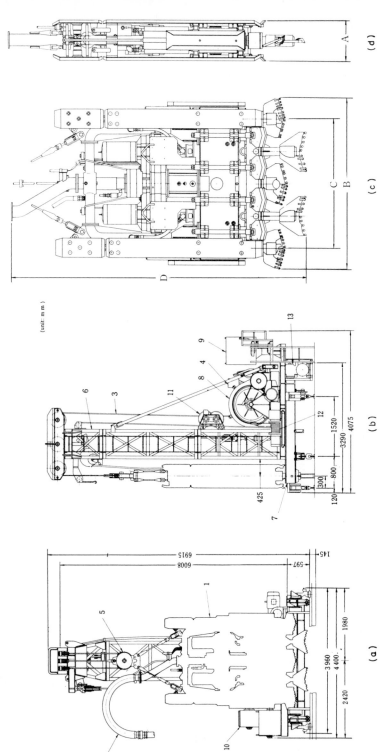

(unit: m m)

(d)

(c)

(b)

(a)

Figure 2-19 The BW system: (*a*) and (*b*) Drilling rig and assembly parts. (*c*) and (*d*) Submersible motor drill. 1 = submersible motor drill. 2 = reverse hose. 3 = hoisting wire rope. 4 = feed indicator. 5 = running block. 6 = derrick. 7 = frame. 8 = hoist. 9 = switchboard. 10 = cable reel. 11 = rope guide. 12 = derrick hoist. 13 = baby compressor for adjustable guide. (*Tone Boring Co.*)

TABLE 2-1 Specifications and Dimensions for BW Long Drill

Model	Bit diameter A (wall width)		Single excavation length B		Effective length C		Height of motor drill D	
	mm	in	mm	in	mm	in	mm	in
BWN-4055	400	15.75	2500	98.43	2100	82.68	4300–4320	169.29–170.08
	450	17.72	2550	100.39				
	500	19.69	2600	102.36				
	550	21.65	2650	104.33				
BWN-5580	550	21.65	2470	97.24	1920	75.59	4525–4555	178.15–179.33
	600	23.62	2520	99.21				
	650	25.59	2570	101.18				
	700	27.56	2620	103.15				
	750	29.53	2670	105.12				
	800	31.50	2720	107.09				
BWN-80120	800	31.50	3600	141.73	2800	110.24	5505–5555	216.73–218.70
	900	35.43	3700	145.67				
	1000	39.37	3800	149.61				
	1100	43.31	3900	153.54				
	1200	47.24	4000	157.48				

Model	Excavation depth		No. of drill bits	Bit rotation at 50 Hz, r/min	ID of reverse pipe		Power required,* kW	Weight of motor drill	
	m	ft			mm	in		kg	lb
BWN-4055	50	164	7	50	150	6	15	7.500	16.500
BWN-5580	50	164	5	35	150	6	15	10.000	22.000
BWN-80120	50	164	5	20	200	8	18.5	18.000	39.700

*×2 sets (6 poles).

Equipment and instrumentation. The assembly consists of the following parts.

1. Long drill, equipped with a prime motor. Main parts are the drill bits, side cutters and guide plates, and reverse-circulation hose.

2. Control system, usually mounted on a derrick. This includes the hoist, cable reel, and operating instruments such as the switchboard, feed indicator, and deflection indicator. A slurry-level indicator is agitated when the slurry level is suddenly lowered.

3. Suction pump, used to maintain reverse circulation. Suction is used to eject soil and cuttings mixed with slurry through the reverse hose and transfer them to mechanical separation units. Alternatively, an air lift is used to remove excavated materials.

4. Mud circulation units, including a vibrating screen to intercept coarse granular soil and dry clay cuttings and a cyclone to intercept finer soil particles.

5. Slurry mixes and storage tanks.

Excavation. This process is shown in the flow diagram of Fig. 2-20. The hose that supplies fresh slurry is usually supplemented by an emergency line to control the slurry level. Drilling is carried out by the bits arranged in two levels to cover the panel pass with adequate overlapping, while side cutters oscillate up and down to trim off soil beyond the bit radius. A portion of the weight is utilized to supply pressure on the bits, while the remaining weight serves to control the true vertical line by gravity.

Cuttings and excavated soil particles are sucked through the center drill stem and forced up to the vibrating screen, and then through the cyclone. The slurry continues its circulation to storage tanks from where it is returned to the trench.

The continuous recirculation of slurry results in a relatively turbulent flow in the pipe circuit, and this process agitates the slurry in the trench continuously. In this condition, the colloidal suspension seldom has a chance to gel in the trench as the excavation continues, and therefore the slurry control limits should be based on the initial rather than on the 10-min gel strength.

Reverse circulation. Reverse circulation is claimed to be more efficient with pump suction than air lift. Efficiency is enhanced when soil materials are handled at the same rate at which they are excavated. In most cases, there is no limit on the pump capacity necessary to match the excavation rate, so that it is possible to provide a coordinated set of pumps, power motors, and hoses.

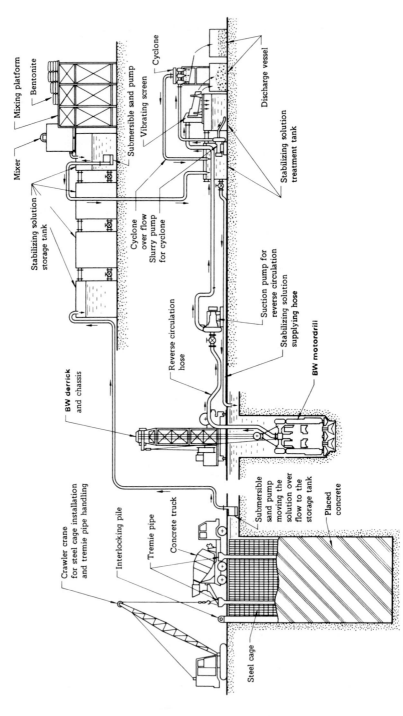

Figure 2-20 Flow diagram of BW system showing excavation and recirculation of slurry.

Mixing platform

Bentonite

Mixer

Submersible sand pump

Vibrating screen

Cyclone

Discharge vessel

Stabilizing solution treatment tank

Stabilizing solution storage tank

Cyclone over flow
Slurry pump for cyclone

Suction pump for reverse circulation

Stabilizing solution supplying hose

Reverse circulation hose

BW motordrill

BW derrick and chassis

Crawler crane for steel cage installation and tremie pipe handling

Interlocking pile

Tremie pipe

Concrete truck

Submersible sand pump moving the solution over flow to the storage tank

Placed concrete

Steel cage

At higher speeds, however, cavitation may occur, tending to inhibit the suction process. Suction is restrained at some specific speed designated as the critical speed for the permissible height of suction lift up to which cavitation is avoided. If v_c denotes the critical speed,

$$v_c = \left(\frac{k}{h}\right)^n \tag{2-1}$$

where h = total suction head and k nad n are appropriate constants. From Eq. (2-1) it follows that the initial speed of the flow will at some point become the critical velocity v_c once the critical height has been reached in the course of excavation.

Pumps with a freshwater capacity of 5 m³/min have been used and found effective in providing suction lift for excavation up to 45 m (150 ft) deep. The basic capacity Q in fresh water is reduced, however, when slurry mixed with soil must be handled, and in this case Q must be multiplied by an empirical reduction coefficient k_1, usually ranging from 0.40 to 0.55 (Ueda, 1974). In addition, the slurry can handle only a certain volume of earth materials as it travels through the hose. This ratio k_2 of solid content to slurry volume is about 0.3 for suction pumps and much less for air lift. Considering also the resulting volume expansion from the original (undisturbed) state to the excavated condition (usually 130 percent), it follows that the practical rate at which excavated materials are removed is

$$Q_p = \frac{Qk_1k_2}{1.3} \tag{2-2}$$

where Q is the initial freshwater capacity quoted for the pump and k_1 and k_2 are given empirically. For example, we consider a pump with initial freshwater capacity $Q = 5$ m³/min, and also assume $k_1 = 0.40$ and $k_2 = 0.30$. The rate of materials handling is

$$Q_p = \frac{5(0.40)(0.30)}{1.3} = 0.46 \text{ m}^3/\text{min} = 27.6 \text{ m}^3/\text{h}$$

The resulting practical rate is compared with the expected drilling rate, and if the two rates are not compatible, a higher-capacity pump is selected. The usual recommended diameter for the reverse circulation hose is 6 in and preferably 8 in.

Comparison of suction pump and air lift. For panel depths exceeding about 40 m (130 ft), the excavated materials are removed with air lift. Compressed air is applied to the center bit and forces mud and cuttings to enter the reverse hose. In purely cohesive soil water jetting is combined with air lift to prevent cuttings from sticking to the drill bits, and the slurry is delivered to the trench using a mud slush pump.

Air lift is not recommended for shallow depths. However, its efficiency is improved with deeper excavations as shown in Fig. 2-21. These diagrams indicate the practical range of either system, and suggest that if conversion from suction pump to air lift is necessary, it can be made at a depth of 100 ft (30 m) where the two systems are equivalent.

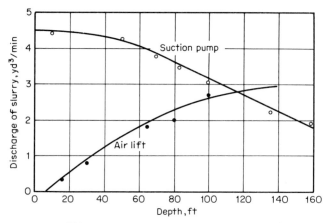

Figure 2-21 Efficiency of suction pump vs. air lift in reverse circulation; suction pump: 6-in-diameter suction, 6-in-diameter delivery, capacity 6.5 yd³/min: air lift 100 lb/in²: air compressor capacity 13 yd³/min. (*From Ueda, 1974.*)

Within their optimum range, suction pumps offer further advantages. By immediately removing the cuttings, there is little chance of dissolving and mixing with the slurry; since the cuttings arrive at the vibrating screen well preserved and compact, they are better separated. Suction pumps extend their transporting range to 500 ft and can handle cohesive as well as granular materials.

Drilling rates. Quoted rates from excavation with the BWN 5580 model in a panel 2.52 m long and 0.6 m wide (cross-sectional area 1.44 m²) are shown in Table 2-2. The drilling rate is the rate of vertical advance, and this multiplied by the panel area gives the excavation rate. These data are based on ideal operating conditions and exclude incidental breakdowns or mandatory shutdowns to service and move the equipment. As expected, better rates are attained in soft or loose soil. Referring to the previous section, a pump with $Q = 5$ m³/min

TABLE 2-2 Drilling Rates of BW Long Drill*

Type of soil	Drilling rate, m/h	Excavation rate, m³/h
Stiff clay	15	21.6
Very stiff clay	12	17.3
Hard clay	8	11.5
Medium sand	12	17.3
Dense sand and gravel	5.5	8.0

*Data taken from actual field tests.

will accommodate the excavation requirements represented by Table 2-2.

Where the machine must be used to penetrate and disintegrate rock or cemented materials, the side cutters are removed since they can slow down drilling. At best, the penetration is very slow and in the range 0.3 to 2.0 m/h (about 1 to 6.5 ft). In these conditions drilling should be implemented by chisels or percussive tools.

Separation units. These include mechanical separators or simple tanks where soil particles suspended in the slurry settle down to the bottom.

Vibrating screens intercept the coarse fraction or clay cuttings as shown in Fig. 2-22*a* and *b*. This assembly has a screen, frame, separator, switchboard, and piping. Its average capacity is 1 to 2 m³/min, and sufficient to accommodate most drilling rates. From the screen the slurry continues to the cyclone. This unit is used either to clean the overflow of slurry and remove sand particles that went through the screen or to reduce the solid content by condensing the underflow of slurry. These processes occur if the slurry has a specific gravity less than 1.15 and a viscosity less than 60 s. Suitable types of screens and cyclones and methods for checking their efficiency are recommended by Tone Boring Co. (1974).

Excavation sequence. Efficiency is maximized if the panel length is optimized in terms of equipment passes. Typically, the excavation can be processed as shown in Fig. 2-23, but the three- and five-pass excavation is most common. The clearance between alternate passes should be less than 3 ft and close to 2 ft so that the resulting thin earth column of the intermediate pass will allow full overlapping. For the arrangement shown in Fig. 2-23 the average panel length is about 5 m (16 ft) for three passes, 7.5 m (25 ft) for five passes, and 10.5 m (35 ft) for seven passes.

(a)

(b)

Figure 2-22 Mechanical separation of excavated soil in a vibrating screen: (*a*) Sand and gravel. (*b*) Clay cuttings.

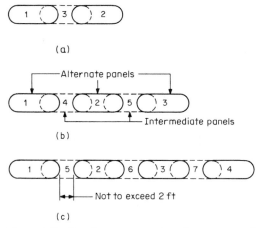

(a)

(b)

(c)

Figure 2-23 Panel arrangement and sequence of passes: (*a*) Three-pass excavation. (*b*) Five-pass excavation. (*c*) Seven-pass excavation.

The time for completing a full pass can be inferred from Table 2-2. The time for a 3-ft short (intermediate) pass is about 30 percent of the time for a full pass. Drilling should not take more than 70 percent of each shift time.

The TBW system

This excavator is operated from a kelly bar set on a special derrick as shown in Fig. 2-24. It excavates rectangular panels with square ends 0.6 m (about 24 in) wide and a basic length 1.500 or 1.940 m (4.9 or 6.4 ft). The trench can be up to 30 m (100 ft) deep. The machine has the following main units:

1. Main drill with a pair of rotary cutters facing each other and rotating in opposite directions. Sliding side cutters with cutting teeth complete the excavation and ensure a vertical face.

2. Hose reels to control the accuracy of the excavation. These are mounted at the rear of a frame tower. The upper reel, shown in Fig. 2-24b, is for the blow or supply hose and the lower for the suction hose.

3. Dual pumping system, a combination of suction pump and blow pump to supply and remove slurry.

4. Slurry treatment plant with separation units and a high-speed coil mixer.

5. Miscellaneous controls and devices to monitor the alignment and check deviations from the true vertical face.

Excavation. The excavator is advanced into the ground by cylinders attached to the tower through a supporting frame. Water jetting is forced through the supply line to prevent the rotary drills from clogging with earth materials. The two hoses for blow and suction are drawn in and out at constant speeds, and for this purpose a traverse apparatus is provided and synchronized with the reel drum, operated automatically from the control panel.

The quoted efficiency indicates penetration rates 10 to 15 ft/h. The excavator can be used in various soils including gravel and hard clay. The rotary cutters can consolidate gravel up to 8 cm (3 in) in size. Boulders and other obstructions must be broken and consolidated with a chisel and then removed with a grab. These tools must therefore be available at the site as standby equipment.

The Romill excavator

This machine consists basically of a heavy steel frame on which are mounted two large contrarotating milling wheels powered by hy-

(a)

(b)

Figure 2-24 The TBW system: (*a*) Excavator and rig. (*b*) Mechanical separation units and hose reels. (*Takenaka Komuten Co.*)

draulic motors. The system is lowered progressively into the trench and excavates and crushes soil or rock. These by-products are simultaneously mixed with the bentonite slurry and removed to the surface by a reverse-circulation mud pump located just above the cutting wheels. Recirculated clean slurry is fed back to the trench to maintain the slurry level. This approach is essentially similar to the rotary drills discussed in the foregoing sections.

The Romill excavation is shown diagrammatically in Fig. 2-25 and is produced by Rodio in Italy. Other versions of this system have been developed in France by Soletanche, referred to as the Hydrofraise, discussed in other sections (Fenoux, 1982), and in Germany by Bauer, referred to as City Cutter. Interestingly, this excavator has demonstrated constructional feasibility for trenches 100 m (330 ft) deep.

As shown in Fig. 2-25, major operational parameters are (1) excavation depth and excavation rate, (2) rotational speed and torque of each milling wheel, (3) flow and pressure of mud pump hydraulic system, and (4) vertical thrust exerted on the soil by the excavator.

With regard to variation in the thrust, tests show that the effective weight of the excavator influences the excavation directly. In soft or loose soil, for example, overthrust may induce a punching effect with sudden deviations, whereas in compact soil or rock the entire weight must be used to increase the ripping action of the teeth. Variation of the relative rotational speed of the milling wheels affects the inclination of the whole machine in the longitudinal plane. Extending the upper frame shield (marked c in Fig. 2-25) introduces an action similar to a hydraulic jack: the shield acts on the walls of the excavation and forces the excavator to change direction transversely as shown.

Counterflow reverse-circulation systems

Figure 2-26 shows excavation with a counterflow reverse-circulation system that normally is used in hard compact soils or in thick stratified formations. Likewise the slurry serves a dual purpose, for face support and as transporting agent for excavated materials. The cutter is a drilling bit of diameter equal to the trench width or a percussive tool penetrating the soil by up-and-down movement. Linear elements are excavated by the extended action of the cutter while the rig is moved horizontally and the bit works vertically, as shown in Fig. 2-26b.

Circular drills

RRC drill. The rodless reverse-circulation (RRC) drill shown in Fig. 2-27 is used for large-diameter foundation elements excavated under

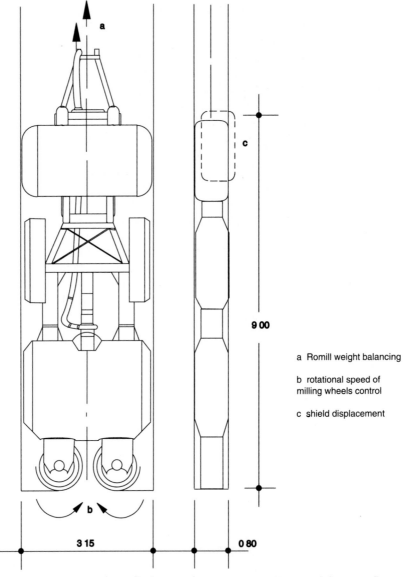

Figure 2-25 Drawing of Romill, showing the directional drilling capabilities. (*a*) Romill weight balancing. (*b*) Rotational speed of milling wheels control. (*c*) Shield displacement.

slurry (see also Chap. 5). The drill is available in three different models for holes with diameter 1 to 3 m (3.3 to 10 ft) and to a maximum depth of 80 m (260 ft). Because the torque on the drilling bits is offset by the motor drill, the machine does not require drill rods but can be cable-suspended from ordinary service cranes. Fresh slurry is

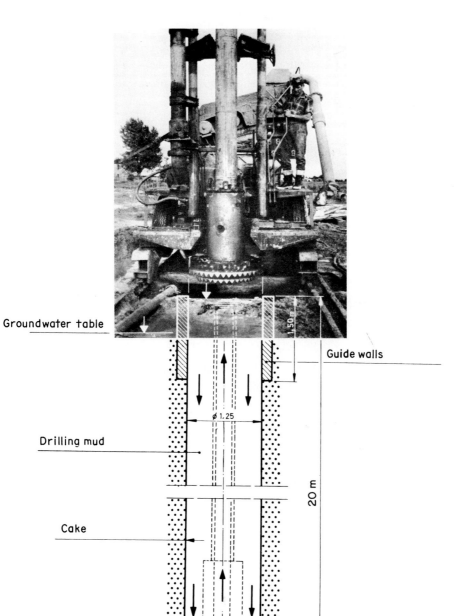

Groundwater table

Guide walls

ø 1.25

Drilling mud

Cake

20 m

(a)

Figure 2-26 Counterflow reverse-circulation system: (*a*) Equipment and section through trench. (*b*) Diagrammatic illustration of the excavation process. (*Radio-Marconi.*)

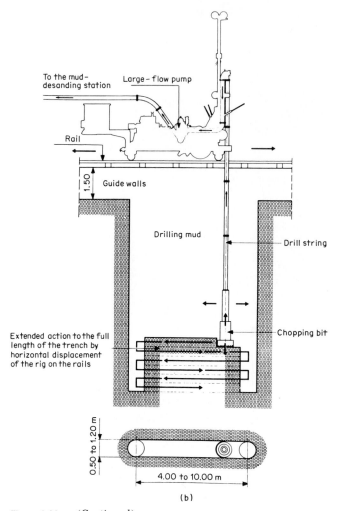

Figure 2-26   *(Continued)*

delivered to the excavation, and cuttings are continuously ejected mixed with slurry through air lift. Because of the special motion of the cutting blades of the bits, gravel or rock fragments are forced toward the reverse gate and large boulders are crushed against the walls of the hole before the smaller pieces enter the reverse circulation.

The drill excavates the bottom of the hole flat and finished according to the bearing requirements. Cleanout is done with an air lift. Since visual inspection is excluded, clean base must be ensured by the reverse circulation with reliance on the skills of the operator.

Figure 2-27 The RRC drill for large-diameter foundation elements excavated with slurry. (*Tone Boring Co.*)

Direct circulation

In relatively shallow trenches and in certain conditions, excavated materials can be removed by direct circulation. In this process slurry is pumped into the trench under pressure through a supply line extended almost to the bottom. As materials are excavated, they are compelled by the flow of slurry to travel upward near the surface and are held in suspension by the system. A main disadvantage of direct circulation is the unusually high percentage of soil retained in the slurry volume and the resulting high slurry density.

2-12   Tools and Equipment for Hard Ground and Boulders

Rock, boulders, cobbles, and other hard materials are not always removed with standard equipment. When the size and shape of obstructions and boulders does not exceed the trench width, they can be picked up with an extractor such as a cable-suspended grab. If the obstruction is too large or too tightly held to be removed in this manner, it must be broken up or loosened first, usually by dropping on it a kelly equipped with a chisel. Loosened or broken pieces are then picked up and extracted by the grab. A standard chisel is shown in

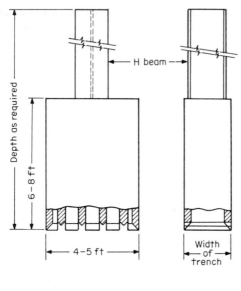

Figure 2-28 Typical chisel details for breaking embedded boulders in slot excavations.

Fig. 2-28; this device consists of several hard metal plates beveled to form cutting teeth and welded to form a compact solid frame embracing almost the entire trench width. The frame is usually attached to a steel H beam as shown.

Percussive tools. Layered rock or cemented soil of moderate thickness can be consolidated and broken up by chiseling and then removed with a clamshell. When penetration cannot be affected in this manner, it may be necessary to resort to percussion either as a supplementary or as an independent method.

Percussive tools derive their name from the violent striking of hard bodies and the shock produced as they fall upon such bodies. They may be cable-suspended, or they may be attached to a drill rod. Percussive tools can also be driven by special impact or vibratory hammers. A percussive tool for hole excavation is shown in Fig. 2-29.

Excavation with clamshells and percussive tools

Single-stage excavation. This is usually done in soft to medium hard soil, either granular or cohesive but without major obstructions. Av-

Figure 2-29 A percussive tool for hole excavation. (*ICOS.*)

erage panels usually are excavated in three passes as shown in Fig. 2-30. The first pass begins away from the last concreted panel to give extra time for the concrete to set. Where the range of clamshells available at the site cannot accommodate the excavation taking into account all relevant factors, the work can be carried out solely with percussive tools.

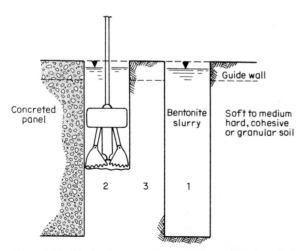

Figure 2-30 Single-stage panel excavation with clamshell bucket: passes 1 and 2: spread of clamshell bucket; pass 3: spread of clamshell bucket minus clearance for grab to embrace soil.

Panel excavation with pilot holes.   If the ground contains some boulders and obstructions, clamshells and grabs can be combined with pilot holes. The holes are initially predrilled at suitable intervals, using either percussive tools or rotary drills, as shown in Fig. 2-31. This preboring is useful in overcoming the difficulty of grabing soil when obstructions are encountered. Proper hole spacing ensures that the excavating implement will move down unrestricted to secure a full bite. Two-stage panel excavation is feasible as long as the pilot holes can be bored. Where the excavation must reach considerable depth, consideration should be given to the interlocking elements, briefly discussed in Sec. 1-11.

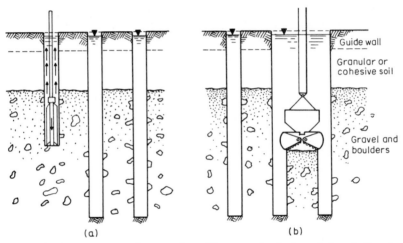

(a)   (b)

Figure 2-31   Two-stage panel excavation with percussive tools and clamshell grab: (*a*) Excavation of pilot holes with percussive tools. (*b*) Panel excavation with clamshell bucket.

The Hydrofraise system

This machine, developed by Soletanche (Parkinson and Gilbert, 1991), has been designed to excavate cohesionless soils as well as hard rock in one single pass and without chiseling. As a work unit, it consists of four principal components: (1) a heavy-duty crawler crane, 100 to 150 ton capacity; (2) a hydraulic power pack; (3) the Hydrofraise equipment; and (4) the slurry treatment plant. Schematically, the assembly is shown in Fig. 2-32. At the base of the frame there are three hydraulic motors; two operate the cutting drums (drilling tools), and the other operates a special pump mounted centrally just above the cutting drums. The spoil removal is therefore similar in principle to the reverse-circulation systems discussed in the foregoing sections.

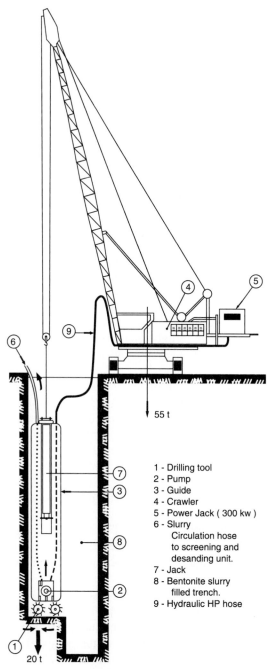

1 - Drilling tool
2 - Pump
3 - Guide
4 - Crawler
5 - Power Jack (300 kw)
6 - Slurry
    Circulation hose
    to screening and
    desanding unit.
7 - Jack
8 - Bentonite slurry
    filled trench.
9 - Hydraulic HP hose

55 t

20 t

Figure 2-32 The Hydrofraise system and its components. (*Soletanche.*)

The slurry plant consists of a slurry preparation unit, holding tanks, and a desander working continuously to screen and centrifuge slurry mixed with soil cuttings arriving from the trench.

In a single cut the machine excavates a panel section 2.4 m (8 ft) long; this is the overall length defined by the exterior of the cutter drums measured along the wall axis. The width of the trench may be varied by changing the drums from a minimum of 25 in to 5 ft, which is the practical maximum for most diaphragm walls. The operational depth is usually up to 90 m (300 ft), but greater depths have been attained. An example is the diaphragm wall at the Navajo dam in New Mexico that has a depth of over 400 ft (Soletanche, 1987), and the Mud Mountain dam project in Washington State where the cutoff wall reached a depth of 420 ft (Soletanche, 1988).

Panels and panel joints. A slurry wall constructed using this system consists of primary and secondary panels, with a distinct way of forming the joints. Primary panels usually consist of three to five full-depth bites. Figure 2-33 shows the excavation sequence for a five-joint panel. The main bites are 8 ft long and separated by a soil wedge about 3.5 ft long, excavated by the fourth and fifth bite, giving a wall panel about 31 ft long. Likewise, a three-bite panel consists of two main bites and an intermediate soil wedge to give a total length $2 \times 8 + 3.5 = 19.5$ ft.

A secondary panel is formed between the primary panels by a single bite that typically accommodates the length range of the machine, or 8 ft long. As the equipment descends, it excavates a soil or rock panel length of 7 ft 4 in and thus encroaches on the adjacent primary sections. This arrangement allows the machine to cut and trim off a 4-in fillet from each end of the primary concreted panels. This cutting ability is extended to hard rock and concrete materials with strength up to 15,000 lb/in^2, so that the overlapping between primary and secondary panels is attained routinely.

The panel joints produced in this manner consist of a serrated surface resulting from the formation of grooves cut in the concrete of primary panels, with a tight concrete-to-concrete contact between sections. These joints are reported to be watertight.

Verticality control. The intent to produce overlapping panels with transversely interacting construction joints requires adequate verticality control. In a test carried out in 1979, the maximum deviation at a depth of 330 ft was kept to less than 6 in, resulting in a vertical accuracy of 0.15 percent. Several mechanical features of the system ensure the necessary vertical accuracy. These include four high-precision inclinometers, with read-out dials located on the main control

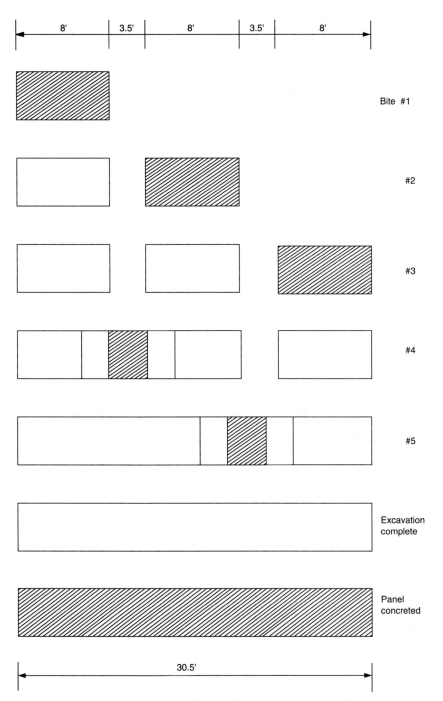

Figure 2-33 Construction sequence of a typical five-bite primary panel.

panel monitored by the operator. The continuous monitoring of verticality is feasible in both the longitudinal and transverse direction, and allows corrective action as soon as deviations are observed. Longitudinal deviations along the line of the wall are corrected by increasing the rotational speed of one of the cutter drums. Lateral corrections are made by activating hydraulic jacks built into the system, which can tilt the entire cutter-drum assembly with respect to the rest of the frame.

Excavation performance. The suggested upper limit of rock and material hardness is an unconfined compressive strength of 15,000 lb/in^2, although the machine can be adapted to excavate harder rock. Excavation rates generally vary inversely with rock hardness. The machine is also used in soft ground such as clay, sand and gravel, and residual soils. A relatively recent example is a viaduct at Cadola, Italy, where the equipment was used to excavate the foundation elements. This foundation penetrates 20 ft into rock overlain by 130 ft of normally consolidated clay. The teeth of the cutter drums and the slurry screening system were modified in this case to accommodate excavation in clay. These foundation elements are rectangular linear panels 3 by 9 ft, also referred to as "barrettes" (see also Chap. 5).

A limiting condition on the use of the Hydrofraise is the presence of boulders or extremely hard rock. When the size exceeds 4 in, their removal through the spoil stream is retarded and the use of the machine is not recommended.

The cutting action of the drums is said to be free of shocks and vibrations, even when working in rock. This is an advantage for slurry wall excavations in urban sites and for dam repair work.

Example. A recent project is the cutoff plastic concrete diaphragm wall for Britain's first Pressurized Water Reactor Nuclear Power Station on the Suffolk Coast (Contractors World, 1990). This project is 1256 m (4120 ft) long, and 55 m (180 ft) deep, built in a series of interlocking elements. The panels were excavated with the three-bite sequence, and concreted with two tremie pipes. The wall is sealed into typical London clay, and consists of plastic concrete for most of its length (Xanthakos, 1979).

The pretrench was initially excavated to a depth of 5 m (16.5 ft) using conventional backhoes or crane-mounted grabs under bentonite slurry. The Hydrofraise machine was inserted and continued the excavation with two primary and one secondary bites. The control and monitoring devices maintained the excavation within an average recorded vertical deviation of 1:500.

References

Anon, 1988: "Diaphragm Walling for Size w11 B Sets Records," *Ground Eng.,* vol. 22, no. 3, Apr. 19–25.

Bruce, D. A., et al., 1989: "Monitoring and Quality Control of a 100 Meter Deep Diaphragm Wall," *Intern. Conf. Piling and Deep Found.,* London, May.

Contractors World, 1990: "Constructing Europe's Deepest Diaphragm Wall," *Technology in Action,* vol. 3, BICC, London.

De Paoli, B., 1984: "Evolution de la technologie des parios moulees en Italie—Procedes et outillages," *Symp. sur Technologie et Organisation de l'Execution des paois moulees dans la construction d'ouvrages hydrauliques,* Sofia, Sept. 14–15.

Dupeuble, P., 1985: "CWS System and Joints between Diaphragm Wall Panels," *Ground Eng.,* September, London.

Fenoux, G. Y., 1982: "La troisieme generation d'outillages pour parois et ses applications a l'etranger," *Travaux,* no. 571, p. 78.

FPS, 1974: *Specifications for Cast-in-Place Diaphragm Walling,* Federation of Piling Specialists, London.

Fuchsberger, M., 1974: "Some Practical Aspects of Diaphragm Wall Construction," *Proc. Diaphragm Walls Anchorages, Inst. Civ. Eng. London.*

Koden, 1984: Drilling Monitor, DM, 686 III/688, Japan.

Mud Mountain, Washington State, 1988: Internal Report, Soletanche Enterprise, Nanterre, France.

Namy, D. L., 1979: "Site Conditions Specific to Slurry Wall Construction," *Proc. Slurry Walls for Underground Transp. Syst.,* U.S. DOT, Cambridge, Mass., Aug. 30–31, pp. 56–79.

Navajo Dam Repair, New Mexico, 1987: Internal Report Soletanche Enterprise, Nanterre, France.

PCSA, 1968a: Cable-Controlled Power Cranes, Draglines, Hoes, Shovels, Clamshells," *Tech. Bull.* 4, Power Crane and Shovel Assoc., Milwaukee, Wis. 1968b: Crane and Excavator Standards No. 1, 2, and 3, Power Crane and Shovel Assoc., Milwaukee, Wis.

Parking Garages, Assemblee Nationale, Paris, 1980: Internal Report, Soletanche Enterprise, Nanterre, France.

Parkinson, J. J., and C. M. Gilbert, 1991: "Design and Construction of Slurry Walls," *ASTM Intern. Symp.,* Atlantic City, N.J., June 27–28.

Powers, T. C., et al., 1955: "Permeability of Portland Cement Paste," Portland Cement Assoc. *Res. Bull.* 53, Chicago, 1959: "The Flow of Water in Hardened Portland Cement Paste," Portland Cement Assoc., *Res. Bull.* 106, Chicago.

Ressi, A., 1974: "Excavating Systems," *Conf. Underground Constr. Fluid Trenches, Univ. Ill.,* Chicago Circle, April.

Sliwinski, Z., and W. G. K. Fleming, 1974: Practical Considerations Affecting the Construction of Diaphragm Walls, *Proc. Diaphragm Walls Anchorages, Inst. Civ. Eng. London.*

Soletanche, 1988: "Mud Maintain," *Washington State Internal Report,* Soletanche Enterprise, Nanterre, France.

Tone Boring Co., 1974: "Manual for Stabilizing Fluids," *Bull.* BW 121, Tokyo.

Troxell, G. E., et al., 1968: *Composition and Properties of Concrete,* 2d ed., McGraw-Hill, New York.

Ueda, S., 1974: Excavation with the BW system, personal communication.

Valenta, O., 1968: "Durability of Concrete," *Proc. 5th Int. Symp. Chem. Cement,* Tokyo, pt. III, p. 193.

Xanthakos, P. P., 1979: *Slurry Walls,* McGraw-Hill, New York.

Xanthakos, P. P., L. Abramson, and D. A. Bruce, 1994: *Ground Control and Improvement Technologies,* Wiley, New York.

3

Geotechnical Considerations

3-1 Introduction

Geotechnical issues relevant to the construction and design of slurry walls usually are articulated with reference to three distinct phases. The first is trench excavation under slurry protection, and the associated stability requirements. The second is the general excavation when the wall acts as ground support, and the associated limitations on ground movement. The third and last stage is when the wall interacts with other structural components as part of the permanent structure.

The geotechnical requirements for each successive stage differ considerably. During trench excavation under slurry, concern is with practical matters such as stability of the open trench, nature of soil and the presence of obstacles, fluid loss potential through highly pervious zones, sloughing and peeling off in unstable layers, and effects of construction procedures.

During the excavation period the wall is subjected to lateral earth stresses, water pressure, and effects of surcharge loads. Vertical loads may be induced from superimposed dead weight, interaction with the superstructure, and other conditions such as inclined anchorages. Where a diaphragm wall is designed and built to act as permanent component of the final structure, final loading conditions, load effects, and distribution may differ considerably from the loads that existed during the construction period. In addition, the soil behavior may revert to the long-term drained condition, markedly different from the short-term construction period, particularly for cohesive soils. Where the groundwater chemistry is uncertain, its potential adverse effects on concrete and reinforcement must be considered.

Conventional or special soil tests and subsurface investigations are thus a prerequisite to the economical design of slurry walls, and must be devised and carried out in connection with the forementioned issues. The broad categories of data acquisition include soil investigations, simple index property tests, engineering properties of cohesive soils, and groundwater chemistry.

Groundwater and soil chemistry.   Routine chemical tests of groundwater will disclose conditions that may cause an unstable bentonite slurry. This problem may relate to excessive viscosity, flocculation, slurry loss, and spalling of the excavated face. Among the factors most likely to affect the slurry are the pH, and contamination by salt, calcium, or organics. The simplicity of pH and conductivity tests on groundwater samples warrants the cost and effort; these tests can be performed routinely in the field. Variations that disclose anomalies in these characteristics should indicate the need to perform water quality analyses on selected representative samples.

Raveling ground and obstructions.   This potential exists with the presence of rubble fill, nests and cobbles, building demolition debris, and materials with relatively large voids. Buried foundations or existing utilities will have a direct impact on the feasibility of excavation. Hence the geotechnical site investigation must include location of utilities and a routine research of the site history with the identification of former structure locations, walls, and pile foundations (see also Sec. 2-2). Filled-in former depressions may be relevant to stability evaluation and analysis. The presence of rock may be an obstruction to excavation since it will require special equipment and will result in slower excavation rates. The rock hardness, degree of fracturing, and weathering are important criteria.

Groundwater table.   Trench stability is commonly ensured by a heavier fluid and with a positive head above the piezometric level. Most stability analyses suggest a level differential of about 5 ft, with 3 ft minimum. The investigation therefore must include data concerning loss of drilling water while making borings, identify highly pervious strata, and provide information about piezometric levels. Artesian conditions such as the one shown in Fig. 3-1 should be identified.

In this case, the piezometric level in the underlying stratum C is at a higher elevation than in the near surface layer A. As a result, there will be a reduction of slurry head relevant to the piezometric level in

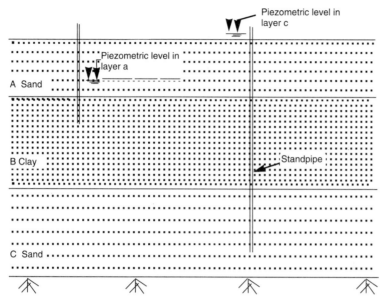

Figure 3-1 Artesian case in slurry wall excavation.

stratum C with a possible ground loss that may or may not be detected during trench excavation.

3-2 Geotechnical Parameters Relevant to Structural Performance

General excavation phase. During this phase the wall resists essentially lateral loads. In addition, the wall may be required to transfer vertical loads such as vertical components of tiebacks, or to reduce deformations and displacements outside the excavation. This performance may be evaluated from a total stress analysis (undrained shear strength) or from an effective stress analysis (drained conditions). These concepts are expressed in terms of several soil parameters: (1) the undrained (undisturbed) shear strength s_u; (2) the lateral earth pressure coefficient K; (3) the effective overburden stress σ_v'; (4) the angle of friction between wall and soil δ; (5) the ultimate bearing capacity q_u; and (6) the bearing capacity factor N_q.

Lateral wall displacement is a criterion that often leads to the selection of diaphragm walls over other support methods, particularly when the usage eliminates underpinning (see also other sections).

Permanent conditions. The long-term vertical load capacity is essentially the same as during the excavation phase. However, for the distribution and magnitude of horizontal earth stresses a distinction must be made between the construction period and long-term service. Typically, under long-term conditions the initial earth pressure at rest is expected to be restored. In this case the relevant parameter is the at rest earth coefficient K_0.

Summary of geotechnical data. Conventional borings may be supplemented by machine-excavated test pits to explore for obstructions, rubble fill, or materials that may deter the construction process. Simple laboratory tests should be performed on a routine basis to assist in the identification of soil types.

Grain-size analysis. In granular soils this gives an indication of soil permeability. In addition it gives an index of probable wall texture and finish. Grain-size tests provide data on the amount of fines that may be suspended in the slurry based on its 10-min gel strength.

Atterberg limits. This parameter represents an important index for preliminary assessment of engineering properties of cohesive soils. The limits are indicators of sensitivity (strength lost upon remolding), of overconsolidated ratio, and of expansion potential.

Rock data. The presence of rock can influence excavation rates and panel length, bearing capacity, and water inflow when excavating to subgrade. A geologic assessment is necessary for the general design and can disclose anomalous behavior. These data are particularly useful if the diaphragm wall is terminated on rock formations for bearing. In Boston, for example, the argillite has been locally altered to a clay-like material that may be subjected to softening upon exposure. Likewise, some schists in New York may be softened upon removal of overburden.

The investigation should include rock coring, with records of drilling rates and water loss. Packer tests for rock permeability, and also pumping tests, are an appropriate index of rock fracturing. In addition, rock hardness RQD (Rock Quality Designation) and slaking will provide relevant information.

Permeability. The colloidal action of bentonite is expected to produce an effective filter cake at the interface and prevent slurry loss to the ground. This interaction is expected to occur in soils with permeability less than about 10^{-2} cm/s (see also other sections). Higher soil permeability may require additional slurry controls and the addition of suitable agents to seal the excavation and prevent slurry from escaping to the ground.

Initial assessment of soil permeability is made during site investigation. Occurrence of fluid loss during drilling will indicate potentially pervious conditions, and this information should be recorded and articulated. In these cases in situ permeability tests are warranted, and a simple procedure is a constant-head or falling-head test out of the casing. More accurate techniques include water inflow tests, either by bailing the casing or by applying a vacuum pump to a short section of wall screen.

Laboratory and in situ permeability tests may be justified depending on the suspected permeability established by visual observations, drilling fluid loss, grain size, etc. Such tests are useful if they are correlated with other indicators. This program should be compatible with the uncertainty of site conditions and stratigraphic complexity.

Other parameters. Conventional unconfined compression or vane tests provide a basis for estimating the undrained shear strength of cohesive soils. Where soils are soft or highly sensitive to disturbance, the data should be obtained by in situ vane shear tests.

Consolidation tests are useful for estimating the magnitude and rate of rebound-recompression process resulting from stress release by excavation and reapplication of permanent service loads. In addition, they give an indication of the swell characteristics of highly overconsolidated soils and thus provide a basis for assessing the soil potential for excessive lateral expansion or heave.

Triaxial compression tests are justified where it is necessary to determine the soil modulus for finite-element analyses. The soil modulus obtained in laboratory tests may be somewhat smaller than the actual soil modulus in situ. Thus laboratory programs to establish modulus should have intermediate rebound-reload cycles as well as measurement of tangent and secant modulus. Likewise, comparison of data from laboratory tests with field measurements on similar soils should be desirable.

3-3 Stability of Unsupported Trenches

A vertical cut in cohesionless soil is feasible only if the face is protected. An inclined cut in clean dry sand generally is stable regardless of height as long as the angle i which its slope makes the horizontal is smaller than the angle of friction ϕ of the sand in a loose state. The factor of safety for such a slope usually is defined as the ratio $(\tan\phi)/(\tan i)$. The only unknown factor is an appropriate value for the angle ϕ that can be estimated with sufficient accuracy.

A trench in cohesive soil can stay open without slurry support as long as the site is underlain by firm materials. This problem can be analyzed noting that saturated clays, when loaded under conditions causing no changes in water content, behave with respect to the ap-

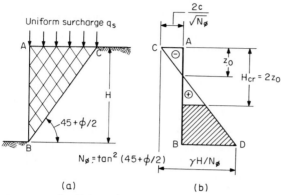

Figure 3-2 Conditions of a cut in cohesive soil at slip failure: (*a*) Section through cut. (*b*) Horizontal earth-stress diagram.

plied stresses at failure as purely cohesive materials; i.e., the angle of shear resistance is zero. The stability is then investigated on the basis of limit theory. Terzaghi and Peck (1948, 1967) present the analysis shown in Fig. 3-2. Slip failure occurs along plane surface BC, making an angle with the horizontal as shown in Fig. 3-2*a*. The following expressions are easily derived:

$$z_0 = \frac{2c}{\gamma} \tan \left(45 + \frac{\phi}{2} \right) \tag{3-1}$$

and

$$H_{cr} = 2z_0 = \frac{4c}{\gamma} \tan \left(45 + \frac{\phi}{2} \right) \tag{3-2}$$

where z_0 = depth at which the horizontal stress is zero
γ = unit weight or bulk density of soil
c = cohesion factor
H_{cr} = maximum height for which the cut is stable for factor of safety 1
ϕ = angle of shear resistance

The stress diagram corresponding to this condition is shown in Fig. 3-2*b*. The assumption $\phi = 0$ reduces the foregoing expressions to

$$z_0 = \frac{2c}{\gamma} \tag{3-1a}$$

and

$$H_{cr} = 2z_0 = \frac{4c}{\gamma} \tag{3-2a}$$

If a uniform surcharge q_s acts on the surface, these relations are easily modified to include its effect. The critical height is now

$$H_{cr} = \frac{4c - 2q_s}{\gamma} \tag{3-3}$$

At any depth less than z_0 the soil is in tension; hence tension cracks tend to develop near the surface, associated with the horizontal stretching resulting from the active state of stress. If tension cracks propagate to a depth z_t, the initial equilibrium is disturbed and the maximum unsupported height is $H_{cr} = 4c/\gamma - z_t$. Terzaghi (1941) and Terzaghi and Peck (1967) have estimated that tension cracks may extend to a depth about one-half of the total height of the cut. However, in most practical problems tension cracks are disregarded below the depth z_0 since the soil in this region is in compression. For this condition the critical height is

$$H_{cr} = \frac{2c}{\gamma} = z_0 \tag{3-4}$$

From the foregoing analysis it follows that the development of tensile stresses is a major factor in trench stability, and in some cases it may be quite unsafe to assume that the ground can withstand horizontal tension. Where the water table is at or near the surface, tension cracks are unlikely to develop below depth z_0. The action of a uniform surcharge q_s results in compressive stresses that tend to close the tension cracks. If $q_s > 2c$, tension cracks can be ignored, but in this case H_{cr} is negative; i.e., the trench cannot be excavated.

In some instances failure may be temporarily delayed or prevented by artificial increase of the tensile strength of the soil, particularly in the upper layers. An example is frost action in cold regions.

The $\phi = 0$ assumption implies a theoretical failure plane inclined at 45° to the horizontal. Analysis based on circular failure arcs leads to similar expressions except that the numerical coefficient 4 is replaced by 3.85. This corresponds to the stability number computed by Taylor (1948). The foregoing equations may be used in slurry trench excavations to estimate a practical depth up to which the trench can be excavated before slurry must be introduced.

3-4   Stability of Slurry-Filled Trenches in Clay

General method of analysis

Nash and Jones (1963) have analyzed trench stability on the basis of limit theory. The supporting element is the hydrostatic thrust exerted by the slurry against the face. If this thrust is not diminished by slurry escaping to the ground, equilibrium essentially requires balancing the forces. Referring to Fig. 3-3a, the forces that must be balanced are as shown. The active wedge ABC tends to slide along plane BC, but this tendency is resisted by the shear force C and by the full hydrostatic thrust P_f of the slurry. The condition $\phi = 0$ yields $\alpha = 0$ and $\theta = 45°$. Expressing all the forces in the polygon of Fig. 3-3b in terms of H, c, γ, and γ_f, and summing up we obtain

$$-0.5\gamma_f H^2 + 0.5\gamma H^2 - 2cH = 0 \tag{3-5}$$

which gives

$$H_{cr} = \frac{4c}{\gamma - \gamma_f} \tag{3-6}$$

If a uniform surcharge q_s acts on the surface, the critical height is

$$H_{cr} = \frac{4c - 2q_s}{\gamma - \gamma_f} \tag{3-7}$$

Experience shows that Eqs. (3-5) and (3-6) provide satisfactory results for the conditions under which they are applied, namely, (1) the trench is long compared with its depth; (2) the cohesion c is fairly

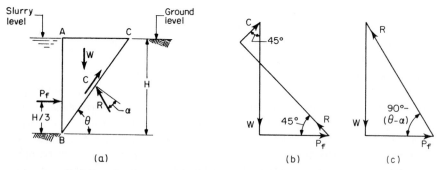

Figure 3-3 Stability of a slurry trench: (a) Section through trench. (b) Force polygon for purely cohesive soil ($\emptyset = 0$). (c) Force triangle for purely cohesionless sand ($c - 0$).

representative for the trench depth; and (3) there is no fluid loss through the interface. The thrust of the slurry inhibits the development of cracks and fissures, and although this effect is enhanced by a heavier slurry, other factors place an upper limit on this weight (see also other sections).

Validity of the $\phi = 0$ concept. The $\phi = 0$ analysis in cohesive soils has obvious practical significance but is valid where the soil is stressed under undrained conditions, i.e., where there is no change in the water content. Examples are saturated clays where a cut is excavated quickly. For ordinary slurry trench excavations, the open trench is a temporary condition merely to allow the concrete placement. This time is short compared with the time required for excess pore pressures within the soil to dissipate. In this case it is appropriate to use the $\phi = 0$ concept and apply undrained loading to trench stability. This leads to a practical simplification of the analysis and allows the use of Eqs. (3-6) and (3-7), in which the factor c is replaced by the undrained shear strength s_u, usually quoted as one-half of the unconfined compressive strength.

If the trench is intended to remain open for a long time, the resulting changes will include swelling and changes in pore pressure and effective stress (Lambe and Whitman, 1969). This means that the soil will become weaker and will therefore exert a greater thrust. For this condition an effective stress analysis is indicated.

The two methods can be related by comparing the factor of safety with plastic failure (Bishop and Bjerrum, 1960). For a soil entering this state the factor of safety should be 1 regardless of the method used in the analysis. In this respect both methods agree since they both yield a factor of safety of 1 for a soil on the verge of collapse caused by a change of stress under undrained conditions. This factor is the same, but the theoretical location of the failure surface depends on the value of ϕ, so that as this value approaches the true angle of shear resistance the position of the failure surface becomes more realistic. However, the total stress analysis does not establish this surface since the $\phi = 0$ assumption typically implies a failure plane at 45° with the horizontal. This discrepancy is rectified by noting that in a triaxial test it is not necessary to know the exact location of the failure plane. The $\phi = 0$ analysis is valid if we assume that failure occurs when the maximum shear stress reaches the maximum shear measured at failure in a corresponding triaxial test. Thus it is valid to analyze trench stability without really knowing the exact inclination of the failure plane.

There are, however, situations where the $\phi = 0$ analysis is not valid. Examples are partially saturated soils, trenches in stiff fissured and weathered clays, situations where field measurements of pore pressure are used as control, and prolonged construction operations. In these cases the total stress analysis may lose its meaning or it may lead to predictions that are either unsafe or too conservative.

Example of slurry trench in soft clay, semiempirical analysis

For the construction of a railway and a subway tunnel in Oslo, two slurry trench projects were completed, identified as S.L. and J.B.T., respectively. The S.L. project involves a two-story tunnel that required a trench excavation 15 m deep in soft clay with properties as shown in Fig. 3-4. The longitudinal tunnel slurry walls were first constructed to a depth of 20 m. Cross walls in slurry trenches were constructed at 4.5-m intervals along the tunnel. Concrete was placed in the cross trenches in the lower 5 m below tunnel bottom. Their purpose was to prevent bottom heave (see also other sections) and also to brace the tunnel walls near the bottom.

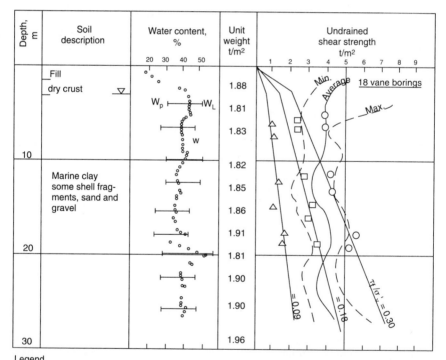

Legend
w_L = liquid limit, w_p = plastic limit. ○-active triaxial test, △-passive triaxial test, □-direct shear test.

Figure 3-4 Soil parameters and geotechnical data, S. L. tunnel, Oslo. (*From Karlsrud et al., 1979.*)

Stability of trench. A test panel was excavated to assess the matter of stability and under the effect of different types of supporting fluids (DiBiagio and Myrvoll, 1972b). The operation was carried out in the following steps:

1. A trench of a minimum size the bite of the excavating equipment was excavated to a depth of 28 m (92 ft) under a slurry with unit weight 12.4 kN/m^3 (1.26 t/m^3). Deformation and pore pressure changes were observed.

2. The excavation was enlarged to form a trench 1 × 5 × 28 m. Deformations and pore pressures were monitored for 12 days for the same slurry weight as in 1.

3. The slurry was diluted to a unit weight of 11.0 kN/m^3 (corresponding to a specific gravity of 1.12) and observations continued for 7 days.

4. The slurry was displaced by water and observations continued for 11 days.

5. The water in the trench was replaced with concrete by the tremie method, and the response of the surrounding soil was observed.

Observed changes in the trench configuration are summarized in Figs. 3-5 and 3-6. At each state of loading the creep rate is almost

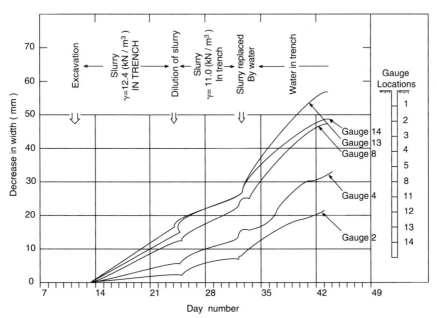

Figure 3-5 Change in width for typical gage points, test panel. (*From DiBiagio and Myrvoll, 1972b.*)

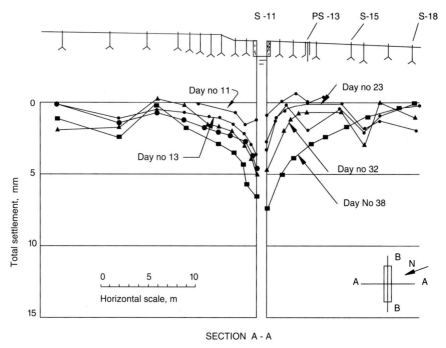

Figure 3-6 Settlement profiles at key stages of test panel. (*From DiBiagio and Myrvoll, 1972b.*)

constant, and the maximum settlement at the end of the testing period is only 8 mm (0.3 in). Prior to the placement of concrete (or 31 days after the trench was excavated) the maximum decrease in width of the completed trench is about 5.5 cm (2.2 in) near the bottom. Apparently, the soil moved always at a decreasing rate, although the specific gravity of the slurry was reduced from 1.26 to 1.00 (plain water), and the trench was stable with only water.

The horizontal deformations (inward movement) measured along the 5-m length at a depth of 15.5 m indicate the importance of the end restraint on the displacement field around the excavation. At this depth the average horizontal displacement was about two-thirds of the maximum value measured at the center of the panel. It appears, therefore, that the analytical studies of trench stability have a limited value unless the geometry factor is considered. This arching action in the ground may be manifested as shown schematically in Fig. 3-7; the tendency of the soil to creep inward near the centerline of the panel is relieved by transfer of load toward the ends of the panel through thrust lines as shown.

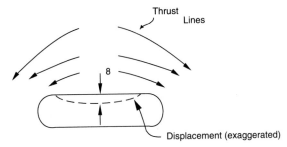

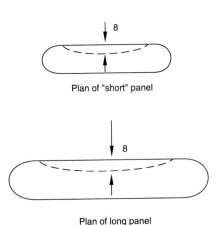

Plan of long panel

Figure 3-7 Arching effect of trenches in clay.

Semiempirical method of analysis. Following the experience gained from the foregoing test, a semiempirical method was developed (Aas, 1976) with assumed failure conditions as shown in Fig. 3-8. Note that the fluid level is lowered as shown so that the depth from ground surface to fluid surface is $D - \beta D = D(1 - \beta)$. The assumed failure block consists of two separate volumes, a lower wedge-shaped body assumed to slide down and into the trench along two planes at 45°, and an upper body assumed to move only vertically. The relevance of this type of body failure is related to observed displacement patterns.

Karlsrud et al. (1979) suggest that the anisotropic nature of the undrained shear strength should be taken into account when evaluating proper parameters for the purpose of analysis. Referring to Fig. 3-8, on the two 45° planes of the lower block the undrained shear strength determined by triaxial compression tests must be applied,

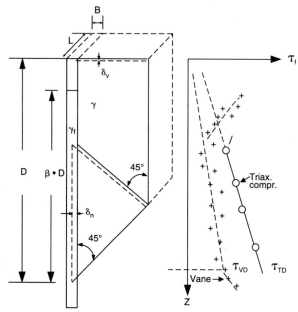

Figure 3-8 Assumed failure condition in trench; semiempirical approach, trenches in Oslo clay. (*From Karlsrud et al., 1979.*)

whereas on the vertical side (upper block) and on the end planes shear strength parameters determined from in situ vane tests are relevant. However, the analysis must also consider rate effects and possible tension cracks in the upper weathered layers. For the Oslo conditions, Aas (1976) has proposed a simplified method of analysis considering the foregoing factors, leading to the following expression for the factor of safety:

$$F = \frac{\tau_{VD}}{D(\gamma_f - \beta^2 \gamma_f)} \left(2\frac{\tau_{VD}}{\tau_{TD}} + 0.6 + 0.86 \frac{D}{L} \right) \tag{3-8}$$

where all symbols correspond to the notation of Fig. 3-8, and γ = unit weight of clay, γ_f = unit weight of fluid in the trench, τ_{VD} = vane shear strength and depth D, and τ_{TD} = triaxial compression strength at depth D. The expression in Eq. (3-8) has a form similar to the bearing capacity equations, but in this case the stability number is dependent upon the anisotropy of clay as well as upon the trench geometry (see also Sec. 4-5).

Considering a trench 15 m deep and 4.5 m long excavated in the clay of Fig. 3-4, and applying Eq. (3-8), the safety factor using a fluid equivalent to water is 1.4 to 1.5, which is adequate. Using an average undrained shear strength 3.5 t/m² from Fig. 3-4, and a soil unit weight

1.88 t/m^3, the critical trench height with only water in the trench is obtained from Eq. (3-6) as H_{cr} = (3.5 × 4)/(1.88 − 1.00) = 15.9 ft. Thus, for a trench 15 m deep, Eq. (3-6) gives a factor of safety 15.9/15 = 1.06; i.e., the trench would be on the verge of collapse.

For the J.T.B. tunnel, the presence of buildings (4 to 5 stories) within a distance 3 to 5 m from the trench required a heavy slurry with unit weight 13 kN/m^3 (1.33 t/m^3). A heavy slurry was required also in the same area when for practical reasons the trench excavation was started from a level 2 m below the original ground surface.

3-5 Special Considerations for Excavations in Clay

Circular cuts. In a circular cut hoop stresses act normal to the radial planes. Near the face they are roughly equal to the vertical stresses, but away from the face both hoop and radial stresses approach the earth stresses at rest.

Shallow circular cuts. These are defined as having a depth-to-diameter ratio less than 12. Meyerhoff (1972) has derived an approximate solution beginning with the expression

$$p_z = (\gamma - \gamma_f)z - 2c = (\gamma' - \gamma_f')z - 2c \qquad (3\text{-}9)$$

which generally is true for long excavations. In this case p_z is the net active pressure for a completely saturated soil at depth z. For a shallow circular cut the coefficient 2 in Eq. (3-9) is replaced by a factor K such that

$$K = 2 \left[\ln \left(\frac{2d}{b} + 1 \right) + 1 \right] \qquad (3\text{-}10)$$

where d is the depth and b is the diameter (or width) of the cut. From these considerations Eq. (3-6) is rewritten by replacing total weights by effective weights and the factor $4c$ by $2Kc$ so that

$$H_{cr} = \frac{2Kc}{\gamma' - \gamma_f'} \qquad (3\text{-}11)$$

The stability number $2K$ increases with increasing depth-to-diameter ratio d/b. The K function in Eq. (3-10) is plotted in the upper curve of Fig. 3-9, which is for an l/b ratio of 1 and therefore applies to circular shapes. The inclination and shape of this curve indicate that although K increases with increasing d/b ratios, this increase is not linear. Accordingly, the factor of safety H_{cr}/H_{actual} decreases with

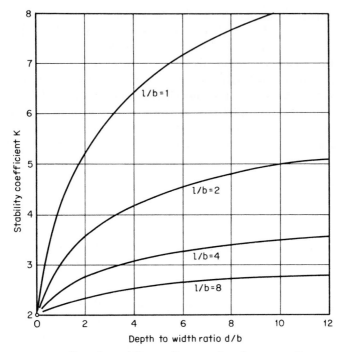

Figure 3-9 Chart for stability coefficients of earth stresses. Rectangular cuts in clay; l = length, b = width, and d = depth. (*From Meyerhof, 1972.*)

increasing depth, and therefore the stability conditions become critical at the maximum excavation depth.

Deep circular cuts. When the d/b ratio exceeds about 12, the earth stress and stability of circular or square cuts approach the bearing capacity problem of a deep vertical strip foundation with an overburden stress equal to the earth stress at rest. Meyerhoff (1972) presents the solution

$$H_{cr} = \frac{Nc}{K_0 \, \gamma' - \gamma'_f} \tag{3-12}$$

where K_0 is the coefficient of earth stress at rest and N is a bearing capacity factor for deep strip foundations. For rigid plastic materials $N = 8.28$.

Since the analysis does not include the lateral shear resistance at the bottom of excavation, the results are conservative. If this resistance is included, N approaches 9.34, or an increase of about 1 in its value. This corresponds to a 12 percent increase in the critical height.

Analysis of short rectangular trenches. For a rectangular trench of length l, width b, and depth d, an approximate but conservative analysis is obtained if we consider the earth stresses along the perimeter of two end zones of width b and length $b/2$ the same as for a square or circular cut. For the remaining length $l - b$ the earth stresses are the same as for a long trench. The coefficient K in Eq. (3-10) increases from 2 for $d/b = 0$ to a maximum value

$$K = 2\left(1 + \frac{3b}{l}\right) \tag{3-13}$$

Likewise the factor N increases from 4 for $d/b = 0$ to a maximum value

$$N = 4\left(1 + \frac{b}{l}\right) \tag{3-14}$$

For both K and N the maximum values occur at fairly great depths. For intermediate depths both K and N are estimated by interpolating between these limits (Hansen, 1961). For convenience the results are shown in Figs. 3-9 and 3-10 ignoring base shear, from which K and N can be obtained graphically.

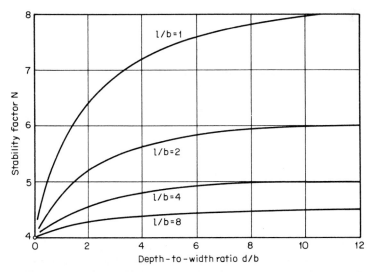

Figure 3-10 Chart for stability factors. Rectangular cuts in clay; l = length, b = width, d = depth. (*From Meyerhof, 1972.*)

If a uniform surcharge q_s acts on the surface or if the excavation is in stratified soil, the foregoing analysis is readily extended to give

$$p_t - p_f = Nc \tag{3-15}$$

where p_t = maximum total horizontal thrust from the soil including any surcharge and p_f = total slurry pressure.

Lateral earth displacement. The inward creep articulated in Figs. 3-5 and 3-7 is associated with a lateral earth displacement when the at rest earth stress is replaced by slurry pressure during excavation. An approximate estimation of soil movement is obtained if we consider the stress-strain relationship and assume a soil that is homogeneous and isotropic with a geostatic stress.

For a deep circular cut the radial deformation at depth z is given by Timoshenko and Goodier (1951) as

$$\Delta = \frac{(1 + \mu)p_z b}{2E_i} \tag{3-16}$$

where p_z is the net lateral stress at depth z, μ is Poisson's ratio, and E_i is the initial tangent modulus of the clay. For saturated clay, $\mu = 0.5$, and for a slurry-filled cut, $p_z = (K_0 \gamma' - \gamma_f')z$. If p_z is positive, the movement of the face is toward the excavation and vice versa. Substituting the value of p_z in Eq. (3-16) gives

$$\Delta = 0.75(K_0 \gamma' - \gamma_f') \frac{2b}{E_i} \tag{3-17}$$

The lateral displacement at the center of the long side of a deep rectangular cut of length l is obtained in a similar manner as

$$\Delta = 0.75(K_0 \gamma' - \gamma_f') \frac{2l}{E_i} \tag{3-18}$$

3-6   Stability of Slurry-Filled Trenches in Sand

Trenches in dry sand

The method of analysis introduced for clay (Nash and Jones, 1963) is extended to dry cohesionless sand as shown in Fig. 3-3a and c. The active wedge ABC is prevented from sliding by the frictional resistance along plane BC and by the thrust of the slurry P_f. Summing up the equilibrium forces and solving for tan α gives

$$\tan \alpha = \frac{\gamma - \gamma_f}{2\sqrt{\gamma\gamma_f}} \tag{3-19}$$

The factor of safety against sliding is defined as the ratio (tan ϕ)/(tan α), from which it follows that

$$F = \frac{2\sqrt{\gamma\gamma_f} \tan \phi}{\gamma - \gamma_f} \tag{3-20}$$

From Eq. (3-20) it follows that for simple wedge failure the stability of slurry-filled trenches in dry sand is independent of the excavation depth and depends only on the soil properties and the slurry density. For the same soil parameters and trench conditions, stability is improved with heavier slurry.

Trenches in sand with water

Trench stability is difficult to maintain where the free water level is near the ground surface. This condition may require one or all of the following: (1) lower the groundwater table; (2) raise the slurry level by building the guide walls higher; (3) use a heavy slurry; and (4) resort to other factors, i.e., short panels to take advantage of arching effects.

Disregarding the interaction between slurry and adjacent ground, the stability analysis may be carried out assuming drained conditions whereby the soil stress is an effective stress and the pore pressure is static water pressure. For a water table at ground surface this requires

$$\tfrac{1}{2}\gamma_f H^2 = \tfrac{1}{2}\gamma' H^2 K_a + \tfrac{1}{2}\gamma_w H^2$$

where γ' is the effective soil weight. This relation yields

$$K_a = \tan^2\left(45 - \frac{\phi'}{2}\right) = \frac{\gamma_f - \gamma_w}{\gamma'}$$

Setting $\gamma_f - \gamma_w = \gamma_f'$ and solving for tan ϕ' under a safety factor F gives

$$F = \frac{2\sqrt{\gamma'\gamma_f'} \tan \phi'}{\gamma' - \gamma_f'} \tag{3-21}$$

which is also derived from Eq. (3-20) by substituting effective weights for total weights. A simple relation is

$$\gamma_f = K_a \gamma' + \gamma_w \qquad (3\text{-}22)$$

which relates the soil and slurry parameters to stability for a factor of safety of 1.

Consider, for example, a trench in loose saturated sand with $\phi' = 28°$ and $\gamma' = 115 - 62.5 = 52.5 \text{ lb/ft}^3$. We compute $K_a = (1 - \sin \phi')/(1 + \sin \phi') = (1 - 0.42)/(1 + 0.42) = 0.40$. The minimum slurry weight, factor of safety 1, is now obtained from Eq. (3-22) as

$$\gamma_f = 0.40 \times 52.5 + 62.5 = 83.5 \text{ lb/ft}^3$$

Variation in the slurry and groundwater level.   The general case of stability with arbitrary groundwater and slurry levels is shown in Fig. 3-11. The water table and slurry level are located with reference to the bottom of the trench as shown. The analysis considers total stress above the water table and effective stress below the water table. This condition leads to the expression

$$\gamma_f = \frac{\gamma(1 - m^2)K_a + \gamma'm^2K_a + \gamma_w m^2}{n^2} \qquad (3\text{-}23)$$

If we take $m = n = 1$, Eq. (3-23) reduces to Eq. (3-22). The angle ϕ is taken the same for both dry and saturated soil. Any saturation of soil above the free level is likely to increase the assumed dry weight. From the foregoing it appears that stability problems can conceivably arise when slurry trenches are excavated in sand and near large bodies of natural water.

Example.   A trench failure in water-bearing ground has been reported by Morgenstern and Amir-Tahmasseb (1965). The trench col-

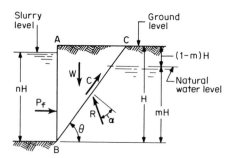

Figure 3-11 Stability of a trench for arbitrary slurry and natural water level.

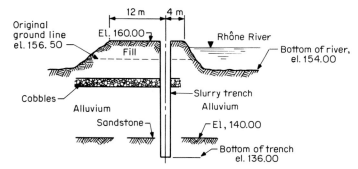

Figure 3-12 Pierre-Benite site. Typical cross section adjacent to river.

lapsed during construction of a cutoff wall to protect the main power station at Pierre-Benite, France, along the banks of the Rhône River. A typical section of the trench is shown in Fig. 3-12. A fill embankment was placed to raise the construction level above the highest river flood level. The initial slurry density was raised as the trench was excavated to 1.20 t/m³ (75 lb/ft³) by retaining soil particles.

The slips occurred in the fill portion of the trench after heavy rainfall that raised the groundwater level almost to the top of the fill. The collapse was extended along the entire length of the panel.

The results from the analysis of the failure are shown in Fig. 3-13, for two angles of friction, 30° and 35°. Taking the tip of the slips at elevation 156.50, the top of the fill at 160.00, and a slurry level 15 cm from the top, n is calculated as 0.96. Three values of m are used, 0.87, 0.93, and 1.00. For the assumed values of the angle ϕ', and taking $n = 0.96$ and $\gamma = 1.85$ t/m³, the graphs of Fig. 3-13 provide a direct assessment of trench stability. For a slurry density varying from 1.20

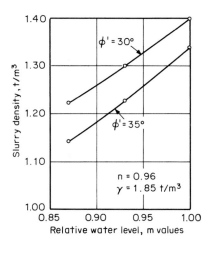

Figure 3-13 Relation of slurry density (measured) to relative water level. Slips at Pierre-Benite. (*From Morgenstern and Amir-Tahmasseb, 1965.*)

to 1.25 t/m³ (the measured slurry density range), and assuming a groundwater level near the top (say $m = 0.95$), the trench is on the verge of slip failure.

3-7 Special Considerations for Excavations in Sand

For routine problems the analysis of trench stability can be carried out assuming the trench to be infinitely long; i.e., the geometry and shape of the trench are ignored. Slip failure is assumed to occur when the total thrust from the active wedge begins to exceed the total slurry pressure. Referring to Fig. 3-14, this condition is reached when the area of the stress diagram, at any depth, shown on the right of Fig. 3-14a to c, equals the area of the slurry pressure diagram shown on the left.

The stability criteria can also be expressed in terms of unit stress, and an example is Eq. (3-22). This concept is not convenient for clays but applies readily to sands. The total thrust method is equivalent to the unit stress approach for the case shown in Fig. 3-14b, but not for the case shown in Fig. 3-14c. For multilayered soil, stability is better analyzed by the unit stress method.

Equal stress method. Figure 3-15 shows a section through a trench. Using a slightly different notation, at depth h_x stability is expressed as

$$p_f = p_w + p_a \tag{3-24}$$

where p_f = hydrostatic slurry pressure
$\quad p_w$ = groundwater pressure (static)
$\quad p_a$ = horizontal active earth stress

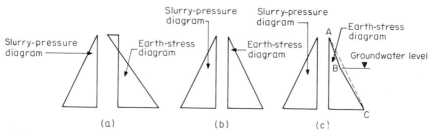

Figure 3-14 Stress diagram for slurry trenches: (a) Trench in clay. (b) Trench in dry sand or in fully submerged sand. (c) Trench in sand with water table below the ground surface.

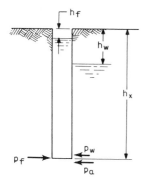

Figure 3-15 Trench in sand with variable slurry and groundwater level.

The following relations hold:

$$p_f = \gamma_f(h_x - h_f) \quad \text{and} \quad p_w = \gamma_w(h_x - h_w)$$

If $\quad\quad h_x \leq h_w \quad\quad$ then $\quad p_a = \gamma h_x K_a$

If $\quad\quad h_x > h_w \quad\quad$ then $\quad p_a = [\gamma h_w + \gamma'(h_x - h_w)]K_a$

and if $h_f = h_w = 0$, Eq. (3-24) yields Eq. (3-22).

Arching effect of short trenches.   In short trenches arching is developed when the part of the soil along the excavation tends to yield but this tendency is resisted at the ends of the panel, which form the boundary lines between yielding and stationary soil. Kowalewski (1964) has suggested that in a trench of finite dimensions arching occurs in a manner similar to the ground response across the crown of a tunnel.

Figure 3-16a shows the slip conditions of a short panel. The Coulomb edge is assumed to have the shape of a segment of a parabolic cylinder $ABC - A'B'C'$, so that failure occurs as sliding along plane $A'B'C'$ inclined at an angle θ to the horizontal. The stability can be checked with the use of nomographs of Fig. 3-16b (Piaskowski and Kowalewski, 1965), representing a soil type of a given strength and density. Evidently K_a decreases with increasing h_x/l ratio, so that the earth thrust per unit length is less for a short trench than for a long one, the depth h_x being the same. In these graphs h_w defines the groundwater table as shown in Fig. 3-15.

For short trenches the coefficient K_a can also be adjusted as proposed by Huder (1972), by applying a reduction factor A given by

$$A = \frac{1 - \exp(-2nK_a \tan \phi)}{2nK_a \tan \phi} \tag{3-25}$$

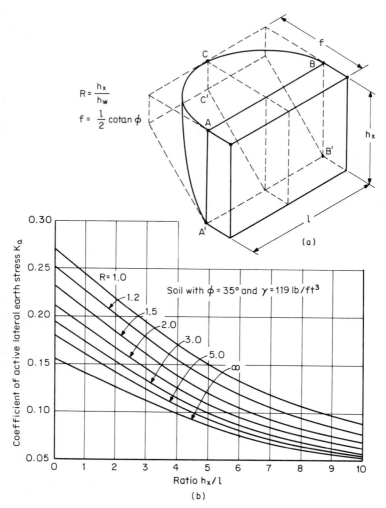

Figure 3-16 Variation of active earth-stress coefficient with trench dimensions. (*From Piaskowski and Kowalewski, 1965.*)

The active pressure is now calculated as

$$p_a = [\gamma h_w + \gamma'(h_x - h_w)]AK_a \qquad (3\text{-}26)$$

where m = ratio of depth to length = h_x/l. Values of A for the most usual cases can be found graphically with the help of Fig. 3-17.

As an example, we can compare the two methods for the soil of Fig. 3-16 ($\phi = 35°$) and an h_x/l ratio of 3. The unfactored active stress coefficient K_a is computed as the ratio $(1 - \sin \phi)/(1 + \sin \phi) = 0.31$. From the graphs of Fig. 3-16, and using $R = 1$ (water level at the

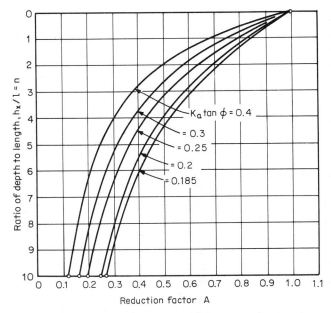

Figure 3-17 Reduction factor A for lateral earth stress in trenches. Idealized soil without cohesion. (*From Huder, 1972.*)

base of the trench), we obtain graphically the factored K_a as 0.19. Hence $A = 0.19/0.31 = 0.61$. Likewise, for the unfactored K_a we compute $K_a \tan \phi = 0.31 \times 0.61 = 0.19$. Using this value and $h_x/l = 3$, we enter the graphs of Fig. 3-17 and we obtain graphically the reduction factor A as 0.62.

The arching effect of short panels has also been investigated by Schneebeli (1964) based on the theory of lateral earth stresses for silos (Caquet and Kerisel, 1956). For a panel length l in cohesionless soil, the horizontal stress σ_z at depth z is

$$\sigma_z = \frac{\gamma l}{N_\phi \sin 2\phi} [1 - \exp(-n \sin 2\phi)] \qquad (3\text{-}27)$$

where $n = z/l$ = ratio of depth z to length l and N_ϕ = flow factor = $(1 + \sin \phi)/(1 - \sin \phi)$. When the depth z becomes very large compared with the length l, the horizontal stress approaches the asymptotic value

$$\sigma_{\max} = \frac{\gamma l}{N_\phi \sin 2\phi} \qquad (3\text{-}28)$$

According to the Schneebeli analysis the horizontal stress attains a maximum value at some depth and remains constant thereafter, whereas according to the Huder theory the reduction factor A approaches a limiting value but the horizontal earth stress continues to increase with depth.

Arching may be caused by the lateral movement of the soil toward the trench just before yielding and is associated with a vertical shortening. Frictional resistance along the boundary edges where the sliding soil meets stationary soil opposes subsidence and thus supports part of the weight of the sliding soil. Just before failure, the principal vertical stress in the lower wedge gets smaller and less than the overburden stress. In analyzing the arching effect the final depth is not necessarily the most critical depth. This assessment will depend on the details of the problem and on the method of analysis.

Example. Figure 3-18 illustrates the application of the Schneebeli method to trench stability problems. For this example, $\phi = 35°$, $\gamma = 120$ lb/ft^3, and the groundwater level is at elevation -5.00. The slurry weight is 70 lb/ft^3. Line AEE_1 represents the net hydrostatic pressure, i.e., slurry minus groundwater pressure. Without arching effects the lateral earth stress appears to exceed the net hydrostatic pressure at a depth of about 28 ft (obtained graphically). Next, the arching effect is considered for a panel 10 ft long, the value of σ_{max} is computed from Eq. (3-28) for both dry and submerged weight, and the curves ABB_1 and ACC_1 are drawn accordingly. Beginning at point B, the curve BD

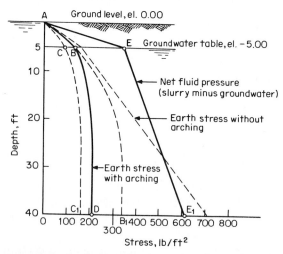

Figure 3-18 Application of arching effect to trench-stability problems. Earth stresses according to the Schneebeli theory.

is drawn parallel to curve CC_1 ($CB = C_1D$). The resulting curve ABD is the lateral earth stress diagram with the arching effect. Under this effect the trench is stable, and the difference between net fluid pressure and lateral earth stress increases with depth.

For short trenches, stability is thus enhanced by arching effects that help redistribute lateral stresses within a disturbed soil mass. There exists both a horizontal and a vertical arching effect, but none of the foregoing methods quantifies the arching mechanism. Solutions thus obtained are therefore reliable if the underlying assumptions are understood and the three-dimensional nature of the problem is explained. Relevant tests using centrifuge models to check trench stability are discussed in subsequent sections.

Stability of multilayered soil. The equal stress method is convenient when the soil is stratified and has nonuniform profile. Considering a soil profile with n different layers above the groundwater table and m different layers below this level, the stability can be expressed in terms of the slurry unit weight as

$$\gamma_f = \frac{K_a}{h_x - h_f}\left(\sum_{i=1}^{n} \Delta h_i \gamma + \sum_{i=1}^{m} \Delta h_i \gamma'\right) + \frac{\gamma_w(h_x - h_w)}{h_x - h_f} \quad (3\text{-}29)$$

where h_x, h_f, and h_w correspond to the notation of Fig. 3-15 and h_i is the thickness of each individual layer. Where ϕ is not the same for all layers, each factor $\Delta h_i \gamma$ should be multiplied individually by the corresponding value of K_a. The factor of safety is obtained from the expression

$$F = \frac{\gamma_{fa}(h_x - h_f) - \gamma_w(h_x - h_w)}{\gamma_f(h_x - h_f) - \gamma_w(h_x - h_w)} \quad (3\text{-}30)$$

where γ_{fa} is the actual unit weight of slurry and γ_f is the slurry weight required for a factor of safety of 1.

Effect of groundwater level. The sensitivity of trench stability to the groundwater level becomes apparent from Eq. (3-23). Useful data on this variability are also provided by the graphs of Fig. 3-19, where the parameter γ_f (slurry unit weight) is plotted vs. the groundwater table for soil with $\phi = 35°$ and $\gamma = 1.9$ t/m^3. Other symbols correspond to Fig. 3-15.

The following conclusions are important: (1) if h_w is below a certain value h_0 (for the example shown, 0.88 m), γ_f decreases with increasing critical depth h_c, but this behavior is reversed when $h_w > h_0$; (2) the

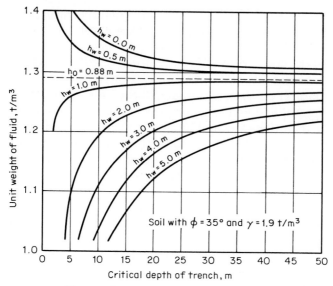

Figure 3-19 Unit weight of fluid vs. critical depth of trench. (*From Piaskowski and Kowalewski, 1965.*)

asymptote of the function $\gamma_f = f(h_c)$ in either case is a line parallel to the h_c axis at a distance h_0 as shown; and (3) for a given soil and a value of h_f, there is a certain value of h_0 for which γ_f is the same for any value of h_c.

Ground settlement. A case study of the variation of ground settlement, caused by slurry trench excavation as a function of the factor of safety, is presented in Fig. 3-20. These data are taken from tests reported by Elson (1968). The factor of safety is expressed as the ratio (tan ϕ)/

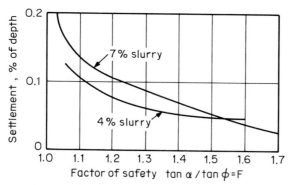

Figure 3-20 Percentage of settlement in sand vs. factor of safety. (*From Elson, 1968.*)

(tan α) and tan α is estimated from Eq. (3-19). Although these results cannot be considered general, it appears that when F exceeds 1.5 the probable settlement is less than 0.05 percent of the trench height. This settlement is assumed to extend across the theoretical sliding wedge, but in reality it is greater near the face.

3-8   Further Topics on Trench Stability

Trenches in cohesive soil

Some investigators treat trench stability as a bearing capacity problem. For the trench configuration shown in Fig. 3-21a and for the general soil with parameters γ, s_u, and N_c, the bearing capacity requires

$$\gamma_f H + N_c s_u \geq \gamma H + q \tag{3-31}$$

The N_c value may be taken as 4 at ground level, i.e., for shallow trenches, but increases as a function of the depth/length ratio, approaching a maximum 8 (Huder, 1972). Consider, for example, a trench with $H = 30$ m, $\gamma = 1.80$ t/m^3, $\gamma_f = 1.25$ t/m^3, $q = 0$, $N_c = 6$, and $s_u = 2.75$ t/m^2. We compute $1.25 \times 30 + 6 \times 2.75 = 54$, and $1.80 \times 30 = 54$. The trench is stable, therefore, with a factor of safety of 1.

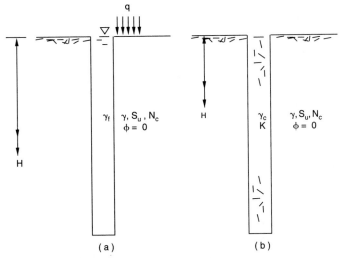

Figure 3-21   Stability of trench in clay: (a) With slurry. (b) With fresh concrete.

Of special interest is the term $s_u/\gamma'H$, the ratio of the undrained shear to the effective overburden stress. For the foregoing example, a ratio of $(s_u/\gamma'H) > 0.12$ is necessary to keep the trench stable.

Stability during concreting.   For trenches in soft clay, another question is whether the soil will support the pressure of the fresh concrete. The analysis of this problem is similar to the stability of the slurry-filled trench. Referring to Fig. 3-21b where γ_c and K are the concrete unit weight and pressure coefficient, respectively, stability requires

$$\gamma H + N_c s_u \geqslant K \gamma_c H \qquad (3\text{-}32)$$

Referring to the same example, and using $\gamma_c = 2.4$ t/m^3 and $K = 0.8$, we compute

$$\gamma H + N_c s_u = 1.80 \times 30 + 6 \times 2.75 = 70.5 \qquad \text{and} \qquad K \gamma_c H$$

$$= 0.80 \times 2.40 \times 30 = 57.6 < 70.5 \qquad \text{OK}$$

Pore pressure changes.   Pore pressure changes are shown in Fig. 3-22 for the test panel discussed in Sec. 3-4, shown in Figs. 3-4, 3-5, and

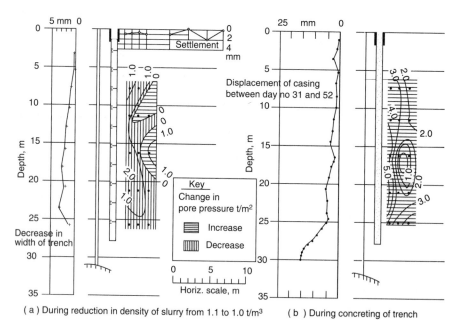

(a) During reduction in density of slurry from 1.1 to 1.0 t/m³   (b) During concreting of trench

Figure 3-22 Measured movement and changes in pore pressure: (a) During reduction in density of slurry from 1.1 to 1.0 t/m³. (b) During concreting of trench. (*From DiBiagio and Myrvoll, 1972b.*)

3-6. Figure 3-22a illustrates the change in pore pressure caused by an unloading of the sides of the trench as the slurry density is reduced from 1.1 to 1.0 t/m³. Figure 3-22b depicts the change caused by loading the sides of the trench occurring during the placement of fresh concrete (DiBiagio and Myrvoll, 1972b).

In Fig. 3-22a the contours express the change in pore pressure (t/m²) at the time of completion of the exchange of water for slurry (density 1.10 t/m²) with respect to the values measured just prior to the exchange. The changes in width of the trench and the observed settlement that occurred during the same interval are also shown and may be referenced to Figs. 3-5 and 3-6.

The variation in the pore pressure caused by the substitution of water by fresh concrete is shown in Fig. 3-22b. Likewise, the values represent the difference between measurements just prior to and immediately upon completion of the concrete placement. The maximum pore water pressure changes throughout the test program were recorded during this phase. The approximate displacement of the inclinometer casing is also shown. Since no inclinometer measurements were recorded prior to concreting the trench, the change in position is computed relative to Day 31, and therefore it includes the inward movement that occurred while the trench was filled with water and during concreting (composite movement). Although the displacement line does not represent the absolute movement during concreting, it shows nonetheless a definite slight bulging developed in the lower section of the trench as the concrete was rising.

Potential drainage problem.   In connection with excavations in soft clay in Oslo, settlement can become a serious problem if drainage of rock occurs. Owing to the permeability of the rock and the presence of a gravel layer over the rock, this drainage affects a large area. Whereas excavations in clays are usually free of drainage problems, the overlying soft clay is normally consolidated, producing large settlements. In Oslo, a common solution is to set tubes in the slurry walls for a later grouting of the rock, if necessary. The pervious layers above rock should be effectively sealed by the walls. In addition, water injection tubes to rock can be mounted outside the excavation to compensate for possible drainage.

Changes in the properties of adjacent soil

For convenience, trench analysis ignores the interaction between the soil and the slurry, the assumption being that the filter cake separates the soil from the slurry and allows the latter to develop its full hydrostatic thrust. This condition is typical for soils of low permeability such as clays and fine silts, but appreciable penetration by slurry may occur into the pores of coarse granular materials and gravels until a seal is formed and stops further penetration. Excessive penetration of the slurry can have an adverse effect on stability involving a failure surface with the slurry-saturated zone. Factors relevant to the analysis are therefore (1) strength changes of the soil caused by slurry impregnation and (2) a slurry thrust less than the full hydrostatic pressure.

Impregnation of soil.   Voids generally allow slurry to escape to adjacent soil. The extent of this penetration depends on pore size, differential hydrostatic head, and shear strength of slurry. Slurry gelled in the pores may impart a certain shear strength to the soil. This problem has been investigated by Elson (1968) ignoring changes in the friction angle.

Figure 3-23 shows the stress diagram for a zone impregnated with slurry. Diagram ABC represents the stress without filter cake, and ACD corresponds to the stress condition with filter cake. The symbols τ_f and r are the gel strength of the slurry and the mean pore radius of the soil, respectively. From triangle ABC the factor C_a is obtained as

$$C_a = \frac{2\tau_f l^2}{r \cos \theta} \tan \phi \tag{3-33}$$

If the filter cake is formed at the left boundary, C_a may be obtained from triangle ACD as

$$C_a = \frac{4\tau_f l^2}{r \cos \theta} \tan \phi \tag{3-33a}$$

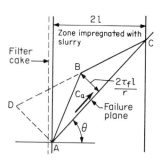

Figure 3-23 Stress diagram in zone of soil impregnated with slurry: ABC = without filter cake; DAC = with filter cake.

This is the apparent increase in the shear strength of the soil. The horizontal component is

$$C_h = 2C_a \cos\left(45 + \frac{\phi}{2}\right)$$

(3-34)

or
$$C_h = \frac{8\tau_f l^2}{r} \tan\phi$$

that may be included in the analysis as a net reduction in the active thrust of the soil. Conversely, the impregnating slurry may be only a dilute fluid with associated softening effects, in which case the active thrust of the soil is increased. Because of the difficulty of selecting soil parameters, Eq. (3-33) is useful for comparison purposes only.

Stability without filter cake.   Without filter cake the slurry is most likely to continue to flow toward the ground. The associated effects are (1) its actual thrust may be less than the theortical and (2) diluted slurry may reduce the friction angle of soil particles.

Müller-Kirchenbauer (1972) presents a simple analysis of stability without filter cake that involves the so-called stagnation gradient i_0. For a slurry with a differential head h, penetrating the soil for a distance l as shown in Fig. 3-24c, the stagnation gradient is the ratio h /l.

Figure 3-24a and b shows how the thrust of the slurry may be applied if there is no filter cake. The actual thrust exerted is

$$P'_f = V i_0 \gamma_{fP}$$

(3-35)

where P'_f = actual thrust of slurry without filter cake
    V = volume of zone within active wedge penetrated by slurry (*ABC*)
    γ_{fP} = slurry weight in penetrated zone, usually = γ_f

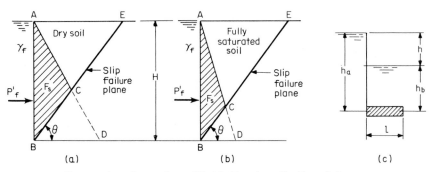

Figure 3-24   Penetration of granular soil by fluid and application of slurry pressure.

If F_s denotes the area of triangle ABC, then

$$P'_f = F_s i_0 \gamma_f \qquad (3\text{-}35a)$$

P'_f is much smaller than the full thurst P_f, and a comparison can be made noting that

$$\frac{P'_f}{P_f} = \frac{\text{triangle } (ABC)}{\text{triangle } (ABD)}$$

Likewise, a smaller factor of safety will result if the slurry effect is a reduced friction angle. In some instances, this reduction has been quoted at as much as 5°.

Stability with permeable filter cake.   A permeable filter cake may be the result of several causes such as loss of colloidal stability or contamination with soil and salts. In this case, the actual thrust of the slurry is between P_f and P'_f.

Figure 3-25 shows a permeable filter cake. As it penetrates the soil matrix it carries a fraction of colloid and noncolloid solids. For a volume element and a corresponding penetration dl the following notation is used:

n_1 = void volume of soil in situ = porosity ratio
n_2 = void volume of filter cake = porosity ratio
i_{01} = stagnation gradient of slurry related to soil
i_{02} = stagnation gradient of slurry related to filter cake
dV, V = volume of slurry element including all solids

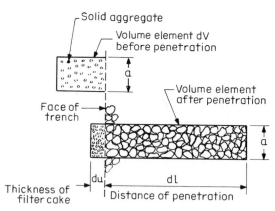

Figure 3-25   Formation of surface filtrate by penetration of suspension containing solid aggregate.

dV_s, V_s = volume of all solids (colloid and aggregate) in element
γ_s = unit weight of aggregate (soil)
γ_f = unit weight of slurry without aggregate
γ_{fs} = unit weight of slurry with aggregate
z = depth of trench
h = head of slurry, generally $< z$
h_1 = fraction of h transmitted to the soil
h_2 = fraction of h transmitted to filter cake
m = concentration factor = V_s/V (not related to bentonite concentration)

When we consider the surface area of a single volume element, it is evident that for $a = 1$

$$dV_s = mdV = (dl\ n_1 + du)m$$

and also

$$dV_s = du\ (1 - n_2)$$

When combined, these relations yield

$$\frac{du}{dl} = \frac{mn_1}{1 - n_2 - m} = \lambda \tag{3-36}$$

The following are true by definition of the stagnation gradient

$$\frac{dh_2}{du} = i_{02} \quad \text{and} \quad \frac{dh_1}{dl} = i_{01}$$

Combined with Eq. (3-36), we obtain

$$\frac{dh_2}{dh_1} = \frac{h_2}{h_1} = \lambda \frac{i_{02}}{i_{01}} \tag{3-37}$$

where $h_1 + h_2 = h$
If the stagnation gradients are known, the fraction heads and the dimensions l and u can be estimated from the foregoing expressions. For a slurry of unit weight γ_{fs} rather γ_f, the head at depth z is adjusted accordingly, so that

$$h_2 = \frac{1}{\gamma_f} \int_0^z \gamma_{fs}\ dz \tag{3-38}$$

Now the fraction of slurry pressure p'_{f1} and p'_{f2} transmitted to the soil and the filter cake, respectively, is from Eq. (3-35)

$$p'_{f1} = i_{01}\gamma_f l \qquad (3\text{-}39a)$$

and

$$p'_{f2} = i_{02}\gamma_f u \qquad (3\text{-}39b)$$

and also

$$p'_{f1} + p'_{f2} = p'_{fs} = h_2\gamma_{fs} \qquad (3\text{-}40)$$

The estimation of stagnation gradients requires a simple test (see also other sections).

3-9   Effect of Gel Strength of Slurry on Stability

For most slurry trench excavations the slurry is continuously agitated within a range that extends from mild stirring to turbulent conditions as the excavation equipment works to complete the operation. In some instances, the slurry may intentionally be allowed to develop a shear strength, and an example is the solidified cutoff wall. A small shear of the order of 10 to 15 lb/ft^2 can improve the stability conditions considerably.

The problem is equivalent to the compression of a perfectly plastic material squeezed between two rough rigid plates. This concept has been extended by Bishop (1952) to the computation of active stress of a puddle core in earth dams. The slurry trench problem basically is the opposite of the earth stress condition induced in the puddle core.

For a trench of height H and width $2a$ it can be shown that the total resistance provided by the slurry is

$$P_f = \frac{1}{2}\gamma_f H^2 + \frac{\tau_f H^2}{2a} + \frac{1}{2}\pi\tau_f H \qquad (3\text{-}41)$$

Since the term $\frac{1}{2}\gamma_f H^2$ is the hydrostatic thrust of the slurry, it follows that the cohesion factor due to the shear strength of the slurry τ_f is

$$C_f = \frac{\tau_f H^2}{2a} + \frac{1}{2}\pi\tau_f H \qquad (3\text{-}42)$$

Equations (3-41) and (3-42) are general and can be used for stability analyses in any type of soil.

In dry cohesionless soil a trench is stable if P_f is equated to the active thrust of the soil $\frac{1}{2}\gamma H^2 K_a$ which gives

$$H_{Cr} = \frac{\pi \tau_f}{\gamma K_a - \gamma_f - \tau_f/a} \tag{3-43}$$

Likewise for clay with $\phi = 0$ and cohesion c, the critical height is

$$H_{Cr} = \frac{4c + \pi \tau_f}{\gamma - \gamma_f - \tau_f/a} \tag{3-44}$$

From the foregoing it follows that relatively narrow trenches are more stable than wide ones for the same value of τ_f.

3-10   Stability under Dynamic Loading

Dynamic loading can be induced during an earthquake or from the application of a vibratory excitation such as the passage of railroad loading. The effect on trench stability is partly an increase in the shear stress under which sliding occurs, and partly a decrease or loss of strength during cyclic loading. The analysis usually involves a modification of the limiting equilibrium method to include a dynamic factor.

Effect of ground vibrations.   Vibration analyses are usually based on the theory of a surface load on an elastic half-space, supplemented by the lumped-mass approach and refinements in the elastic half-space theory. The principal difficulty in current vibration analyses is in determining representative soil properties of shear modulus and Poisson's ratio as input into the differential equations that describe the vibration motion. The general principles of vibration theory are beyond the scope of this text; hence this section discusses the trench response to these effects in a conceptual manner.

If saturated cohesionless soil is subjected to ground vibrations, the result is an increase in the pore water pressure due to movement of water from voids as the soil is compacted and densified. The corresponding decrease in effective stress may turn the sand into a "quick," or liquefied, condition for which the soil strength is practically zero; thus no load can be supported. This situation arises primarily in loose silts and sands and eventually will lead to trench collapse.

Vibrations can also cause problems in clay deposits and result in unstable excavation, and this condition is more critical in highly sensitive clays. If soft clays contain sand lenses, their liquefaction will contribute to the development of a slide.

In general, ground motion produces a corresponding acceleration that can alter the state of stress in the active wedge. For a potential circular arc failure ground acceleration causes an active moment about the center of the arc, thus adding to the overturning moment. This is particularly critical in earthquakes and large explosions or blasting operations. More often, however, it is necessary to estimate the effect of moving loads alongside an excavation or the effect of vibrations from construction equipment.

A relevant factor to trench stability is the energy released to the active wedge. This can be represented by the amplitude of the motion produced, the frequency of this motion, the resulting acceleration, the force delivered to the wedge, or the energy itself defined in terms of the motion velocity. All these concepts are subject to direct measurements under various combinations to correlate the observed results.

Effect of moving loads and construction equipment. This situation has been assessed in full-scale field tests. A test of this type has been performed for the excavation shown in Fig. 3-26. In this case, a trench was excavated adjacent to a railroad track, while various measure-

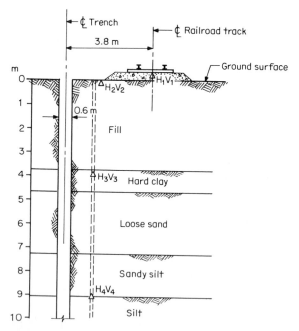

Figure 3-26 Test panel for the study of the effect of dynamic loads. V = vertical component of vibration. H = horizontal component of vibration. (*From Saito et al., 1974.*)

ments were taken to study the effect of moving trains and locomotives and the effect of drills and chiseling (Saito et al., 1974).

Dynamic measurements. The vibrations induced just beneath the ballast by the passage of trains are reduced at the hard-clay layer, but little reduction is observed from the hard clay down to the loose sand and silt since this soil is conducive to vibrations. The vibration pattern is shown in Fig. 3-27 for various construction stages.

Response spectra are shown in Fig. 3-28. The period for V_1 is between 0.01 and 0.3 s. The period for H_1 has some peaks between 0.08 and 0.1 s. Figure 3-28b to d shows response spectra for V_3 at various stages of construction. Acceleration varies with excavation, and its level increases with excavation depth but is reduced after completion of the concrete wall. These effects may be assessed by comparing the relative acceleration values. If the relative acceleration level 0.6 m from the face is taken as 1, during construction it changes as follows: 0.94 for excavation depth 3 m, 1.25 for excavation depth 8 m, 1.24 for excavation depth 40 m, and 0.46 after completion of the concrete wall.

The dynamic effect of construction equipment, i.e., a chisel used for hard obstacles, is a corresponding impact imparted to the ground. Maximum acceleration occurs just below the operating level and generally is more severe than the impact induced by passing trains. A chisel affects both faces to the same extent, whereas train passage affects only the adjacent face since the vibrations are not transmitted across the trench.

The last comment suggests the usefulness of slurry trenches built to intercept vibrations. An example given by Xanthakos (1974) in-

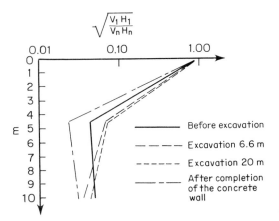

Figure 3-27 Decrease of the intensity of vibration with distance and through different soil layers. (*From Saito et al., 1974.*)

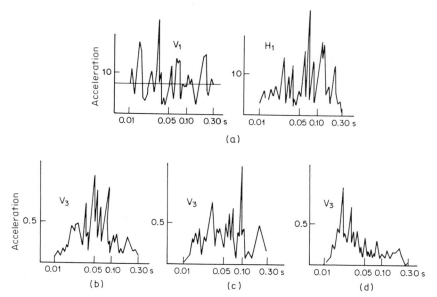

Figure 3-28 Response spectra: V = vertical component of ground vibrations; H = horizontal component of ground vibrations. (a) Pattern of vibrations induced in the ground just beneath the ballast; patterns of vibration of V_3. (b) Before excavation. (c) For excavation at 40 m. (d) After completion of the wall. (*From Saito et al., 1974.*)

volves a trench 45 ft deep, excavated close to the outside wall of a building in Berlin and filled with gelled bentonite slurry to intercept construction vibrations and isolate the building from train effects. A complete report on this project was provided after the project was completed, and some essential points are mentioned here:

1. The damping and absorbing effect of a gelled slurry in a trench increases with the energy of vibration. Since vibration damage is associated with vibration velocity, it is interesting to note that a velocity amplitude of 5 mm/s reaching the trench was reduced to 1 mm/s.

2. The reduction of the horizontal component of a periodically excited vibration is more efficient than that of the vertical one, but in the case of impact the opposite was observed.

3. While the damping effect of deep narrow trenches is confirmed in practice, difficulties were encountered with soil pollutants attacking the bentonite slurry, with subsequent slurry losses. The remedies included additional stability controls and pouring extra slurry.

4. Where this application is considered, studies of the soil chemistry and groundwater are essential to determine the control measures

necessary to maintain colloidal stability. It is conceivable that under the most adverse conditions a continuous buildup of soil particles along the initial filter cake may cause it to increase across the entire width. This bridging may restore the ground with the subsequent loss of the damping effect.

Strain measurements. For the test of Fig. 3-26, the passage of trains produced strains of the order of 5.0×10^{-5} for H_3 and 1.0×10^{-4} for H_4. Strains caused by chiseling were 2.7×10^{-5} for H_3 and 9.4×10^{-4} for H_4. These strain levels are well below the dynamic yielding strain and the liquefaction limit of loose sand and silt.

Pore water pressure measurements. Dynamic pore water pressure measurements generally are difficult to obtain. For the test panel of Fig. 3-26, measurements were obtained, however, for both static and dynamic conditions; the results are shown in Fig. 3-29, associated with passing trains. The pore water pressure begins to increase as the train enters the trench zone and reaches a maximum when the vibration level becomes maximum. The component due to vibrations is about 0.01 kg/cm², or 20.5 lb/ft² (Saito et al., 1974), and this is fairly nominal. These data are, however, approximate since vibration strains are too small for proper instruments to trace short-term pressure changes with better accuracy.

From Fig. 3-29 the maximum measured pore water pressure is 0.05 kg/cm² (102 lb/ft²). For a static train loading KS-18 (Japanese Standard) the corresponding earth pressure is 0.076 kg/cm² using the Westergaard distribution theory, so that the pore water pressure coefficient is 0.66. Pore water pressure changes are greatest when the chisel operates near the recording instrument. For this example the maximum measured pore water pressure is 0.056 kg/cm² (115 lb/ft²).

The foregoing results indicate that the dynamic effect of conventional moving loads on trench stability in loose or in soft soils reaches a peak near the upper part of the excavation and diminishes gradually

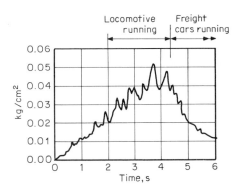

Figure 3-29 Variations in the pore water pressure due to the passage of trains. Point 8 m deep when excavation reached a depth of 6.6 m. (*From Saito et al., 1974.*)

in deeper parts. The effect of chiseling is more pronounced near the source level but diminishes away from this level, so that it does not have a global influence on trench stability with the exception of some localized sloughing.

3-11   The Cylindrical Surface Method

This analysis assumes that a rotational type of failure occurs along a slip surface approximating a circular arc. The rotational character of some slides in deep excavations and particularly in soft or loose soils has been established beyond doubt. In this case the trench analysis requires the determination of a circle that best represents the surface along which sliding will occur. This critical circle satisfies the condition that the ratio of the moment causing sliding and the moment resisting it is a maximum. The investigation is therefore within the category of maximum and minimum solutions exemplified by the Coulomb theory and involves possible combinations of cohesion and friction that may give the minimum factor of safety. Slight variations in geometry (assumed center and radius of circle) have minor effects on stability, but errors in assumed panel boundaries, stress distribution, and soil parameters are more critical.

All potential circles have one common point, which is the intersection of the vertical face and the bottom line of the trench. Once the center and radius are determined, the analysis is carried out as shown in Fig. 3-30. All forces and loads within the active wedge are computed and their line of action located. The summation of their moments about the center of notation O is the overturning moment M_0 that tends to cause sliding along curved surface BC. The resisting moment M_r is provided by (1) the shear resistance along BC represented by

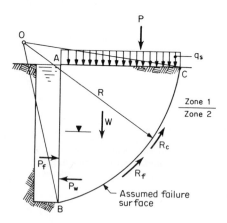

Figure 3-30 Analysis of trench stability according to the cylindrical surface method.

the friction R_f and the cohesion R_c, (2) the slurry thrust P_f, and (3) the shear resistance at the ends of the cylinder ABC. The factor of safety against sliding is

$$F = \frac{M_r}{M_0}$$ (3-45)

The length of the cylindrical section must be selected first, since it is relevant to the factor of safety. Since the shear resistance at the end returns is the same regardless of trench length, it follows that short panels are safer than long ones. For continuous trenches, the longer the length the less significant the effect of the end returns, and in many instances it may be ignored.

According to these principles, a concentrated load (point or line) acting on the surface of the sliding wedge makes a contribution that depends only on the distance from center O, and the farther the load is from O the greater the resulting moment. Hence the sliding surface method may be overly conservative when there are such loads on the surface, and a more appropriate method may be to use principles from the theory of elasticity.

Examples of external concentrated loads are adjacent foundations, underground structures, heavy moving loads, and loads incidental to construction. Elastic solutions are obtained assuming that soil is homogeneous and isotropic. There may be cases, however, where it is best to recognize the limitations of theory and resort to empirical criteria. For instance, the effect of certain concentrated loads such as foundations may be compensated for by limiting the panel length. This helps stability in two ways: (1) arching takes effect, redistributing the stresses, and (2) the existing foundation usually possesses sufficient longitudinal rigidity to span over weak spots, tending to ignore localized loss of strength and adjust the load transfer by overloading the soil beyond the boundaries of the panel.

These solutions have been tried empirically and found to work well. Relevant tests are reported by ICOS (1968) in conjunction with the metropolitan subway extension in Milan, Italy, constructed in cut-and-cover excavations in soil with sand and gravel (Xanthakos, 1974). In these tests artificial spread footings were built within 1.5 ft from a contemplated trench. After the trench was excavated under slurry to a depth of 25 ft and with dimensions 2×6 ft, the footing loads were increased from 8.6 to 12 kips/ft^2 and ultimately 17 kips/ft^2. Thereafter the load was decreased to 10.4 kips/ft^2 as the trench length was incrased to 18 ft by extending the initial excavation on both sides by 6 ft. The test was concluded while gradually lowering the slurry level and simultaneously removing the foundation loads. When the level reached about 7.5 ft from the surface, the first cave-in occurred, and as pumping continued more cave-ins followed with only the weight of the foundation loading the soil.

3-12   Trenches with Horizontal Curvature, Case Study

Figure 3-31 shows two excavations with horizontal curvature. Figure 3-31a is a circular cut, and Fig. 3-31b is a circular trench. For the latter, stability depends on both the concave and the convex face. As a first approximation the stability of the outside face (concave) is roughly equivalent to the stability of a circular cut of the same geometry if changes in the bottom of the hole are not considered. The convex face undergoes different stretching and deformation; hence its stability may be more critical. An indication of stability criteria for the two different surfaces is obtained if we consider a curved trench of finite length and include the effect of end returns, as in short trench panels. For the convex face the end panels converge, resulting in a sliding wedge of less volume but also of less sliding surface, hence less sliding resistance. For the concave face the end returns diverge, resulting in a sliding wedge with more volume but also with more sliding surface, hence more sliding resistance.

The stability of circular trenches has been analyzed by Lorente De No (1969) for both convex and concave faces using finite-difference methods. Certain assumptions are that the soil is homogeneous and isotropic, and the elastic medium is assumed frictionless. The excavation is considered dry. To avoid problems in simulating the increasing excavation depth, the excavation is assumed to have been carried out in a weightless medium to the final depth, and thereafter the overburden is increased until failure occurs.

First yielding occurs at the bottom, and failure is determined by the difference of the principal stresses. This difference increases with depth except when K_0 approaches 1. However, the analysis presented

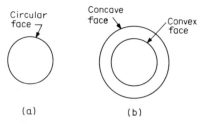

Figure 3-31   Excavations with horizontal curvature: (a) Circular cut. (b) Circular trench.

here is based on a value of μ (Poisson's ratio) of 0.25, so that K_0 derived from the relation $K_0 = \mu/(1 - \mu)$ is not 1 (a $K_0 = 1$ would require $\mu = 0.5$).

Results of analysis. Figure 3-32 shows the deformation of the model. Figure 3-32a is for a concave slope, and a strip excavation (infinite rectangular cut) is shown in Fig. 3-32b. Both the vertical settlement at the ground surface and the inward movement of the face are less for the concave face. Figure 3-33 shows the deformation of a compound excavation that has a concave and convex vertical face. When the two sketches are superimposed, they provide the deformation of a circular trench. For the same curvature and depth the concave slope causes less surface settlement and inward movement.

Figure 3-34 shows a plot of the factor $f = \gamma H/c$ vs the ratio $r = R/H$ of the circular trench. R is the horizontal radius, and H is the height. The upper curve is for concave slopes and the lower for convex.

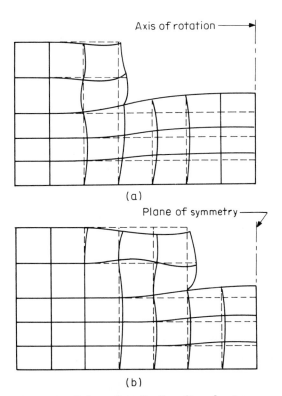

(a)

(b)

Figure 3-32 Deformation of soil medium due to excavation: (a) Circular excavation. (b) Long rectangular cut. (*From Lorente De No, 1969.*)

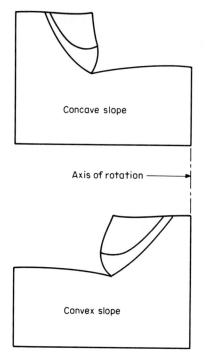

Concave slope

Axis of rotation

Convex slope

Figure 3-33 Typical plastic zones at failure for concave and convex slopes. (*From Lorente De No, 1969.*)

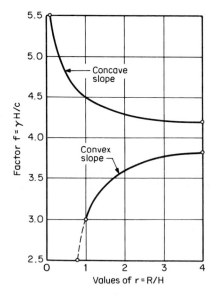

Figure 3-34 Chart for factor $f = \gamma H/e$, concave and convex slopes. Variable values of $r = R/H$, where R = radius of horizontal curvature and H = height of excavation.

The lower limit for the concave and the upper limit for the convex face is obtained as $r \to \infty$ (linear trenches), and is represented by the asymptote for $f = \gamma H / c = 4$.

As a first approximation, f can be obtained from the expressions

Concave slopes:
$$f = 4 + \frac{2}{3r + 1} \qquad (3\text{-}46)$$

Convex slopes:
$$f = 4 - \frac{2}{3r - 1} \qquad (3\text{-}47)$$

that apply to dry excavations. The classification of the excavation as very deep or shallow is with reference to the ratio R/H. The factor f approaches a maximum of about 6 for concave slopes as r approaches zero, but convex vertical faces appear to approach the asymptotic line for r values close to unity ($R = H$) with a lower limit of about 3. In fact, Eq. (3-47) gives better results for $r \geq 1$. When $r < 1$, plastic flow reaches the axis of symmetry before it is developed at the surface, creating a tension zone around this axis and causing failure by the combined action of shear and tension cracks. If tension cracks are present, this analysis is not valid because of discontinuities and geometric changes.

For a slurry-filled circular trench the analysis may be approximated by estimating f from Eqs. (3-46) and (3-47), and then entering Eq. (3-6), replacing the coefficient 4 by f. In the lower zone of r the results may be misleading for the convex face but acceptable for routine analysis.

3-13 Performance Monitoring

General principles

There are several reasons for using instrumentation to monitor the performance of slurry walls and adjacent structures during and after construction. During construction of a slurry wall (trench excavation to concrete placement), the following performance criteria must be ensured and quantified:

1. Trench stability
2. Verticality of trench
3. Guide wall stability

During and after excavation (general) alongside a finished diaphragm wall, the performance criteria are extended to include the following:

1. Sufficient prevention and control of ground movement behind the wall.
2. Adequacy of lateral support systems (usually cross-lot bracing or ground anchors).
3. Prevention and control of bottom heave (base stability).
4. Control of groundwater level to avoid distress to nearby structure.

Instrumentation is therefore a routine phase of the construction program. Parameters of interest in using instrumentation are summarized in Table 3-1 together with possible measurement methods.

Measurement Methods

In general, instrumentation methods are available for three main activities: (1) deformation measurements, (2) load and stress measurements, and (3) water and earth pressure measurements. The following sections give a review of the use of the measurement method, the principle of operation, and some data on various practical details (Dunnicliff, 1979).

Deformation measurements. These are associated with the initial trench excavation, concrete placement, and general wall and ground movement during and following the excavation.

Optical survey. Horizontal movement of ground surface, guide walls, or the top of the finished diaphragm wall normally is measured by holding a steel tape or scale at right angles across a line of sight between a fixed transit position and a permanent foresight. It is important to ensure that the endpoints of the line of sight are stationary, and if there is a possibility of movement, distance should be chained from these points to permanent points more remote from the excavation. Accuracy is about ±0.01 ft.

Vertical movements of the ground surface, guide walls, or the top of the wall are usually measured by second- or third-order optical leveling to an accuracy of ±0.01 ft. Simple studs are designated as measuring points on concrete surfaces, but on the ground surface steel or wooden stakes may be driven to create a measuring point. Where soil moisture changes or frost action could cause natural distortion of the reference point, a Borros anchor should be set about 5 ft below ground surface to ensure datum stability and serve as a surface measuring

TABLE 3-1   Problems and Measurement Methods in Slurry Walls Construction

Geotechnical problem	Parameters of interest	Possible measurement methods
Trench stability	Width of trench	▪ Trench width gage ▪ Inclinometer
	Horizontal and vertical movement of adjacent ground	▪ Optical survey* ▪ Inclinometer ▪ Subsurface settlement gage*
Verticality of trench	Alignment of sides of trench	▪ Inclinometer in temporary casing
Guide wall stability	Horizontal and vertical movement of guide wall	Optical survey*
Ground movement behind wall	Horizontal movement of ground	▪ Optical survey* ▪ Inclinometer in or behind wall ▪ Horizontally installed multipoint extensometer ▪ Tape extensometer across excavation ▪ Piezometer
	Vertical movement of ground	▪ Optical survey* ▪ Subsurface settlement gage*
	Movement of adjacent buildings	▪ Photography ▪ Optical survey* ▪ Tiltmeter ▪ Crack gage
Lateral support with cross-lot bracing	Load in bracing	▪ Strain gage
Lateral support with tie-backs	Movement of anchor Load in anchor	▪ Telltale ▪ Load cell
Basal stability	Bottom heave or horizontal movement of ground	▪ Heave gage* ▪ Piezometer ▪ Inclinometer
Retention of groundwater level	Groundwater level Pore pressure	▪ Observation well ▪ Piezometer
Full-scale test panels for research purposes	All above parameters Earth pressure between wall and soil outside excavation Stress in wall	See above ▪ Earth pressure cell ▪ Strain gage

*Requires installation and use of deep benchmark to a depth below seat of settlement of heave.

point. Measurements of vertical movement require use of a good benchmark.

Inclinometers. Their use allows measurement of subsurface horizontal movement, either of the slurry wall or of the ground behind the wall. They can also serve to check the verticality of the excavated trench.

An inclinometer system has a pipe installed in a vertical borehole, with internal longitudinal guide grooves. A torpedo containing an electrical tilt sensor is lowered in the pipe on the end of a graduated electrical cable, whereas orientation is controlled by wheels riding in the guide grooves. The cable is connected to a remote readout device indicating tilt of the torpedo with respect to vertical. Tilt readings and depth measurements establish the alignment of the grooved pipe, and changes in this alignment constitute horizontal movement data.

For slurry wall measurements a precise tilt sensor is used, preferably a closed-loop force balance servo accelerometer with a measuring accuracy of about ±0.2 in in 100 ft of depth. Since the calculation process is laborious, data reduction should be performed by computer.

Details reflecting good practice are noted by Dunnicliff (1979). After a set of readings have been taken within the grooved pipe, a repeat set should be taken with the torpedo rotated about 180° in the grooves, basing the computations on the difference between the two sets. This will negate any zero drift in the sensor and will average groove irregularities. If the grooved pipe is installed in holes deeper than about 60 ft, a survey should be made of in-place groove twist using a suitable device. Twist can be present in the pipe prior to installation and can be aggravated during installation; any undetected twist will result in false data on the direction of horizontal ground movement. The torpedo should be check-calibrated frequently, using either a test stand obtained from the manufacturer, a homemade stand of a suitably sturdy wall, or a grooved pipe installed in a remote area away from the movement zone. The inclinometer system does not provide a measurement of absolute horizontal position, but essentially relative to one end of the grooved pipe. Great caution is suggested so that the bottom of the pipe is installed deep enough using base fixity as a reliable reference, calculating data from the bottom upward. Where this is not certain, periodic optical survey measurements should be made on the top of the pipe to determine the top location, calculating data from the top downward. At best both should be done to check the assumption of base fixity.

An "in-place" version of inclinometers is available, with the tilt sensors locked in place at various depths along the grooved pipe. Data can be obtained rapidly and telemetered to a remote location.

Inclinometer pipes installed in soil are usually backfilled with a weak grout or pea gravel injected in the annular space between pipe and soil. Inclinometer pipes installed within the slurry wall are usually set within a 4-in PVC pipe attached to the reinforcing cage, the annular space between pipes filled with weak grout. For measuring verticality of the trench grooved pipe sections are lowered in the slurry-filled trench, and forced against the wall using special hydraulic jacks. Readings are made as usual, the jacks are retracted, and the pipe is withdrawn.

Subsurface settlement gages. These provide data on vertical ground movement adjacent to a slurry wall, and therefore on trench stability during trench excavation and on general stability during excavation between slurry trenches. Shallow subsurface settlement gages can also be used to create surface measuring points below the zone of seasonal moisture changes and frost action.

These devices fall into two general categories, single-point and multipoint gages. The most frequently used single-point gage is the "Borros" anchor consisting of a steel anchor mechanically set at the bottom of a borehole. A small-diameter riser pipe extends from the anchor to the ground surface, and optical survey elevations are taken on top of the pipe to check anchor settlement. A larger-diameter sleeve pipe protects the riser pipe from vertical movement of soil above the anchor. Problems may arise because of binding between the bottom of the sleeve pipe and the riser rod. Accuracy of measurement normally is ±0.01 ft.

Multipoint inductive coil settlement gages can be used to determine a full pattern of subsurface settlement with depth. These gages consist of a corrugated plastic pipe installed in a nominally vertical borehole with stainless-steel wire rings around the pipe placed at 5- to 10-ft intervals. The annular space between pipe and borehole wall is grouted with a mix having a modulus similar to the soil modulus. A probe containing an inductive coil is lowered within the pipe on the end of an electrical cable and survey tape. Readings at the ground surface provide data for calculating settlement. Normal accuracy is ±0.01 ft, but greater accuracy is possible by modifying the basic arrangement.

Combined inclinometer and multipoint subsurface settlement gages. It is possible to combine these two devices so that they can be installed in a single borehole to obtain both horizontal and vertical subsurface movement from one installation. This arrangement requires careful sizing of the inclinometer pipe and the corrugated plastic pipe, packing the intervening space with grease, and selecting a grout mix mechanically compatible with the surrounding soil to fill the annular space between corrugated pipe and soil.

Multipoint extensometers. These are installed vertically to monitor subsurface settlement on the outside of slurry walls, but they can also be installed horizontally or inclined to monitor horizontal movement of the wall and the soil.

A horizontally installed multipoint extensometer consists of up to six separate anchors placed at various depths in a drill hole, with a sleeved rod connected to each. The rods pass through a head set in the slurry wall, and relative movement between the end of each rod and the head gives data of movement. Zero relative movement between the two deepest anchors usually is interpreted to mean that both are beyond the active movement zone. Quoted accuracy is of the order of ±0.005 in, usually attainable with the use of a permanent-magnet sensor attached to each rod.

The annular spaces between rods and sleeves should be filled with a light oil. A disconnect should be provided between the inner end of each rod and its anchor, using a simple bayonet arrangement. In this way, if questionable readings are made, the appropriate rod can be disconnected from its anchor by gripping and turning at the head, while free sliding within its sleeve is verified. If the rod does not slide freely, the sleeve will have been squeezed so that data from the anchor will not be reliable.

Heave gages. These are used to monitor base heave of an excavation between slurry walls, and therefore serve as an index of base stability. There are two basic categories: (1) gages that require lowering rods or a probe in a hole to locate a buried component, and (2) electrical gages that give measurements of heave with respect to a deep anchor and thus do not require lowering rods or probe.

With the first category the simplest method is to install a conical steel point, facing upward. At any time during excavation a probing rod of known length is lowered in the borehole to mate with the conical point. The elevation of the top of the rod is determined by optical leveling, giving the elevation of the conical point. Accuracy is ±0.01 ft.

The secondary category requires drilling a hole to a depth below the expected level of heave, setting an anchor with an attached sleeved rod. The rod terminates at an electrical linear displacement sensor set below the eventual bottom of the excavation, so that any changes in distance between sensor and deep anchor causes an identical movement within the sensor itself. A cable runs up the borehole to the current bottom of the excavation, and the cable terminals can be set below the excavation bottom using a packer device so that excavation can proceed without damaging the cables. Quoted accuracy may be as high as ±0.005 in. The second category is more expensive and recommended if the desired accuracy must be higher than ±0.01 ft.

Tape extensometers. These are devices used to measure the width across an excavation between slurry walls, and hence to provide a check of horizontal movement measurements obtained by optical survey or inclinometers.

Studs are attached to the walls, and the portable extensometer is mated with the studs and stretched across the excavation at the time of reading.

Telltales. These serve to monitor movement of ground anchors with respect to the wall face and thus provide an indication of load loss in the anchor with possible ground and wall movement. They normally consist of a small-diameter rod within an oil-filled sleeve. A disconnect arrangement between the rod and its anchor provides the means for checking that the rod is free to move correctly within its sleeve.

Benchmarks. Benchmarks established on permanent structures should not contribute errors to vertical movement measurements. However, benchmarks placed at a shallow depth in soil may move to an extent sufficient to interfere with the survey accuracy. Exempting frost heave and seasonal moisture changes, construction activities may cause a surface bench to settle as a result of extension strains.

If a suitable stationary structure is not available away from the zone of possible vertical movement, a deep benchmark should be installed to a depth below the seat of vertical movement. It may consist of a pipe, anchored at depth, and surrounded by and disconnected from a sleeve pipe to protect the inner pipe from vertical movement caused by soil movement. The space between the two pipes should be filled with a bond-breaking material.

Trench width gages. These measurements are usually associated with full-scale test panels rather than with routine construction monitoring. Dunnicliff (1979) describes two types of gages used in such tests, one in Norway and one in Boston. The Norwegian example is reported by DiBiagio and Myrvoll (1972b) and used a hydraulic gage (see also Sec. 3-4). The Boston case (Goldberg et al., 1976) required monitoring of trench width without reinforcing cage, but both prior to and after concreting. The absence of steel bars allowed the use of the "soil strain gage" inductive principle. This system consists of opposing 12-in-diameter coils installed directly on the surface of the trench walls after excavation. The coil separation distance (and hence change of trench width) at the coil location is determined by sending an electric current through one of a pair of coils installed on opposite sides of the slurry trench. For the Boston experience, measurements were taken while the trench was filled with slurry, after concrete placement, and after concrete set with a quoted accuracy of ±0.1 in.

Unlike an inclinometer, the trench width gages do not indicate displacements relative to initial conditions, nor do they separate unequal movement of the two sides of the trench. They provide, however, data relative to localized surface sloughing of the trench walls and indicate actual changes in trench width.

Crack gages. A preconstruction survey of buildings adjacent to slurry wall excavations is made as a legal record to establish building conditions prior to construction (see also Sec. 2-2). This survey is supplemented by descriptions and photo records. The width of existing cracks can be monitored using an optical crack width gage. Selected cracks may also be gaged with a portable mechanical gage by attaching permanent studs on each side of the crack. Subsequent readings with the gage provide evidence of change in crack width.

Tiltmeters. These are used to monitor verticality of buildings adjacent to slurry wall excavations. Normally ceramic plates are attached to the walls at representative locations, and readings of plate verticality are made using a portable tiltmeter.

Load and stress measurements. These may be desired to establish load in bracing and anchors, and stresses in the wall to confirm the design or a part of full-scale tests on panels for research purposes. The usual methods involve the use of strain gages and load cells.

Strain gages. These have been used to monitor loads in cross bracing, and measure stresses in the finished wall under load.

For monitoring bracing loads the most effective method has been the use of vibrating wire strain gages mounted on studs welded to struts. Interestingly, the process must recognize the effect of details. The thermal coefficient of the gage should be close to the thermal coefficient of the strut to ensure a stress field independent of temperature. The gage should be at least 5 ft from the end of the strut to avoid end-detail effects. For measuring stresses caused by bending and axial load, three gages are needed on a pipe strut and four on a wide flange strut.

Recently, weldable gages have been used successfully in cross bracing. They are available in both vibrating wire and resistance strain gage versions. If the resistance strain gage is used, careful consideration should be given to proper gage circuitry using high-quality environmental connectors.

For monitoring stresses in the wall, three methods are described. The first involves attachment of strain gages, usually the resistance type, to the steel. The second makes use of embedment strain gages in the concrete. The third is based on the use of sister bars, short lengths of reinforcing steel gaged with a full bridge of resistance strain gages and cast in the concrete.

Load cells. These are used on selected ground anchors to provide load data, and hence a fair indication of load distribution and magnitude patterns. These data give warning of imminent problems and instability conditions. Strain gages have also been used but their success is not documented to the same extent. Load cells are doughnut-shaped so that the anchor passes through a central hole in the cell. They are available in different sizes to accommodate anchor bars and bundles of stranded tendons. The devices are normally gaged with resistance strain gages and should have sufficient gages to create insensitivity to nonuniform loading. As an alternative, a telltale arrangement may be used as a load indicator, with a quoted accuracy of ±5 kips.

A relevant comment is on load measurement while locking off ground anchors. Specifications usually stipulate proof-testing each anchor to a certain load, and locking it off at a specified lower load (Xanthakos, 1991). The use of a calibrated hydraulic jack is not suitable for this purpose because the laboratory calibration does not model field conditions correctly (ram travel can cause frictional buildup and an actual applied load up to 25 percent less than the load indicated by the hydraulic pressure gage and calibration). A load cell in this case should always be used in series with the jack when stressing the anchors, and a high-quality mechanical load cell is often more convenient than an electrical strain-gaged cell because of the absence of cables and a separate readout box.

Water and earth pressure measurements. Measurements are often necessary in connection with the retention and monitoring of groundwater level and wall response to earth pressures. The usual methods involve the use of observation wells and piezometers, and earth pressure cells.

Observation wells and piezometers. Observation wells are very useful to monitor the groundwater level, and hence to check the effects of excavation on water table drawdown that may result in settlement. They usually consist of a slotted wall screen attached to a steel pipe, installed in a borehole in a sand environment.

A piezometer in the soil provides information on (1) drainage of pore water from the soil toward the excavation, and therefore an advance warning that consolidation settlement may result in some form of damage; (2) shear deformation of the soil toward the excavation (this process in normally consolidated clay causes a rise in pore pressure, but in overconsolidated clay a reduction in pore pressure), and therefore a warning of possible adverse effects; and (3) progress of heave beneath the base of excavation, and therefore an indication of base stability.

If rapid response to changing pore pressure conditions is not required, an open-standpipe piezometer is suitable. If rapid response is contemplated, a diaphragm-type piezometer is necessary. If piezometers are installed in soils containing sand size or larger particles, the drill casing should not be left in place, as this involves the risk of pore pressure leakage between the soil and the outside of the casing.

Earth pressure cells. In several cases the earth pressure acting on a slurry wall is measured to confirm the intent of the design or for research purposes. For this purpose pneumatic or vibrating wire earth pressure cells are satisfactory. DiBiagio and Myrvoll (1972a) describe the procedure used in slurry wall tests in Oslo clay. An inexpensive hydraulic jack is used to position each cell against the wall of the trench, and hold it in position while the panel is concreted. The cells and the hydraulic rams are attached to the preassembled reinforcing steel cage before it is lowered into the slurry trench. Each cell is first mounted in the center of a flat steel plate so that the membrane is flush with the surface of the plate. The assembly is then attached using a flexible coupling to the body of the hydrualic jack, and a reaction plate of similar size is fastened to the piston end. Forces on the steel cage during installation of the cells are avoided by placing the body of the jack inside a short length of pipe welded to the cage, so that the jack can slide freely. When a hydraulic pressure is applied to the jack, the piston is forced out until the reaction plate comes in contact with the soil. When this happens, the piston ceases to move and the body of the jack is displaced on the opposite side of the trench. At this stage, the force developed by the jack is transmitted directly to the sides of the trench and not to the reinforcing cage. Once the cell and the reaction plate are in contact with the sides of the trench, the ram pressure is increased until the desired seating force is obtained. This pressure is maintained while the panel is concreted and is released when the concrete is set.

If effective stress rather than total stress is required, each earth pressure cell must be accompanied by a piezometer, installed in a similar manner or in nearby boreholes in the soil.

Selection of monitoring method

Specific guidelines on the selection or an appropriate arrangement to monitor the construction and performance of slurry walls depend mainly on the project requirements and cannot be generalized. The selected instrumentation program is intended to confirm design assumptions and answer questions expected to arise when the system becomes operative. This means that the design should articulate features based on questionable assumptions or uncertain factors of safety, and engage an instrumentation program to support the analytical decisions.

Several common guidelines are given by Dunnicliff (1979). The most frequent performance monitoring procedures include optical surveys to monitor buildings, ground surface and guide wall movement, and wall movement during general excavation. If both horizontal and vertical subsurface movement measurements are contemplated, the locations can be arranged to provide a cross-check between data, for example, arranging inclinometers, horizontal multipoint extensometers, and support load measurements at the same station. In general, it is more efficient to select several representative stations and instrument them fully, and use minimal instrumentation at other stations to check that the primary stations represent the critical conditions.

3-14   Soil-Slurry Interaction

Certain aspects of this interaction have an immediate geotechnical interest, while others relate to practical problems such as slurry loss, sloughing, and even loss of stability.

Formation of seal

In general an impermeable barrier is formed at the interface, with a twofold function: separate the soil from the slurry and enable the latter to exert its full hydrostatic thrust. The deposition of colloid-type particles along the interface causes a seal to be formed according to "thixotropy."

This interaction is demonstrated in Fig. 3-35. Two compartments of a glass tank are filled with sand and a bentonite suspension. The separating barrier is then gradually lifted, allowing the suspension to penetrate the sand according to a hydrofracture pattern. Although this behavior is not necessarily typical, it confirms an important fact: a seal is formed within the soil and restricts further flow of slurry. In water-bearing formations any flow that occurs until the barrier is formed is toward the ground as long as the slurry is heavier than plain water and its level is higher than the groundwater table.

Penetration and filter cake.   Figure 3-36 shows schematically how a colloidal slurry penetrates a granular medium. First, the slurry enters the pores under a pressure differential (Fig. 3-36a), and in the process solid particles are deposited in the voids. In Fig. 3-36b the slurry continues its filtration as more particles accumulate in the pore space and form a packed zone of solid materials, commonly called "filter

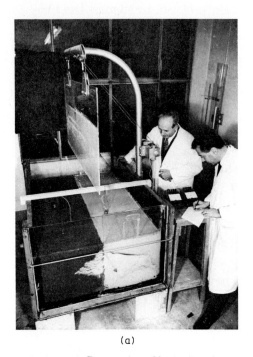 

(a)   (b)

Figure 3-35 Penetration of bentonite slurry into a granular medium: (*a*) General view of the glass tank. (*b*) Tree-shaped triangular intrusion. (*ICOS.*)

cake." In the final stage, the cake gels while it is covered by a layer of bentonite particles that provide a protective film, as shown in Fig. 3-36*c*. At this stage the barrier resists penetration.

For a cake to be formed there must be filtration of slurry; hence this process is influenced by the permeability of the soil. Thus the filter cake will not be formed where there are large voids or where the penetration is close to zero.

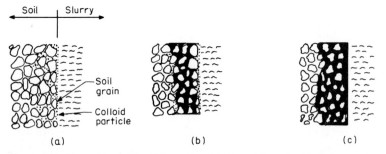

Figure 3-36 Formation of the filter cake: (*a*) Deposition of colloid fraction in the soil voids. (*b*) Filtration of slurry. (*c*) Formation of impermeable film along the face.

If we consider a tube of diameter $2r$ and length l as an idealized representation of the soil pores and assume that the tube is filled with slurry, the pressure difference Δp necessary to displace the slurry and produce flow is related to the shear strength of the slurry. The slurry is on the verge of shear failure if

$$2\pi r l \tau_f = \pi r^2 \, \Delta p$$

which gives

$$\Delta p = \frac{2\tau_f l}{r} \tag{3-48}$$

This relation is easily modified to include the so-called critical hydraulic gradient. The slurry therefore penetrates the soil to different distances l that depend on pore size, the shear strength of slurry, and the pressure differential.

The formation of the filter cake is a time-dependent process. In practice, the filter cake is assumed to be formed when there is a sudden decrease in the rate of slurry loss. It can be inferred, therefore, that the mass of the filter cake increases not only with depth but also with time as long as flow continues. In general two theories have been suggested to explain this process. The first suggests that under pressure differential, the slurry is filtered under the mechanism of Fig. 3-36. The second theory assumes that, as slurry is delivered to the trench, a potential difference is spontaneously created through electrochemical effects generated from the interaction of slurry, groundwater, and soil, stimulating bentonite particles to move toward the face of the trench where they are intercepted and form deposits.

For continuous filtration, we can consider the three times given in Fig. 3-37 (Nash, 1974). This leads to the expression

$$u = \sqrt{\frac{2k_c(1 - n_f)(\gamma_f z_1 - \gamma_w z_2)}{(n_f - n_c)\gamma_w}} \sqrt{t} \tag{3-49}$$

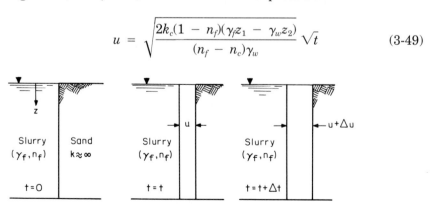

Figure 3-37 Theoretical formation of filter cake with time.

where n_f, γ_f relate to slurry
   k_c, n_c relate to cake
   γ_w, z_2 relate to groundwater

Filter-cake test. Figure 3-38 shows results from a filter-cake test in fine granular soil. The slurry used in the test has bentonite concentrations 6, 8, and 10 percent under pressure differences 0.5, 1.0, and 2.0 kg/cm² , respectively. The data are recorded after certain times from the start of the test, as shown. For practical purposes the filter cake is seen to achieve its final strength about 1 min after the slurry-soil interaction begins. The permeability continues to decrease for about 4 more minutes, at which time it reaches a value of 1×10^{-8} cm/s.

Seal mechanism. The formation of a seal can occur according to several mechanisms characterizing the soil range from fine-grained to open gravel. The three basic modes are as follows.

Surface filtration. In this process the filter cake is formed at the interface as a net packing of material. The barrier is essentially watertight, and any water percolating through it is referred to as filtered water. Water loss during surface filtration consists of two parts: (1) initial slurry loss that extends over the period required for the formation of the cake, and (2) steady fluid loss obeying the flow

$$v = mT^{-1/2} \tag{3-50}$$

where v = flow rate
   T = time after filter cake formation
   m = constant

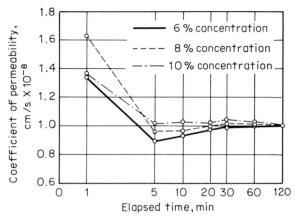

Figure 3-38 Variation in the permeability of filter cake with time. Data obtained with Japanese bentonite.

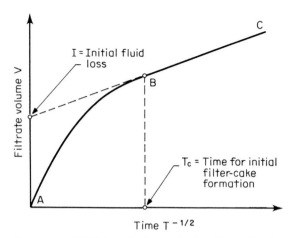

Figure 3-39 Fluid loss during and after filter-cake formation. (*From Hutchinson et al., 1974.*)

Slurry loss during and after filter-cake formation may be represented as shown in Fig. 3-39. Evidently, for the filter-cake test of Fig. 3-38, the T_c time is 1 min.

Deep filtration. This mechanism is prevalent in medium to coarse soil. It is similar to surface filtration but the penetration extends deeper. The dense packing of colloid particles forms a barrier and stops further penetration. The interception and deposition of bentonite particles in the soil pores near the interface means that the escaping fluid gradually becomes thinner since it loses its colloid fraction, and eventually this fluid approaches a waterlike liquid.

Rheological blocking. In this case the slurry flows into porous soil such as gravel until flow is restrained by its own shear strength. The penetration increases with depth and exemplifies a hydrofracture pattern. This behavior can be described by the relation between the shear stress and the resulting rate of shear. This mechanism takes effect with fairly large pores and is characterized by a gradual gelation of slurry in the zone of penetration. A convenient theoretical expression is Eq. (3-48) where τ_f is the shear strength of gelled slurry in the pores. Of these distinct mechanisms surface filtration is the preferred way of obtaining a seal because it minimizes slurry loss and does not result in soil changes.

Slurry loss. Figure 3-40 shows initial slurry loss vs. bentonite concentration. A cutoff concentration is evident on the curve, and for the type of bentonite used (Berkbent) it is between 4 and 4.5 percent. Below that the initial slurry loss increases sharply.

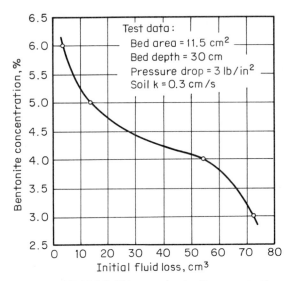

Figure 3-40 Initial fluid loss vs. bentonite concentration. (*From Hutchinson et al., 1974.*)

The presence of a small quantity of sand in the slurry can alter the sealing mechanism in open ground ($k = 1$ cm/s) from rheological blocking to deep filtration, as shown in Fig. 3-41, with a subsequent reduction demonstrated in Fig. 3-42. Although there will always be some suspended fine materials in the slurry as by-product of the ex-

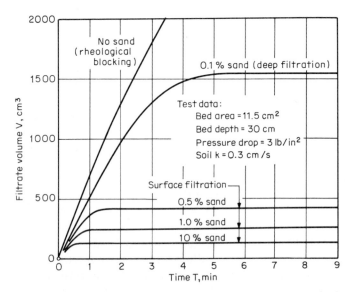

Figure 3-41 Effect of sand on filtration of 5 percent Berkbent fluid through fine gravel bed. (*From Hutchinson et al., 1974.*)

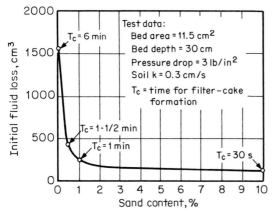

Figure 3-42 Effect of sand content on initial fluid loss through fine gravel bed. (*From Hutchinson et al., 1974.*)

cavation, for trenching in open ground adding a small fraction of fines to the slurry may be beneficial.

The gradual loss of diluted fluid or water in surface or deep filtration means that the slurry in the trench may become heavier in terms of the colloid concentration, with subsequent changes in flow properties. The rate of slurry loss is not necessarily pressure-sensitive since it depends also on other factors. This behavior should be understood since it affects the selection of slurry control limits and dictates performance monitoring.

Thixotropic gelation

For the purpose of this application thixotropy means slurries and gel setting times of the order of minutes. For slurries that gel when allowed to stand, thixotropy results in an isothermal, reversible, time-dependent sequence occurring under conditions of constant composition and volume whereby the slurry stiffens to a gel while at rest and liquefies upon stirring or remolding. In this behavior the interparticle force mechanism and principles of aggregation and dispertion are quite important.

The tendency of particles of the same nature to adhere upon contact is relevant to thixotropy. Very fine particles exhibit a lack of balance of forces at their surface, satisfied either by contact or by adsorption of ions from an adjacent phase. This explains thixotropy on the basis of an attraction-repulsion force balance. There is evidence that at times two separate zones of thixotropic behavior exist for the same material. For example, reversible hardening-liquefaction effects may first occur at very low salt concentration, but higher salt content may lead to a stable system. Further increase in salt content causes the thixotropic characteristics to reappear. This behavior is quite important in the control of slurries (see also Xanthakos, 1979).

Thixotropy occurs preferentially, and almost exclusively, in systems with elongated particles such as clays. Thixotropic suspensions of bentonite have been observed in which particles come to rest although there is no material contact between them. Conversely a suspension of graphics in mineral oil is nonconducting in a liquid state but conducting after gelation, indicating that particles now must be in contact to form a continuous network.

Reversibility. The sol-gel transformation of thixotropic suspensions commonly used as slurries is reversible. When shaking or stirring of the suspension stops, the slurry gels. When stirring or agitation starts again the slurry liquefies, and this reversibility can continue indefinitely. Reversibility can also occur with more concentrated systems, although in this case it may be limited.

A practical aspect of reversibility in slurries is the linkage between colloid particles to form an assembly that within a short time (usually seconds) causes the system to gel in the soil pores. Thus, for colloid concentrations that are practical and attainable in slurry trench excavations gelation leads rapidly to the buildup of the filter cake. Although theoretical thixotropic strength change relations are not available to permit direct correlation of thixotropic effects with field problems, this behavior can be reasonably practical by means of simple tests (see also Xanthakos, 1979).

Sloughing and peel-off

The plastering effect of the filter cake on the interface compels individual soil particles and grains to remain in the earth structure. This is important in granular soil where kinetic and rolling friction are the only forces that keep outermost particles at the exposed face from collapsing under gravity. If enough soil grains could break away, the result would be sloughing and peel-off.

Sloughing and peel-off can be represented theoretically if we consider an idealized soil system. If the average soil grain is represented by a sphere of diameter D submerged in a slurry of shear strength τ_f, motion can occur in any direction if the applied force exceeds the total shear resistance on the surface of the sphere. This shear resistance is

$$T = \frac{\pi D^2 \tau_f}{4} \tag{3-51}$$

The sphere is prevented from downward movement if T exceeds the buoyant weight of the particles with respect to the slurry. This weight is

$$W' = \frac{\pi D^3}{6}(\gamma - \gamma_f)$$

and the requirement $T = W'$ yields

$$D_v = \frac{3}{2}\frac{\tau_f}{\gamma - \gamma_f} \tag{3-52}$$

where γ is the density of the grain (without voids) and D_v denotes the diameter for vertical movement. Equation (3-52) does not relate the stability of particles with respect to movement toward the face. Resistance in this case depends on grain orientation, the inclination of the bearing area for a given particle, and the shear effect of the deposited filter cake. A theoretical presentation of this behavior is given by Xanthakos (1979).

Peel-off test. Figure 3-43 shows a device used to test the stability of a soil sample against peel-off. A container is filled with the sample, placed so that the vertical face becomes horizontal inside the container. The sample may be saturated before starting the test. A bentonite suspension is poured into the container until it fills it to the

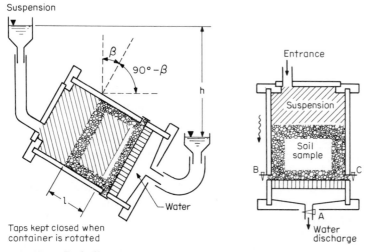

Figure 3-43 Peel-off test to investigate stability of individual grains at various angles of inclination.

top, and at the same time the bottom valve is open to allow a small quantity of water to be discharged. The valves are then turned off and the container is rotated as shown to allow peel-off to occur under gravity. The interface may remain stable when it reaches a vertical position, and in this case the rotation continues until it completes 145° from the initial position. If no particles fall off, the sample is stable against peel-off. Sample disturbance and volume distortion in the conduct of the test can alter behavior and cause misinterpretation of results. However, the test is simple and useful, and can be carried out several times using different slurry compositions.

As shown in Fig. 3-43, a small quantity of water remains inside the container for a given pressure head h depending on the inclination of the apparatus. The ratio h/l is the stagnation gradient discussed in the next section.

Stagnation gradient

By definition, this is the ratio h/l of the pressure head to the penetration distance. For convenience the boundaries are taken as shown in Fig. 3-25.

Rewriting Eq. (3-48) and setting $\Delta p = h \gamma_f$, we obtain

$$\frac{h}{l} = \frac{2\tau_f}{r} \frac{1}{\gamma_f}$$

and setting $h/l = i_0$,

$$i_0 = \frac{2\tau_f}{r} \frac{1}{\gamma_f} \tag{3-53}$$

relating the stagnation gradient i_0 to the parameters τ_f and r. Unless the average pore diameter $2r$ and the in situ gel strength τ_f of the slurry are accurately determined, Eq. (3-53) has little practical significance. Thus, in addition to the standard tests, predictions can be made from stagnation gradient tests. Since the intent is to establish a relationship $i_{01} = f(i_{02})$, at least two tests are necessary, one using pure slurry and the second using slurry mixed with some soil from the excavation. Referring to Fig. 3-25 and Sec. 3-8, m is always the total solid ratio by volume.

Figure 3-44 shows a typical apparatus used for the stagnation test. It consists of a pipe with an upper chamber separated from the pipe by means of a tap and a disk. The pipe is filled with a soil sample in a saturated state. The tap is then closed, and the chamber is filled with a colloidal suspension. Subsequently, the tap is open and the disk is removed, allowing the suspension to penetrate the sample, as shown

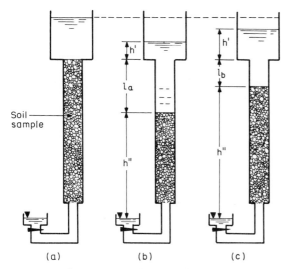

Figure 3-44 Stagnation-gradient test for determination of the values i_0 and i_{01}/i_{02}: (a) Situation before starting test. (b) Penetration without filtrate. (c) Penetration with filtrate.

in Fig. 3-44b. At this stage the penetration occurs without filter cake, and the fluid loss is the initial loss. By definition the stagnation gradient is

$$i_{01} = \frac{h_a}{l_a} = \frac{h' + l_a + h''(\gamma_w/\gamma_f)}{l_a} \tag{3-54}$$

which actually gives a numerical value for i_{01} since all parameters are known (measured directly). Figure 3-44c shows the penetration with a filter cake, assumed to be relatively impermeable. This penetration is $l_b < l_a$. Likewise

$$h_b = h' + l_b + h'' \frac{\gamma_w}{\gamma_f} \tag{3-55}$$

With i_{01} and h_b computed from Eqs. (3-54) and (3-55), respectively, the fraction of slurry pressure transmitted actually to the filter cake is, from Eq. (3-40),

$$p'_{f2} = p'_f - p'_{f1} = h_b \gamma_f - i_{01} \gamma_f l_b \tag{3-56}$$

and the thickness of the filter cake is computed from Eq. (3-36) as

$$u = \lambda l_b \tag{3-57}$$

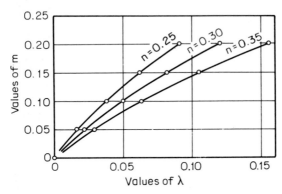

Figure 3-45 Relation between λ and the concentration m of solid matter in suspension (for $n_1 = n_2$).

which requires λ to be known. We can assume that $n_1 = n_2$, and in this case λ can be computed from Eq. (3-36) or with the help of Fig. 3-45. The stagnation gradient i_{02} corresponding to a filter-cake thickness u is

$$i_{02} = \frac{h_b - i_{01}l_b}{u} \tag{3-58}$$

If the test is carried out using a slurry aggregated with soil from the excavation, the head h_b is adjusted noting that just above the top of the pipe the slurry weight is γ_{fs} but just below the boundary the weight is γ_f. The head h_b is now

$$h_b = h' \frac{\gamma_{fs}}{\gamma_f} + l_b + h'' \frac{\gamma_w}{\gamma_f} \tag{3-59}$$

If the filter cake has permeability equal to zero, l_b is also zero and h_b is the actual pressure head. Then from Eq. (3-56) the fraction pressure transmitted to the filter cake is the total hydrostatic pressure.

Alternatively, the fraction pressure transmitted to the slurry may be estimated from a different consideration. We can rewrite Eq. (3-56) as

$$\frac{p_{f2}'}{p_f'} = 1 - \frac{i_{01}l_b}{h_b} \tag{3-56a}$$

which is generally valid for thin filter cake. In practice, however, any excess material deposited on the face is scraped off by the excavating tool so that a reasonable u_{max} is about 1 cm (⅜ in). The fraction pres-

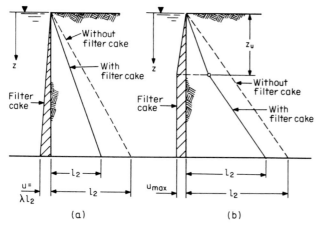

Figure 3-46 Zones and shape of penetration: (*a*) Filter cake of increasing thickness. (*b*) Filter cake of limited thickness.

sure head transmitted to the region beyond the filter cake is now increased according to

$$p'_{f1} = h\gamma_{fs} - i_{02}\gamma_f u_{max} \tag{3-60}$$

Figure 3-46 shows schematically a filter-cake penetration where the thickness increases as $u_2 = \lambda l_b$ and a filter cake of increasing thickness to u_{max} that remains constant thereafter. It can be shown that

$$z_u = \frac{\gamma_f}{\gamma} u_{max} \left(i_{02} + \frac{1}{\lambda} i_{01} \right) \tag{3-61}$$

Example. The stagnation gradient test is a time-dependent process; i.e., the results are valid for the time when measurements are made. In this context the test is useful regardless of soil conditions. However, this procedure is not a permeability test. Undisturbed samples must be obtained, especially from considerable depths, but where this is not possible suitable samples can be prepared in the laboratory and densified as the in situ soil.

As an example, we consider a trench in sand assuming that the slurry penetrates through a relatively permeable filter cake of limited thickness as shown in Fig. 3-47. The properties of the soil are as follows:

$$\phi = 30° \qquad \gamma = 120 \text{ lb/ft}^3$$

$$n_1 = 30 \text{ percent} \qquad \gamma_s = 150 \text{ lb/ft}^3$$

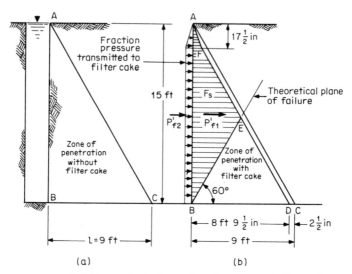

Figure 3-47 Stability analysis of trench under permeable filter cake.

The bentonite concentration in the fluid gives γ_f = 66 lb/ft³, raised to γ_{fs} = 75 lb/ft³ as soil is mixed with slurry. The porosity of the filter cake is taken as n_1. On the basis of the impermeable membrane theory, the stability is checked by Eq. (3-20), given F = 1.9. This factor is obtained for γ_f = 66 lb/ft³.

Next we consider the analysis with a relatively permeable cake. Stagnation tests give i_{01} = 2, and i_{02} = 10. The value of u_{max} is taken as 0.4 in. The analysis is carried out according to the following steps.

Step 1. Compute λ either from Fig. 3-45 or from Eq. (3-36), or λ = 0.05.

Step 2. Calculate z_u from Eq. (3-58)

$$z_u = \frac{66}{75}(0.4)\left(10 + \frac{2}{0.05}\right) = 17.5 \text{ in}$$

Step 3. Referring to Fig. 3-47, compute the penetration and depth 15 ft

$$l = \frac{15}{2}(1.20) = 9 \text{ ft} = 108 \text{ in}$$

(Note that 1.20 is the specific gravity for γ_{fs} = 75 lb/ft³.)

Step 4. At depth 17.5 in compute penetration with and without filter cake (from $u = \lambda l_b$)

$$l = \begin{cases} \dfrac{0.4}{0.05} = 8 \text{ in} & \text{with filter cake} \\[2mm] \dfrac{17.5}{2}(1.20) = 10.5 \text{ in} & \text{without filter cake} \end{cases}$$

Note that the difference $10.5 - 8 = 2.5$ in is the distance DC in Fig. 3-47b.

Step 5. Calculate the area of penetration $ABEF = F_2$ and compute p'_{f1}. This area is approximately 32.5 ft². Then $p'_{f1} = 2(32.5)(66) = 4290$ lb/ft of trench

Step 6. Estimate the fraction force P'_{f2}. First find

$$P'_{f2} = 10(75)\left(\frac{0.4}{12}\right) = 25 \text{ lb/ft}^2$$

at depth 17.5 in and constant thereafter. Hence

$$P'_{f2} = 25(14.27) = 360 \text{ lb/ft}$$

The total force mobilized against the face is $4290 + 360 = 4650$ lb/ft compared with the total hydrostatic thrust of 8450 lb/ft. Since the actual thrust exerted by the soil (active state) is 4500 lb/ft, the factor of safety is now 1.03.

Effect of penetration on soil properties

Effect on clay. Trench excavations in clay usually have surface filtration. If the soil has very low permeability, filtration is unlikely and a protective cake will not be formed. In many instances a trench in clay can be excavated using only plain water merely to keep the face stable.

When a cut is made, the lateral stress along the vertical face is reduced to zero, and along the section the pore pressure is negative, i.e., in tension. When the trench is filled with slurry, the two pressures tend to equalize. The soil absorbs water near the face, accompanied by a corresponding loss of strength. This softening dissipates away from the face, and as long as it does not extend more than a few inches, its effect on stability is not serious. A small permeability in a clay matrix causes colloid-size particles to be deposited at the interface to form a protective film. Nash and Jones (1963) have reported permeability coefficients of the order of 2.3×10^{-9} cm/s for films in contact with London clay.

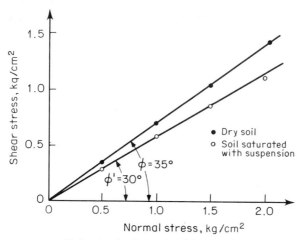

Figure 3-48 Reduction in the angle of friction due to saturation with bentonite suspension. (*From Müller-Kirchenbauer, 1972.*)

Effect on granular soil. Figure 3-48 shows results of tests on samples of coarse sand and sandy gravel. In the natural state and water content this soil has a friction angle of 35°. When the samples were saturated with slurry, the friction angle was reduced to 30° (Müller-Kirchenbauer, 1972). Similar results have been reported by Farkas (1971).

The practical implications of these results are in connection with trench stability. It is not always certain under what conditions to expect changes in the properties of granular soil because of slurry trench excavation. Useful guidelines are given by Xanthakos (1979).

Changes in slurry density. Invariably a certain quantity of solids from the excavation is mixed with the slurry. This imparts to the slurry a density higher than the original. In this process the actual thrust changes because of the heavier slurry with an immediate benefit on trench stability.

The amount and type of soil particles left in the trench depend on (1) the gel strength of the slurry; (2) the type of equipment; (3) the type of excavated soil; and (4) the method of materials handling. An indication of the probable changes in slurry properties is provided by the data of Fig. 3-49, taken from actual construction sites. The excavating techniques are not identified, but other conditions are average. This information is useful and can be obtained by monitoring the excavation of the first panel while keeping relevant records.

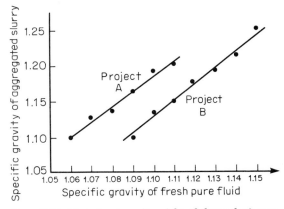

Figure 3-49 Variation in unit weight of slurry during excavation. Data from actual construction.

Effects of lowering the slurry level

Unintentional lowering of the slurry level is shown in Fig. 3-50. In this example, trenching begins as shown in part a and continues through the water-bearing sand and silty clay without incident. When the excavation reaches the gravel layer, slurry begins to escape toward the ground as shown in Fig. 3-50b by the direction of the arrows. This flow is accelerated by the high permeability of the gravel, the absence of groundwater at this level, and the pressure differential. The slurry level drops below the sand layer as shown in Fig. 3-50c, and at this stage pore water pressure is applied to the filter cake from the outside and causes its disintegration. Without filter cake and hydrostatic sup-

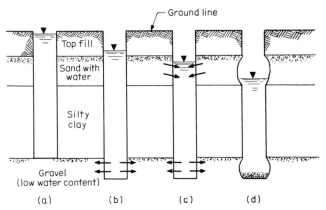

Figure 3-50 Consequence of lowering the slurry level. Loss of ground caused by water infiltration.

port, the groundwater flows into the trench as shown in Fig. 3-50*d* while the sand caves in. Such incidents are common and can be dealt with if they can be predicted. Shorter panels and extra supply of slurry could prevent this problem.

Slurry trenches in urban sites are often excavated from a platform below the street level. In this case it is conceivable that the ground-water table is much higher than the slurry level, rendering the operation impracticable from the viewpoint of stability. The excavation must now be preceded by dewatering (if this is feasible), selecting the dewatering points so that the system does not draw slurry from the trench.

If the alignment of a trench intercepts groundwater flow, the trench may function as dam and change the flow pattern. Similar changes in the flow and groundwater level will occur if a long trench is excavated across a valley. The same effects have also been observed at the closure position on the perimeter of a site that is completely enclosed by a slurry trench. A typical example is the construction of a deep basement; during the slurry wall excavation the water table inside the enclosed area rose more than 1 m (3.5 ft), and the face collapsed while the last panel was excavated.

References

Aas, G., 1976: "Stability of Slurry Trench Excavation in Soft Clay," *Proc. 6th European Conf. Soil Mech. Found. Eng.,* Vienna, vol. 1.1, pp. 103–110, Also published in Norwegian Geotechnical Inst., Oslo, *Publ.* 111.

Bishop, A. W., 1952: "The Stability of Earth Dams," Ph.D. Thesis, University of London. 1954: "The Use of the Slip Circle in the Stability Analysis of Slopes," *Geotechnique,* vol. 5, pp. 7–17 and L. Bjerrum, 1960: "The Relevance of the Triaxial Test to the Solution of Stability Problems," *Proc. ASCE Res. Conf. Shear Strength Cohesive Soils,* Boulder, Colo., pp. 437–501.

Bjerrum, L., 1973: "Problems of Soil Mechanics and Construction on Soft Clays. State-of-the-art report to Session IV, *Proc. 8th Intern. Conf. Soil Mech. Found. Eng.,* Moscow, vol. 3, pp. 111–159. Also published in Norwegian Geotechnical Inst., Oslo, *Publ.* 100.

Caquet, A., and J. Kerisel, 1956: *Traite de mecanique des sols,* 3d ed., Gauthier-Villars, Paris.

DiBiagio, E., and F. Myrvoll, 1972a: "Earth Pressure Measurements on a Braced Slurry-Trench Wall in Soft Clay," *Proc. 5th European Conf. Soil Mech. Found. End.,* Madrid, 1972. vol. 1, pp. 473–483. Also published in Norwegian Geotechnical Inst., Oslo, *Publ.* 91.

DiBiagio, E., and F. Myrvoll, 1972b: "Full Scale Field Tests of a Slurry Trench Excavation in Soft Clay," *Proc. 5th ECSMFE,* vol. 1, pp. 461–471. Madrid.

Dunnicliff, J., 1979: "Performance Monitoring of Slurry Wall Construction," *Symp. Slurry Walls for Underground Transp. Systems, U.S. Dot,* Cambridge, Mass., Aug. 30–31, pp. 197–214.

Eide, O., G. Aas, and T. Josang, 1972: "Special Application of Cast-in-Place Walls for Tunnels in Soft Clay in Oslo," *Proc. 5th European Conf. Soil Mech. Found. Eng.,* Madrid, 1972. vol. 1, pp. 485–498. Also published in Norwegian Geotechnical Inst., Oslo, *Publ.* 91.

Elson, W. K., 1968: "An Experimental Investigation of the Stability of Slurry Trenches," *Geotechnique,* vol. 18, no. 37, pp. 39–49.

Farkas, J., 1971: "Stability of Slurry Trench Walls," *Proc. 4th Budapest Conf. Soil Mech.,* pp. 397–403.

Goldberg, D. T., M. D. Gordon, and W. E. Jaworski, 1976: "Lateral Support Systems and Underpinning," *Reports No. FHWA-RD-75-129 and 130,* U.S. DOT, Fed. Highway Administration.

Hansen, J. B., 1961: The Ultimate Resistance of Rigid Piles against Transverse Forces, *Dan. Geot. Inst. Bull.* 12, p. 5.

Huder, J., 1972: "Stability of Bentonite Slurry Trenches with Some Experience in Swiss Practice," *Proc. 5th European Conf. Soil Mech. Found. Eng.,* Madrid, vol. 1, pp. 517–522.

Hutchinson, M. T., et al., 1974: "The Properties of Bentonite Slurries Used in Diaphragm Walling and Their Control," *Proc. Diaphragm Walls Anchorages, Inst. Civ. Eng., London.*

ICOS, 1968: "Trench Excavation Close to Heavy Footings," *Internal Report,* Milan.

Karlsrud, K., 1972: "Finite Element Analysis of the Cast-in-Situ Wall at Kogens Gate," 8th Norwegian Geotechnical Inst., Oslo, *Internal Report* 52601-4, p. 7.

Karlsrud, K., 1975: "Practical Experience from the Excavation of Slurry Trenches in Oslo Clay," Norwegian Geotechnical Inst., Oslo, *Publ.* 110, 1976. First published in Norwegian in Nordisk geoteknikermode, Copenhagen, 1975. Foredrag, Copenhaven Polyteknisk Forlag, pp. 529–542.

Karlsrud, K., and F. Myrvoll, 1976: "Performance of a Strutted Excavation in Quick Clay," *Proc. 6th ECSMFE* (also *N.G.I. Publ.* III), Vienna.

Karlsrud, K., E. DiBiagio, and G. Aas, 1979: "Experience with Slurry Walls in Soft Clay," *Symp. Slurry Walls for Underground Transp. Systems, U.S. Dot,* Cambridge, Mass., Aug. 30–31, pp. 383–408.

Kowalewski, Z., 1964: "Parcie czynne gruntu w wycopie a skonczoney dlugosci," *Blul. Inf. Naun-Techn.,* Warsaw.

Lambe, T. W., and R. V. Whitman, 1969: *Soil Mechanics* M.I.T., Wiley, New York.

Lorente De No, C., 1969: Stability of Slopes with Curvature in Plane View, *Proc. 7th Int. Conf. Soil Mech. Found. Eng.,* Mexico City, pp. 635–638.

Massachusetts Bay Transportation Authority, 1978: Plans and Specifications for Construction of Harvard Square Station.

Meyerhof, G. G., 1951: "The Ultimate Bearing Capacity of Foundations," *Geotechnique,* vol. 2, p. 301. 1972: "Stability of Slurry Trench Cuts in Saturated Clay," *Proc. Conf. Performance Earth Earth-Supported Struct., Purdue Univ.,* vol. 1, pt. 2, pp. 1451–1466.

Morgenstern, N. R., 1963: "Comments," *Symp. Grouts Drilling Muds,* Butterworths, London and I. Amir-Tahmasseb, 1965: "The Stability of Slurry Trench in Cohesionless Soils," *Geotechnique,* vol. 6, no. 4, pp. 387–395 and V. E. Price, 1965: "The Analysis of Stability of General Slip Surfaces," *Geotechnique,* vol. 15, pp. 79–93.

Müller-Kirchenbauer, H., 1972: Stability of Slurry Trenches, *Proc. 5th European Conf. Soil Mech. Found. Eng.,* Madrid, vol. 1, pp. 543–553.

Nash, J. K. T. L., and G. K. Jones, 1963: *The Support of Trenches Using Fluid Mud,* Butterworths, London.

Nash, J. K. T. L., 1972: "The Design of Slurries for Use in Civil Engineering Projects," *1st Iranian Congr. Civ. Eng. Pahlavi Univ., Shirar, Iran.* 1974: "The Stability of Trenches Filled with Fluids," *Symp. Underground Constr. Fluid Trenches,* University of Illinois, Chicago Circle.

Piaskowski, A., and Z. Kowalewski, 1965: "Applications of Thixotropic Clay Suspensions for Stability of Vertical Sides of Deep Trenches without Strutting," *Proc. 6th Int. Conf. Soil Mech. Found. Eng.,* Montreal, vol. 2, pp. 526–529.

Puller, M. J., 1974: "Slurry Trench Stability: Theoretical and Practical Aspects," *Ground Eng.,* vol. 7, no. 5, pp. 34–36.

Saito, J., Y. Goto, and H. Sato, 1974: "Stability of Trench against Dynamic Loads during Slurry Excavation," *Kajima Corp., Spec. Bull.,* Tokyo.

Schneebeli, G., 1964: "Le Stabilite des tranchees profondes forees en presence de boue," Houille Blanche, vol. 19, no. 7, pp. 815–820.

Skempton, A. W., 1948: "The $\phi = 0$ Analysis of Stability and Its Theoretical Basis," Proc. 2d Int. Conf. Soil Mech. Found. Eng., Rotterdam, vol. 1, pp. 72–78 and H. Q. Golder, 1948: "Practical Examples of the $\phi = 0$ Analysis of Stability of Clays," Proc. 2d Int. Conf. Soil Mech. Found. Eng., Rotterdam, vol. 2, pp. 63–70 and P. LaRochelle, 1965: "The Bradwell Slip: A Short Term Failure in London Clay," Geotechnique, vol. 15, pp. 222–242.

Taylor, D. W., 1948: Fundamentals of Soil Mechanics, Wiley, New York.

Terzaghi, K., 1941: "General Wedge Theory of Earth Pressure," Trans. ASCE, pp. 68–97. 1943: Theoretical Soil Mechanics, Wiley, New York and R. B. Peck, 1948, 1967: Soil Mechanics in Engineering Practice, Wiley, New York.

Timoshenko, S., and J. N. Goodier, 1951: Theory of Elasticity, McGraw-Hill, New York.

Xanthakos, P. P., 1974: Underground Construction in Fluid Trenches, Colleges of Engineering, University of Illinois, Chicago.

Xanthakos, P. P., 1979: Slurry Walls, McGraw-Hill, New York.

Xanthakos, P. P., 1991: Ground Anchors and Anchored Structures, Wiley, New York.

4

Analysis and Design Considerations

4-1 Ground Response in Supported Excavations

Theoretical background

Ground response during and after an excavation is fundamental for the analysis and design of diaphragm walls. This review discusses key principles that are not necessarily new discoveries or developments but rather factors often misunderstood or ignored. A routine approach to the engineering of an excavation and its support system is to employ analytical techniques to predict performance and compare these results with the measured and observed field record.

In general, excavation is the removal of a mass of soil and water. Total stress release is a process that causes unloading. Where it must be done in the dry and other controls are not feasible or available at the site, the groundwater outside the excavation must be lowered artificially; i.e., the soil is dewatered. The result of these processes is movement of the surrounding soil, and control of this movement is essential in engineering the excavation. In most instances, ground movement must be further controlled and limited so that adjacent properties and utilities are not adversely affected.

Ground response is influenced by several key factors. These are (1) dimensions of the excavation, (2) soil properties, (3) groundwater control, (4) time element and sequence of construction steps, (5) the type of ground support and its bracing, (6) the presence of structures and utilities, and (7) transient surcharge loads. The larger the excavation the greater the decrease of total stress, and thus the larger the movement of the surrounding ground. At the extreme case, an excavation may be so deep and poorly supported that it may result in a complete shear failure.

Soil properties, groundwater control, and time are closely interrelated. If an instantaneous earth removal could be made, the soil around it would strain under undrained conditions. If the same excavation could be made at an infinitely slow rate, the surrounding soil would strain under fully drained conditions. Actual excavations are completed over a finite time period and under conditions that are partially drained. As a practical matter, excavations in sands are typically assumed to be drained, and cuts in clay are treated as undrained except near the clay boundaries; excavations in silts usually are assumed partially drained.

Effect of groundwater. If the groundwater level is unchanged, the water continues to act against the support and thus contributes to the total lateral stress. Conversely, a decrease in groundwater pressure can cause an increase in effective earth stress with accompanying ground settlement. In routine practice, engineers choose to estimate the total lateral thrust acting against the support from two components: effective earth stress and pore water pressure.

If a watertight wall penetrates an impervious formation below the base, the water conditions can be assumed static, resulting in a simple water pressure distribution against the wall. This condition is likely with diaphragm walls and watertight joints. With more conventional temporary supports ideal water cutoff is unlikely, and a more complex pattern of water inflow should be expected (Lambe, 1970). The latter case warrants the analysis of pore water flow. If a two-dimensional steady-state flow can be assumed, pore pressures may be estimated from flow nets or from finite-element solutions. The complexity of this analysis becomes obvious if pertinent factors are included, for example, in situ permeability, pore pressure caused by changes in total stress, flow parallel to the wall, and time necessary to complete the construction including effects on consolidation. Usually, pore pressures are likely to be less than static, but dynamic conditions can result from certain events such as broken mains outside the excavation.

The effective overburden stress σ_v' outside an excavation can be estimated assuming geostatic conditions so that

$$\sigma_v' = \sigma_v - u \tag{4-1}$$

where σ_v is the total overburden stress and u is the pore pressure near the support. Figure 4-1 shows the distribution of vertical stresses for

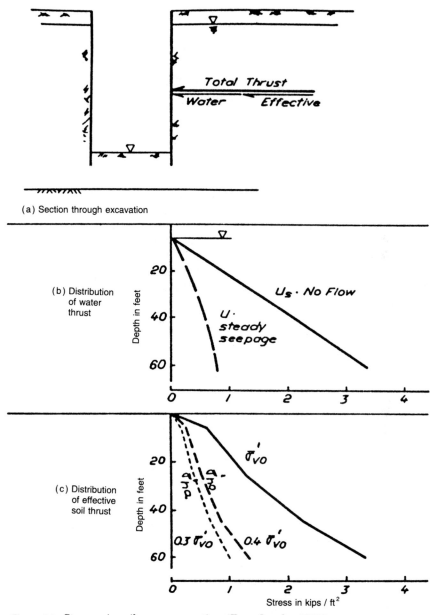

Figure 4-1 Stresses in soils near excavation. (*From Lambe, 1970.*)

static pore pressure conditions and for a groundwater level about 6 ft below the surface. The two horizontal stress diagrams correspond to 0.4 σ_v' and 0.3 σ_v', respectively. The distribution diagram for $\sigma_{h0}' = 0.4$ σ_v' approximates horizontal stresses for the K_0 state and for normally consolidated soil. The distribution for $\sigma'_{ha} = 0.3\ \sigma'_v$ represents the active state for a soft soil.

The pore water pressure can be a significant component of the total thrust acting on the support. Outside the excavation, a decrease in pore pressure results in increase in the effective stress leading to settlement. For the permanent condition it is common practice to consider pore water pressure in the analysis. For temporary supports this is not always necessary, and only the two extreme situations are usually evaluated, fully drained with zero pore pressure, and undrained with only total stress treated.

Soil stresses and strains near an excavation. A soil element experiences stresses and strains as shown in Fig. 4-2 (Lambe, 1970) for two distinct locations A and B. The effects of the excavation are (1) a reduction of total vertical and horizontal stresses, (2) changes in equilibrium pore water pressure, and (3) the apparent dependence of wall movement on the horizontal thrust. The stress paths apply to soils normally consolidated to an isotropic stress state. Since excavation

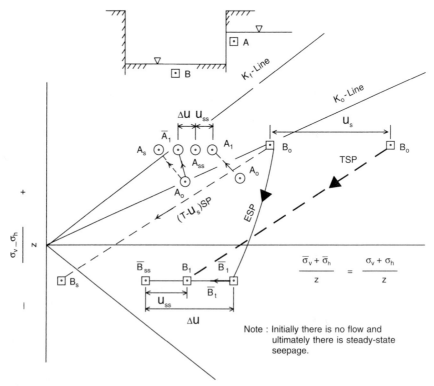

Figure 4-2 Stress paths for soil elements near excavation. (*From Lambe, 1970.*)

causes unloading, it also alters the boundary pore pressure on the inside. If it remains long enough to allow steady-state seepage to develop, the equilibrium pore pressures essentially are the same as in a flow net.

Stress and strain changes caused by excavation and steady-state seepage are summarized in Table 4-1. Soil element A outside the excavation shows a tendency to settle, but the soil beneath the excavation tends to expand. According to these strains, an increase in shear strength should be expected for element A, and a slight increase for element B.

Stress paths and corresponding horizontal strains are shown in Fig. 4-3 for an element outside the support. The numbers 1 through 5 characterize the sequential changes in stress and strain. The soil is initially consolidated to the stress system indicated by point 1, unloaded to the stress-strain system shown by point 2, and so on. The variation in horizontal stress for element A can cover a broad range depending on the inward or outward wall movement.

The stress-strain plots of Figs. 4-2 and 4-3 show soil behavior following an excavation, but they do not include the effect of friction at the wall-soil interface, and they ignore changes caused by the excavation sequence and bracing. The plots are general and intended merely to demonstrate the phenomena involved.

Effects associated with construction

Changes in the state of stress of the soil are caused by (1) trench excavation under slurry whereby the slurry hydrostatic pressure replaces the original at rest condition, (2) replacement of the slurry by fresh concrete whereby the hydrostatic pressure changes to the thrust

TABLE 4-1   Stresses and Strains for Soil Elements near an Excavation

Condition	Soil element A	Soil element B
Initial (static) pore pressure u_s	$A_0\overline{A}_0$	$B_0\overline{B}_0$
Pore pressure at steady-state flow u_{ss}	$A_1\overline{A}_{ss}$	$B_1\overline{B}_{ss}$
Pore pressure upon unloading	Decreases	Decreases
Pore pressure during consolidation	Decreases	Increases
Strain upon unloading	Vertical compression	Vertical extension
Strain during consolidation	Vertical compression	Vertical extension
Undrained shear strength during consolidation	Increases	Decreases

From Lambe, 1970.

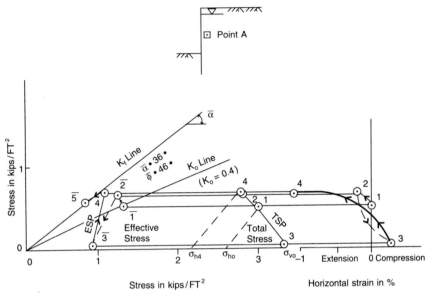

Figure 4-3 Stress paths and strain. (*From Lambe, 1970.*)

exerted by the rising fresh concrete, and (3) the general excavation and bracing sequence. Other factors affecting changes are the dimensions of the excavation and mainly its depth, the presence of structures and foundations, and transient surcharge loads.

The tendency to have settlement patterns caused by excavation summarized and predicted in a general manner will in most cases inhibit the decision on the degree and kind of protection necessary to ensure controls. The choice of diaphragm walls as ground support in built-up areas is often interpreted to mean adequate stability and confinement of ground movement to the inconsequential range. However, the broad range of performance patterns resulting from different scenarios of construction methods and soil conditions hardly justifies a general approach. Instead, ground movement should be studied by correlating its pattern and magnitude to relevant aspects and phases of construction (see also subsequent sections). The stress-strain relationships and groundwater flow patterns discussed in the preceding section form a conceptual basis for much of the analysis but must be interfaced with physical activities and construction events to investigate the composite effects.

In general ground response can be articulated for three distinct stages: (1) initial excavation before any bracing is installed, (2) excavation to subgrade after the top braces are installed, and (3) removal of the bracing (substitution with the permanent structure).

An excavation usually is carried down to a level, usually 15 to 20 ft, at which the first bracing is installed (cross beams, anchors, etc.). During this stage the wall deforms as a free cantilever. The horizontal strains reflect this mechanism by developing a triangular contour pattern that decreases with depth and distance from the wall.

After the uppermost bracing is in place, the wall is restrained against lateral movement at this level, although the displacement does not necessarily stop completely. If anchors are used, preloading can be used at this level to control further movement as it will cause a corresponding recompression of the soil analogous to passive resistance. In the deeper portion of the cut the wall continues to bulge inward and cause tensile strains. When the intermediate bracing is installed, movement is again restrained.

As the bottom braces are sequentially removed to construct the underground structure, further inward movement occurs at these locations. When the upper braces are removed while the lower section is braced by the permanent structure, the wall reverts to the cantilever pattern. Movement stops when the upper portion of the excavation is braced, or backfilled and compacted.

4-2 Heave in Narrow Excavations Supported by Diaphragm Walls

Background. In soft plastic clays instability is approached where the weight of soil beside an excavation tends to displace the underlying soil toward the excavation. The clay beneath the base acts primarily as frictionless material under undrained conditions. In the past the problem has been avoided by adapting special construction procedures whereby sheet piles are installed with a suitable embedment, followed by the placement of the roof. Thereafter the excavation is completed under compressed air. Other alternatives are the use of artificial freezing, or excavation by dredging under water.

A basic analysis of the heave problem suggests a mutual relationship between the transition from elastic to plastic failure within and below the zone of influence of the cut, the influence of the lateral support, including its stiffness and embedment below excavation level, and the presence of a firm stratum, which the wall may or may not reach. Other factors influencing base instability by heave are the configuration of the cut and the strength of material acting as surcharge above excavation level.

A simple theoretical model showing the contribution of ground support to base stability of cuts in soft clay is presented in Fig. 4-4. An element outside the wall is considered in the active state, and an ele-

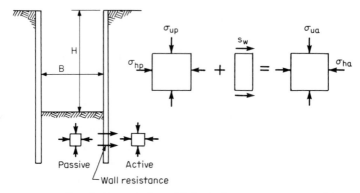

Figure 4-4 Rough theoretical model for inelastic movement and base instability for cuts in soft clays: $\sigma_{ha} - s_w - \sigma_{hp} = 0$ $\sigma_{va} - \sigma_{ha} = 2s_u$ $\sigma_{hp} - \sigma_{vp} = 2s_u$ $s_w = \gamma H - 4s_u$

ment below the base is in the passive state. The difference between active stress and passive resistance must be sustained by the strength of the wall in a comparative form; otherwise plastic failure will result.

Base instability can be analyzed by considering the deformation of the ground beside and beneath the excavation. During removal of earth, shear stresses are set up beneath the excavation as a result of the surrounding soil pushing the clay first inward and then up onto the excavation. If the shear strength of the clay in the affected zone is sufficient, the base is stable. If this strength is exceeded, the ground beside the cut will start sinking, forcing the bottom upward. Solutions are presented by Terzaghi (1943), Terzaghi and Peck (1967), and Tschebotarioff (1973).

If the wall extends below excavation level, the stability is improved by mobilizing the shear strength at the interface of the embedded portion as the clay mass tends to move upward. If the problem is investigated in soft clay, the shear strength at the interface will be the undrained shear strength since the adhesion factor is unity (see also Sec. 5-8). This analysis is valid for temporary excavations and does not consider changes in shear strength that may occur with time.

Cross-wall bracing. The cross walls mentioned briefly in Sec. 3-4 in conjunction with the Oslo subway serve a double purpose: brace the lower part of the walls, especially the embedded portion, and provide extra shear resistance to improve stability against base heave. The transverse trenches are excavated from a convenient level but to the same depth as the long side walls, and the concrete for the cross walls is cast only to the underside of the base slab. Since the cross walls are not to be exposed and act mainly in compression, they need only nominal reinforcement.

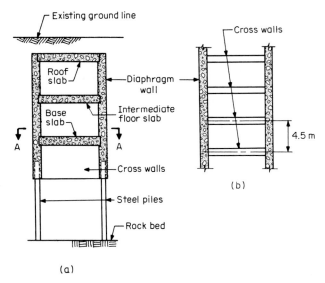

(a)

Figure 4-5 A two-level subway tunnel with cross walls for bottom bracing: (*a*) Subway cross section. (*b*) Sectional plan *A-A*. (*From Eide et al., 1972.*)

Cross-wall bracing for the diaphragm walls built in soft clay for the Oslo subway is shown in Fig. 4-5. Bracing at other levels is provided by the permanent floor slabs cast downward.

The overall stability of the longitudinal trenches is not necessarily a critical problem. However, a special problem with the cross-wall trenches is that only a small block of clay is left between adjoining cross-lot walls (for the construction of Fig. 4-5, this block is only 3.5 m wide). Since the cross trench is filled with concrete only to the excavation level, backfilling of the remainder of the trench can adversely affect the stability of the next trench to be excavated. A solution is to use crushed stone as backfilling with provisions for complete drainage after backfilling to ensure high frictional resistance. Different alternatives are shown in Fig. 4-6. For the Oslo project (Karlsrud et al., 1979) the selection was based on a special test trench (Karlsrud, 1975; Aas, 1976) showing that alternatives *A* and *B* would require a heavy slurry of unit weight 11 to 12 kN/m³ (specific gravity 1.12 to 1.22). Using alternative *B*, problems with loss of slurry from a trench under excavation into the drained crushed rock of the previously finished trench occurred on three occasions and caused collapse. The work continued using alternative *C*, where half the trench is backfilled with low-grade concrete. By dividing the cross trench into two halves and backfilling opposite halves with lean concrete, and then continuing with the section to be backfilled with crushed rock, the procedure en-

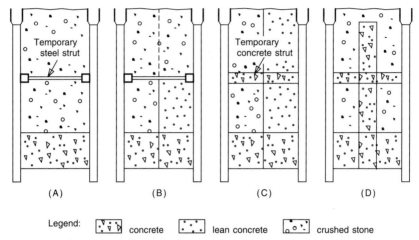

(A)   (B)   (C)   (D)

Legend: [concrete] concrete [lean concrete] lean concrete [crushed stone] crushed stone

Figure 4-6 Alternate methods of constructing cross-lot walls in long narrow excavations. (*From Karlsrud et al., 1979.*)

sures that next to a trench under excavation there is either intact clay or a trench filled with lean concrete.

Heave analysis of ordinary strutted excavations. Such an excavation is shown in Fig. 4-7. Either there is no embedment of the ground support below excavation level, or its effect is disregarded. The term "strutted" means that the ground is prevented from moving toward the cut. The analysis is based on the stability number N_c (Bjerrum and Eide, 1956). This number depends on the excavation form but mainly on the width-to-length and depth-to-width ratio. The values of N_c are essentially the same as those given by Skempton (1951) for bearing capacity failures.

For the cut of Fig. 4-7 the factor of safety against base heave failure is expressed as

$$F = N_c \frac{s_u}{\gamma H + q} \tag{4-2}$$

where F = factor of safety
H = height (or depth) of excavation
γ = soil density
s_u = undrained shear strength of clay below and around excavation level
q = surcharge load at ground surface
N_c = stability number

Values of N_c are estimated with the help of the diagrams of Fig. 4-7 using $D = H$ and then are entered in Eq. (4-2).

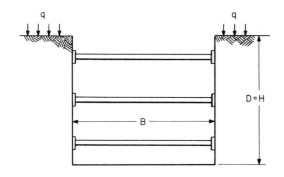

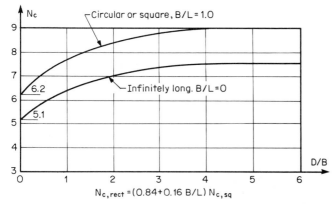

Figure 4-7 Values of stability number N_c for heave analysis of braced excavations. (*From Bjerrum and Eide, 1956.*)

Heave analysis with wall embedment.   In this case the analysis includes the shear mobilized at the interface of the embedded wall portion. This effect becomes more pronounced with increased embedment and where the undrained shear strength increases with depth. For infinitely long cuts ($B/L = 0$), the factor of safety is expressed as

$$F = \frac{N_c s_u + (2h/B)\alpha s_u}{\gamma H + q} \tag{4-3}$$

where h = wall embedment below excavation level
α = adhesion factor
B = width of excavation (see also Fig. 4-8)

and other parameters are as before. N_c is now estimated from Fig. 4-7 using $D = H + h$.

Heave analysis with cross walls, single opening.   Likewise, for excavations supported by diaphragm walls and cross walls, as shown in Fig.

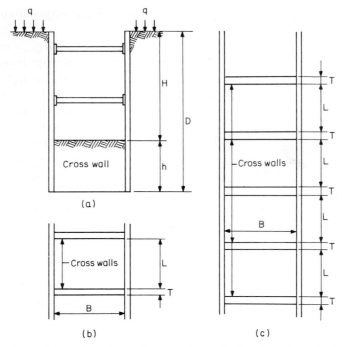

Figure 4-8 Typical plan and section for analyzing stability against bottom heave: (a) Section showing longitudinal walls and cross walls. (b) Plan for a single opening. (c) Plan for analyzing stability through two or more openings.

4-8, the stability against bottom heave is expressed as

$$F = \frac{N_c s_u + [2(B + L)h/BL]\alpha s_u}{\gamma H + q} \qquad (4\text{-}4)$$

where D, H, h, B, and L conform to Fig. 4-8 and N_c is again obtained from Fig. 4-7 considering the ratio D/B.

Since bottom heave is analyzed through a single opening, the depth-to-width ratio should be taken as D/L if $L < B$ in estimating N_c. If the walls are extended deeper by support on piles, subpiers, or stilts (an arrangement that excludes vertical displacement), the shear resistance at the exterior interface mobilized when the overburden begins to settle following the tendency to heave may be considered. This effect is not included in the present analysis.

Heave through two or more openings.   In this case, a further factor improving stability is the downward resistance on the underside of the transverse walls (Eide et al., 1972), assumed evenly distributed over the area under consideration. For two openings (Fig. 4-8c), we consider the parameter

$$q_1 = \frac{TBNs_u}{B(2L + T)} \tag{4-5}$$

in which N can be taken as 7.5. Then the factor of safety is

$$F = \frac{N_c s_u + [4(B + L)h/B(2L + T)]\alpha s_u + q_1}{\gamma H + q} \tag{4-6}$$

Likewise the factor of safety against heave through an infinite number of openings (long excavation) is

$$F = \frac{N_c s_u + [2(B + L)h/B(L + T)]\alpha s_u + q_1}{\gamma H + q} \tag{4-7}$$

where

$$q_1 = \frac{TBNs_u}{B(L + T)} \tag{4-8}$$

and N can again be taken as 7.5.

A suggested factor of safety is 1.5, especially for prolonged excavations. If the undrained shear is estimated with good accuracy and the cut remains open for a short period, the value of F may be reduced to 1.3. The tendency of the base to heave is aggravated if the bracing is not adequate and the walls begin to move. Where the upper layers are stiff compared with the clay below excavation level and the cut is shallow, base heave is influenced to a lesser degree by the wall bracing.

Results from excavations in Oslo.   For the cut-and-cover tunnels in soft Oslo clay mentioned in Sec. 3-4, the maximum bottom heave with cross walls as shown in Fig. 4-5 was confined between 20 and 30 mm, indicating that the cross walls functioned as intended in preventing bottom heave failure. The theoretical factor of safety computed from the foregoing analysis is 1.3 to 1.4. Interestingly, small lateral displacements of the tunnel walls indicated convergence because of incomplete or imperfect contact between the cross walls and the tunnel diaphragm walls. Continuing settlements after completion of the tunnel were probably associated with pore pressure changes and consolidation of the clay.

Initially, the pore pressure was hydrostatic, corresponding to a groundwater level +4.0, with +6.85 taken as the ground level (m). The slurry trench excavation resulted in a 3-m increase in piezometric elevations closest to the trench, indicating that some water escaped from the trench to the surrounding ground. The pore pressure remained at this level until tunnel excavation started and resulted in a steady decline in pore pressure. After completion of the tunnel, the pore pressures reached a new constant level that was 2 to 3 m below normal along the outside face of the tunnel. A tendency was also evident for flow down below and up through the bottom of the tunnel.

Example.   Referring to Fig. 4-8, the following data are given: $D = 60$ ft, $H = 40$ ft, $B = 30$ ft, $h = 20$ ft, $L = 12$ ft, $T = 3$ ft, $q = 100$ lb/ft^2. The clay has undrained shear $s_u = 600$ lb/ft^2 and $\gamma = 120$ lb/ft^3. The adhesion factor α is 1.

Stability without diaphragm walls.   Evidently $D/B = H/B = 40/30 = 1.33$, and $B/L = 0$, so that $N_c = 6.6$ (from Fig. 4-7). The factor of safety is computed from Eq. (4-2) as

$$F = \frac{6.6(600)}{120(40) + 100} = \frac{3960}{4900} = 0.81 \qquad \text{not enough}$$

Stability with diaphragm walls but no cross walls.   Evidently $D/B = 60/30 = 2$, and $B/L = 0$, so that $N_c = 7$ (from Fig. 4-7). When Eq. (4-3) is applied, the factor of safety is

$$F = \frac{7(600) + [2(20)/30](600)}{4900} = \frac{4200 + 800}{4900}$$

$$= 1.02 \qquad \text{still inadequate}$$

Stability with cross walls, single opening.   Evidently $L < B$, so that $D/L = 60/12 = 5$ and $N_c = 9$. The factor of safety is now computed from Eq. (4-4) as

$$F = \frac{9(600) + [2(30 + 12)(20)/(30)(12)]600}{4900}$$

$$= \frac{5400 + 2800}{4900} = 1.67 \qquad \text{OK}$$

Long excavation with cross walls.   First the factor q_1 is computed from Eq. (4-8):

$$q_1 = \frac{3(30)(7.5)(600)}{30(12 + 3)} = 900$$

For $D/B = 2$ and $B/L = 0$, $N_c = 7$ (from Fig. 4-7). Next we compute the factor

$$\frac{2(B + L)h}{B(L + T)} \alpha s_u = \frac{2(30 + 12)(20)(600)}{30(12 + 3)} = 2240$$

From Eq. (4-7)

$$F = \frac{4200 + 2240 + 900}{4900} = \frac{7340}{4900} = 1.50 \quad \text{OK}$$

4-3 Wall Bracing Systems

Bracing with struts. Figure 4-9 shows three different types of internal bracing that can be used for diaphragm wall construction. The cross bracing with struts shown in Fig. 4-9a is typical for narrow excavations in cut-and-cover. The raker system shown in b is used in relatively large building excavations and requires an artificial countersupport to receive and transfer the lateral thrust back to the ground. The diagonal bracing shown in c is used in square cuts, and its main advantage is the release of a large unobstructed area inside the excavation.

Effect of brace stiffness. At each level of brace applications secondary wall movement can occur as a result of compression at loose connection points, horizontal bending of wale beams, and elastic shortening of the braces. In practice, the effective stiffness of a brace, expressed as the ratio of preload to apparent deformation, may be markedly less than its ideal elastic stiffness (O'Rourke, 1981). Studies by Palmer and Kenny (1972) during open cut excavation for the Oslo subway show that the effective brace stiffness was only $\frac{1}{50}$ the ideal elastic stiffness. Other studies (Jaworski, 1973; Scott et al., 1972) confirm that significant horizontal displacement occurs when braces lack tight connections with the wall and where compressive materials are use to shim separations at connection points.

Braces can be preloaded to ensure rigid contact between interacting members. A typical preloading arrangement, shown in Fig. 4-10, includes the brace connection details with a plot of observed stiffness. Preloading is introduced by inserting a hydraulic jack at each side of an individual pipe strut between the wale beam and a special jacking plate welded to the strut. The increase in separation between the strut and the wale is measured, as is the lateral displacement of the vertical piles at this level and on opposite sides of the cut. The pile displacement is substracted from the increase in separation to give the apparent deformation of the strut.

The effective stiffness K_E of the strut is

$$K_E = \frac{P}{\Delta S} \tag{4-9}$$

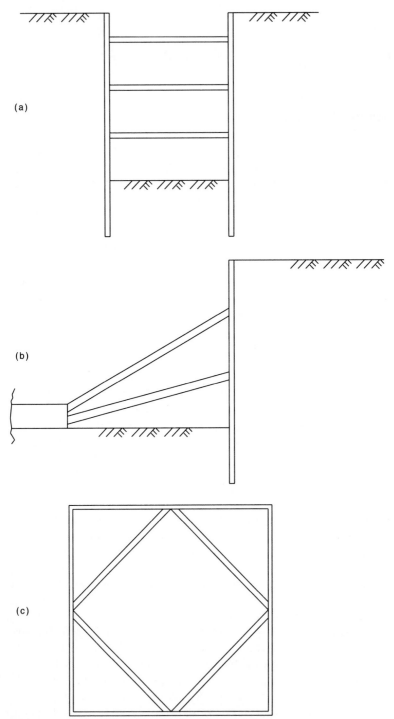

Figure 4-9 Interior bracing systems for supported excavations. (*a*) Conventional bracing. (*b*) Raker supports. (*c*) Plan view of diagonal bracing.

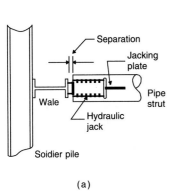

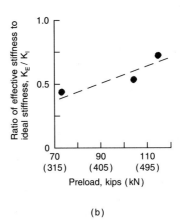

(a)   (b)

Figure 4-10 Preloading arrangement and measured brace stiffness. (*O'Rourke, 1981.*)

where P is the average preload and ΔS the average apparent deformation. The ideal stiffness of the strut is

$$K_I = \frac{EA}{L} \tag{4-10}$$

where E is the modulus of elasticity of the strut material and A and L the cross-sectional area and length of the strut, respectively.

In Fig. 4-10*b* the ratio K_E/K_I is plotted vs. the preload, from data obtained from cut-and-cover construction. The relative high percentage of ideal stiffness attained at each strut level documents the effectiveness of preloading in producing rigid supports. The strut stiffness increases with preload, but very high preload levels are not necessarily more advantageous.

The strut bracing detail shown in Fig. 4-10 is suitable for the soldier pile and concrete panel walls discussed in Sec. 1-7 and shown in Figs. 1-25 and 1-26. Alternatively, the struts may be part of the permanent inside framing system.

For all-concrete diaphragm walls, strut bracing can be combined with the considerable wall stiffness to eliminate the use of wale beams. Rigid connections of wales to a diaphragm wall are difficult and costly, and result in gaps and loose fit, with subsequent stress concentrations at the contact areas. The struts in this case can be directly connected to the wall by means of shear plates, as shown in the detail of Fig. 4-11. The wall is designed as a two-way slab. The wall thickness is usually sufficient to resist punching shear provided the size of the bearing plate is selected accordingly, and the system

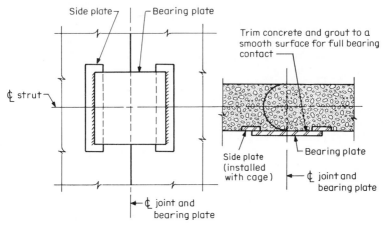

Figure 4-11 Connection details for strutted diaphragm walls.

as a whole possesses adequate rigidity to ensure a uniform distribution of lateral earth loads.

Bracing with rakers.   The use of preload in conjunction with rakers does not necessarily provide control of movement. Elastic analysis shows that the transfer of the thrust to one or two caissons embedded in the ground may result in overall movement of the order of 3 in for construction conditions typical in Chicago.

An idealized wall deformation associated with lateral loading and a combined raker-caisson bracing is shown in Fig. 4-12a, and it is apparent that at this stage the wall approaches cantilever behavior. As more construction is completed and the foundation slabs are in place, the caisson is further restrained and makes the raker system more effective. In Fig. 4-12b the bracing functions under stable conditions so that the wall movement is inward bulging that can be controlled by the wall stiffness. Although the volume of incremental displacement in a and b may be essentially the same, the pattern of movement is dissimilar.

Unsupported slopes and berms.   Slopes and berms may be provided as part of the bracing as shown in Fig. 4-13, where the associated instability problems are also indicated. In Fig. 4-13a the excavation is made as a combination of cut slope and braced cut. The unsupported slope begins at the top of the braced support and continues to ground line. In Fig. 4-13b the slope is made part of the bracing; instability in this case will deprive the wall of lateral support.

In most large excavations berms are left in place as part of a sequential construction or as designated lateral bracing. Usually, how-

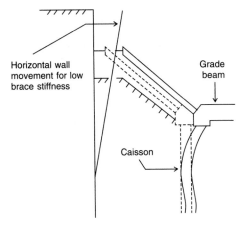

(a) Lateral deformation of caisson

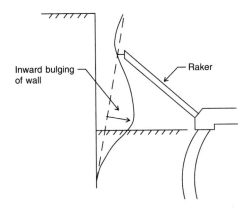

(b) Caisson stabilized

Figure 4-12 Wall deflection caused by raker and caisson bracing. (*O'Rourke, 1981.*)

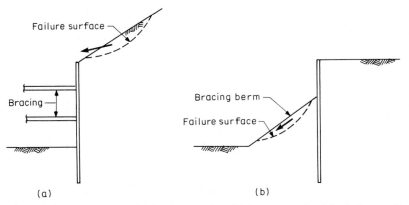

Figure 4-13 Overall stability of walls braced with berms. (*a*) Combined slope and braced wall. (*b*) Braced wall supported by berm.

ever, sloughing, seepage activity, creep, and continuous construction operations lead to gradual distortion and deterioration of the berm. As a bracing, berms appear to be more effective if they supplement a more rigid lateral support near the top of the wall. Where clay berms brace the wall temporarily in its entirety, they are almost certain to result in excessive lateral movement, in spite of wall stiffness.

Berms for excavations in soft to medium clay exhibit a higher dependence of time vs. movement because of distinct creep effects. Examples that articulate the sensitivity of excavation to raker and berm bracing in soft and medium clay are presented by O'Rourke (1981). The time dependence of berm deformations because of creep and gradual attrition from construction events contributes to displacement. Several investigators (Clough and Derby, 1975) have attempted to quantify the effects of berm bracing using finite-element analysis and checking the results against case histories. The conclusion is that providing a generous berm can have a decisive effect on reducing movement in weak soils but is less important in stronger soils. Nonetheless, at least 75 percent of the theoretical passive wedge must be present in the berm for an effective reduction of movement.

Walls braced with permanent structure. Where the architectural and structural requirements of the superstructure are compatible with the prefounded column method (discussed in other sections), the usual procedure is to complete the first stage of construction by installing the exterior diaphragm walls and the foundation portion of the interior columns. The second stage begins by general excavation and placement of concrete floors in a downward process where each slab is cast directly on the ground when the proper level is reached and serves to brace the walls.

If the excavation is relatively shallow and lateral wall movement is not critical, the construction can proceed as shown in Fig. 4-14 consisting of the following stages: (1) Excavate to final level providing also a generous berm as shown in A; at this stage the wall is braced along its entire height by the berm alone. (2) Construct the permanent

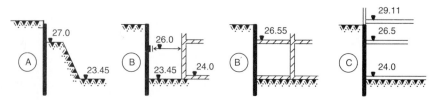

Figure 4-14 Temporary bracing with berm, followed by the permanent bracing with final structure.

underground structure except the outer bay, as shown in B, install a temporary upper strut just below the permanent floor, and remove the berm; at this stage the wall is braced by the upper strut and by its embedment below excavation level. (3) Install bottom floor and upper slab in outer bay as shown in B', and remove strut; at this stage the wall is braced by the permanent structure. (4) Proceed with the erection of the superstructure as shown in C.

Bracing by embedment. For walls braced with multilevel bracing, embedment below final excavation level for either static equilibrium or control of movement is not necessary. Wall embedment may, however, be selected explicitly as bottom bracing, especially where dense and stiff ground is available or where rock exists at shallow depth. In this case, two considerations must be emphasized.

1. It has been demonstrated that in sands considerable movement, of the order of 1 to 3 percent of the wall height, is necessary to mobilize full passive resistance depending on the sand density. This movement is unrealistic and clearly intolerable. As a result, it has been suggested to reduce passive earth pressure coefficients by as much as 50 percent in the worst case, which corresponds to a design condition of loose sand with a high angle of wall friction. The development of passive pressure is also much dependent on vertical motion of the wall. The same problem in cohesive soils, particularly with reference to effective stresses, does not appear to have attracted the same attention, probably because these effects are likely to be of less importance than in the case of high internal soil friction.

2. Where embedment is extended to limit wall movement, the method of analysis and design must be correlated with the actual conditions. For example, in the case of a cantilever wall or a wall braced at the top artificially and at the bottom by embedment, working bending moments are deduced from a wall penetration into the ground corresponding to a factor of safety for rotational stability equal to unity. In order to ensure stability, either the active pressure is increased or the passive pressure is reduced by a factor of safety, and from these revised pressures a new wall penetration is determined for equilibrium. Thus the working bending moments do not correspond to the actual installed depth, and occasionally unrealistic features, such as higher shear forces in the wall, become apparent.

Bracing with ground anchors. Limiting conditions for a wall supported at the top by a single row of anchors and at the bottom by embedment are shown in Fig. 4-15. In part a the wall is overloaded beyond its structural capacity and is on the verge of failure, which may pull the anchor out of its fixed zone.

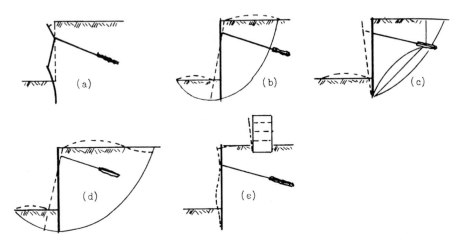

Figure 4-15 Limiting condition for anchored walls as they relate to fixed anchor location.

With insufficient anchor length beyond the slip plane and also with insufficient wall embedment, the system may shift by rotating as shown in *b*. Passive resistance below excavation level is manifested in connection with the slip plane and is perceptible through measurement of wall deformation. Equilibrium is established by increasing wall embedment, which will also result in a longer anchor zone.

In *c* the wall has sufficient embedment and is stable below excavation, but it tilts forward because the anchor is too short and is fixed within a zone that slips. In this case stability is restored after the fixed anchor zone is moved beyond the potential slip plane.

The condition shown in *d* involves slipping of the ground mass and wall rotation. It occurs because of two unstable factors: insufficient wall embedment and fixed anchor zone within a ground mass prone to failure. As in *c*, ground deformation measurements can be used to monitor this condition and provide indication of pending failure.

The condition shown in *e* involves stable structure-anchor-soil interaction in static terms, but excessive ground deformation associated with large lateral wall displacement results in unstable foundation conditions for the existing building. Incidents of this nature can be avoided with appropriate serviceability criteria based on deformation controls.

Figure 4-16 illustrates a problem common with deep vertical cuts. The rock anchor is inclined at 45° to reduce overall length, and this results in a downward load component essentially the same as the horizontal earth thrust, exerted by the diaphragm wall on the rock. The stability in this case is not only a matter of material strength but also depends on the presence of fissures, clay-filled seams, weak joints,

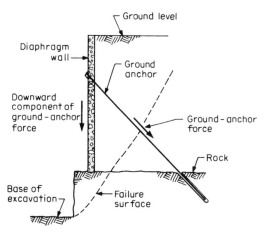

Figure 4-16 Vertical loads from anchor tension and chiseling into rock, causing shear failure in the rock mass below the base of the wall.

and cracks. At worst, the vertical anchor component may result in shear failure as shown. The potential of vertical drawdown of the wall under excessive anchor load is demonstrated in both soil and rock; it is avoided by decreasing the vertical anchor component, by increasing the bearing capacity of the wall, or both.

It appears from these brief comments that the mechanism of an anchored wall is complex since the ground, wall, and anchors must interact and work together in order to resist earth loads and surcharges and also restrict deformations.

4-4   Prediction and Control of Movement

Although it is rather unorthodox to isolate movement from earth stresses and vice versa, movement of an excavation is often more critical because it can affect buildings and adjacent utilities. An added complexity is the fact that slurry walls are built in most soil conditions, and often in poor soil and with high groundwater table.

With the evolvement of a well-defined technology, the complacency that set in with procedures largely developed in the 1940–1950 period does not necessarily produce now the safest or most economical solutions. Thus examples of poor behavior for supported excavations suggest that significant improvements in the design of excavations and underground works are possible if the analysis considers also performance characteristics so that engineering solutions can be used to their best advantage.

Settlement detrimental to surroundings

The usual approach to the settlement problem is to compile a record of existing buildings, structures, streets, and utilities and supplement it with an up-to-date survey (see also Sec. 2-2). The next and most important step is to establish a range of tolerable differential settlement, but the wide disparity of results and views on the subject make general guidelines difficult to lay down.

The settlement caused by open cut excavation that a building can withstand is less than the settlement that the same structure can undergo without damage under the effect of its own weight. Settlement caused by subway construction can occur rapidly and produce erratic effects. Damage to nearby buildings will depend first on the type, foundation, age, and general condition of the building (D'Appolonia, 1971). A comprehensive summary of settlement that may be damaging to surroundings is provided by Skempton and MacDonald (1956). Useful classifications of allowable and detrimental settlements are also given by Sowers (1962) and by Grant et al. (1972).

Differential movement, usually expressed as angular distortion, is of much greater concern than uniform settlement or tilting. From theoretical studies, tests, and field observations, it appears that a building undergoing an angular distortion greater than $\frac{1}{300}$ is likely to suffer some form of damage, but this is not necessarily true in every case. The settlement corresponding to this distortion will generally vary and depend on the soil type, rigidity of the foundation, and distance between exterior columns and walls.

If an entire structure moves vertically some amount or rotates as a plane rigid body, this will generally not cause structural or functional distress. For example, if a building settles 1 in (2.5 cm) on one side and 3 in (7.5 cm) on the other with a linear variation between the two points, the building will have settled 1 in and tilted an amount $x = (3 - 1)/L$. Local settlements below the tilt line between the two sides are likely to cause distress, and these are the differential settlements that must be controlled since they determine structural and functional acceptability. Differential settlement is thus the settlement between two adjacent points.

For a given magnitude of differential settlement a building resting on sand may suffer more damage than one founded on clay. This is generally true for buildings that settle under the effect of their own weight, the reason for the difference being that settlement in clay occurs over a longer period and the structure has more time to adjust to this deformation. The same guidelines should not be used for settlements due to excavation. In this case, the settlement may be irregular and occur during the excavation period.

The tolerance of underground services and utilities to differential settlement is more difficult to quantify. The most susceptible facilities are old sewers and tunnels of brittle materials, and where joint leakage can be caused by minor disturbance. Utilities made of ductile materials can deform without distress even under the rigorous conditions imposed in areas of mining subsidence, but problems may still be encountered if there is a large relative movement across a structural discontinuity.

A convenient trend is to allow damage in some instances to occur and institute repairs afterward. The basis for this approach is that the cost of repairs usually is less than the cost of extra procedures used solely for preventing damage, but this is true mainly of buildings of small value and limited functions.

Movement and settlement due to excavation

Typical patterns of movement are presented in Fig. 4-17. In part *a* the movement occurs as lateral yielding of soft soil above stiff soil for a cut supported by a flexible wall. In part *b* the lateral yield of soft clay occurs above and below the base of the cut, and the soil at the base tends to move upward (heave). Figure 4-17*c* and *d* is for the same excavation but with a rigid support. In both cases, movement is as-

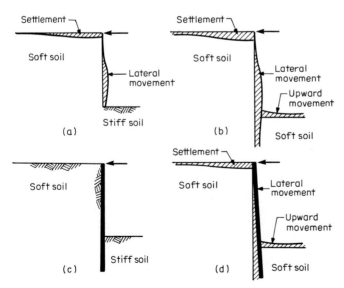

Figure 4-17   Settlement due to lateral movement: (*a*) and (*b*) Flexible wall. (*c*) and (*d*) Rigid wall. The top of the wall is restrained against movement and may or may not have intermediate bracing.

sociated with (1) lateral displacement of the support above and below the excavation level as the work continues to a lower level and before the next bracing is installed; (2) some yielding of the bracing; and (3) elastic deformation of the wall between bracing points.

Movement above excavation level. The installation of any bracing tier normally is preceded by excavation to an appropriate level. The associated stress release and relative freedom of the wall below the last bracing cause it to move. Thus wall movement above the excavation level reached at any time is controlled mainly by the procedure and execution of bracing, degree of preloading, and stiffness of the medium where the forces from the bracing are eventually transferred. If these details do not receive proper execution, lateral wall movement above excavation can be significant.

Movement below excavation level. Lateral yielding of the support below a given excavation level will occur irrespective of the capacity and preloading of the bracing above that level. The lower part of the wall is restrained against movement by the passive resistance of the soil and by the wall stiffness. This movement increases in soft or loose soil, with increasing wall flexibility, and with reduced wall embedment. Where the stability number N is greater than 6 for excavations of ordinary dimensions and shape, base instability by heave is rapidly approached, leading to more movement.

Observed movement

The conceptual presentation of the causes of movement in the foregoing section does not solve practical problems, unless this process can be quantified. The most serious problem concerning movement occurring during excavation generally is with clays. As a braced excavation in clay is deepened, ground movement around the excavation increases. The primary cause for this increase is the additional shear stresses applied to the soil as the factor of safety against base heave diminishes.

For a general excavation (other than the narrow cuts discussed in Sec. 4-3), the relation between ground movement and tendency for base heave is shown by the data of Fig. 4-18. Although the support in this case is a sheet pile wall, the results are general. The maximum lateral movement measured in the soil behind an excavation in San Francisco Bay mud is plotted vs. the factors of safety against base heave. The lateral movement δ_H is expressed as a nondimensional parameter by dividing by the excavation depth H. Movement increases fast as the factor of safety drops below 1.5. This result is important

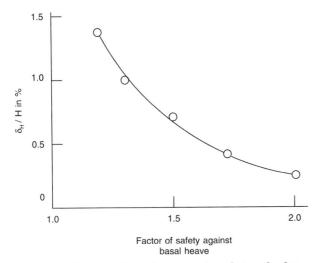

Figure 4-18 Maximum lateral movement vs. factor of safety.

since it demonstrates the nonlinear response of the soil. For a linear elastic soil medium, movement increase would remain constant regardless of factor of safety.

Walls braced before excavation. Wall movement can be reduced to inconsequential levels, and even eliminated, if the lateral support and its bracing can be constructed in its final position before general excavation. If that is possible, wall displacement is associated with elastic deflections between bracing points and with some yielding of bracing already installed. In this manner ground movement becomes independent of soil type and is influenced mainly by the stiffness of the support system.

Walls braced with crosswalls. Figure 4-19 shows section and construction sequence for the Studenterlunden tunnel in Oslo mentioned also in other sections. Concreting of the panels caused permanent outward displacement of the walls, corresponding to a 10-mm increase in width. After concreting, the panels settled as much as 10 cm (4 in) until the steel piles were inserted through open steel tubes grouted to interact with the steel reinforcement. This settlement was predicted and was considered in positioning the reinforcing cages to maintain the joints with the tunnel slabs at the correct alignment and level.

According to the construction sequence, the top slab was cast prior to any excavation, and therefore the walls were braced at the top and bottom before any unloading. The excavation was carried out under the roof, and the intermediate floor slab braces the walls at midheight. Actual wall movement registered maximum value near midheight and

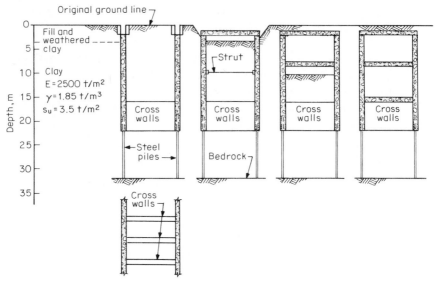

Figure 4-19 Construction of a subway section in Oslo. Diaphragm walls braced at the bottom with cross walls. (*From Eide et al., 1972.*)

before the bracing at this level was installed. The measured displacement was close to 5 mm (0.2 in) and occurred as elastic deformation between lateral supports.

Walls braced by embedment into rock.   This solution may be economical if the distance between walls is considerable and rock exists at shallow depth. An example of bottom bracing with a rock socket is shown in Fig. 4-20, giving also data on soil and rock characteristics. The lower crust of the clay layer is occasionally sandy and contains some gravel.

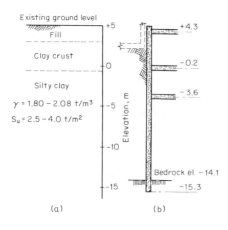

Figure 4-20 Construction of a deep basement in Oslo. Diaphragm walls braced at the bottom by embedment into rock: (*a*) Soil data. (*b*) Section through wall. (*From DiBiagio and Roti, 1972.*)

The diaphragm walls are 1 m thick (40 in) and are keyed into the rock. The total wall height is 20 m (66 ft), braced by the permanent concrete floor slabs, 40 cm (16 in) thick. During excavation a small pore pressure decrease was recorded (1.5 m loss in the hydraulic head). When bedrock was reached, the pore pressure decreased markedly as a result of dewatering through the rock.

Ground settlement and wall movement are shown in Fig. 4-21. The reference day 46 is the last day of observations before excavation. The settlement for day 238, which is the end of the excavation period, is 23 mm (0.92 in) maximum, and exhibits a constant rate. Since there was no significant change in pore pressure during the same period, this settlement is the result of lateral movement. At the end of this period the excavation remained open and unsealed for considerable time to construct the basement, and the settlement continued beyond day 238 as a result of pore pressure loss and consolidation effects. The

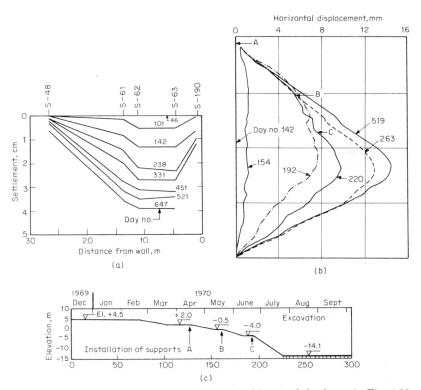

Figure 4-21 Observed excavation for the office building in Oslo shown in Fig. 4-20: (a) Ground settlement as a function of time. (b) Lateral wall movement at various excavation stages. (c) Construction sequence as a function of time. (*From DiBiagio and Roti, 1972.*)

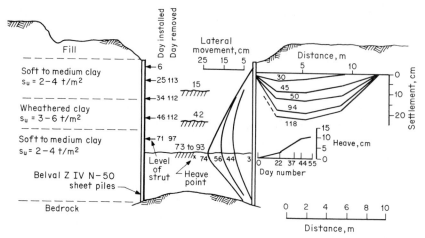

Figure 4-22 Excavation, lateral movement of sheeting, and settlement of adjacent ground. Open cut in soft Oslo clay. (*From NGI 1962–1966.*)

settlement stopped when the rock socket was sealed and the pore pressure in the clay began to build up again.

The lateral wall movement shown in Fig. 4-21*b* refers to day 142, almost 2½ months after starting excavation, at which time more than 3 m (10 ft) of earth had been removed. The data are adjusted slightly so that all curves pass through a point corresponding to zero movement at the uppermost bracing level. The movement reaches a maximum of 15 mm (0.6 in) at a depth of 12 m, but total movement from the beginning of excavation is close to 25 mm (1 in).

For comparison, Fig. 4-22 shows a similar excavation in Oslo clay, of similar geometry and soil conditions, but with a flexible wall. Steel sheeting is driven to rock but does not penetrate hard material and is therefore free to move laterally. The data show wall movement and ground settlement relative to the insertion of the struts as the excavation was carried down, but they do not represent long-term changes. Both inward wall movement and ground settlement are nearly 10 times those of Fig. 4-21. Contributing factors are movement below excavation level, base heave, elastic deflection associated with flexible support, and yielding of the bracing.

Walls braced with struts.   Figure 4-23 shows a section and soil data for the Embarcadero Station, BART (Kuesel, 1969). The diaphragm walls are internally braced by 7 levels of struts, in an excavation 60 ft deep. With ordinary ground support the stability can be analyzed by referring to Eq. (4-2). Using $B = 55$ ft, $H = 60$ ft, $N_c = 6.4$, and $s_u =$

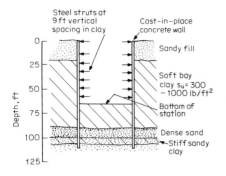

Figure 4-23 Excavation, soil profile, diaphragm walls, and bracing for the Embarcadero Station, BART. (*From Kuesel, 1969.*)

1000 lb/ft², the factor of safety against base heave is $(6.4)(1000)/(120)(60) = 0.88$.

The diaphragm wall is embedded 50 ft below excavation level. Using $D = H + h = 60 + 50 = 110$ ft, and $D/B = 110/55 = 2.0$, the stability number N_c is 7.0, and $h/B = 1$. From Eq. (4-3) the factor of safety is $[7(1000) + 2(1000)]/7200 = 1.25$, or adequate. Added protection is also provided by the presence of the firm layer of dense sand and stiff clay into which the wall penetrates.

The wall is a composite steel I beam and concrete panels 4.5 ft thick. At the end of excavation and with all the struts in place, maximum wall deflection was from 1 to 1.5 in (2.5 to 3.75 cm). The insertion of the top strut, close strut spacing, and well-executed details contributed to the control of movement, but this case demonstrates also the effect of bottom bracing by extending the rigid support into firm ground.

Figure 4-24 shows data for an excavation in subway section D of the Massachusetts Bay Transportation Authority. The medium blue clay is slightly overconsolidated in the upper crust and shows a decrease in the undrained shear with depth as it becomes normally consolidated. For an excavation 50 ft deep the factor of safety against base heave is slightly greater than 1.0 (D'Appolonia, 1973).

A sheet pile wall supported the excavation for most of its length except for a length of 200 ft adjacent to the Don Bosco School, where a 3-ft-thick diaphragm wall protects the excavation and also serves as underpinning. In both cases the bracing consists of interior struts of similar configuration, the only difference being the support stiffness. The measured pore pressure behind the diaphragm wall at the end of excavation was 10 to 15 percent less than static (Lambe, 1970).

Excavation of the slurry trench caused an inward movement of the face by 1 in (2.5 cm). At the end of excavation and with all struts in place, the diaphragm wall had moved laterally from ½ to 1½ in. The

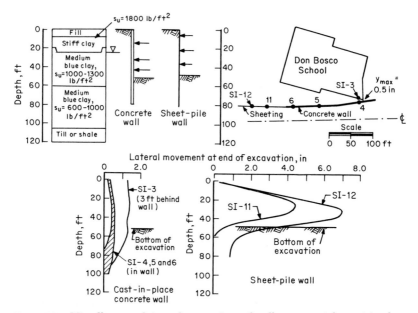

Figure 4-24 Miscellaneous data and comparison of wall movement for cast-in-place diaphragm wall and sheeting. Excavation in Boston medium clay. (*From D'Appolonia, 1973.*)

lateral movement of the sheet pile wall was from 4.5 to 7.0 in, or several times the movement of the diaphragm wall.

Walls braced by permanent floors. The New Palace Yard car park, London, is 16 m (52.5 ft) deep and was constructed in fissured London clay. The exterior diaphragm walls are within a few meters of the foundations of both the clock tower (Big Ben) and Westminster Hall. The first construction stage included the installation of the diaphragm walls and the foundation part of the interior column (prefounded column method, discussed in other sections). The steel columns of the substructure were lowered into cased boreholes and grouted into position. The construction was completed in a downward process where each slab was cast directly on the ground and the concrete floor was used as bracing.

The ground is typical London clay overlain by a layer of water-bearing gravel and fill. The clay has an average undrained shear strength of 100 kN/m^2 (about 2400 lb/ft^2) and a K_0 value varying from 2 to 3.

Wall and ground movement is shown in Fig. 4-25 and refers to the time when the excavation was completed. The profile of the lateral wall displacement shown in Fig. 4-25b is with all five floors in place

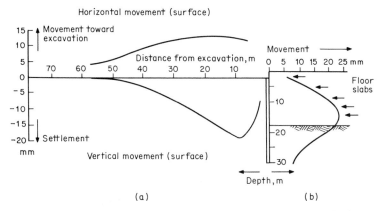

Figure 4-25 Observed wall and ground movement. New Palace Yard car park, London: (*a*) Vertical and horizontal surface movement. (*b*) Movement of wall toward excavation.

but before the bottom slab was cast. The diagram confirms two important effects: (1) part of the wall movement (about 5 mm) was due to initial shrinkage of the concrete floors, and (2) the wall stiffness and embedment were effective in limiting wall movement below excavation level. Interestingly, the permanent floors do not take effect until the concrete has hardened sufficiently. Conversely, the excavation is carried under "roof," and cannot continue until the concrete floor above becomes self-supported. In this case, preloading is not possible, and this precludes partial compensation of movement.

The ground movement shown in Fig. 4-25*a* shows vertical settlement at the surface and horizontal movement toward the excavation as a function of the distance from the wall. The settlement curve shows the distinct effect of shear resistance mobilized at the wall-soil interface, and also suggests the presence of a downdrag force on the wall. Ground movement is inconsequential by most standards and criteria, but it extends along a zone 4 times the depth of excavation.

Excavation under high water table. Figure 4-26 shows a cross section of a four-level basement built on a site with a water table 1.2 m (4 ft) below the surface (Huder, 1969). The ground consists of glacial till, varved decomposed moraine, and lacustrine deposits. The materials of the moraine are mainly of a clayey nature, somewhat sandy to gravelly, and in some places with lenses of silt. The undrained shear strength is 0.2 kg/cm^2 for the lacustrine deposit and 1.4 kg/cm^2 (2800 lb/ft^2) for the undisturbed moraine. The excavation is 17 m (56 ft) deep.

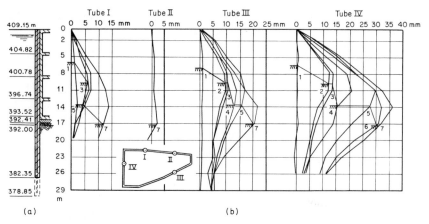

Figure 4-26 (*a*) Section through a four-level basement in Switzerland. (*b*) Observed wall movement. Bottom of wall elevation: tube one = 382.35 m; tube two = 380.00 m; tube three = 380.00 m; tube four = 382.35 m. (*From Huder, 1969.*)

The diaphragm wall was built to a depth of 27 to 35 m (88 to 114 ft) to provide a cutoff. Outside the excavation the water table was left undisturbed, but the interior was dewatered to a level 50 ft below surface. At the end of excavation, the probable water head was 12 m (40 ft).

Lateral wall movement is shown for four locations marked I, II, III, and IV on the plan. The wall depth is 27 m (88 ft) for tubes I and IV, and 29 m (95 ft) for tubes II and III. Bracing is provided by the permanent floors as in the example of Fig. 4-25. The zero deflection shown at the surface is used for reference and is not actual deflection. The movement profiles show that the wall continued to deflect at the upper floors as the next lower floors were placed, as a result of shrinkage and elastic shortening under more lateral load. Tube IV registered more than twice the deflection of tube I, although the wall has the same depth. The greater movement for tube IV was caused by the loose soil, and by more shrinkage and elastic shortening of the longer floor slab.

Tubes II and III are opposite, adjacent to the moraine, and have the same depth. Behind tube III, the natural ground rises about 20 ft (6 m) above the top of the wall, and subsequently there is a tendency for a net movement of the entire structure from that side to the opposite side containing tube II. The minimal wall movement shown for tube II is thus an adjusted deformation profile and includes the composite movement. Huder (1969) suggests that exact correlation of movement is further complicated because of variations in wall stiffness. It is conceivable that construction tolerances resulted in deviations of ±30 percent in the theoretical wall stiffness.

Anchored walls.   Representative examples of anchored walls are available for anchorages fixed in stiff clay or in rock.

Neasden Underpass, London. A cross section for this excavation is shown in Fig. 4-27. The excavation is 8 m (26 ft) deep, with a 5-m (16-ft) wall embedment. The London clay exists to a depth of 28 m (92 ft) and is underlain by the much stronger Woolwich and Reading beds that have an undrained shear strength close to 300 kN/m^2 (about 6200 lb/ft^2).

The walls were braced with four rows of anchors extending to twice the excavation depth, and with a moderate inclination fixing the anchorage zone in the clay. The walls began to move with excavation, and the lateral movement extended well below the bottom of the inclinometer tubes. Toward the end of excavation and subsequently the walls underwent more inward movement as well as settlement. The displacement trajectories of various points showed that outside the anchorage zone, ground movement was essentially horizontal. The vertical wall displacement toward the end of excavation was caused by the vertical component of the anchors as the lateral thrust was increased.

Figure 4-27*b* shows the lateral movement of the tops of the three inclinometer tubes with time. Time-dependent movement is clearly the case, and extends back beyond the anchorage region. This ground movement is therefore related to the bracing procedure as the ground stretches to mobilize resistance to the anchor load.

Guildhall Precincts Development, London. A section of the diaphragm wall and the anchorage is shown in Fig. 4-28*a*. The excavation is 10.4 m (34 ft) deep, and the wall thickness is 50 cm (20 in).

Lateral wall movement at various excavation stages is shown in Fig. 4-28*b* to *i* (Littlejohn and MacFarlane, 1974). The displacement profiles are plotted relative to the toe of the wall, so that no account is given of the overall movement except when it is measured during a general survey, as in profiles *e* and *i*.

Profile *b* shows wall rotation toward the excavation which is superimposed on the cantilever action above the first excavation level. The maximum differential displacement between the toe and the top occurred at this stage (10 mm), corresponding to a rotation or slope of $\frac{1}{970}$. The effect of prestressing the top anchor is evident in profile *c* showing the wall drawn back toward its initial profile. The difference in profiles *c* and *d* reflects time effects, in this case 4 days, and indicates anchor displacement in the zone of load transfer. Likewise the bulging that occurred below excavation level in profile *f* as earth moving continued to the second level is seen to have disappeared when the second anchor was prestressed in profile *g*. This bulging continued

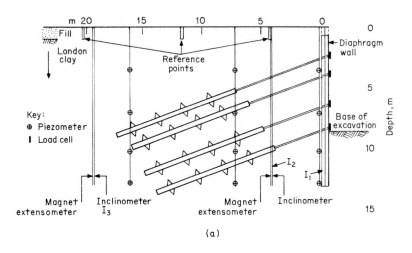

(a)

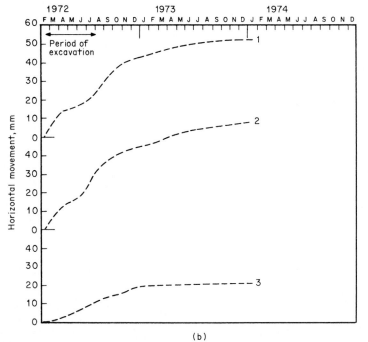

(b)

Figure 4-27 Neasden Underpass, London: (*a*) Section through diaphragm wall showing tiebacks and instrumentation. (*b*) Horizontal movement of the top of the three inclinometer tubes: 1 = in the wall; 2 = 4.3 m behind the wall; 3 = 19.3 m behind the wall.

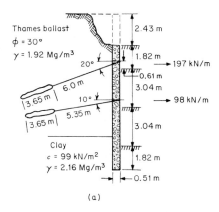

(a)

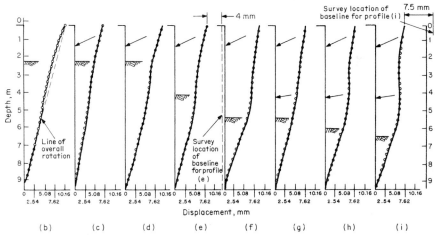

Figure 4-28 Guildhall Development, London: (*a*) Section through diaphragm wall. (*b*) to (*i*) Observed wall movement during excavation. (*From Littlejohn and MacFarlane, 1974.*)

as the excavation was taken to its final level, as shown in profiles *h* and *i*.

The measured vertical settlement indicated negligible scattered changes around the wall and at ground surface. The upper anchors were monitored for 103 days, and during this period the prestress remained essentially unchanged, indicating that there was no relative movement between the fixed anchor zone and the wall.

Keybridge House, Vauxhall, London. A section of the diaphragm wall, together with the anchorage and soil data, is shown in Fig. 4-29*a*. The excavation is 14.5 m (48 ft) deep, and the wall is embedded 2.2 m (7.2 ft) below excavation level.

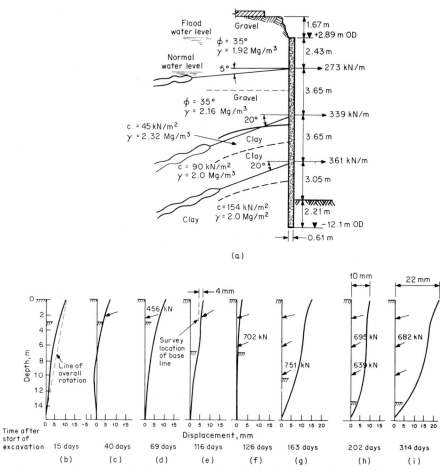

Figure 4-29 Excavation for the basement of the Keybridge House, Vauxhall, London: (*a*) Section through diaphragm wall. (*b*) to (*i*) Observed wall movement at various construction stages. (*From Littlejohn and MacFarlane, 1974.*)

Lateral wall movement is shown in Fig. 4-29*b* to *i*. In profile *b* the cantilever deflection is combined with wall rotation to produce the displacement shown. Stressing the first anchor to 450 kN draws the wall back as shown in profile *c*. About 29 days later the wall had reverted to the shape of profile *d*, although no major change in the prestress level was detected.

Following excavation to the second level (6.8 m), the wall deformation below the depth 6.5 m shown in profile *e* was almost the same as the wall deflection of profile *d*, but an inward displacement of the toe (2.5 mm) occurred as a result of consolidation of the clay on the cut side. The development of beam action below the anchor level offset the initial cantilever effect.

With two levels stressed as shown in profile *f*, the top and toe of the wall converged, and their differential displacement became smaller. Following excavation to the third level (10.4 m) the differential displacement increased to 13 mm, and in spite of the stressing of all three anchor levels. At the final excavation level the toe of the wall moved a moderate 1.5 mm toward the cut. It might appear from profile *h* that the wall underwent some rotation about a point between the two upper anchors, which reduced the differential top/toe displacement to 10 mm. The wall settlement at final stage was 12 mm (0.5 in) and reflects the movement necessary to mobilize side shear and base bearing.

The time effects on wall movement become evident from profiles *h* to *i*, reflecting a 3-month period. During this time, the differential deflection between top and toe more than doubled, although the load at the center anchor registered only a slight loss of prestress. This suggests the possibility of consolidation of the stressed soil around the fixed anchor zone, and confirms movement of the entire mass of ground behind the wall and within the zone of influence of the anchorage.

World Trade Center, New York. For this project the anchors were fixed into rock and served temporarily as bracing until the permanent structure was in place. Typical wall sections are shown in Fig. 4-30 for the three monitored panels, generally 70 ft deep. The diaphragm walls were keyed into rock primarily to transfer the considerable vertical load imposed by the anchorage and the depth of excavation. The panels were supported by four to six anchor rows installed at 45° and

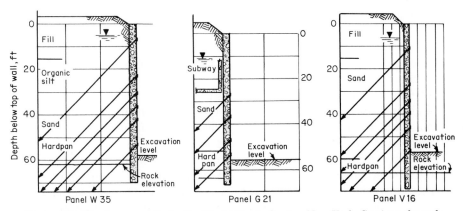

Figure 4-30 Diaphragm walls for the World Trade Center, New York. Sections through panels W35, G21, and V16. (*From Saxena, 1974.*)

penetrating 30 to 35 ft (9 to 10.5 m) into rock. The anchors were pre-stressed to the corresponding design load, sometimes as high as 600 kips. The wall thickness is 3 ft and has a stiffness EI 1.5 × 10^6 kip · ft^2 in the uncracked condition.

Figure 4-31a shows lateral wall movement for panel W35 (Saxena, 1974). The anchors are stressed to 100 percent of their design load. The wall continued to move toward the soil as the excavation proceeded to lower levels. The total movement at the top is 6.6 cm (0.2 ft), and occurred from the beginning to the end of excavation as tilting (rotation) of the wall about its toe. The wall moved very little in the same direction during the 10 months following the excavation. As a result of this movement the anchors experienced loss of prestress associated with anchor shortening.

The horizontal movement for panel G21 is shown in Fig. 4-31b. Anchors were omitted in the upper part of the wall because of the existing subway structure, so that the first row of bracing was about 25 ft (8 m) below the top of the wall, with cantilever function above this bracing level. The anchors of this row were stressed only to 40 percent of their design load to avoid overstressing the structure. The panel continued to move toward the excavation in spite of the prestress applied to the lower anchor levels, and reached a maximum movement of 0.2 ft (6 cm), one-half of which occurred during excavation to the second tieback level. A small increase in load for anchor T_1 reflects a different magnitude and pattern of lateral earth stresses. The loss of prestress for the remaining three anchor levels appears to be nominal.

The wall movement for panel V16 is shown in Fig. 4-31c. The uppermost anchors were installed 12 ft (3.7 m) from the top, with cantilever action above this level. As the remaining anchors were installed and prestressed, the wall moved away from the cut, and upon completion of excavation the tip and top of the wall were essentially at their initial position.

Free cantilevers. Cantilever walls (without bracing other than embedment below excavation level) are seldom used in urban excavations or in deep cuts, but they are feasible in relatively shallow excavations and provided the resulting movement can be tolerated.

Figure 4-32a shows lateral movement of a cantilever wall at various times and construction stages. The excavation is for the Reading bypass in London. The depth of this cut is the same as in the Neasden underpass shown in Fig. 4-27. The total wall height is 17 m (56 ft) from ground surface, 9 ft of which is used as embedment below excavation level. The ground consists of London clay in the upper crust, with the toe of the wall keyed into the much stronger Woolwich and

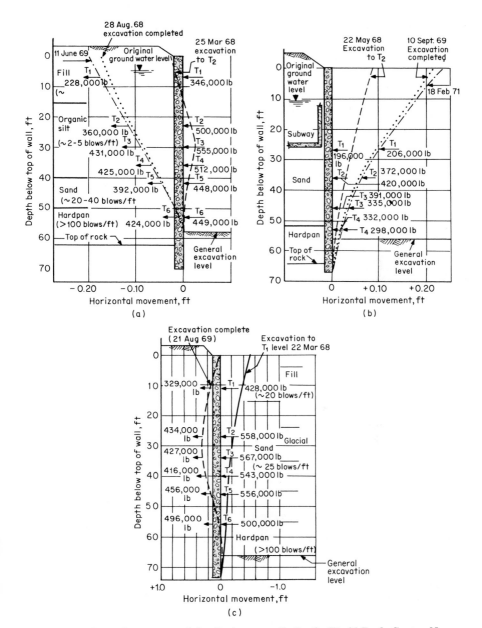

Figure 4-31 Lateral movement of the diaphragm walls for the World Trade Center, New York: (*a*) Panel W35. (*b*) Panel G21. (*c*) Panel V16. (*From Saxena, 1974.*)

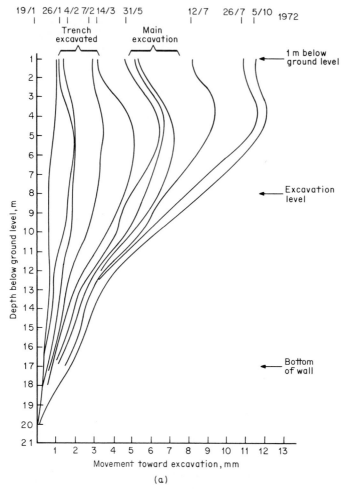

Figure 4-32 (*a*) Lateral movement of the cantilever diaphragm wall for the Reading bypass in London. (*b*) Horizontal and vertical ground movement. (*From St. Johns, 1975.*)

Reading beds. Figure 4-32*b* shows the distribution of surface movement.

Combined bracing.   Combined bracing includes struts, anchors, rakers, and berms, all combined or used in conjunction with wall embedment.

Central YMCA, London.   Figure 4-33*a* shows a typical section for the underground portion of this building. The basement is 16 m (52.5 ft) deep, but the diaphragm wall is extended only 2 to 3 m (6 to 10 ft) below excavation level.

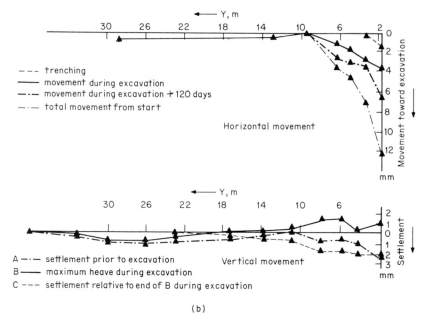

A —·— settlement prior to excavation
B —— maximum heave during excavation
C – – – settlement relative to end of B during excavation

(b)

Figure 4-32 (*Continued*)

The excavation was carried out in three basic stages, shown in Fig. 4-33a. In stage 1 excavation was completed to a level of 10 m (33 ft) while the wall was braced with a row of anchors installed 3.5 m (11.5 ft) from the top. A concrete slab 30 cm (12 in) thick was cast on the ground at the 10-m level and braced the wall at this point. The excavation continued under this floor in two stages. In stage 2, the central portion of the remaining basement was excavated, leaving the berm and casting the central portion of the basement slab. In stage 3 the perimeter berm was removed sequentially in short lengths, and the basement floor was completed in the same manner.

Wall and ground movement is shown in Fig. 4-33b for the period during construction. Excavation to the 10-m level caused inward wall bulging, and the removal of the perimeter berm caused movement that increased rapidly with time. This movement occurred as rotation about the 10-m floor slab. It is conceivable that if the base slab had been delayed further, a plastic hinge might have been developed at the 10-m level followed by rotational slip below this level. With the last stage of excavation there was a corresponding increase in surface settlement.

Brittania House, London.   The basement for this building is 20 m (66 ft) deep, and was built as shown in Fig. 4-34. The tower raft is 27 m (89

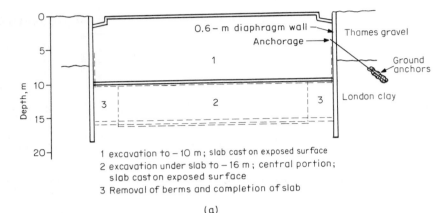

1 excavation to − 10 m; slab cast on exposed surface
2 excavation under slab to − 16 m; central portion;
  slab cast on exposed surface
3 Removal of berms and completion of slab

(a)

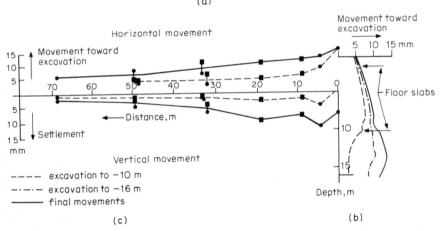

(c)   (b)

Figure 4-33 YMCA building, London: (a) Diagrammatic presentation of the excavation sequence. (b) Lateral movement of the diaphragm wall. (c) Ground movement and settlement. (*From St. John, 1975.*)

ft) wide and 70 m (230 ft) long, located almost centrally in the east-west direction and close to the north site boundary in the north-south direction. Figure 4-34a shows a section through the east and west wall, and Figure 4-34b shows a section through the north wall.

The ground at the site was reduced from + 11.0 m (ODN) to 7.00 m to provide a better construction platform for the diaphragm walls. The walls are 80 cm (32 in) thick and extend 22.5 m (74 ft) below the original ground. Bulk excavation was carried out to the level shown in Fig. 4-34 working southward away from the north wall. A continuous berm was left along the perimeter as temporary bracing, and the excavation slope was covered with a protective thin concrete layer to delay deterioration of the clay berm. When the excavation reached the raft level, a 0.9-m-thick concrete slab was placed to prevent swelling

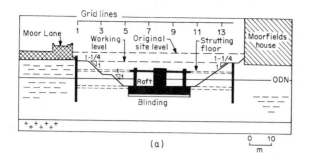

(a)

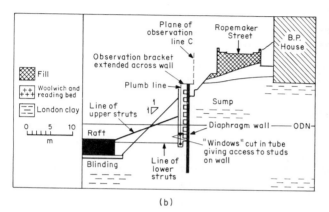

(b)

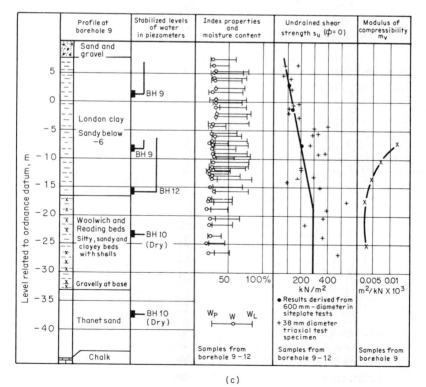

(c)

Figure 4-34 Construction of the 20-m-deep basement for the Brittania House, London: (a) Section through the east-west walls. (b) Section through the north wall. (c) Pertinent soil data; ODN = ordinance datum Newlyn. (*From Cole and Burland, 1972.*)

and consolidation of the clay. The 3.3-m-thick raft was then constructed in alternate bays to allow for shrinkage effects (Cole and Burland, 1972).

The excavation sequence along the north wall is shown in Fig. 4-35a along grid line 8, or approximately at the center of the wall between the east and west boundaries. The lateral movement of the top of the north wall is shown in Fig. 4-35b. Considerable lateral support was provided at the extremities of this wall by the east and west slopes excavated as shown in Fig. 4-34a. Wall movement at three levels with time is given in Fig. 4-35c, together with the settlement reading in the street adjoining the north wall. The first of the top struts was placed on July 21, 1963, 10 days after casting the concrete raft. Excavation of the top of the north berm continued, and by Aug. 19 the entire row of upper rakers was in place and wedged against the raft. The removal of berm beneath this bracing began after Aug. 19, and placing of the bottom rakers started at the end of the same month.

The excavation procedure for the west and east walls was somewhat more complex. Earth moving initially was carried out from north to south, as shown in Fig. 4-35a. West wall movement at the top with time is shown in Fig. 4-36 along the same section of Fig. 4-34a. Excavation from the working level at grid line N (the line where the movement is shown) started after June 21, 1963, and was substantially completed by the end of July for the construction of the raft, cast on July 30. Partial berm removal was necessary on Sept. 20, and by Nov. 20 the propping floor braced the wall as shown in Fig. 4-36.

From Fig. 4-35b and c it appears that the ground response to excavation was slow. With the excavation almost halfway down (level ODN, Nov. 6), the top movement of the north wall was only 3.5 mm (0.14 in), but it accelerated rapidly as the excavation approached full depth and reached 13 mm (0.5 in) on June 21. The movement continued steadily until July 2, when the excavation reached the profile shown in Fig. 4-35a, at a rate of 1.8 mm/day. Thereafter, the movement rate was slower, and with the struts in place it was reduced to 0.44 mm/day. Likewise, after an initial lag the movement of the west wall accelerated and reached 0.8 mm/day, but was reduced to 0.25 mm/day at the time the raft was cast. Thus this wall moved some 16 to 18 mm during the 2 months following the excavation when it was braced only with the earth berm. The total movement of the west wall was increased to 62 mm (2.5 in) by the time the propping floor was in place.

It appears that the movement associated with this excavation was largely time-dependent, and for both the north and west wall the movement during excavation was only a fraction of the total move-

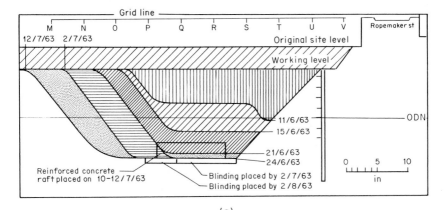

(a)

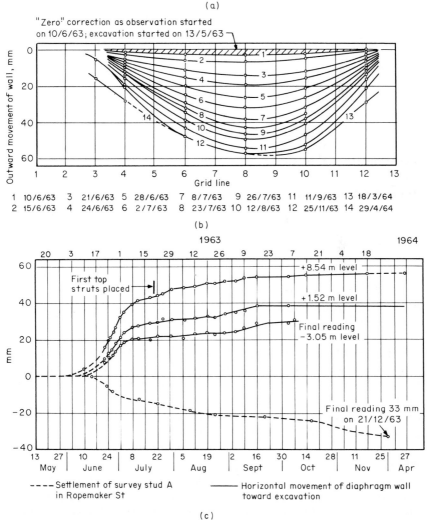

(b)

(c)

Figure 4-35 Data from the excavation of the Brittania basement, London: (*a*) Excavation schedule shown along a section normal to the north wall. (*b*) Lateral movement of the top of the north wall. (*c*) Movement of the north wall at three levels; ODN = ordinance datum Newlyn. (*From Cole and Burland, 1972.*)

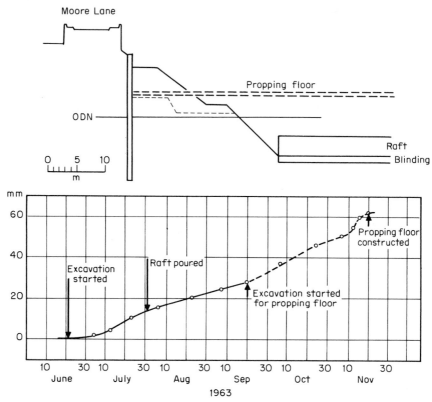

Figure 4-36 Movement of the west wall, basement of the Brittania House, London. (*From Cole and Burland, 1972.*)

ment. The difference in the rate of movement between the two walls may be due to different lateral bracing conditions and the fact that the west berm was less steep than the north slope.

Southern Pacific Excavation, San Francisco. Figure 4-37 shows plan and cross section of this excavation, together with soil data (Clough, 1975). The excavation was carried out in very soft clay to a depth of 11 m (36 ft) using top and bottom bracing only in conjunction with a temporary earth berm. The diaphragm wall is 75 cm (2.5 ft) thick and penetrates 12 m (40 ft) into the ground below excavation level. The top bracing consisted of the two cross-lot struts and some diagonal bracing located as shown, and a group of rakers braced the wall at excavation level. A cap beam was cast on top of the wall to reduce the inward bulging by stiffening the wall longitudinally. The earth berm was left against the wall until the lower-level rakers were in place.

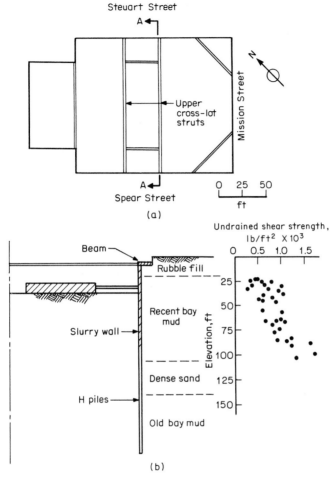

Figure 4-37 Plan, section, and soil data for the Southern Pacific
excavation, San Francisco: (*a*) Plan view. (*b*) Section *A-A*. Prestress
loads: upper struts 2900 lb/ft; lower struts 6000 lb/ft.

Because the wall carries significant vertical loads, it is supported on
piles.

Wall movement and ground settlement are shown in Fig. 4-38. Both
the top and bottom braces were prestressed to the levels mentioned
in Fig. 4-37. The largest lateral wall movement occurred adjacent to
Steuart Street where the clay is weakest and the excavation was deepest. The top of the wall moved inward by more than 2.5 cm (1 in) as
a result of yielding of the bracing and wall bulging between supports.

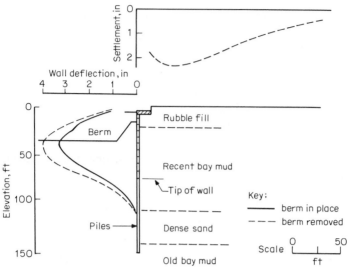

Figure 4-38 Measured movement and settlement, Southern Pacific excavation, San Francisco. (*From Clough, 1975.*)

The wall moved 10 cm (4 in) into the excavation at and below the base of the cut, and its tip displacement was about 3 cm (1.2 in). Evidently most of this lateral deformation occurred as movement below excavation level, and although it is not shown as a function of time it is assumed to have been time-dependent.

Comments on reducing movement and settlement

The foregoing examples articulate the process of movement in excavations in conjunction with the soil type and the bracing system. Although the results are not quantified, it appears that the soil stiffness or density and the stiffness of the support are the most important single parameters influencing the magnitude and pattern of movement. Time effects are important for excavation in clay. In addition to the wall stiffness, the stiffness of the bracing influences movement of the system. The effective stiffness of the supports is influenced by the horizontal and vertical spacing, the structural section properties, and the type and execution of connections. Goldberg et al. (1976) suggest that the support spacing and wall properties can be combined into a general stiffness parameter defined as EI/h^4, where EI is the flexural wall stiffness and h is the vertical spacing of the supports.

Case-history data on maximum diaphragm wall movement in clays are presented in Table 4-2 (Clough and Schmidt, 1977) together with the respective values of EI/h^4 and the factor of safety against base heave. These results show several trends:

1. Although in some instances the factor of safety against base heave is rather low, the movement does not exceed 0.2 percent of the wall height, and this confirms the conclusion that a stiff wall system is effective in reducing movement.

2. In some of the examples of Table 4-2 the movement is relatively large and approaches or exceeds 1 percent of the wall height. In two cases, opening of holes for caisson construction inside the excavation resulted in large movement. In a third case, wide spacing between supports (9 m) reduced the system stiffness and in spite of a stiff wall. A suggestion has been (Peck, 1969) to keep the bracing spacing to less than $2c/\gamma$ in soft clays, where c = undrained cohesion and γ = unit weight, in order to control movement.

Some other factors influencing movement are discussed in the following sections.

Preloading.   Preloading is becoming a routine practice for ground anchors and has been common for struts. Preloading may be estimated from a Rankine active state (triangular), according to an apparent pressure diagram (Peck et al., 1974), from a condition corresponding to the rest earth stress, or a preload can be applied until 1 in of onward movement is observed (see also subsequent sections).

Clough (1979) presents the diagrams shown in Figs. 4-39 and 4-40, for sands and stiff clays, respectively. Results from field data and model tests were used to produce these plots. According to these diagrams, the preload has a strong effect on system movement and can be used to reduce movement. There is, however, a limit beyond which further increase in preload does not produce appreciable reduction in movement, and thus very large prestress loads are not indicated.

Optimal distributions of design preload diagrams can be trapezoidal, rectangular, or triangular. Trapezoidal diagrams result in higher preloads for the uppermost supports and would normally be used where large movement is expected in the initial excavation stage. Triangular distributions result in higher preload forces for the lowest supports, and theoretically they should be effective where a large component of displacement is movement below excavation level. This may, however, be academic since in most cases large movement has occurred before the lowest supports are in place.

TABLE 4-2 Movements of Slurry Walls in Clay

Reference	Location	EI/h^{4*} kN/m²/m	Factor of safety basal heave	Max. movement Exc. depth, %	Comment
Lambe (1970)	Boston	1,470	2.0	0.2	
DiBiagio and Roti (1972)	Oslo	4,300	1.3	0.1	
Armento (1973)	San Francisco	26,600	1.4	0.15	
O'Rourke et al. (1976)	Chicago	1,420	1.4	0.5	
O'Rourke et al. (1976)	Chicago	3,020	1.3	1.8	Problems caused by nearby foundation construction
O'Rourke et al. (1976)	Chicago	6,490	1.4	2.0	Problems caused by nearby foundation construction
Clough and Derby (1977)	San Francisco	109	1.7	1.0	Vertical strut spacing = 9 m
Johnson et al. (1977)	Boston	2,200	4.0	0.2	

Adapted from Clough and Schmidt, 1977.
*Based on moment of inertia of concrete section only.

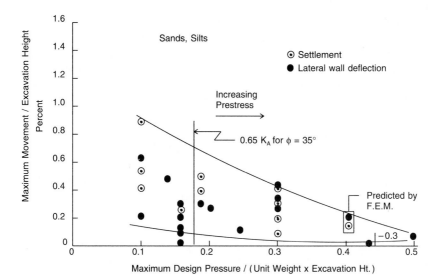

Figure 4-39 Effect of prestress load on movements of wall systems in sands. (*From Clough, 1979.*)

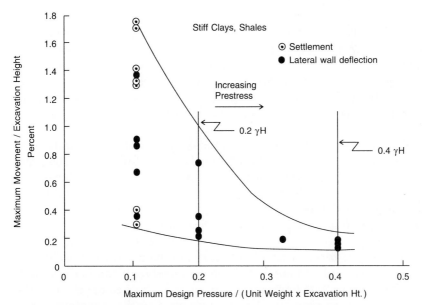

Figure 4-40 Effect of prestress load on movements of wall systems in stiff clays. (*From Clough, 1979.*)

Applying preloads to recreate the at-rest pressure is compatible with the goal of design but should not be expected to eliminate system movement. In applying at rest preloads, only the lateral component of stress relief is compensated for, but not the vertical stress relief across the bottom of excavation. Interestingly, the pattern and level of preload will determine the lateral earth stresses acting on the wall.

Earth berms. In addition to the comments made in Sec. 4-3, several trends have been observed for excavations braced with berms. In general the earth berm-raker system in soft clay may be expected to move more than the cross-lot bracing, and this is because a considerable part of the excavation must be completed before the bracing is installed.

Premature removal of the berm, or local slope failure in the berm caused by seepage, softening during rainy weather, and softening by repeated movement of equipment, all will result in more movement. Large or flat berms should not be expected to have significant stabilizing effects on base heave. In most cases the clayey soil simply moves beneath the subgrade and carries the berm with it.

There is a clear linkage between the effectiveness of a given berm size in controlling movement and the basic stability requirements of the excavation. Nonetheless, the successful use of an earth berm is enhanced if the period during which it is expected to be the major support is reduced.

Supports below excavation level. Movement in clay develops below excavation level after the initial excavation stage. Bottom bracing with cross walls or rock sockets should be effective in controlling this movement. Wall embedment below excavation level can be almost as effective, particularly in stiff clay, and examples are the excavations in London clay mentioned in the foregoing sections.

General guidelines. Movement in excavations, and occasionally local failure, has been often attributed to delayed installation of the bracing, pile driving, caisson construction, water loss through holes and leaking joints, remolding and undercutting of clay berms, and heavy surcharge loads from construction equipment. Because these factors are individual system parameters whose influence and contribution cannot be isolated, no attempts can or should be made to include them in quantitative terms. Consideration should be given to consolidation settlement caused by lowering of the water table. If the material outside the excavation is fairly incompressible, such as compact sand, the water table there may be allowed to respond to the dewatering conditions inside the excavation. If the soil is compressible, the walls must isolate the construction; otherwise the groundwater table outside the excavation must be maintained by a recharge scheme.

Cross-lot bracing with struts may be supplemented with preloading for the rebound of the wall to its initial position and to compensate for yielding of the bracing. In spite of current trends, preloading does not appear to be as necessary as it is with flexible walls unless the excavation is unusually wide, in which case struts would not ordinarily be used. Instead, it is better to concentrate on the construction procedure, reduce the time between bracing installations, and emphasize connection details. The extra wall stiffness allows greater unbraced heights, but initially this is not an advantage since large movement can occur in soft clay as the excavation is taken down to the next bracing level if the bracing interval is too large. This strength is an advantage, however, after the top and bottom braces are in place, at which time some intermediate struts can be removed provided the reamining struts can resist the lateral load.

Bracing with the permanent floors may result in less movement if the top uppermost floor is cast before any excavation. Movement associated with this bracing is initial shrinkage and elastic shortening of the concrete. Consider, for example, a 50-ft-wide excavation braced with concrete floors. The initial shrinkage at each floor level is of the order of ¼ in (0.6 cm), and the elastic shortening corresponding to a compressive (lateral) load of 30 to 50 kips/lin ft will be close to 0.1 in (0.25 cm), giving a total length change of about 0.35 in (0.9 cm) distributed at both ends. If the same excavation is braced with struts stressed to 20 ksi (1400 kg/cm^2), the elastic shortening of the steel will be about 0.4 in (1 cm). Premature excavation before the concrete floor has hardened should be avoided, and a rule of thumb is to start earth moving when the concrete floor can support its own weight in bending. If the walls are too far apart, shrinkage, creep, and elastic shortening will be major components of movement.

Anchored walls.   The position of the top row of anchors is usually dictated by the balance between the initial cantilever and the final moment, and limitations on wall movement. The first row is often 4 to 5 m (13 to 16 ft) from ground level. However, considerable movement can occur during the cantilever stage (sometimes as much as 50 percent of the total movement), and in soil that becomes progressively stiffer it may take the form of rotation about the tip of the wall. Accordingly, the first row of anchors should be as close to the ground as possible. A suggested depth is 1.5 m (5 ft) provided local ground failure behind the wall does not occur during prestressing of the anchors.

Very significant is the time-dependent movement observed for excavations in clay. For the Neasden excavation (Fig. 4-27) the movement of the top of the wall during the 18 months following the excavation was almost 150 percent of the movement recorded at the end of excavation. For the Keybridge excavation (Fig. 4-29) the time effects on movement become apparent during the 3-month period following the excavation, when the differential deflection between top and tip of the wall more than doubled. This effect may indicate consolidation of the soil around the fixed anchor zone, or it may be transition from elastic to plastic behavior.

The variance that often characterizes the design approach is demonstrated by referring to the two examples of Figs. 4-28 and 4-29. In both cases the prestress level is based on a modified trapezoidal diagram of apparent pressure with $p = \gamma HK$ where γ = soil unit weight, H = excavation height, and K = empirical coefficient (0.2 to 0.4). For the Keybridge excavation (Fig. 4-29), a back analysis indicates that probable value of K is 0.3, with the apparent pressure diagrams modified to give more load for the bottom rows and less load for the upper row. For the Guildhall excavation (Fig. 4-28) a probable value of K is 0.2, with the apparent pressure diagram modified to give more load for the upper row.

4-5 Special Problems in Excavations

Effects of anisotropy. Anisotropy, as a difference in response to loading in the vertical and horizontal direction, is manifested in most natural clays, and its effect on the undrained behavior of soft to medium clays is now recognized in most analyses. In braced excavations anisotropy reflects physical differences in soil behavior: behind the wall (active side) the soil is acted upon by vertical gravity, but the soil on the passive side (inside the excavation) is loaded horizontally by the thrust of the wall.

Beginning with the Terzaghi base heave theory, Clough and Hansen (1981) have extended the analysis to include anisotropic behavior. A strength variation is introduced along potential failure planes so that stress reorientation is applicable. Furthermore, it is useful to consider the ratio R of the factors of safety for the anisotropic and the isotropic stage given by

$$R = C_1 C_2 \qquad (4\text{-}11)$$

where $C_1 = N_c^*/N_c$ = ratio of the anisotropic bearing capacity factor to the bearing capacity factor normally used for isotropic soils, and C_2 is given in terms of the undrained shear strength, the dimensions of the excavation, and the anisotropic strength ratio K_s. Clough and Hansen (1981) define the ratio K_s as $s_{u(90)}/s_{u(0)}$ where $s_{u(0)}$ and $s_{u(90)}$ is the

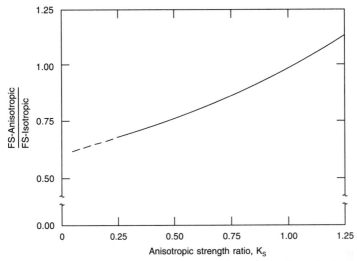

Figure 4-41 Ratio of factor of safety against base heave for anisotropic soil to that for isotropic soil for wide excavation.

undrained shear strength of the clay at $\beta = 0°$ and $90°$, respectively, and β is the angle of major principal stress change to the vertical. The factor C_2 approaches unity for soft to medium clays for excavation width >15 m (50 ft) and for $K_s \geqslant 0.25$, yielding $R = N_c^*/N_c$.

Figure 4-41 gives the ratio R as a plot vs. K_s. If $K_s < 1$, the factor of safety against base heave for anisotropic behavior is less than the same factor for isotropic behavior, and this difference is amplified as K_s decreases further. For K_s close to 0.25 the factor of safety for anisotropic conditions is 30 percent less than the same factor for isotropic conditions. When the excavation width and term K_s are outside the range $C_2 = 1$, the influence of anisotropy becomes more dominant. These results suggest that base heave factors determined from conventional analysis overestimate the factor of safety for the anisotropic form, and this error becomes more critical as the degree of anisotropy increases.

Likewise movement can be doubled, earth pressure distribution altered, and strut loads markedly increased as soil behavior shifts from isotropic to anisotropic. These potentially detrimental effects become more serious if the factor of safety against base heave is reduced below 1.4.

Time effects.   Several walls of Table 4-3 were monitored while the excavation depth remained unchanged. These projects were in San Francisco Bay, and the ground support was a sheet pile wall.

TABLE 4-3 Data from Case Histories; Base Heave and Movement for Excavations in Clay

Case no.	Location	Wall type	Wall end condition[†]	Final depth of excavation, m	Average S_u, tons /m²	Clay Properties			Minimum factor of safety FS	Movement, cm	
						w_p, %	w, %	S_1		δ_H	δ_V
1	San Francisco, Calif.	Sheet pile	Fixed	13.5	3.5	15–40	45–60	4–8	1.3	19.3	15.2
2	San Francisco, Calif.	Sheet pile	Fixed	14.0	3.5	15–40	45–60	4–8	1.3	15.0	14.4
3*	San Francisco, Calif.	Sheet pile	Fixed	14.0	3.5	15–40	45–60	4–8	1.3	10.2	
4	San Francisco, Calif.	Sheet pile	Free	9.1	2.4	35–60	55–90	4–8	1.3	3.8	
5	San Francisco, Calif.	Sheet pile	Fixed	9.1	2.1	35–60	75–100	8–20	1.0	25.4	
6	Oslo, Norway	Sheet pile	Fixed	11.0	2.5	15–30	20–45	2–6	1.0	23.5	23.3
7	Oslo, Norway	Sheet pile	Fixed	11.0	3.0	10–35	20–45	2–6	1.1	14.2	14.0
8	Oslo, Norway	Sheet pile	Free	9.2	3.0	10–35	20–45	3–7	1.3	18.5	11.6
9	Boston, Mass.	Sheet pile	Free	15.2	6.6	11	30	—	1.6	11.5	
10	Chicago, Ill.	Soldier pile	Fixed	13.4	1.9	10–20	20–40	—	1.2	8.9	
11	Bowline Point, N.Y.	Sheet pile	Fixed	9.8	3.9	10–40	35–65	4–8	2.4	5.1	8.0

From Mana and Clough, 1981.

*Local unusual construction effects. Affected data not used.

†Fixed end refers to wall tip embedded in underlying stiff layer; free end, tip in soft to medium clay.

NOTE: S_u = undrained shear strength; w_p = plasticity index; w = water content; S_1 = sensitivity.

252

In this area the assumption is often made that time-dependent effects in excavation are caused by undrained creep in the bay mud. However, a general constitutive model that can adequately predict the time-dependent deformation of cohesive soils under arbitrary three-dimensional stress is yet to become available. Considerable information on time-dependent behavior is available for certain cases such as one-dimensional compression, plane strain, and undrained triaxial creep.

The general theory is formulated on the concept of pseudo-linear elasticity. Representations for volumetric and deviator soil deformations including time effects are developed from existing models that account for restricted boundary conditions. These representations can be applied to the case histories of Table 4-3, and more particularly to the San Francisco studies to predict the response of remolded bay mud in triaxial compression tests, subject to arbitrary stress paths and drainage conditions. The results obtained from this analysis are compatible with the observed performance (Kavazanjian and Mitchell, 1980). Likewise, immediate pore pressures are predicted with sufficient accuracy.

For the example of Table 4-3, if the logarithm of the rate of observed lateral movement (taken as $\Delta S / \Delta t$) is plotted vs. the logarithm of time t, the resulting path has a linear form showing that the rate of movement decreases rapidly with increasing time. The same pattern also suggests that higher creep rates are associated with a smaller factor of safety. Thus short-term, time-dependent movement should be expected for braced excavations in clay, particularly with reduced safety factors.

Pore pressure dissipation. The undrained condition assumed for excavations in clay reflects an end-of-construction stage, but it is not always clear whether this assumed behavior actually applies. For example, the presence of a drainage layer in the clay matrix can enhance consolidation during excavation, and in this case the fallacy of idealized assumptions is obvious (see also Sec. 4-1).

The occurrence of consolidation around an excavation is a complex phenomenon, and its quantification a difficult problem. As earth removal begins and continues, the drainage boundaries are likely to change, and this will allow consolidation to occur at increasing rates. Conversely, the presence of impervious barriers in the path of flow impedes the process and complicates consolidation further.

An example of supported excavation in linear elastic low-permeability soil ($k = 1 \times 10^{-8}$ cm/s) is given by Osaimi and Clough (1979), analyzed within the matrix of finite-element solutions. The support is a 2-ft-thick diaphragm wall penetrating the full depth of the clay and assumed to be hinged at the level of a rigid base. As expected, the deformations of the soil mass were reduced with the wall in place. Along the face of the slope movement was about two-thirds of that without the wall. However, negative pore pressures were larger with the wall present since this system is impervious and inhibits lateral drainage. Pore pressures in the soil mass directly below the excavation in front of the wall were basically similar to those that would be expected for simple one-dimensional vertical drainage. Since consolidation is retarded by the presence of an impervious wall, undrained loading conditions can be assumed in the analysis.

Collapsible soils. By definition metastable or collapsible soils are unsaturated soils undergoing a radical particle rearrangement and considerable volume loss upon wetting with or without additional loading (Clemence and Finbarr, 1981). Difficulties associated with the use of these soils as foundation support have long been recognized, but until recently concern was limited because such soils were located in arid regions with modest economic development potential. With recent advances in irrigation these regions have been made available for industrial development and associated construction, and collapsible soils are becoming relevant to the analysis and design of excavations.

Probably the most extensive deposits of collapsible soils are the Aeolian, or wind-deposited, sands and silts (loess). In addition, alluvial floodplains, mud flows, colluvial deposits, residual soils, and volcanic turfs can produce collapsible soils. In technical terms, these deposits are characterized by loose structures of bulky-shaped grains in the form of silt to fine sand size. Comprehensive reviews are given by Clemence and Finbarr (1981), Northen (1969), Sultan (1969), and Dudley (1970). Since 1970, major effort has focused on determining the mechanism of collapse, on predictive techniques and treatment methods, and on evaluating case histories.

4-6   General Stability of the Ground-Anchor-Wall System

A comprehensive treatment of anchors and anchored walls is given by Xanthakos (1991). This section covers, therefore, the basic principles in conjunction with the analysis and design of diaphragm walls.

Ground stability with nearly horizontal anchors

A frequent practical case involves shallow anchors installed with a small inclination as shown in Fig. 4-42. This situation occurs where

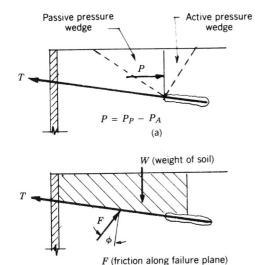

Passive pressure wedge   Active pressure wedge

$P = P_P - P_A$

(a)

W (weight of soil)

F

ϕ

F (friction along failure plane)

(b)

Figure 4-42 Failure mechanism of soil mass. Inclined anchors with shallow depth.

diaphragm walls must be braced near the top for control of movement, where a deep anchorage zone is not available, and where the vertical component of the anchor force must be restricted. Failure is characterized by pullout of the anchorage and a mass of soil in front of the installation. As the anchor is stressed, the force is transmitted to the surrounding soil mass, which begins to yield in front of the anchorage. Under more load a shear failure plane is produced, followed by pullout of the anchor. This mechanism is similar to the general shear failure of shallow footings.

The stability can be analyzed in two ways: (1) by assuming that failure occurs as shown in Fig. 4-42a where active and passive pressures are developed in the corresponding zones when sufficient movement occurs; and (2) by comparing the shear resistance mobilized along a plane coinciding with the anchor axis and the force applied to the anchor, as shown in Fig. 4-42b. Both failure conditions must be checked, and the zone of influence in the horizontal profile of the anchorage must be defined geometrically for each anchor. As long as the anchor profile is 4 m (13 ft) or more from the ground surface, failure of the soil mass in a mechanism shown in Fig. 4-42 is unlikely even in soft or loose soil.

For the condition shown in Fig. 4-42a, the resistance of the soil mass to failure is $P = P_p - P_A$, where the terms P_p and P_A are the passive and active pressure based on $0.5 \, \gamma h^2 K_i$ where h is the common height of the active-passive wedge. The fixed anchor zone must be far enough away from the wall for the wedge to be formed. If T_h is the horizontal component of the anchor, stability requires that

$$T_h = \frac{P}{F} \tag{4-12}$$

where F = factor of safety, not less than 1.5.

General stability of ground-multianchored wall

Analysis with plane failure surface. A simple method of analysis based on limiting equilibrium is shown in Fig. 4-43, based on the assumption that slip failure develops according to a planar configuration. The force acting in this manner is compared with the resisting force developed along the slip surface, and a factor of safety is established. Deformations are not computed but are lumped into the factor of safety. In the simplest form the plane failure surface begins at the base of the ex-

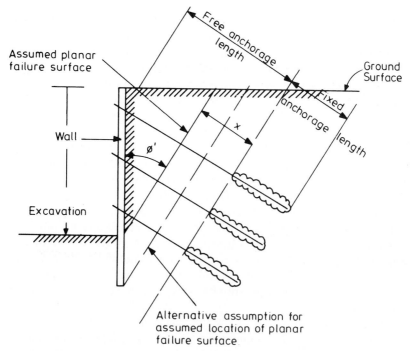

Figure 4-43 Stability analysis of anchored wall based on limiting equilibrium with plane failure surface.

cavation and extends at an assumed angle. From these considerations the fixed anchor zone begins at some point beyond the assumed failure surface. Alternatively, and more realistically, the failure plane is assumed to begin at the tip of the wall. Dimension x is determined from these considerations.

Analysis with circular slip surface. Probably a more realistic assumption of limit equilibrium analysis is failure along a circular slip surface as shown in Fig. 4-44. The method most commonly used in Europe is the Fellenious slip circle, supplemented by Huder (1965), Locher (1969), and Malijain and Van Beveren (1974). Likewise, the fixed anchor zone is located outside the most critical failure surface, so that additional checks are necessary to ensure that the anchors are not too short for these conditions.

The sliding block (Kranz) method. This procedure, initially formulated by Kranz (1953), was expanded by Ranke and Ostermayer (1968). The objective is to simplify the analysis by replacing the actual experimental failure shown in Fig. 4-45a by a composite surface shown in b and c, which is a modified version of the method (Pfister et al., 1982). The failure prisms in active pressure (dce) as well as in passive (bhg) are replaced as a second step by equivalent forces P_a and P_p as shown in c. With this simplification the analysis shifts from the complex system wall-ground-anchors to the soil mass M represented by the block ecbf. The wall and the anchor are replaced by their reactions on the mass, $-P_A$ for the wall and A for the tension in the anchor. The analysis is carried out for a unit length of excavation (see also Fig. 4-46).

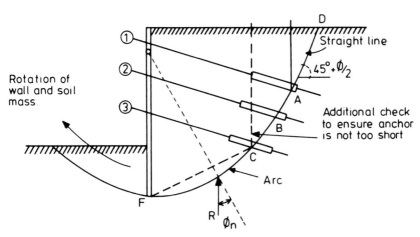

Figure 4-44 Stability analysis of anchored wall based on limiting equilibrium with circular slip surface.

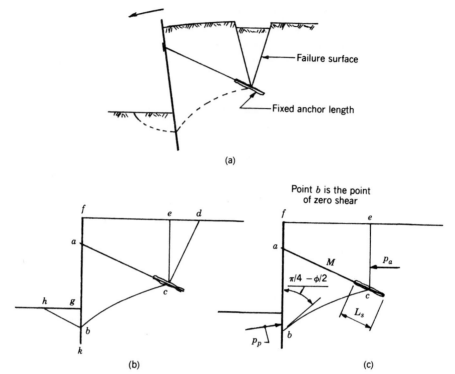

Figure 4-45   Failure of an anchored wall–ground system: (a) Actual mode of failure. (b, c) Simplification of the wall anchor system for stability analysis, using the sliding block method.

Analysis with one row of anchors.   The soil mass M is defined by planes bf and ce, and by a curved failure line bc, where b is the point of zero shear in the wall. Point c is located on the axis of the anchor at either of the following distances from the end:

- Half the fixed anchor length L_s if the spacing B between two adjacent anchors of the same row is less than or equal to $L_s/2$
- Equal to B where $B > L_s/2$

The failure curve bc represents a circle whose tangent at point b has an angle $(\pi/4 - \phi/2)$ with the wall as shown. This assumption is probably as close to reality as possible, since a straight line between points b and c may yield conflicting results. The forces involved in the equilibrium of the block, shown in Fig. 4-46, are as follows:

1. Known forces. These are W = weight of soil mass M, $-P_A$ = wall reaction equal to active pressure on height bf, and P_a = active pres-

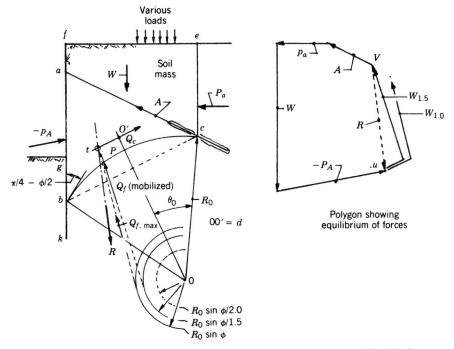

Figure 4-46 Assumed condition, forces and equilibrium diagrams for a sliding block necessary for stability analysis.

sure on plane *ec*. These three forces are estimated using effective stress analysis ignoring hydrostatic pressure since this cannot stabilize the soil mass M. Hydrostatic forces may have to be introduced, however, as horizontal component in P_a and vertical component in W. Other known forces are A = tension force in the anchor and F_e = exterior forces applied to the soil mass but having no stabilizing effects.

2. *Unknown forces.* These are the two components due to friction and cohesion *c* of the reaction along surface *bc*. The cohesion component Q_c is parallel to *bc* and has a magnitude $2cR_0 \sin \theta_0$ acting at distance $d = R_0\theta_0/\sin \theta_0$ from center 0 (distance $00' = d$). The friction component Q_f is tangent to a circle with radius $R_0 \sin \phi$. The forces Q_c and Q_f as defined are limit values of the two components corresponding to the failure state (Pfister et al., 1982).

Computation procedure. The analysis is carried out according to the following steps: (1) determine direction and magnitude of resultant R of forces W, $-P_A$, P_a, A, and F_e, and (2) establish the intersection point *t* between the line of action of the resultant R and the Q_c axis. Initially the force polygon is drawn for the components A, P_a, W, and $-P_A$ as shown in Fig. 4-46, terminating at point u. A factor of safety is then selected and the polygon is completed from point u by adding two vectors as follows: (1) a vector equal to Q_c/F_s and (2) a vector parallel to the tangent drawn from point t to the circle with radius $R_0 \sin \phi / F_s$ centered at 0. The actual value of the factor of safety is determined by trial-and-error procedure until the polygon of forces is closed exactly at point V. This factor is preselected by the designer.

The analysis is considered satisfactory if (1) the value of F_s is at least 1.5; (2) point P where the Q_f support line intersects circular surface bc is located in the central area of bc; and (3) the average stress along bc is the allowable (working) obtained from the ultimate (failure) using a factor of safety of 3.

Analysis with multiple rows of anchors. The equilibrium conditions for a soil mass supported by a multianchored wall are shown in Fig. 4-47. Certain conditions must be satisfied: (1) the wall embedment below excavation level is compatible with the passive resistance in this area, and (2) the fixed anchor length is located beyond the unstable zone. The stability of soil mass M is checked under the same procedure, but modifying the rear limit of mass M, the shape of slip surface, and the tension forces in the anchors.

Rear limit of mass M. Conceivable cases are shown in Fig. 4-47 where the actual volume of mass M is represented by the shaded areas. The rear limit of soil mass engaged in the interaction is defined by the lowest low of anchors and is the vertical line through point c_3.

Shape of slip surface. If the wall embedment is small, it may be ignored in the analysis (parts a, c, and e). In this case the mass M can be treated as a gravity wall with surface foundation. The slip surface is plane bc_3. If the embedment is considerable and must be considered (parts b, d, and f), the slip surface approaches a circle with a tangent at an angle $\pi/4 - \phi/2$ at point b of the wall.

Tension in the anchors. If the fixed anchor zone is placed beyond the boundary of mass M, it is possible for the force engaged in the stability of the soil mass to be less than the actual force in the anchor A. This case will arise if one anchor in the group is much longer than its neighbors. Under these conditions part of the cone defined by the angle $\beta = \pi/4 - \phi/2$ will pass below the rear limit of mass M. An example where this problem will not arise is shown in Fig. 4-48.

Computation approach. Likewise, the system is acted upon as in the single-row case. With the exception of the slip surface within a planar configuration, the maximum value of Q_f corresponds to its angle

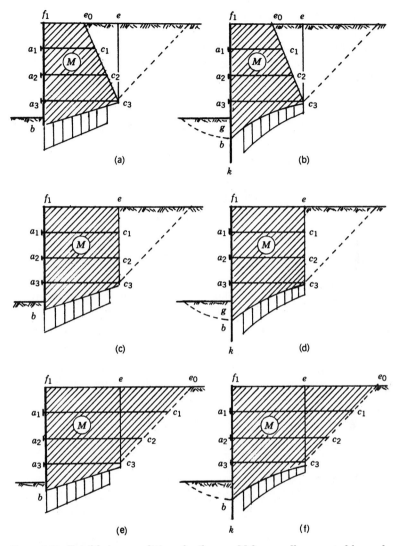

Figure 4-47 Equilibrium condition of soil mass M for a wall supported by multiple row of anchors.

$(\pi/2) - \phi$ with the slip surface, and the maximum Q_f is borne by the straight line bc. Furthermore, for a planar slip surface Q_f is defined by the angle $(\pi/2) - (\phi/F_s)$, which is made with the slip surface bc, and this is intended to represent the condition of limited wall embedment corresponding to the procedure of surface foundations.

Application of principles. The foregoing principles can be applied directly to the anchored wall of Fig. 4-49, supported with two rows of

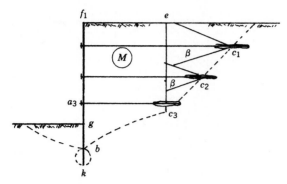

Figure 4-48 Equilibrium condition of a multianchored wall supporting a soil mass M; unequal length anchors and location of fixed zones with respect to stability of mass M.

anchors. The two masses M_1 and M_2 correspond to the two anchorages a_1 and a_2. The frictional forces Q_1 and Q_2 are defined by the angle $\pi/2 - \phi$ with respect to the slip surface, taken as planar for simplicity. At each stage M_i, the system is stable if

$$A_i' \geq F_s A_i \qquad (4\text{-}13)$$

where F_s = factor of safety, not less than 1.5, and A_i' is obtained from the polygon of forces as shown. This approach is different from the

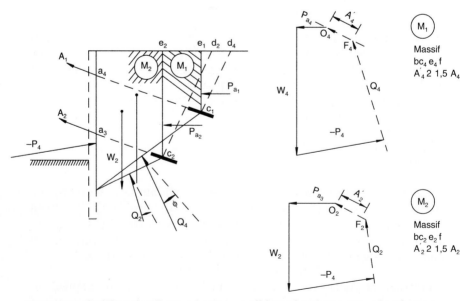

Figure 4-49 Stability of wall-ground system, wall braced with two rows of anchors.

procedure of Fig. 4-46, where the factor of safety relates to Q_c and Q_s, but it requires a trial-and-error analysis until the polygon is closed at the desired point.

4-7 Lateral Earth Stresses

In simple terms, the formulation of the problem of predicting lateral pressures and deformations is essentially the definition of appropriate limiting conditions. This requires knowledge of the initial stress conditions in the ground, the constitutive relations for the soil, and the correct or most realistic boundary conditions.

Formulation of problem

Earth pressures are redeveloped during soil displacement (or strains), but until the soil is on the verge of failure (as defined by Mohr's rupture envelope) the stresses are indeterminate. They are also somewhat indeterminate at rupture since it is difficult to simultaneously produce everywhere a plastic equilibrium state in the soil mass, where this is usually a progressive event.

Figure 4-50a shows Mohr's circles for the K_0 condition and at plastic equilibrium. The two circles are drawn having common point A and tangent to the rupture line, and both represent a state of plastic equilibrium in plane strain. One of the other circles such as EA or AF would be a steady-state condition depending on the overconsolidation ratio (OCR).

Initial stresses.   In sedimentary soil, as the buildup of overburden continues there is vertical compression of soil because of increase in vertical stress, but there should be no significant horizontal compression. In this case the horizontal earth stress is less than the vertical, and for sand deposits K_0 usually ranges between 0.4 and 0.5 (values of ϕ' between 27° and 34°). Thus, for initial loading the expression proposed by Jaky is confirmed (Bishop, 1958) so that

$$K_0 = 1 - \sin \phi' \qquad (4\text{-}14)$$

With the exception of certain soils such as normally consolidated soils, the initial effective stresses are seldom known with confidence. There is also evidence that the horizontal stress can exceed the vertical if the soil has been heavily preloaded in a process where the stress remained locked and did not dissipate when the preload was removed. The coefficient K_0 may now approach 3, and under certain conditions it may come close to K_p (Brooker and Ireland, 1965; Skempton, 1961).

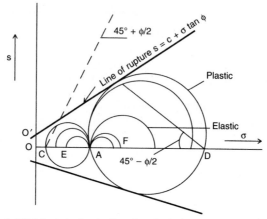

(a) Mohr's circles for the K_o and at plastic equilibrium (or rupture).

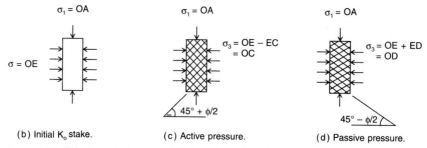

(b) Initial K_o stake.   (c) Active pressure.   (d) Passive pressure.

Figure 4-50   Elastic and plastic equilibrium; in both active and passive condition the slip lines are idealized.

Referring to Fig. 4-50a where the applied stresses OA and OE are vertical and horizontal stress, respectively, by definition $K_0 = OE/OA$.

Constitutive equations.   Although the nature of constitutive equations for sands and normally or lightly overconsolidated clays is adequately understood, natural soils or soils placed under field conditions are not always fully represented, since they may display anisotropic, nonhomogeneous, and time-dependent characteristics (see also the foregoing sections). In addition, discontinuities give rise to size effects in response to loading.

Boundary conditions.   These are more reliable if they represent actual construction procedures and a pragmatic interaction between structure and soil, including the bracing.

Where the prediction of deformations is essential, the problem is usually approached with linear elastic theory. If maximum lateral pressure or resistance is the criterion, limiting equilibrium methods are typically used to estimate these forces. In this case little, if any, consideration is or can be given to actual deformation and associated movement. In other instances, such as braced walls, movement is usually reduced if not completely stopped, and this affects the distribution of lateral earth stresses. In this case, semiempirical methods are used to arrive at a reasonable solution. Likewise, preload and system stiffness affect movement and cause changes in the magnitude and distribution of earth loads.

Elastic methods of analysis

This procedure involves both linear and nonlinear stress-strain relations. The former requires judgment in selecting an appropriate modulus. Nonlinear analysis should include studies of several stress paths to select relations that are not unduly restrictive. Linear analysis can be used to calculate both small and relatively large deformations by changing the elastic modulus. Problems involving large deformations and simulation of yielding are better approached with nonlinear models.

Linear analysis.   A good example for linear analysis is excavation with a high factor of safety and small deformations. If this excavation is in clay, base failure will occur under undrained condition if

$$\gamma H = N_c s_u \qquad (4\text{-}15)$$

which is similar to Eq. (4-2), and all symbols are similar. Terzaghi and Peck (1967) have introduced the dimensionless number $N = \gamma H/s_u$ as an index of probable base failure. If $N = 3$ to 4, some plastic yielding is likely, but according to Alberro (1969) for $N < 4$ pressures and deformations can be computed from elastic theory. If $N_c = 6$ is taken as typical for most excavations and $N = 3$ to 4, a criterion is manifested for the applicability (lower bound) of elastic theory (Morgenstern and Eisenstein, 1970). Until recently, however, this criterion was limited to excavations in deep soft and medium clays.

The effect of K_0 on stresses and deformations is documented by DiBiagio (1966) in finite-element schemes. Maximum heave appears to be insensitive to K_0, but maximum lateral displacement is basically linearly dependent on this coefficient. If K_0 is taken as unity for soft clays with initial undrained modulus 1500 lb/in², the maximum lateral displacement in an excavation 25 ft deep will be 3 in, but for stiff clays with modulus 1500 lb/in² it is only 0.3 in. It follows, therefore,

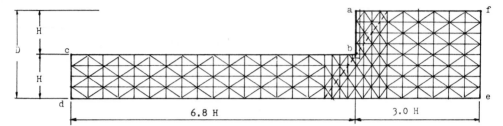

Boundary Conditions
a-b : Wall, rigid and smooth, allowed to yield
b-c : Free surface
c-d : Fixed side boundary, rigid and smooth
d-e : Base, rigid and either rough or smooth
e-f : Fixed side boundary, rigid and smooth
f-a : Free surface

Figure 4-51 Excavation supported by a rigid, smooth wall; element idealization of a problem of earth pressure behind a yielding wall. (*From Morgenstern and Eisenstein, 1970.*)

that if elastic theory is used, maximum displacement should not exceed a few inches. When large displacements are expected, considerable yielding should be predicted, so that either the modulus should be adjusted or nonlinear relations introduced.

The significant effect of boundary conditions is confirmed in studies by Morgenstern and Eisenstein (1970), and an example is shown in Fig. 4-51. The wall supporting the excavation is rigid but smooth with respect to vertical displacement and can simulate a diaphragm wall with internal bracing or anchors. Earth pressures are computed from elastic theory for differing boundary conditions. The soil behind the wall has the following parameters: $E = 65,000$ lb/in²; Poisson's ratio $\mu = 0.3$; and bulk density $\gamma = 125$ lb/ft³. The initial earth stresses are derived from the relation

$$K_0 = \frac{\mu}{1 - \mu} \qquad (4\text{-}16)$$

so that for $\mu = 0.3$, $K_0 = 0.43$.

Earth pressures against the wall are computed for the position of zero lateral yield when the excavation of height H is taken down to a rigid base. As expected, the computed lateral pressures for both rough and smooth base are the same as the initial horizontal stresses (Fig. 4-52), since neither lateral nor vertical displacement has occurred and the presence of excavation has no influence on the stress environment.

Figure 4-52 shows also earth pressure distribution for the condition of no lateral yield but with the rigid base at distance $0.5H$ and H beneath the base of excavation. In these cases earth pressure distri-

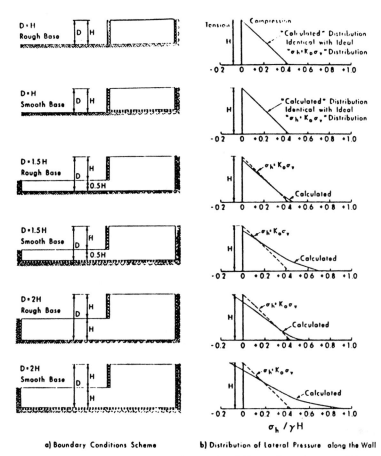

a) Boundary Conditions Scheme   **b) Distribution of Lateral Pressure along the Wall**

Figure 4-52 Lateral pressure distribution for different boundary conditions, wall of Fig. 4-51; condition of no lateral yield. (*From Morgenstern and Eisenstein, 1970.*)

bution changes markedly, although the wall has not moved, because of the ability and freedom of materials to flow beneath the wall. This effect is amplified when the rigid base changes to smooth and is located deeper below excavation level (cases $D = 1.5H$ and $D = 2H$). Interestingly, the maximum horizontal pressure at the base increases while stresses at the top reverse to tension.

For the same example lateral earth stresses are computed for wall displacement toward excavation $0.0025H$, which is less than the displacement necessary for the active state. The results are shown in Fig. 4-53. The boundary condition along the rigid base is now more significant when it is close to the base of excavation. As excavation is carried down to the rigid base the pressure behind the wall is reduced by 50

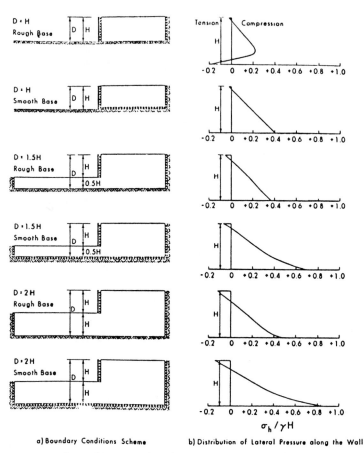

a) Boundary Conditions Scheme   b) Distribution of Lateral Pressure along the Wall

Figure 4-53 Lateral pressure distribution for different boundary conditions, wall of Fig. 9-51: pressure diagrams for wall yielding $0.0025H$ toward active state. (*From Morgenstern and Eisenstein, 1970.*)

percent from the K_0 state for the rough base, but only by 10 percent for the smooth base. For the former, the larger reduction is partly due to the presence of tension along the base, but in reality this is not feasible. A nonlinear stress distribution is developed as the rigid base is taken below excavation level.

Likewise, lateral earth stresses are computed for a small displacement $0.0025H$ toward the ground approaching the passive state and are shown in Fig. 4-54. The passive resistance increases considerably owing to the presence of the rough rigid base, but the effect of conditions along the rigid base decreases as this base is taken farther down.

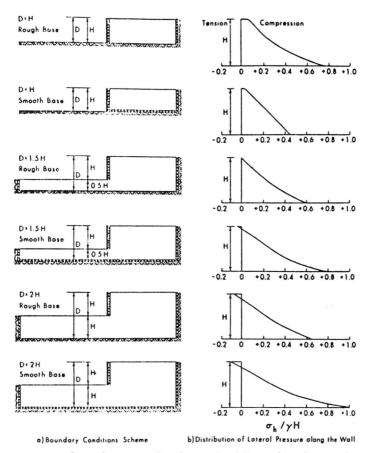

a) Boundary Conditions Scheme   b) Distribution of Lateral Pressure along the Wall

Figure 4-54 Lateral pressure distribution for different boundary conditions, wall of Fig. 4-51; pressure diagrams for wall displacement toward the ground (passive state) 0.0025*H*. (*From Morgenstern and Eisenstein.*)

Earth pressures in the elastic range are sensitive to changes in lateral deformations when the rough rigid base is close to excavation level.

Nonlinear analysis. For such soils as loose sands and compacted clays, it is difficult to fit material behavior within the scope of linear analysis, even with a high factor of safety. Typical examples are walls associated with fill operations. Nonlinear support behavior and nonlinear soil resistance have been considered and yield satisfactory results if properly represented.

The analysis requires successful interpretation of results from triaxial compression tests to establish realistic stress-strain relations. Finite-element techniques are used to solve the problem incrementally.

Limiting equilibrium methods

Referring to Fig. 4-50 where $\sigma_1 = OA =$ vertical stress, we have the definition $\sigma_h = K_0\sigma_1$, which is triangular since at any depth z the vertical stress is $\sigma_1 = \gamma z = \sigma_v$.

Active state.   Considering a normally consolidated cohesionless soil in dry condition, the active pressure shown in Fig. 4-50c is represented by the stress $\sigma_3 = \sigma_h$. In this case

$$\sigma_h = K_a\sigma_v \qquad (4\text{-}17)$$

where $K_a = \tan^2(45 - \phi/2) = (1 - \sin\phi)/(1 + \sin\phi) =$ coefficient of active pressure.

A major point of interest is the very small displacement required to reduce the earth pressure in sand to almost the full active state. This is less than -0.4 percent, but a horizontal compression of 0.4 percent produces only about one-half the maximum passive resistance.

Passive state.   Likewise, this state is represented in Fig. 4-50d where $\sigma_3 = \sigma_h$ again. In this case

$$\sigma_h = K_p\sigma_v \qquad (4\text{-}18)$$

where $K_p = \tan^2(45 + \phi/2) = (1 + \sin\phi)/(1 - \sin\phi) =$ coefficient of passive pressure. If the difference in the friction angle ϕ is ignored, $K_p = 1/K_a$. Usually, a movement of 1.0 to 2.0 percent is necessary to produce a full passive condition, but it may be much higher.

Soil with water.   If a soil is saturated with static water, the coefficient of lateral earth stress is related to the effective vertical stress $\sigma_v' = \sigma_v - u$, where u is the pore water pressure. The foregoing relations are modified as follows:

Active: $\sigma_h = K_a'\sigma_v' + \gamma_w h$ (4-17a)

Passive: $\sigma_h = K_p'\sigma_v' + \gamma_w h$ (4-18a)

where $\gamma_w h$ is the static water pressure at depth h and K_a', K_p' are for friction angle ϕ'.

Limiting equilibrium theories.   Invariably, these are formulated on the concept of soil strength expressed by the Coulomb-Mohr failure criterion, as presented in Fig. 4-50. They differ, however, in the shape and location of the failure surface and in the application of statics. The Coulomb theory is based on the concept of a failure wedge with a planar surface that passes through the toe of the wall. A second assumption is that the thrust on the wall acts on some known direction, so that the resultant thrust can be determined by statics. A further assumption is that there is wall friction; i.e., as the failure wedge moves with respect to the backface of the wall a friction force is developed between wall and soil under a friction angle δ. The Rankine theory assumes no wall friction, and thus the direct relationship between vertical overburden stress and lateral pressure is expressed as in Eqs. (4-17) and (4-18). Otherwise stated, the presence of the wall introduces no changes in shear stresses at the wall-soil interface. Other theories are based on logarithmic spiral slip surfaces, slip along a circular surface, and the concept of slices. In the Sokolovski method (Sokolovski, 1965) the equations of equilibrium and the failure criterion are explicitly satisfied for each infinitesimal element responding to failure.

Active and passive state in soil with cohesion.   The foregoing theory is modified to include soil with cohesion. The effect of cohesion on the passive thrust is assumed to be applied at a rate that does not cause excess pore pressure. Setting $N_\phi = (1 + \sin \phi)/(1 - \sin \phi) = 1/[\tan^2 (45 - \phi/2)]$, the following are derived:

Passive state: $$\sigma_h = N_\phi \sigma_v + 2c\sqrt{N_\phi} \qquad (4\text{-}19)$$

so that with cohesion c present N_ϕ is not the ratio of horizontal to vertical stress. The second term of Eq. (4-19) has two components: a factor that has a linear variation with depth, and a factor that represents a constant stress with depth, so that the resultant thrust is located between the midpoint and the lower-third point.

Active state: $$\sigma_h = \sigma_v \frac{1}{N_\phi} - 2c \frac{1}{\sqrt{N_\phi}} \qquad (4\text{-}19a)$$

Equations (4-19) and (4-19a) are easily modified for effective stress and water pressure. Note that $1/N_\phi = K_a$.

Although Eq. (4-19a) indicates a negative pressure near the top of the wall, meaning that the soil adheres to the interface, this adherence is doubtful in practice. It is better, therefore, to ignore cohesion and assume a fictitious triangular pressure using an arbitrarily selected friction angle.

TABLE 4-4   Usual Range of Earth Pressure
Coefficients

State of stress	Cohesionless soil	Cohesive soil
Passive	3–14	1–2
At rest	0.4–0.6	0.4–0.8
Active	0.22–0.33	0.5–1

The strain necessary to bring a clay to the limit state is a matter that has been modestly investigated. To produce the active state about 1 to 2 percent strain is required, but much more is necessary to produce the passive state. A usual range of earth pressure coefficients is shown in Table 4-4.

Stresses for undrained conditions.   A special case is $\phi = 0$ that applies to a saturated soil undergoing undrained loading. The analysis is now simpler and is carried out using $N_\phi = 1$ and replacing c by s_u. The corresponding critical-failure plane is inclined at 45°.

Analysis with friction.   Wall friction is one of the two factors that have a critical effect on the coefficients of earth pressure. The other is seepage pressure. The commonly used Rankine theory does not use wall friction and tends to give a somewhat more conservative (larger wall pressure) solution than the Coulomb analysis.

A complete evaluation of the active and passive state with friction becomes complicated owing to the variation and pattern in the inclination of the slip planes. Solutions have been presented by Janbu (1957, 1972), Sokolovski (1944), and Harr (1966). The role of friction is also discussed by Xanthakos (1979, 1991).

Wall movement and earth pressures.   Clough and Duncan (1991) have compiled Table 4-5 from experimental data and finite-element analyses. These results give approximately magnitudes of wall movement required to reach minimum active and maximum passive earth pressure conditions, and supplement the guidelines presented in the foregoing sections. Relevant conclusions are: (1) The required movement for the extreme conditions is approximately proportional to the wall height; (2) the movement required to reach the maximum passive pressure is about 10 times that required for the minimum active pressure, for the same wall height; and (3) the movement required to reach limit conditions for dense and incompressible soils is smaller than that for loose and compressible soils.

The value of earth pressure coefficients varies with displacement, but after the limit value is reached these coefficients remain constant

TABLE 4-5 **Approximate Magnitudes of Movements Required to Reach Minimum Active and Maximum Passive Earth Pressure Conditions**

	Values of Δ/H^*	
Type of backfill	Active	Passive
Dense sand	0.001	0.01
Medium dense sand	0.002	0.02
Loose sand	0.004	0.04
Compacted silt	0.002	0.02
Compacted lean clay	0.01†	0.05†
Compacted fat clay	0.01†	0.05†

After Clough and Dancan, 1991.

$^*\Delta$ = movement of top of wall required to reach minimum active or maximum passive pressure, by tilting or lateral translation

H= height of wall

†Under stress conditions close to the minimum active or maximum passive earth pressures, cohesive soils creep continually. The movements shown would produce active or passive pressures only temporarily. With time the movements would continue if pressures remain constant. If movement remains constant, active pressures will increase with time, approaching the at-rest pressure, and passive pressures will decrease with time, approaching values on the order of 40 percent of the maximum short-term passive pressure.

and independent of further displacement. The rate of pressure change also varies with the type of soil, so that the pressures in dense sand change more quickly with wall movement. These effects are illustrated in Fig. 4-55 for various types of sand.

Semiempirical methods

Apparent pressure diagrams. The introduction of apparent pressure diagrams (Peck, 1969) was not intended to represent the actual distribution of earth stresses but instead constitutes a method of calculating strut loads that might be approached but not exceeded during excavation. The origin of these diagrams was the measurement of strut loads behind flexible walls. The behavior of these walls during excavation suggests a case of rotation about the top, as opposed to rotation about the tip or lateral translation, which is the assumed motion in the Coulomb and Rankine theories.

Strut loads in sand. The probable explanation of the considerable increase of the lateral pressure near the top is the condition of true

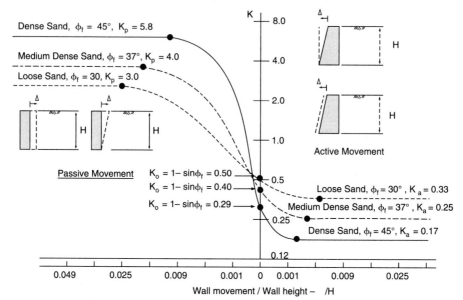

Figure 4-55 Relationship between wall movement and earth pressure. (*After Clough and Duncan, 1991.*)

arching. A stable condition of arching requires a major rotational movement about the top while the wall itself sustains the arch and remains unyielding. The squeezing of grains occurs as long as they are hard and nondeformable; hence it cannot develop in plastic clays. In this case, the pressure diagram used to determine strut loads is as shown in Fig. 4-56a. A condition favoring arching is the nature of sand

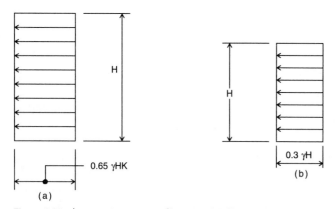

Figure 4-56 Apparent pressure diagram: (*a*) Excavation in sand. (*b*) Excavation in stiff clay or when $N < 4$; H = excavation depth. (*From Peck, 1969.*)

deposits that are not too loose. If the sand is submerged and lacks the apparent cohesion of moist sand, the tendency of the soil to wedge will densify the materials before an arch can develop.

From Fig. 4-56a the total thrust assumed to be transmitted to the struts is $0.65\gamma H^2 K_a$ or 30 percent higher than the total active thrust. It is, however, less than the total thrust based on the K_0 condition, and the denser the soil the greater the difference.

Strut loads in clay. The behavior of an excavation in clay is influenced by the stability number $N = \gamma H/s_u$ (Peck, 1969; Flaate and Peck, 1973). Where $N < 4$, earth pressure theories should not be used since they may reduce the theoretical pressure to zero, which conflicts with reality. This discrepancy arises probably because a theory of plastic equilibrium cannot be applied to a material that is not in a plastic state. Instead, Peck proposed a trapezoidal diagram with a width $0.2\gamma H$ to $0.4\gamma H$ giving a total thrust $0.75\gamma KH^2$ ($K = 0.2$ to 0.4) for $N < 4$. Although a different system behavior might be expected with a stiff wall, the absence of plastic conditions suggests an initial similarity in strut loads. Hence this author modified the Peck diagram to the diagram shown in Fig. 4-56b.

The second distinction was made when $N > 7$. In the cases monitored the soft clay extended to considerable depth below excavation level, and in some instances the clay was softer below the bottom than above. Under these conditions inward movement and settlement were considerable. Strut load measurements showed that the envelope apparent pressure would be approached if in the modified Rankine-Résal coefficient $K_a = 1 - m4s_u/\gamma H$ the value of m was taken as 0.4. This was consistent with the soft clay and the fact that the depth of the failure surface is not necessarily limited to the depth of the cut. A further explanation was offered by Bjerrum et al. (1972) who demonstrated that wall deflection beneath the excavation leads to arching and transfer of earth pressure to the stiffer part of the system, i.e., the strutted part. If the cut is underlain by stiff material expected to limit movement, the depth of the plastic zone may not exceed the depth of excavation, and in this case the apparent earth pressure is more likely to be governed by the unmodified Rankine-Résal coefficient $K_a = (1 - 4s_u/\gamma H)$ and the width of the apparent pressure diagram is $\gamma H - 4s_u$.

The application of these principles to diaphragm walls must recognize the explicit effect of the embedded portion, the considerable wall stiffness, the probable wall behavior according to flexural beam theories, and construction imperfections causing erratic variations in strut loads. Thus, for soft to medium clay this author has suggested using the Peck diagrams but modified as shown in Fig. 4-57.

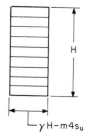

Figure 4-57 Recommended apparent-pressure diagram for determining strut loads for diaphragm walls in soft to medium clay. H = excavation depth, m = 1 normally, and m = 0.4 where large movement is expected and the soft clay extends to a considerable distance below the excavation level. The wall does not penetrate into the stiff layer.

Referring to Fig. 4-56b, the value of $0.3\gamma H$ is justified from a consideration of the total envelope carried by the struts. This load is $0.3\gamma H^2$ and is equal to the total lateral pressures at rest with K_0 = 0.6, which is the earth coefficient for most normally consolidated clays. This satisfies the criterion that the capacity of the system should not be less than the earth load at rest.

Referring to Fig. 4-57, we note that for soft clay (s_u = 500 lb/ft^2 or 2.5 t/m^2), and unless the excavation is very shallow in which case the diagram normally would not be applicable, estimating the strut loads using m = 0.4 is more conservative than using at rest pressure (ϕ = 0, c = 0) redistributed to a rectangular diagram. This difference may be greater than 50 percent. If m = 1 is used and H < 35 ft, the diagram of Fig. 4-57 should not be used since it is less conservative and the expected wall movement is very small. Instead, a redistributed pressure diagram using K = 1 and c = 0 may be more appropriate.

Increased active earth pressure. Several investigators have suggested that where the expected movement should not be sufficient to produce the active state, the lateral earth stress may be obtained from a combination of active and at rest earth pressure as follows

$$K_{eh} = (1 - k)K_a + kK_0 \tag{4-20}$$

where $0 \leqslant k \leqslant 1$, K_{eh} = increased active earth pressure coefficient, and K_a, K_0 are as previously.

Earth pressure in braced walls. Braced walls are discussed in Sec. 4-3, and include bracing with rakers, slopes and berms, the permanent structure, wall embedment, and ground anchors. Restraining effects are manifested by system stiffness and wall fixity against rotation or translation. Both these mechanisms can be available with the bracing techniques commonly used for diaphragm walls.

Four idealized types of wall behavior are shown in Fig. 4-58. The cantilever wall shown in a depends on embedment for stability. The assumed linear earth stress distribution is consistent with wall movement and approaches the active state. The wall in b is supported elast-

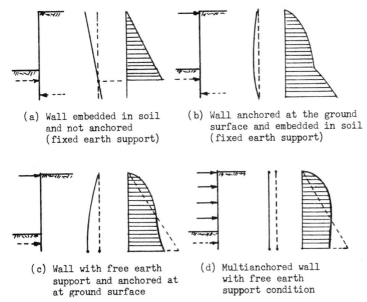

(a) Wall embedded in soil
    and not anchored
    (fixed earth support)

(b) Wall anchored at the ground
    surface and embedded in soil
    (fixed earth support)

(c) Wall with free earth
    support and anchored at
    at ground surface

(d) Multianchored wall
    with free earth
    support condition

Figure 4-58 Basic types of wall supporting excavations; various restraints against rotation and translation.

ically at the ground surface and embedded at the lower end. Its deformation resembles essentially a simple beam, since there are two points in the wall that do not displace laterally. The wall shown in c is also supported at the top, but its small embedment allows some lateral movement, so that stress redistribution occurs to a greater extent. Multibraced or multianchored walls shown in d would be expected to move essentially in translation so that with some preloading the resulting earth pressure diagram deviates from the triangular distribution and approaches a rectangular shape.

For the wall systems shown in Fig. 4-58a and b, an analysis based on the active state is consistent with system behavior as long as the expected movement warrants this condition. For the system shown in Fig. 4-58c and d, the magnitude and distribution of earth pressures will depend on the interaction of local factors, such as the application and level of preload or prestressing, degree of fixity or restraint, system stiffness, and construction procedure. Probable pressure distribution patterns are shown in Fig. 4-59. Within certain limits, but more particularly in connection with the rigidity of the excavation wall, a desired earth pressure distribution can be manifested by a particular arrangement of the bracing and the amount of preload. For example, if for a multianchored wall the distribution must be changed toward the top to produce a resultant that lies in the upper half, it will only be necessary to make the upper anchors longer than the lower ones.

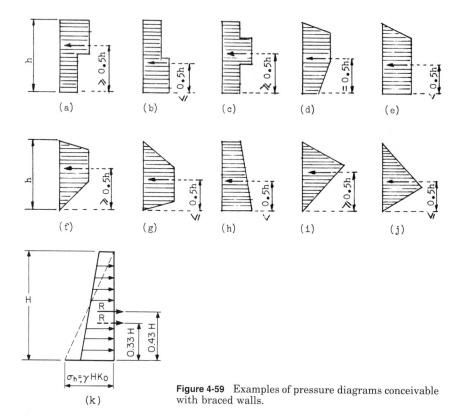

Figure 4-59 Examples of pressure diagrams conceivable with braced walls.

The same effect is produced if the preload level is higher in the upper rows.

Location of horizontal resultant. Data obtained from experimental investigations and field observations appear to confirm that the horizontal resultant pressure, commonly assumed to be located at one-third of total height for triangular distributions, has in reality a point of application above the lower third point (Terzaghi, 1934; Clausen and Johansen, 1972; Sherif et al., 1982).

Terzaghi (1934) found that the resultant was applied at $0.40H$ to $0.45H$ from the bottom of the wall, where H = total wall height and height of pressure diagram. Clausen and Johansen (1972) suggested the same range of resultant locations, and Sherif et al. (1982) recommend $0.42H$ for walls in static active condition. Duncan et al. (1990) suggest that the location of the resultant may be assumed to be $0.40H$ above the bottom of the wall.

Based on a limited record of field studies, Xanthakos (1979) suggested a modified pressure diagram for the short-term condition of diaphragm walls braced at the top with the permanent floor intended to prevent or minimize movement. Whereas the total resultant pressure should be unchanged from the at rest condition, it appears conceivable that the stresses near the top will exceed the at rest values while the stresses near the bottom will be less than the at rest pressures. Accordingly, walls braced at the top by the permanent floor or by other rigid bracing installed before excavation should be checked for the temporary stress diagram shown in Fig. 4-59k.

The purpose of this stress diagram is to recognize the results of field measurements; hence it represents a semiempirical procedure. It is recommended for situations where the soil consists of dry sand or soft to medium saturated clay. This loading may develop toward the end of excavation and persist for some time. It is not an apparent earth pressure diagram but the original earth stress resultant redistributed as shown, with the initial resultant moved from the lower third point $(0.33H)$ to the $0.43H$ point. The ordinate at the top and the base can be computed from statics since both the magnitude and location of the resultant R are known.

4-8   Further Topics on Earth Pressures

Base restraint and passive resistance

For a diaphragm wall restrained by embedment below excavation level but not socketed in rock, equilibrium is satisfied if the passive resistance offers a restraining force with a factor of safety n. This is expressed as

$$F_a \leqslant F_p = P_s/n \qquad (4\text{-}21)$$

where F_a = acting force, F_p = permissible resistance, and P_s = passive resistance.

The parameter F_a is one of the following: (1) for elastically embedded walls F_a is the sum of the positive spring forces (no tension is allowed); (2) for walls considered pinned at the level of the resultant passive force, F_a is the soil reaction or the passive resistance; (3) for fully restrained walls F_a is the shear force at height z_0 corresponding to zero load point, plus the restraining force at the theoretical bottom (the force required to maintain horizontal equilibrium), plus the water pressure between z_0 and the theoretical bottom end.

The parameter F_p is one of the following: (1) for elastically embedded walls or free to rotate at the base and under the condition of earth pressure at rest, F_p is given by the area of the passive earth pressure triangle $A_r = A_p/n - A_a$, where A_p/n is the area of the passive pressure diagram divided by n and A_a in the area of the active pressure diagram; (2) for completely fixed wall F_p is estimated according to appropriate equations, distributed triangularly, and superimposed upon the effective earth pressure.

Statical analogy of wall

The statical analogy of a braced wall is similar to a continuous beam, considered fixed against lateral displacement at the support points and acted upon by earth and water pressures. Wall stability is based therefore on small-deflection theories and first-order analysis. Concentrated forces or moments may act along the wall height. The top of the wall can be assumed to be free, pinned, or fixed against rotation and lateral displacement. The condition of the bottom support may be assumed as one of the following: (1) bottom supported by an elastic spring, and (2) bottom restrained according to Blum's theory. Beneath the point of zero pressure, a triangular counterpressure is assumed.

The method of fixed earth support

A diaphragm wall with free top and fixed bottom is shown in Fig. 4-60 with the corresponding earth pressure diagrams. Passive resistance is developed on the left and right side of the wall, and the wall embedment is sufficient to yield a fixed bottom condition. The two components E_{pL} and E_{pr} can be calculated if the transition from e_{pL} to e_{pr} is known. An exact analysis, therefore, is not possible. For a wall pinned at the top and fixed at the bottom, an approximate analysis can be carried out with sufficient accuracy using Blum's theory.

Blum's elastic line theory by graphical procedure.   The loading diagram shown in Fig. 4-61 is based on the adjacent soil profile. The diagram

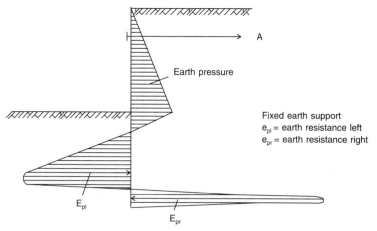

Figure 4-60   Distribution of active earth pressure and passive resistance; wall restrained at anchor level only, and bottom fixed.

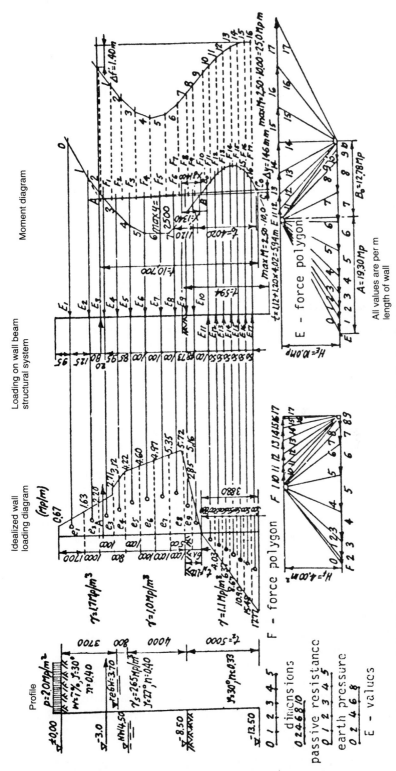

Figure 4-61 Design of singly anchored wall by means of graphical solution for bending moments. *(From Otta et al., 1981.)*

is constructed using the wall, earth, water, and anchor elevations in unit lengths, the lateral earth pressure in force per unit area and the total lateral load in force per unit width of wall (Otta et al., 1981). To take into account any increase in the passive pressure when the wall is inserted into undisturbed, compact earth, the passive earth coefficient may be increased accordingly. The passive resistance on the left side of the wall is considered fully effective to the theoretical bottom point, and the slope of this portion of the loading diagram is given by $(1.5K_{ph} - K_{ah})$ where the subscript h denotes pressure due to horizontal earth volume. At the bottom point the passive resistance is replaced by a concentrated load whose magnitude is determined graphically.

The upper support (anchor or bracing) is assumed nonyielding pinned support, and the bottom (foot) of the wall is considered fully fixed. The embedment t_z is initially assumed and later corrected in the course of the solution.

The wall height is divided into a number of convenient sections, not necessarily of equal width. For each area, the earth pressure is expressed as a concentrated load acting through the center of gravity. A vector diagram (E force polygon) is then drawn as shown. On a horizontal base line, commencing at the right and moving from left to right, the successive loads for the sections from the bottom to the top (E_{10} to E_1) of the equivalent beam are laid off end to end. A pole distance H_E is chosen to some convenient scale approximately equal to $\frac{1}{3}$ (ΣE_a), and the remainder of the loads E_{11} to E_{17} is laid off as shown. The lateral location of the pole E_1 is chosen at any convenient location.

The moment diagram is then constructed beginning at point 0 and drawing the first segment parallel to ray number 1. The moment diagram is completed by adding succeeding segments parallel to rays 2 through 17, respectively. Point A is located by extending the first segment until it intersects the anchor line. Point B is fixed as the intersection of the moment diagram with the elevation of zero force on the loading diagram. A line defined by points A and B is extended to locate point C as the intersection with the moment diagram. The maximum moment, for example, segment 6, is given by the y ordinate (2500 mm) times 10.0 Mp, or 25.0 Mp-m.

A graphical method for constructing the deflection diagram reflects the condition that the area enclosed by the moment diagram can be designated as an "elastic weight" with which the beam is loaded. The deflection curve bears the same relation to the moment curve as the moment curve does to the pressure diagram. These elastic weights F_1, F_2, etc., pass through the centers of gravity of the strips into which the area between the moment curve and the base line is divided. These strips need not be of equal width, and their boundaries are the lines of action of the loads E_4, E_5, etc. Each value plotted is equal to the area of the appropriate strip between the moment diagram and the base line. In drawing the F force diagram it is convenient to start at the bottom of the beam, i.e., at F_{17}. In order to make the base line of the deflection diagram vertical it is necessary to have the last ray F_{17} of the F force diagram vertical. The zero line of the deflection diagram intersects the anchor line at a distance $\Delta f' = 1.40$ m from ray 17 extended.

A potential yield point is A. Since, however, the wall must be fixed at A (unyielding anchor support) the final closing line must pass through A so that $\Delta f' = 0$. Thus the closing line must be displaced at the foot of the wall by an amount Δy either to the left or to the right of point C. If the side AC of the error triangle ACC_0 is taken as 1, its area is obtained as $F = L\Delta y/2$. If this area is assumed to act as a load, the necessary deflection $\Delta f' = 0$ will result. It follows, therefore, that

$$\Delta y = \Delta f' = \frac{3\,H_p}{l^2} \tag{4-22}$$

or

$$\Delta y = 1.4(3)(4)/(10.7)^2 = 146 \text{ mm}$$

By displacing C by $\Delta y = 146$ mm we obtain point C_0. If $\Delta f'$ lies to the left of the base line, Δy must be the distance to the right of C, and vice versa. In this manner the correct position of the closing line and of t_0 is obtained. The depth of embedment is now

$$t = t_N + 1.2t_0$$

or $t = 1.12 + 1.2(4.02) = 5.94$ m, where the factor 1.2 designates a margin of safety. By transferring the final line to the E force diagram we obtain the anchor tensile force $A = 19.3$ Mp. The maximum bending moment is obtained from the moment area, i.e.,

$$M_{\max} = y_{\max}(H_E) \tag{4-23}$$

Blum's equivalent beam method.   This is a simplified form of the graphical solution. Since the moment distribution of the wall (free at the top and fixed by embedment) shows a zero point below the base, the wall can be replaced by two beams hinged together at the point of zero moment. The upper part is considered a simply supported beam, and the lower part a beam pinned at one end and fixed at the other. Since the design of the wall is governed by the maximum moment, it merely is sufficient to design the upper beam as shown in Fig. 4-62. The point

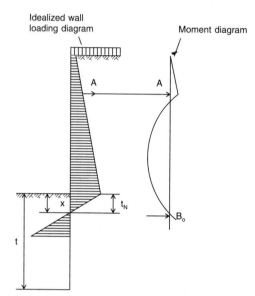

Idealized wall
loading diagram

Moment diagram

Figure 4-62 Blum's equivalent beam method, fixed-earth support.

of zero moment B_0 (the lower end of the beam) is assumed to coincide with the point of zero loading. The beam shown in Fig. 4-62 is then statically determinate with the assumed loading and end conditions.

The theoretical embedment t_0 can be calculated from the equilibrium conditions for the lower beam shown in Fig. 4-63. The moment M at distance z below B_0 is given by

$$M = B_0 z - \gamma(K_{ph} - K_{ah}) \frac{z^3}{6} \qquad (4\text{-}24)$$

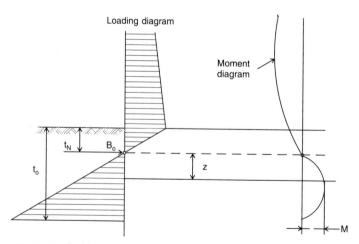

Figure 4-63 Loading and moment distribution, fixed-earth support.

and for $M = 0$ we obtain

$$z_0 = \sqrt{\frac{6B_0}{\gamma(K_{ph} - K_{ah})}} \qquad (4\text{-}25)$$

and

$$t_0 = t_N + z_0 \qquad (4\text{-}26)$$

Thus, for a factor of safety n, the wall embedment is

$$t = t_N + n\sqrt{\frac{6B_0}{\gamma(K_{ph} - K_{ah})}} \qquad (4\text{-}27)$$

The maximum moment is calculated at the point of zero shear. For soil with alternating layers, especially near the base, the point of zero moment (hence the theoretical embedment) can be estimated approximately only.

The method of free earth support

The free-earth method assumes that the wall is rigid and may rotate about the bracing level, so that failure occurs by rotation about the bracing point. Passive pressure develops in the soil in front of the wall, and active pressure develops behind the wall. After the theoretical embedment is computed, its value may be increased 30 to 40 percent, or K_p may be divided by an appropriate safety factor (usually 2). The latter approach, although arbitrary, is favored also as a means of reducing movement toward the excavation.

For the limiting case, the passive resistance E_p shown in Fig. 4-64 is just sufficient to balance the effect of the active force E_Q. The con-

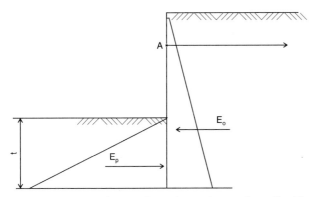

Figure 4-64 Active force and passive resistance in wall with free-earth support.

dition $\Sigma M = 0$ at the brace level gives directly the necessary embedment t, while the condition $\Sigma H = 0$ gives the brace force. The maximum bending moment occurs at $Q = 0$.

Blum's method.   The moment diagram is obtained as for the case with fixed bottom (Fig. 4-61). The closing line, however, is drawn from A to be tangent to the moment diagram. The embedment is determined by point B at which the tangent line touches the moment diagram, as shown in Fig. 4-65.

   In order to determine the loading diagram, the depth of embedment t_z is assumed between 0.5 and 0.6h. The pole distance in the force diagram is set at $0.5\Sigma E_a$. If the tangent point of the line drawn from A to the moment curve cannot be obtained with good accuracy, the embedment is found with the help of the relation

$$t = t_N + \sqrt{\frac{2B}{n}} \qquad (4\text{-}28)$$

Comparison with fixed earth support.   Without fixity at the bottom end of the wall, the maximum bending moment will be greater. Likewise, the embedment for a free-earth condition is less than for a wall with

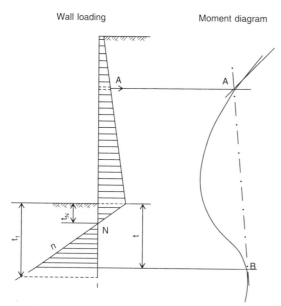

Figure 4-65 Loading and moment diagram in wall with free-earth support.

fixed end support. The choice between the two methods of analysis must therefore consider the soil conditions. Assuming a wall freely supported at its bottom is justified for firm ground conditions.

Analytical solutions. A wall with free earth support conditions can be considered analytically, based on the diagrams of Fig. 4-66. The two different schemes reflect granular and cohesive soil types. The analysis is carried out by satisfying static equilibrium. For an example solution of this problem reference is made to Bowles (1988).

Walls partially restrained at bottom

If a partial embedment condition is chosen, the analysis is essentially the same as for a wall unrestrained at the bottom. Since in this case the depth of embedment is given, either the position of point C or the value of t_0 can be estimated. Thus

$$t_0 = \frac{t - t_N}{n} \tag{4-29}$$

where n is again the factor of safety. In analyzing a wall with partial fixity, the moment diagram is drawn using Blum's method, and the estimated depth t_0 is inserted. In this manner, point C on the moment

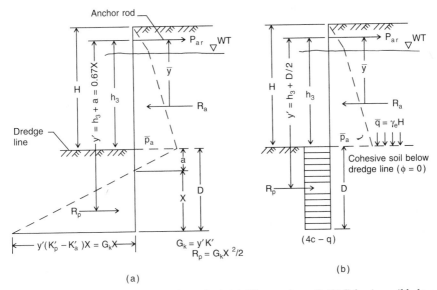

Figure 4-66 Anchored wall free-earth method. (a) All granular soil. (b) Cohesive soil below dredge line with granular-soil backfill.

diagram is determined. By drawing the connecting line AC, the values of B, max y, etc., are found.

Long-term condition

The recommended earth pressures for permanent walls have their origin in the at rest condition. Although during the temporary bracing, the influence of the support system is obvious, it is reasonable to assume that with time the lateral earth stresses ultimately will return to nominal at rest values. These should be linear with depth. The possibility of much larger lateral stresses in overconsolidated clays than existed before construction has been considered but discounted, the contention being that these stresses are somewhat relieved by the horizontal tensile strains accompanying the excavation.

In most instances the earth stresses at rest should be considered in conjunction with full pore pressure unless the site has a permanent groundwater lowering. Good judgment is essential in selecting at rest coefficients, and the subsoil should be grouped on the basis of its origin and index properties.

The method of equivalent tie support for multianchored walls

With little or no prestressing the loads developed in a multianchored wall will correspond to the active state if sufficient movement occurs to yield this condition, or to partially at rest pressures if movement is limited. In any other case, lateral earth stresses behind the walls are manifested by the level and sequence of prestressing.

In practice prestressing is introduced to a level that is quite variable and often arbitrary. A review of methods used to calculate prestress loads is presented in Table 4-6, and evidently these methods cover limiting equilibrium and apparent pressure theories.

TABLE 4-6   Summary of Methods Used to Estimate Prestress Load on Anchors

Reference	Method
Kapp	Percentage of allowable tie-rod load (20–60%)
Mansur and Alizadeh	At-rest pressures
Rizzo et al.	Active to at-rest
Shannon and Strazer	50% anchor yield load
Clough et al. (1974)	Terzaghi-Peck rules ($0.4\gamma H$)
Liu and Dugan	15 × height wall (in lb/ft^2)
Hanna and Matallana	Pressures halfway between active and at rest
Oosterbaan and Gifford	Active pressures
Larsen et al.	Pressures between active and at rest

Multianchored walls may be analyzed by the so-called method of equivalent tie support (James and Jack, 1974). Although this method is based on theory, it presents essentially empirical solutions where flexibility coefficients are used for multiple-anchor analysis.

For a load P that is a function of deformation the following is true:

$$P = \frac{d^4y}{dx^4} EI = yr_s \qquad (4\text{-}30)$$

where r_s is the equivalent spring stiffness of the soil. The wall is considered a series of members connected by nodes. At these points horizontal members simulating the soil stiffness or support joints can be represented as shown in Fig. 4-67. A simple iteration routine and a simplified stress-strain relationship can be used to simulate the elastic-plastic effects of a soil as shown in Fig. 4-68. Estimates of P continue for each deflection profile until convergence to a condition of equilibrium is achieved.

Anchor forces are predicted from a consideration of the temporary effects produced by the passive resistance at intermediate excavation stages. The position and magnitude of a resultant anchor is estimated by treating the wall as a single-anchored structure under the following assumptions: (1) mobilizing and resisting pressures correspond to the Rankine state (this is made for simplicity and is justified where appropriate movement is expected); (2) at failure there is rotation of the wall about a unique point (this enables the use of a simple procedure for calculating the additional anchor force induced when the passive resistance is shifted to a different area during the next excavation stage); and (3) the wall has a length sufficient to provide a factor of safety of 1 against rotation at each excavation stage (this allows estimation of the maximum resultant anchor for free earth support conditions ignoring fixity at the end).

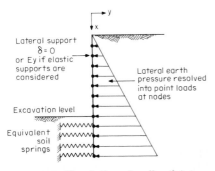

Figure 4-67 Simulation of wall-soil interaction; anchored walls. (*From James and Jack, 1974.*)

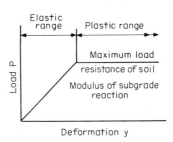

Figure 4-68 Simplified stress-strain relation in elastic-plastic soil.

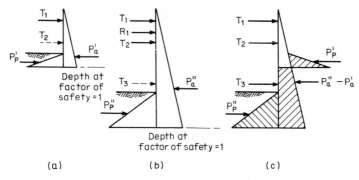

Figure 4-69 Equilibrium conditions for multianchored wall converted to single-anchored wall.

Equilibrium conditions are shown in Fig. 4-69 for various excavation stages. From a we obtain

$$\Sigma F_H = 0 \quad \text{satisfied if } T_1 = P_a' - P_p'$$

$$\Sigma M = 0 \quad \text{satisfied if } M_p' = M_a' \text{ about point } T_1 \tag{4-31}$$

Likewise from part b the following are derived:

$$\Sigma H = 0 \quad \text{satisfied if } T_1 + T_2 = P_a'' - P_p''$$

$$\Sigma M = 0 \quad \text{satisfied if } M_p'' = M_a'' \text{ about the centroid} \\ \text{of } T_1, T_2 \tag{4-32}$$

If R_1 is the resultant of T_1 and T_2 (centroid), then $R_1 = P_a'' - P_p'' = T_1 + T_2$. Combining with (4-31) gives $P_a' - P_p' + T_2 = P_a'' - P_p''$, or

$$T_2 = P_a'' - P_p'' - P_a' + P_p' = (P_a'' - P_a') - (P_p'' - P_p') \tag{4-33}$$

i.e., the additional earth load transmitted to T_2 is the temporary support offered during the previous stage. The equivalent beam load to T_2 is shown hatched in Fig. 4-69c. As long as T_2 is unknown, so are the position and magnitude of R_1. If one is known, the other can be estimated and the initial position checked.

The iteration procedure suggested to ensure convergence to the correct value of the cantilever is illustrated in Fig. 4-70 (James and Jack, 1974). This shows an excavation stage reduced to a position for the

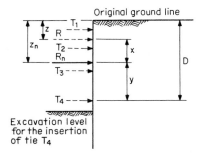

Figure 4-70 Iteration procedure for system equilibrium, multi-tied wall: R = previous resultant tie force; R_n = new resultant tie force; z = previous resultant tie-force level; z_n = new resultant tie-force level; T_1, T_2, T_3, T_4 = individual tie forces.

installation of the force anchor. For equilibrium, the following must be satisfied:

$$\Sigma F_H = 0 \quad \text{or} \quad T_4 = R_n - R$$

$$\Sigma M = 0 \quad \text{or} \quad Rx - T_4 y = 0$$

(4-34)

where $y = D - x - z$ so that

$$f(x) = Rx - T_4 D + T_4 x + T_4 z$$

and substituting in the Newton-Raphson iteration formula gives

$$x_{n+1} = x_n - \frac{Rx - T_4 D + T_4 x + T_4 z}{R + T_4}$$

(4-34a)

where x_{n+1} and x_n are the new and previous estimate of x, respectively. Applications of this procedure in the analysis of multianchored diaphragm walls are reported by Littlejohn and MacFarlane (1974).

4-9 Measured Lateral Earth Stresses on Diaphragm Walls

Walls braced by embedment into rock and by permanent floors

For the deep basement wall of Fig. 4-20 lateral earth pressure measurements were taken for three stages: during concreting of the instrumented panel, during excavation, and for some time after completion of the structure.

The pressure exerted on the sides of the trench during concreting was the hydrostatic pressure of fresh (fluid) concrete only in the upper 5 to 6 m of the column pour and about two-thirds that value in the deeper part of the wall, indicating the obvious effects of the setting process. Upon completion of the pour the total lateral force per linear meter was 235 t.

During excavation the total thrust on the wall decreased from 230 to 170 t/m, but the point of application of the resultant did not vary by more than 1 m. The stress pattern, magnitude, and changes are shown in Fig. 4-71. Excavation to stage II proceeded before the slab at ground level was placed and was accompanied by considerable reduction in earth stresses along the wall. From stage II to stage III the wall was braced at the top by the A floor, but again a decrease in pressure was observed. From stage III to stage IV, with two floors in place, the wall rotated slightly about the B support, and this caused an increase in lateral pressure above that level.

Long-term measurements are shown in Fig. 4-72 for three key stages: day 72, just before the start of excavation; day 344, when the minimum thrust was observed; and day 651. The total lateral earth thrust corresponding to these three stages is 230, 160, and 197 t/m, and the point of application is at the 0.44, 0.45, and 0.44 point of the

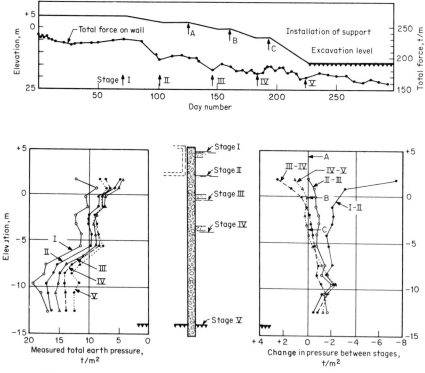

Figure 4-71 Magnitude and changes in total lateral force acting on the wall of Fig. 4-20. (*From DiBiagio and Roti, 1972.*)

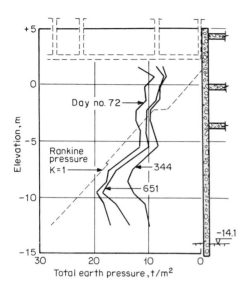

Figure 4-72 Long-term measurements and changes in lateral earth stresses for the wall of Fig. 4-20. (*From DiBiagio and Roti, 1979.*)

wall height from the bottom, respectively, or nearly constant. The dashed line in Fig. 4-72 represents the earth pressure for $\phi = 0$ and ignoring cohesion, so that $K = 1$. The total thrust represented by this line is 248 t/m. Although the resultant thrust on the wall decreased steadily during excavation, it shows a definite tendency to increase again and approach the $K = 1$ condition. Changes in earth stress caused by drainage of the lower part before the rock was sealed are evident in the diagrams.

Walls braced at top and bottom prior to excavation.   Lateral earth stress data are shown in Fig. 4-73 for the Oslo tunnels discussed in previous sections. These structures are similar to Fig. 4-72 in that the walls are braced at the top and bottom before excavation (Karlsrud et al., 1979). Evidently, tunnel excavation caused relatively small earth pressure changes, and as a whole the lateral thrust is close to the theoretical active pressure based on undrained triaxial tests. The pressure distribution, however, shows some arching effects. The earth pressure inside the excavation (passive side) is almost twice the overburden pressure at the end of construction (γz). This relatively high pressure is probably caused mainly by the restraint provided by the cross walls, and to a lesser extent by inward lateral wall displacement. Similar results were obtained at other tunnel locations.

Walls braced with struts.   Figure 4-74*a* shows the measured lateral earth stresses on the walls of the Powell Street Station, BART, for two

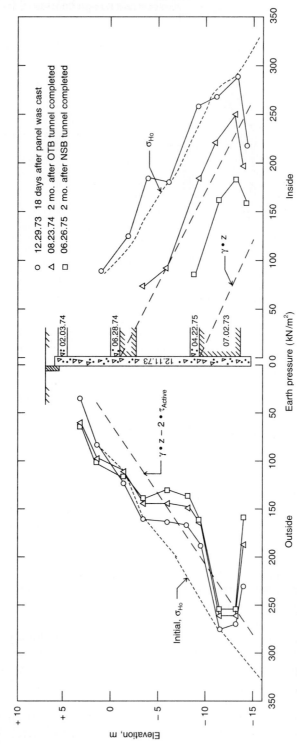

Figure 4-73 Typical earth pressure distribution, Studenterlunden tunnels, Oslo. (*From Karlsrud et al., 1979.*)

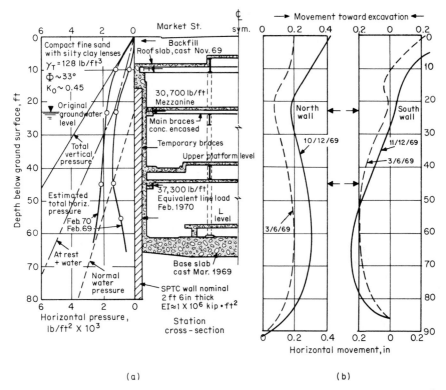

(a)

(b)

Figure 4-74 Powell Street Station, BART: (*a*) Typical section through the structure and pertinent soil data. (*b*) Observed lateral wall movement. (*From Gould, 1970.*)

phases: February 1969 with the excavation nearing completion, and February 1970 with the excavation essentially completed (Gould, 1970). Also shown are the at rest and water pressure $K_0 \gamma' h + \gamma_w h$. These measurements reflect a load variation of 12 percent from the average. The development of strut loads between the two stages is subject to fluctuations because of thermal expansion but shows a tendency for the lateral pressure to increase with time after excavation as the water level was restored.

From the pressure diagram for February 1970 it appears that the loading in the upper part of the profile exceeds the at rest and water pressure, but in the lower part of the profile the loading is less than the at rest and water pressure. For the long-term condition the two resultant pressures tend to be substantially equal.

Figure 4-75 shows field measurements of bracing loads and total pressures for the diaphragm walls of the Civic Center Station, BART.

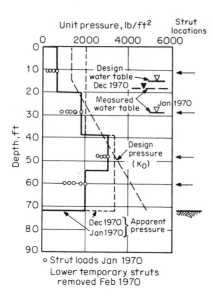

Figure 4-75 Field measurements of bracing loads and total pressure for the diaphragm walls of the Civic Center Station, BART. (*From Thon and Harlan, 1971.*)

The K_0 condition is based on $K_0 = 0.45$, obtained by averaging measured values in the laboratory (Thon and Harlan, 1971).

The apparent pressure derived from the bracing loads is shown for two occasions: (1) during construction, January 1970, with the excavation completed and all bracing levels in place; and (2) for a postconstruction period, December 1970. During construction the water level outside the structure was lower than expected, and the considerable reduction in pressure near the base of excavation may have been caused by a pore pressure decrease in the upper clay layer. The reduction persisted for some time because of the low permeability of the clay. A buildup of pressure is evident (December 1970) owing to the restoration of the water table in the clay layer. The combined soil and water pressure approaches a triangular distribution and is reasonably close to the design curve.

Temporary loads for a strutted excavation. Figure 4-76 shows a section for the diaphragm wall of the basement of the Sears Tower, Chicago (Cunningham and Carpenter, 1975). The excavation is 45 ft deep in soft Chicago clay, but the wall (30 in thick) is extended almost 24 ft below excavation level into stiff clay. The wall was braced during excavation by three tiers of wales and inclined rakers.

The design brace loads shown in Table 4-7 were obtained from the Terzaghi-Peck apparent trapezoidal diagrams. Measured strut loads at the end of excavation are shown for three sides and one corner with all the braces in place. The brace loads for the top tiers are reasonably

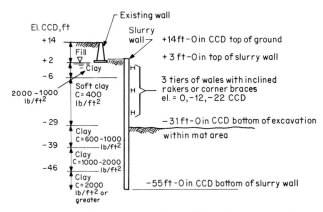

Figure 4-76 Diaphragm wall for Sears Tower basement, Chicago: section through wall and soil data; CCD = Chicago city datum. (*From Cunningham and Carpenter, 1975.*)

close to the design loads, although in some instances much lower or higher. The very low brace loads measured along Wacker Drive are due to the reduced earth surcharge at this location since this is a viaduct structure. Interestingly, the lower tiers received lateral thrusts much lower than predicted from apparent pressure diagrams, in some instances 10 percent of the design loads. This is the composite effect of two factors: (1) bottom bracing was provided by the passive

TABLE 4-7 Estimated and Measured Brace Loads, Sears Tower, Chicago

Mark	Location	Load, lb × 1000	
		Measured	Design
Adams	No. 12 top tier	406	405
	Midtier	250	390
	Bottom tier	73	362
Franklin	No. 31 top tier	295	425
	Midtier	206	461
	Bottom tier	47	405
Adams	No. 11 top tier	461	405
	Midtier	334	390
	Bottom tier	126	362
Wacker	No. 50 top tier	117	250
	Midtier	221	400
	Bottom tier	31	381
16–27	NE first (top) tier	636	500
18–25	Second tier	480	556
19–24	Second tier	350	486
	Third tier	111	486

From Cunningham and Carpenter, 1975.

resistance mobilized behind the considerable embedment in stiff clay, and (2) preload was applied to the upper tiers but not to the lower bracing.

Experimental analysis of strut load distribution. Figure 4-77 shows an experimental enclosure supported by diaphragm walls. The panels are 60 cm (24 in) thick, 5 m (16.5 ft) wide, and 11 m (36 ft) deep. The excavation depth is 7 m (23 ft), and there are seven bracing tiers at 1-m intervals, two sets per panel. The soil is alluvial gravelly sand with bulk density 2.2 Mg/m³, and a friction angle 27 to 35°. The water table is 70 cm below the construction level.

Kastner and Lareal (1974) have investigated the variation and distribution of strut loads, first during excavation and installation of the bracing and then as these loads tended to equalize. The excavation was carried out under minimum lateral movement to warrant the K_0 condition. The struts were installed as soon as the earth moving was

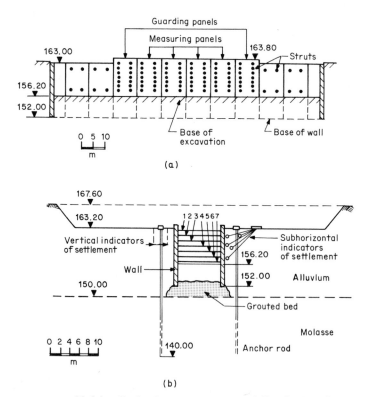

Figure 4-77 Model walls for the measurement and distribution of strut loads: (a) Wall elevation. (b) Section through excavation. (*From Kastner and Lareal, 1974.*)

completed to the appropriate level, and were brought under control for constant length. Each strut was essentially rigid, with a maximum change in length of 0.1 mm.

Apparent pressures are shown in Fig. 4-78a with all tiers in place. Diagram A represents the average estimated pressure (earth plus water) per meter depth of each layer, based on strut load measurements. Diagram B is the apparent pressure (Peck, 1969), and diagram C is the adjusted apparent pressure for effective stress and water pressure. There is considerable difference between apparent and measured pressures. Furthermore, for a system of stiff walls and bracing, differences between strut loads in the same tier are significant. Thus diagram D of Fig. 4-78a shows maximum values measured on one of four pairs of struts. These values are much higher than the average stresses for diagram A and several times the value of the apparent

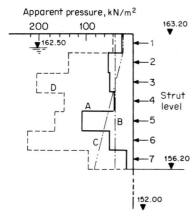

A mean of measured stresses in strut braces
D maximum measured stresses in strut braces
C values given by Peck's modified method
B values given by Peck's method

(a)

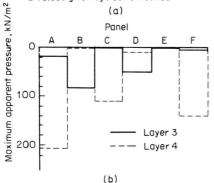

(b)

Figure 4-78 Observed performance of the test panels of Fig. 4-77: (a) Apparent pressures at the end of excavation for each layer. (b) Apparent pressures at the end of excavation for each pair of struts in layers 3 and 4. (*From Kastner and Lareal, 1974.*)

pressures. This divergence is attributed to the rigidity of the system that magnifies the effect of construction deviations.

The redistribution of strut loads, where some struts absorb the load from their neighbors, is shown in Fig. 4-78b. In this case, the two struts in the third layer of panel B are heavily loaded, whereas the two adjoining ones and the pair immediately below (layer 4) are practically unloaded.

In actual construction these results are very unlikely to have direct application to strutted walls since the system stiffness of the example (flexural stiffness divided by strut tier spacing) approaches an upper limit that exceeds several times actual system stiffness. The results demonstrate, however, that variation in actual strut load distribution is greater with increased system stiffness. With stiff walls, the absence of any appreciable deformation to accommodate construction deviations results in some loads receiving considerable load while others receive very little.

Anchored walls.   For the walls of Guildhall development shown in Fig. 4-28, an analysis of lateral stresses has been provided on the basis of an empirical method, taking into account the continuous construction process and excavation stages as well as variations in the soil strata (Littlejohn et al., 1971). The assumption is that the final soil stress distribution is triangular and that the wall yields progressively as the excavation proceeds. In a step-by-step consolidation process the multianchored wall is converted into a repetitive single-tied system whereby wall penetration is estimated by satisfying rotational as well as horizontal equilibrium (see also foregoing sections).

Bending moments for the wall of Fig. 4-28a are shown in Fig. 4-79 for the excavation stages shown in Fig. 4-28b to i. Particularly parts h and i appear to confirm the single-tie response, whereby the support of two anchors is consolidated at a point between them so that the bending moment is negative over this area and positive elsewhere. Further consolidation of the bending moment curve results in a lateral pressure distribution that is more triangular than trapezoidal (note, however, that a back analysis of this wall suggests a trapezoidal diagram with $K = 0.2$ for estimating anchor prestress).

A similar analysis of the Keybridge House wall of Fig. 4-29 produced the bending moment profiles shown in Fig. 4-80. Part b shows also the design and measured moments for the cantilever portion of the wall. The variation in the design and measured moment is probably due to a different water level. The measured moments relate to normal groundwater level, whereas the design curves are based on the flood level.

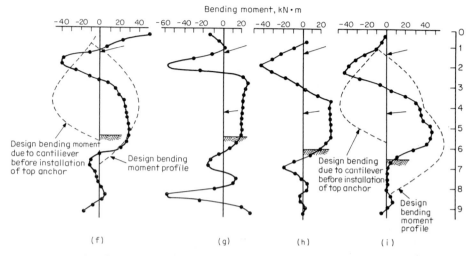

Figure 4-79 Bending moments for the wall of Fig. 4-28 (based on a 0.3-m strip; moment diagrams *f* to *i* correspond to stages *f* to *i* of Fig. 4-28.

Flexible wall in clay. Figure 4-81 shows data and predictions for a sheet pile wall in clay, based on finite-element analysis (Clough, 1980). The initial earth pressure assumed to act on the wall prior to excavation approaches the at rest condition. The wall is braced at four strut levels as shown, and penetrates through a homogeneous clay deposit to an underlying rigid base.

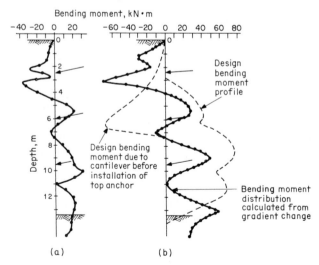

Figure 4-80 Bending moments for the wall of Fig. 4-29*a*, based on a 0.3-m strip; final excavation stage.

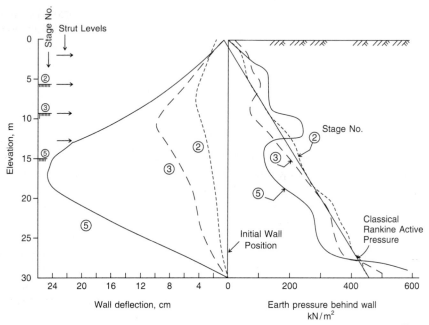

Figure 4-81 Finite element predicted earth pressure distribution on sheet pile wall in clay. (*From Clough, 1980.*)

The earth pressures for stage 2, following excavation to a depth of 5.5 m (18 ft) below the first strut level, are essentially linear and close to the Rankine values. This is compatible with the lateral wall movement that reached values that produce the Rankine state (0.5 percent *H*). At stage 3 the earth pressures around the strut levels are somewhat higher than the Rankine values but lower than Rankine below the struts until a depth of 26 m (85 ft) when the pressures again exceed the Rankine values. At this stage deflection of the sheeting below the last strut level produces an arching effect (Bjerrum et al., 1972). Following final excavation to stage 5, the trend shows increased pressures on the exposed wall portion and decreased pressures on the embedded wall, but the total resultant between stages 2 and 5 is about the same and close to the Rankine active resultant.

These results suggest that during excavation the system load is essentially a fixed parameter when the wall movement is large enough to induce the limiting condition of the Rankine state. The load distribution also shows that the pattern of lateral pressures is influenced by the flexural rigidity of the wall below the last strut level and the degree of stability of the excavation. The larger the movement below excavation level, the stronger is the arching effect whereby the lateral stresses below the excavation level are reduced and the stresses on the strutted wall portion are increased.

4-10   Refined Methods of Analysis

Finite-element techniques, basic principles

Advantages and limitations   It appears from the foregoing that partially integrated techniques inhibit a complete problem formulation since they pursue each phase independently. Thus earth stresses are determined by limiting theory, support loads are estimated empirically, and deformations are predicted by statistical data, elastic theory, and one-dimensional consolidation theory. Limiting equilibrium analysis is simple in predicting collapse loads but does not predict deformations associated with limit loads and provides no information for conditions other than those at the limit.

Finite-element analysis gives solutions based on actual stress-strain relations, boundary conditions, and constitutive relations. As a predictive technique it allows consideration of structures with arbitrary shape and flexibility, complex construction sequence, and heterogeneous soil conditions. Seepage loading and nonlinear soil-interface behavior can be analyzed, and predictions can be made for stress changes and deformations for the soil and the structure for conditions other than at the limit. Where instrumentation is contemplated, the method is a logical supplement to the design.

Two general approaches are followed. In the first, predictions are made and compared with observed behavior. If discrepancies exist and cannot be rectified, the assumptions are modified and the analysis is repeated until convergence is reached. The second approach involves parametric studies of factors influencing wall behavior, from which designs are formulated for different wall functions. Finite-element analyses have been carried out by Cole and Burland (1972), Ward (1972), Wong (1971), Clough (1973), Egger (1972), Tsui (1973), Barla and Mascardi (1974), Clough and Tsui (1974a, b), Clough et al., (1974), Breth and Stroh (1976), Simpson et al., (1979), Stille and Fredricksson (1979), and Pfister et al. (1982).

Limitations are imposed by inability to always prescribe appropriate constitutive behavior and determine the parameters needed for the constitutive models. Accuracy is thus influenced by the availability of input data routinely necessary. The programs typically require soil parameters that must be determined through extensive soil investigations and laboratory tests. It is also conceivable that application of soil-structure interaction involves certain special problems for which solutions are approximated. Other difficulties arise from the simulation of the relative movement between the soil and the structure that must be modeled, and the numerical problems that are intensified by the stress-strain pattern.

Statement of problem. Table 4-8 shows a typical flowchart incorporated in finite-element analysis. The chart lists the steps involved in the investigation, and each step represents an idealized form of the actual problem. Behavioral models are selected for the soil, the structure, and the soil-structure interface. Structural behavior is expressed mathematically, such as elastic, elastic-plastic, and so on. The soil model and the soil-structure interface model are the most difficult to define. Parameters indicating the media properties are selected next, and approximated in nonhomogeneous conditions. The initial stress conditions are defined, the construction sequence is worked out, the finite-element mesh is drawn, and the analysis is carried out.

Simulation of construction sequence. This involves the division of the loading sequence into small increments, analysis of the effects of each increment in sequence, and superposition of the results to obtain the resultant stress and displacement conditions. Diaphragm wall modeling must consider, therefore, trench excavation under slurry, concrete tremie placement, general excavation on one side (probably accompanied by dewatering and recharging), and installation of bracing.

Models for simulating excavation have been proposed by Clough and Duncan (1971) that are general and accommodate excavation in soil and in rock, and can represent in-place structural elements. If the soil

TABLE 4-8 Typical Flowchart and Procedure Leading to Finite-Element Analysis

Statement of problem
↓
Idealization of soil and groundwater conditions
↓
Selection of constitutive modeling techniques
↓
Selection of media properties
↓
Assumption of initial stress conditions
↓
Assumption of construction sequence
↓
Drawing of finite-element mesh to accommodate soil conditions, structural configuration, and construction sequence
↓
Analyses

is assumed linear elastic, results for one- and three-step excavation simulation should be comparable. Dewatering and seepage loading constitute pressure changes on the elements in the mesh, and are merely special cases of the more complex loading produced by the excavation. Installation and preloading of the bracing can be simulated in the form of a restraint or load change.

Among the initial conditions, the simple initial at rest stresses are difficult to conceive, whereas the construction process prompts changes in these stresses. For example, stress-strain changes are induced by operations such as the replacement of soil by slurry to be followed by fresh concrete, and by the installation and preloading of the bracing.

Among the boundary conditions, the representation of the interface is particularly relevant to the model. With diaphragm walls, the soil-slurry interaction must be inferred first, and the shear resistance mobilized at the interface must be obtained as the wall moves with respect to the soil. Activities that are relevant to the wall performance but cannot be simulated are (1) construction-induced movement in certain soft clays or loose sands; (2) overexcavation or delays in support installation; (3) vibrations caused by adjacent work, and subsidence originating by caisson construction; (4) water loss through anchor holes and wall joints; (5) remolding and undercutting of temporary berms left as bracing; and (6) surcharge loads from moving equipment and other contributions.

Case studies of finite-element analysis

Cut-and-cover tunnel in sand. A case study is reported by Clough and Tsui (1974*a*). The soil is considered nonlinear elastic, with a tangent modulus calculated from a hyperbolic stress-strain curve during primary loading and a straight-line unload-reload curve should the shear stress in an element decrease during an increment of loading. Soil data are shown in Table 4-9.

Because of the complex behavior no attempt was made to simulate the slurry trench excavation and the tremie placement of concrete, so that with the walls in place a simple condition at rest was assumed with $K_0 = 0.5$. The friction at the wall-soil interface was taken to correspond to the shear strength of the soil at one-half the friction angle.

Predicted wall movement during the construction stage is shown in Fig. 4-82. Most movement occurred during excavation down to the first brace level, and is essentially parallel translation, as shown in Fig. 4-82*a*, but sufficient to reduce the earth stresses to a nearly active

TABLE 4-9 Soil Data for Finite-Element Analysis, Cut-and-Cover Tunnel of Fig. 4-82*

Type of soil = sand
Unit weight above water table γ = 125 lb/ft^3
Friction angle ϕ = 30°
Poisson ratio = 0.2
Coefficient of earth pressure at rest K_0 = 0.5
Cohesion = 0
Modulus exponent n = 0.5
Modulus number K = 280

From Clough and Tsui, 1974a.
*Initial tangent modulus E_i assumed to vary with minor principal stress σ_3 so that $E_i = K\sigma_3^n$.

state for the portion of the wall above the brace level (see also Fig. 4-83a). The deflection-depth ratio for this stage is 1:850. Excavation below the first brace level with this bracing in place caused the wall to move as shown in Fig. 4-82b, undergoing rotation about the brace point with the bottom part moving away from the soil.

With the water table rising to its normal level following the placement of the top and bottom slab, a small elastic deflection occurred as shown in Fig. 4-82c. Referring to Fig. 4-83b and c the actual earth stresses approach closely the at rest pressure for K_0 = 0.5.

Of special interest is the vertical pressure distribution along the underside of the base slab. This pressure is reduced from Fig. 4-83b to c, after completion of construction, and the resultant is less than the weight of the overburden. The difference can be accounted for by

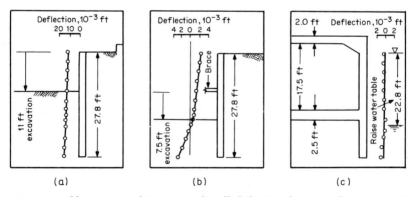

Figure 4-82 Movement and incremental wall deflection for cut-and-cover tunnel built with diaphragm walls: (a) Wall deflection due to excavation to brace level. (b) Wall deflection due to excavation below brace level. (c) Wall deflection due to raising water table with top and bottom slab in place. (*From Clough and Tsui, 1974a.*)

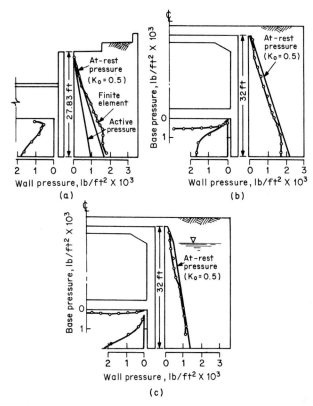

Figure 4-83 Lateral earth stresses on diaphragm-wall cut-and-cover tunnel of Fig. 4-82: effective earth stresses (*a*) at completion of excavation; (*b*) at completion of structure and backfill above structure; (*c*) following restoration of water table. (*From Clough and Tsui, 1974a.*)

the friction developed along the back of the walls, assumed to settle somewhat after the placement of the slabs.

Braced excavations in soft clay. Figure 4-84 shows the predicted earth stresses for the Southern Pacific excavation in San Francisco (Clough, 1975). The stresses, obtained by finite-element analysis, are shown for two stages, one for the lower struts in place but not prestressed, the other with the lower struts preloaded. The analysis assumes the prestress applied to the lower struts was retained without loss (Clough, 1975).

The predicted earth pressure before prestressing was decreased to near active, corresponding to a wall movement 0.9 percent of the excavation height. With the lower struts preloaded the lateral earth

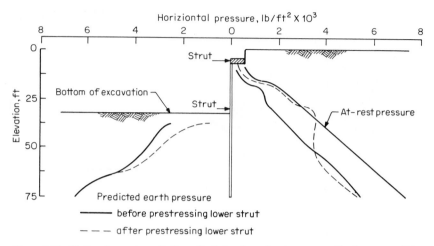

Figure 4-84 Finite-element predictions for lateral earth stresses on diaphragm wall in soft clay. Southern Pacific excavation, San Francisco. (*From Clough, 1975.*)

stresses increased to nearly the original at rest, a response anticipated since the preload was calculated from the at rest diagram. The wall was predicted to move inward toward the soil by 2.5 cm (1 in) during the preload application.

Anchored wall in clay.   Figure 4-85 shows an anchored wall supporting an excavation 10 m (32.5 ft) deep (Tsui, 1973). The soil is homogeneous clay underlain by rock. The diaphragm wall is 60 cm (2 ft) thick, and the anchors consist of steel rods, 1 in² cross-sectional area, with the fixed zone in rock. The prestress loads were calculated from the apparent pressure diagram shown in Fig. 4-85b. The undrained shear strength of the clay increases linearly with depth from 2.0 to 7.0 t/m² (500 to 1400 lb/ft²) at the bottom of the clay layer. The coefficient K_0 is taken as 0.85, and the insertion of the wall is assumed to have no effect on the initial at rest condition. The initial tangent modulus is taken as 400 times the undrained shear strength. The assumption of plane strain is considered valid for a 2-ft-thick wall and anchor spacing less than 3 m (10 ft).

A nonlinear elastic model is incorporated in the analysis, and tangent modulus values are obtained for a stress-strain curve represented by a hyperbola. The interface between the wall and the soil is treated similarly on both sides using a bilinear stress-strain deformation relationship with initial shear stiffness 50,000 lb/ft³ reduced by a factor of 1000 if the yield strength of the interface is exceeded. The construction sequence is simulated by an incremental loading process based

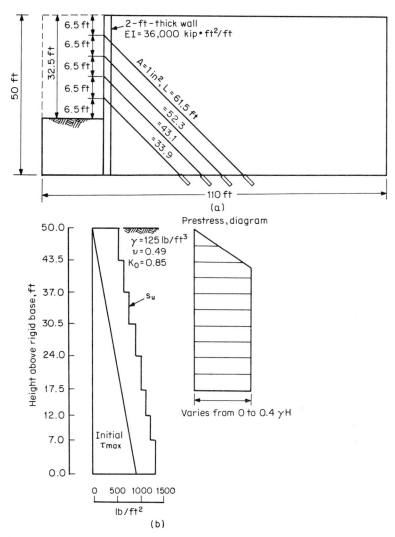

Figure 4-85 A tied-back wall in clay: (*a*) Section through wall. (*b*) Soil data and prestress diagram. (*From Tsui, 1973.*)

on the nine-step modeling shown in Fig. 4-86. Anchor lengths vary from 61.5 to 33.9 ft.

Figures 4-87 and 4-88 show wall and ground movement and earth pressure distribution, respectively, for the two prestress levels and with no prestress, together with anchor loads corresponding to apparent pressure diagrams. Wall movement responds consistently to prestress level, decreasing almost linearly with the amount of prestress-

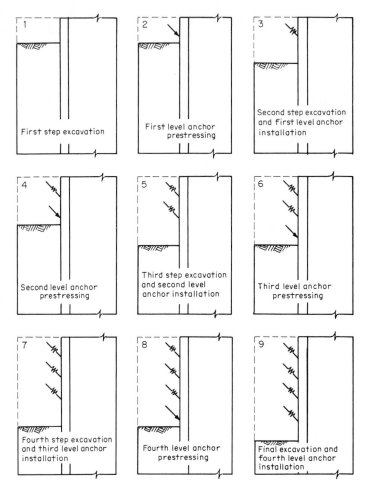

Figure 4-86 Construction sequence. Finite-element analysis of the tied-back wall of Fig. 4-85. (*From Tsui, 1973.*)

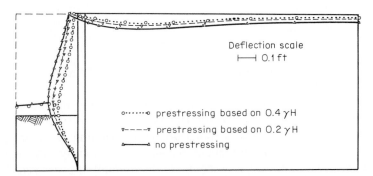

Figure 4-87 Wall and ground movement predicted by finite-element analysis, tied-back wall of Fig. 4-85. (*From Tsui, 1973.*)

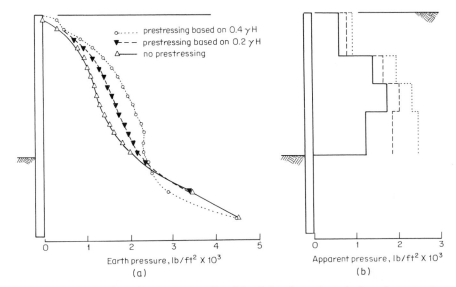

o······ prestressing based on 0.4 γH
▼ − − prestressing based on 0.2 γH
△——— no prestressing

Earth pressure, lb/ft² X 10³
(a)

Apparent pressure, lb/ft² X 10³
(b)

Figure 4-88 Lateral earth pressure predicted by finite-element-analysis and apparent-pressure diagrams, tied-back wall of Fig. 4-85. (*From Tsui, 1973.*)

ing. Likewise, ground settlement behind the wall decreases as the prestress increases, but this effect diminishes as the next higher prestress load is introduced.

The predicted earth pressure diagrams shown in Fig. 4-88a may be compared with the apparent pressures shown in b obtained by distributing the anchor loads over the appropriate spans. The predicted pressures approach the original at rest values and show a triangular distribution. There are no pressure bumps at the anchor points.

A second example of anchored wall in clay modeled by finite-element analysis is shown in Fig. 4-89 (Clough and Tsui, 1974b), and includes two cases, one with four rows and the other with three rows of anchors. Unlike the previous supports, however, the wall is flexible, with stiffness equivalent to PZ-72 sheeting. The anchor prestress is based on apparent pressure diagrams.

The predicted lateral pressures are more triangular than the design trapezoidal diagrams, and this distribution is consistent with actual wall movement. Unlike the previous examples, earth pressures tend to concentrate at anchor points.

Effect of wall and anchor stiffness, and anchor prestressing

Lateral displacement in clay. Wall stiffness is defined as the inverse of Rowe's flexibility number for walls, and is thus expressed as EI/L^4

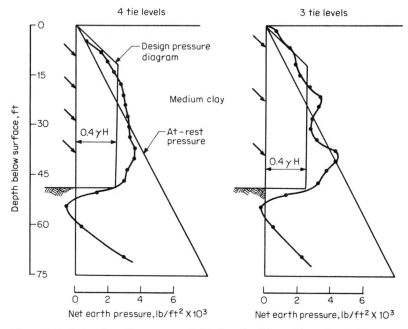

Figure 4-89 Lateral earth pressure behind a flexible wall predicted by finite-element-analysis, prestressed tied-back wall. (*From Clough and Tsui, 1974a.*)

where L is the vertical distance between anchor rows. A plot of observed displacements correlating the stiffness EI/L^4 with the stability number $N = \gamma H/s_u$ is shown in Fig. 4-90 (Goldberg et al., 1976). These data demonstrate that deformation and wall movement in excavations are functions of soil strength and wall stiffness.

By reference to Fig. 4-90 a direct comparison can be made between a sheet pile wall and a diaphragm wall braced at 10-ft vertical intervals. The sheet pile section is PZ-38, and the concrete wall is 30 in thick. The stiffness factors are calculated as follows:

$$\text{Steel sheeting } \frac{EI}{L^4} = \frac{(30 \times 10^6) \times (281)}{120^4}$$

$$= 40.7 \text{ lb/in}^2 = 5.86 \text{ kips/ft}^2$$

$$\text{Concrete wall } \frac{EI}{L^4} = \frac{(3 \times 10^6) \times (\frac{1}{12})(12 \times 30^3)}{120^4}$$

$$= 391 \text{ lb/in}^2 = 56.3 \text{ kips/ft}^2$$

From the plot of Fig. 4-90 the expected maximum displacement for the sheet pile wall is 3 in, and 1.5 in for the stiffer diaphragm wall.

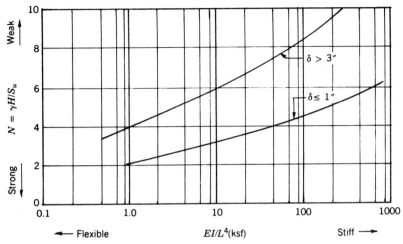

Figure 4-90 Effect of wall stiffness and soil deformability (expressed by the stability number $N = \gamma H/s_u$ or lateral wall deflection (ksF = kilopounds per square foot). (*From Goldberg et al., 1976.*)

Theoretical analysis. Finite-element studies have been carried out by Egger (1972) to investigate the effect of wall stiffness for excavations in sand. The wall height is 10 m (33 ft) and supports an excavation 7.5 m (24.5 ft) deep, giving a wall embedment of 2.5 m (8.5 ft). The construction sequence involves bracing with three rows of anchors installed in three stages. Two wall systems are considered, with a stiffness ratio of 1:100.

Predicted lateral earth pressures are shown in Figs. 4-91 and 4-92 for the flexible and the stiff wall, and for two prestress levels, 1 and 6 t/m, respectively. In the first excavation stage the wall is a free cantilever. Lateral movement, shown in Fig. 4-93, is three times greater for the flexible wall; hence this system mobilizes passive earth resistance near the ground to a much higher level. The stiff wall moves less, and therefore earth stresses are mobilized to a lesser extent, although they cover a markedly greater zone. Likewise, the active earth pressure approaches the at rest condition near the wall base much faster for the flexible wall than it does for the much stiffer wall.

As the prestress is increased from 1 to 6 t/m, the flexible wall receives this supplementary change as a stress concentration between 1.5 m above and 2.5 m below the anchor level. For the stiff wall the resulting earth pressure diagram is essentially uniform from the top down to about 6 m. In the last excavation stages these differences are still observable but less significant, indicating the effect of closer anchor-row spacing on equalizing the stiffness factor EI/L^4.

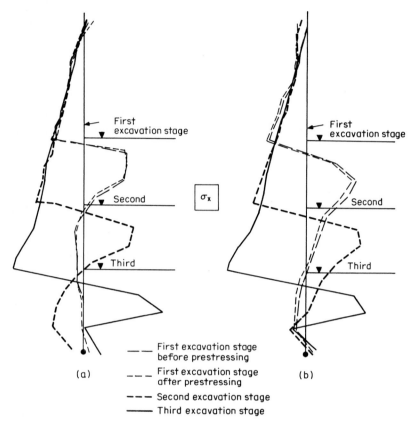

First
excavation stage

First
excavation stage

Second

σ_x

Second

Third

Third

___ First excavation stage
before prestressing

_ _ _ First excavation stage
after prestressing

(a)   (b)

--- Second excavation stage

——— Third excavation stage

Figure 4-91 Lateral earth pressures predicted by finite-element analysis for an excavation in sand: (*a*) Flexible wall. (*b*) Stiff wall. Anchor prestress 1 ton/m. (*From Egger, 1972.*)

The effect of anchor prestressing on wall movement is shown in Fig. 4-93. The prestress of 1 t/m is much lower than the active level, but 6 t/m corresponds nearly to the actual pressures existing at final excavation level. Movement at the top of the flexible wall is reduced from 2.5 to 1.7 cm when the prestress is increased from 1 to 6 t/m. For the stiff wall the same movement is reduced from 2.3 to 1.4 cm with the higher prestress level.

Figure 4-94 shows the increase in the actual anchor force as excavation continues to final level, and for the two prestress levels. With a prestress level 1 t/m, anchor reaction grows quickly and reaches almost the same value for both walls (7.2 t/m). With higher prestress, the increase becomes less significant but still higher than with the lower prestress. At final excavation stage and with 6 t/m prestress, anchor reaction is about 8.8 t/m for both walls.

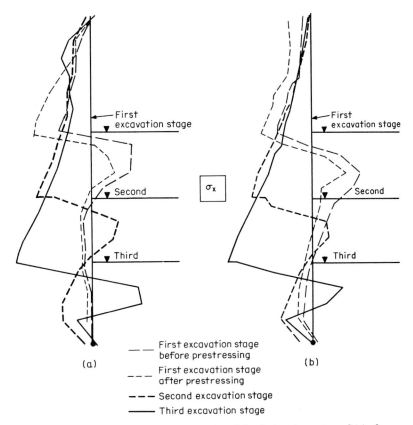

Figure 4-92 Lateral earth pressures predicted by finite-element analysis for an excavation in sand. (*a*) Flexible wall. (*b*) Stiff wall. Anchor prestress 6 tons/m. (*From Egger, 1972.*)

Clough and Tsui (1974*b*) have investigated the effect of prestress under constant wall and anchor stiffness. The wall system has a medium stiffness value of 36,000 kip-ft²/ft, and the anchors are assumed to be steel bars of cross-sectional area 1 in². Predicted wall and soil deformation decreases with increased prestress, and this effect appears more prominent near the top of the wall where the use of prestress corresponding to a trapezoidal diagram loading can practically eliminate movement. However, the prestress is only partly effective in preventing movement near the base of excavation.

The effect of wall rigidity was isolated by keeping the prestress load and anchor stiffness at assigned constant values. Results showed that movement is reduced with increasing wall rigidity, although not linearly proportioned.

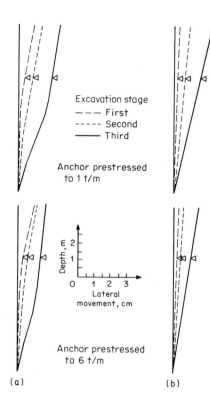

Figure 4-93 Lateral wall movement for a wall in sand predicted by finite-element analysis: (*a*) Flexible wall. (*b*) Stiff wall. Anchor prestress 1 and 6 tons/m. (*From Egger, 1972.*)

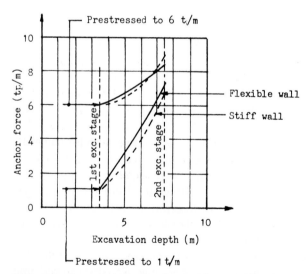

Figure 4-94 Increase in anchor force with excavation depth for two levels of prestress; stiff and flexible wall. (*From Egger, 1972.*)

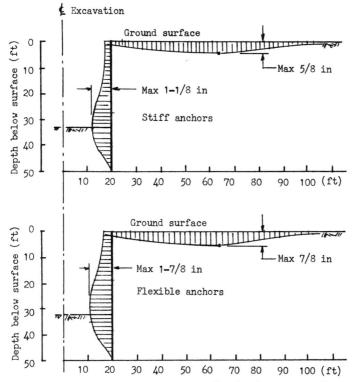

Figure 4-95 Effect of anchor stiffness on wall and soil movement. (*From Clough and Tsui, 1974b.*)

In the same study the effect of anchor stiffness was analyzed for an excavation 32.5 ft deep in a deposit of normally consolidated clay, supported by four rows of anchors. The strength of the clay increases from 600 lb/ft² near the surface to 1800 lb/ft². Two types of anchor tendons were considered, bars 1 in² in cross-sectional area, and strand with cross-sectional area of 0.1 in², giving a stiffness ratio of 1:10. The predicted wall and ground movement is shown in Fig. 4-95 for the stiff and flexible anchors. The former reduce movement, but the reduction is not linearly dependent on anchor stiffness change.

Combined effect of parameters. The combined effect of the three parameters, wall stiffness, anchor stiffness, and prestress, has been studied by Clough and Tsui (1974b). In the first case, a flexible wall is analyzed with a flexible anchor system and without prestress. In the second case, a relatively high prestress load is applied based on a trapezoidal apparent pressure diagram with ordinate 0.68γH with a very stiff wall-anchor system.

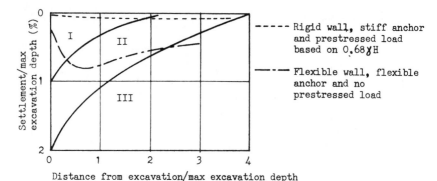

Figure 4-96 Combined effect of parameters on wall movement. (*From Clough and Tsui, 1974b.*)

Wall movement is shown in Fig. 4-96, plotted on a dimensionless diagram. Movement divided by excavation depth is shown vs. distance from the wall divided by excavation depth. The two solid curves divide three zones of behavior as defined by Peck (1969). Zone I represents best soil and construction conditions; zone II, intermediate conditions; and zone III, the worst credible conditions. Without prestress, the resulting settlement brings the system into zone II. The effect of the combined parameter change on predicted settlement in the second case is significant, so that ground settlement is not restricted entirely to zone I.

Plane strain conditions

In general, solutions involving diaphragm walls are based on plane strain conditions. Model tests by Tsui (1973), and Tsui and Clough (1974) have provided criteria and guidelines in assessing the effect of system stiffness, component discontinuity, and repetitious loading. These are summarized as follows (Xanthakos, 1991).

1. A parameter that defines the wall deflection is the characteristic length l_0 expressed as

$$l_0 = \sqrt[3]{\frac{2D(1 - \mu_s^2)}{E_s}} \qquad (4\text{-}35)$$

where E_s and μ_s are the elastic parameters of the soil and

$$D = \frac{Eh^3}{12(l - \mu)^2} \qquad (4\text{-}36)$$

in which h = wall thickness, E = elastic modulus, l = vertical anchor spacing, and μ = Poisson's ratio.

2. Cast-in-place or precast diaphragm walls and certain sheet pile systems may be considered continuous in terms of plane strain behavior. Typical cases analyzed in this manner are a 3-ft-thick diaphragm wall, a 1-ft-thick diaphragm wall, and an MP-116 sheet pile wall. For each example, l_0 is estimated using a soil modulus varying from 50 to 400 t/ft^2 and an assumed μ_s = 0.3.

3. Variation in characteristic length l_0 with soil modulus is shown in Fig. 4-97. At the lowest soil modulus, this length is greater than about 6 ft. For a 10-ft horizontal anchor spacing, the ratio is about 0.6, 1.0, and 1.7 for the 3-ft and 1-ft walls and the sheet pile unit, respectively. If the horizontal anchor spacing is increased to 15 ft, these ratios are 0.9, 1.5, and 2.5. The assumption of plane strain in this case is valid for the diaphragm walls, and acceptable (30 percent deviation) for the sheet pile wall.

4. For the 1-ft-thick wall, the three-dimensional pressure distribution at the anchor level is compared with the uniform pressure assumed in plane strain analysis, and results are shown in Fig. 4-98. The soil is clay with assumed modulus 180 t/ft^2, and the prestress loads are spaced at 10-ft centers. For this condition the ratio s/l_0 is 2,

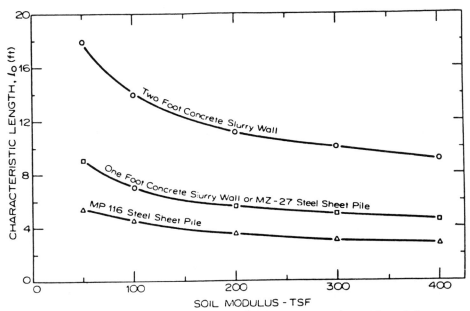

Figure 4-97 Variation in characteristic length of typical continuous walls and dependence on soil modulus. (*From Tsui and Clough, 1974.*)

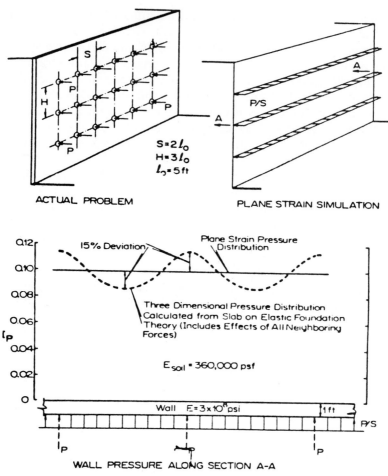

Figure 4-98 Comparison of plane strain and actual pressure distribution for a 1-ft-thick concrete wall. (*From Tsui and Clough, 1974.*)

yielding a deviation of 15 percent from plane strain conditions. It appears therefore that for most diaphragm walls plane strain analysis is applicable and valid.

4-11   Other Loads

Surcharge loads at ground surface.   These include point, line, and strip loads. The resulting lateral pressures may be analyzed by the theory of elasticity, which is combined with empirical data when they are available and modified as necessary to account for the increased stiffness of rigid walls (Terzaghi, 1954; Spangler, 1951). For uniform surcharge loads acting at ground surface, the corresponding lateral stresses are calculated by applying an appropriate coefficient K_a or K_0 so that the surcharge is considered part of the effective lateral earth stress at a particular state.

Other investigators consider the soil elastic but introduce a modulus of elasticity increasing linearly with depth (Turabi and Balla, 1968). Although comparison of measured stresses from the few field cases available with stresses calculated from elastic theory indicates a surprisingly good agreement, in some instances a possible error of ±30 percent may be expected.

The solution commonly used is developed by Boussinesg, expressed in the form

$$\sigma_r = \frac{P}{2n}\left(\frac{3r^2z}{R^5} - \frac{1 - 2\mu}{R(R + z)}\right) \tag{4-37}$$

using trigonometric relationships for θ, r, and R as identified in Fig. 4-99. This form is particularly suitable for programming on small calculators since the point load P is usually fixed with given x, y coordinates, whereas z is varied to obtain the wall pressure profile. Work on the validity of this analysis has been carried out by Spangler and Mickle (1956), Rehnman and Broms (1972), and others. The use of $\mu = 0.5$ (Poisson's ratio) simplifies Eq. (4-37).

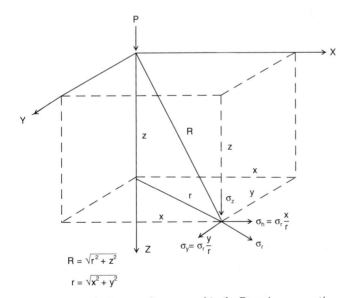

Figure 4-99 Identification of terms used in the Boussinesq equation [Eq. (4-37)] for lateral pressure.

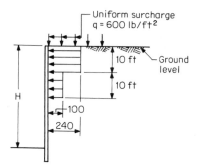

Figure 4-100 Lateral load distribution due to external load at ground level. Gradients shown are pounds per square foot per foot of depth. The diagram is applied to single- and multiple-braced excavation.

An example of lateral load distribution assumed to represent the effect of traffic and construction equipment is shown in Fig. 4-100. It is based on a surcharge load of 600 lb/ft² acting alongside the excavation support and represents essentially a strip load. The ground consists of an upper layer of fill and loose silty fine sand underlain by firm sand. The lateral distribution is independent of the excavation height and affects mainly the upper part of the support system.

Loads within a soil mass. A simplified distribution pattern is shown in Fig. 4-101. The essential points are: (1) the total load is reduced by the weight of the overburden; (2) the lateral load is ignored above the level of load application; and (3) the effect diminishes as the loaded area is away from the lateral support.

For a load within a mass of soil the elastic analysis is complicated by the extension of the elastic soil medium above the plane of load application, so that it often is convenient to resort to a simple distribution. Figure 4-102 shows a simple method for converting a footing (strip) load into a lateral stress. In part *a* the load is distributed first vertically according to angle *α* and then horizontally. In part *b* the angle of inclination is considered together with the failure wedge, and only the portion of the load within this wedge is assumed to cause lateral stresses.

It appears that lateral distribution of external loads is thus based on both elastic and limit theory, with crossover and shifting from one method to the other as different types of loads must be considered. A better analytical consistency may be obtained if conformity between soil deformation and wall movement can be established.

Other causes of lateral pressure. Besides surcharge loads, lateral pressures may be induced in the following situations.

Ice formation. Lateral pressures can be developed when pore water freezes, and this is particularly a problem where the groundwater level is not altered.

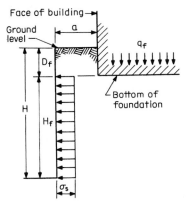

Figure 4-101 Lateral load distribution due to building foundations:

$q_f =$ total live- and dead-load foundation pressure, lb/ft²

$\quad = \dfrac{\text{building load in width } H_f}{\text{area of width } H_f}$

$q_n = q_f - \text{weight of overburden} = q_f - \gamma D_f$

$$\sigma_s = \begin{cases} 0.5q_n \left(1 - \dfrac{a}{1.5H_f}\right) \\ \quad \text{for } 0 < \dfrac{a}{H_f} < 1.5 \\ 0 \\ \quad \text{for } \dfrac{a}{H_f} > 1.5 \end{cases}$$

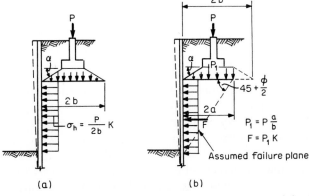

(a)   (b)

Figure 4-102 Lateral stress distribution due to external load within a soil: (a) Vertical and horizontal distribution according to an inclination angle. (b) Distribution taking into account the zone of influence within the failure wedge.

Seismic earth pressure. Diaphragm walls in seismic areas may experience problems related to excessive settlement of adjoining ground or excessive wall movement during an earthquake. A frequently used method for obtaining seismic earth forces is a pseudostatic approach proposed by Mononobe and Okabe, referred to as the M-O analysis (Seed and Whitman, 1970; Elms and Martin, 1979). The method is, however, based on certain assumptions: (1) the wall moves sufficiently to mobilize active conditions; (2) the soil behind the wall is drained and cohesionless; (3) the failure surfaces are plane; and (4) the accelerations are uniform in the soil mass. A review of procedures and relevant theoretical expressions given by Barker et al. (1991) includes a summary of acceleration coefficients.

Swelling pressures. Problems associated with lateral expansion may arise if expansion clays are behind a wall and become excessively wet. In overconsolidated clays, vertical rather than lateral expansion may be a more serious problem.

Thermal expansion. The effect of thermal expansion and contraction of the bracing of two opposite walls is a reversal of ground strain. For long or wide strutted excavations too much contraction of the bracing can bring the system into an active state or cause ground movement beyond the allowable. Too much expansion can reverse the stress condition and induce lateral earth pressures much higher than the design values. In dissimilar ground and under varying initial loading conditions, the expansion of bracing supporting two opposite walls can cause erratic redistribution of stresses that may be difficult to express analytically.

4-12   Design Methodologies

Wall embedment and earth pressures below excavation

Where the reduction of wall movement and protection of the base from groundwater are not factors influencing wall embedment, the latter is estimated from a statical analogy between the lateral pressures acting on either side. Apart from the application of statics, the pressures on the active side may change rapidly from those associated with undrained conditions to values related to fully drained state. Likewise, the passive resistance may be expected to deteriorate at least as rapidly. If a layer of much stiffer soil or rock exists close to the excavation level, it will have a marked effect on reducing toe movement and will also brace the wall at this level. Finally, the possibility of overexcavation should not be discounted.

One of the least understood aspects is the response of the embedded wall portion. Where load diagrams are used, the analysis should articulate the fact that these do not explicitly address the problem since they apply only to the exposed wall section. Interestingly, in many cases structural design based essentially on the exposed wall portion is generally adequate. Referring to Fig. 4-81, wall response is explained by the earth pressure loadings. As arching occurs, soil pressure increase on the exposed wall section is compensated by a corresponding decrease below Rankine active values on the embedded section. Essentially the system moves to attain an equilibrium position, and in the process the pressures on the active side of the embedded wall decrease until they are balanced by the pressures on the passive side. This continues as long as base heave is retarded and the wall can yield plastically or move relatively free within the soil.

Overdesigns may thus result because the soil-structure interaction is not considered in quantitative terms. An example is the assumption of full at rest pressure on the embedded wall portion, justified only if the design intends to provide a wall with a high degree of stiffness to restrict subgrade movement. In this case, the wall ends up receiving loads that could be carried by the soil if enough deformation could be allowed.

Relevant comments

There is considerable evidence suggesting that the passive pressure coefficients for loose sand are often too optimistic considering the large strains necessary to mobilize this condition. The same evidence also demonstrates the considerable complexity of the interaction between walls and soil masses depending on the strain behavior implicit in the system.

Using an empirical or semiempirical method, the results will depend on the experience and judgment of the designer. When large excavations are considered, oversimplification of the wall analysis and soil behavior may lead to an inadequate appreciation of total system behavior, and result in some possible risk to the completed structure. In such cases, refined techniques such as finite-element analysis will be advantageous in modeling the total response of walls and soil mass. Alternatively, basic computer programs, not readily available, may be applied to the design of walls, and constitute an important engineering tool provided their basic limitations are understood.

One of the main advantages of computer usage is the ability to carry out parametric studies. In this case, the effects of changing the variables in the analysis can be quickly and economically examined. Long- and short-term stability may be represented, the various construction stages and bracing installations can be followed, the effects of mis-selection of soil characteristics can be considered, and the general sensitivity of the overall problem in relation to ground conditions and factors of safety may be assessed.

Less serious problems become apparent in routine design. An example is surcharge loading, often due to existing foundations within a retained soil mass. These surcharges may be represented as discussed in Sec. 4-11 by point loads, line loads, or specific loaded areas. Several graphical procedures are available for estimating resulting horizontal surcharges, based on elastic theory. The use of equations based on the Boussinesq solution is simple and convenient, but in practice designers will find considerable differences in the results obtained by the different methods, particularly when heavy footings rest within a short distance above the excavation level within the retained earth.

Another problem relates to the use of effective stress analysis for examining wall stability in clays. This problem arises from the difficulty of assessing how long the excavation will remain open under the worst loading conditions, and whether an effective stress analysis is thus appropriate. Concern with groundwater conditions also arises in design, since it is often difficult to interpret the available data so as to determine the worst credible condition. Care is necessary to avoid water pressure gradients that induce boiling conditions at the toe of walls with short embedment.

Basic design principles

Two design philosophies are currently used: (1) working stress design, also referred to as "allowable stress design" (ASD), and (2) limit states design, also referred to as "load factor design" (LFD) or "load and resistance factor design" (LRFD).

Structures and structure members must have adequate strength, stiffness, and toughness to accommodate the intended functions during service life. The design must ensure reserve strength to account for the possibility of overload. The latter may arise from changes in the structural use, by underestimating load effects, or because of variations in construction procedures. In addition, there must be a provision for the possibility of understrength. This may be caused by dimensional deviations, or actual strength less than the design, all possible within statistically acceptable limits.

Limit states

Diaphragm walls, like other structures, must be designed for specific functions. Rather than using the term "failure," we choose to refer to the "limit state." If a wall ceases to fulfill the intended design function, it is said to have reached a limit state. Limit states are categorized into two types: ultimate or strength limit states, and serviceability limit states. A wall will reach an ultimate limit state when the strength of at least one of its components is fully mobilized or when the structure becomes unstable. In the ultimate limit state the wall may experience distress and structural damage, either local or global. Various failure modes may also be identified in the soil that supports the wall, and these are likewise ultimate limit states; examples are bearing capacity failures, sliding, overturning, and overall instability.

A wall will experience a serviceability limit state when it fails to perform its intended design function, partly because of excessive deformation or movement, or because of deterioration (i.e., excessive leakage). Serviceability limit states include excessive overall or differential settlement, lateral movement, fatigue, vibration, and cracking.

Load factor design (LFD)

This is a strength or limit state design method. Unlike ASD, it considers the random nature of loads and resistances, as well as different levels of uncertainty for different types of loads.

The design loads are determined by multiplying the normally expected values, called "nominal" loads, by load factors typically larger than unity. The design strength or resistance is obtained by multiplying nominal strengths by resistance factors generally smaller than unity. A design is acceptable if the factored resistance exceeds the strength requirement obtained from the factored loads for a given limit state. This is expressed as follows:

$$\phi R_n \geq \Sigma \gamma_i Q_i \quad \text{(effect)} \quad (4\text{-}38)$$

where ϕ = performance factor, R_n = nominal resistance, γ_i = load factor for load component i, and Q_i = load component i.

In this approach the values of the load and performance factors are based on semiquantitative consideration of probabilities, judgment, and previous experience with comparable design methods.

Load and resistance factor design (LRFD)

It appears from the foregoing that both load effects and structural resistance to loads are fundamental variables to be considered. Thus the LRFD approach is also a strength design method and has the same format as LFD, expressed by Eq. (4-38). However, loads and resistance factors are derived differently. Thus the LRFD methodology depends on reliability theories. Loads and resistances are still the random vari-

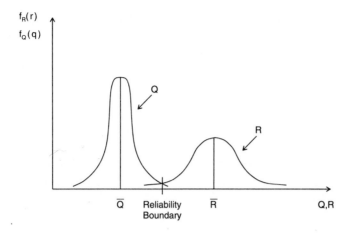

where

    Q : Load
    R : Resistance
    $\overline{Q}$: Mean of Load
    $\overline{R}$: Mean of Resistance

Figure 4-103 Probability density functions for load and resistance.

ables and are represented by their mean and standard deviations. Load and resistance factors depend on the safety index, directly related to the probability of failure. The safety index is chosen so that the probability of failure is small. Probability density functions for load and resistance are shown in Fig. 4-103. The relationship between safety index and probability of failure is presented in Fig. 4-104.

Allowable stress design (ASD)

Traditionally, this method ensures safety by restricting values of stress obtained from elastic analysis to values that do not exceed certain allowable values. Allowable stresses are usually specified on a percentage of the ultimate (yield) strength or capacity of material, based on a global factor of safety. For allowable stress design, Eq. (4-38) may be reformulated as follows:

$$\frac{\phi R_n}{\gamma} > \Sigma Q_i \tag{4-39}$$

Because the method uses deterministic values for loads and resistances, the random nature of these parameters is not explicitly considered. The ASD method does not take into account, therefore, the different degree of uncertainty for different types of loads. Live and dead loads are treated similarly, and both are assumed to have the

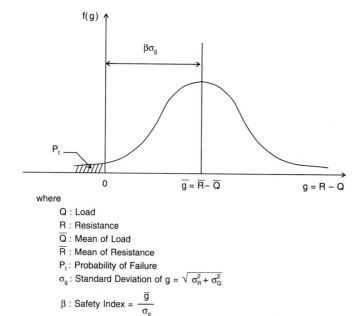

where

    Q : Load
    R : Resistance
    $\overline{Q}$: Mean of Load
    $\overline{R}$: Mean of Resistance
    P_t : Probability of Failure
    σ_g : Standard Deviation of g = $\sqrt{\sigma_R^2 + \sigma_Q^2}$

    β : Safety Index = $\dfrac{\overline{g}}{\sigma_g}$

Figure 4-104   Definition of safety index.

same average variability. Another disadvantage of the method is inability to rationalize the uncertainties in the strength of materials and the ultimate resistance of structural components.

4-13   Safety, Loads, and Performance Factors

Allowable stress design (ASD), safety factors

A safety factor is typically used to provide structural safety. It is not determined consciously by the use of probabilistic methods, and thus these values are the result of experience and engineering judgment. Typical values of safety factors used in common cases of underground construction work are shown in Table 4-10 (See also Chap. 5). Safety factors for anchorages and anchored structures are given by Xanthakos (1991).

Strength design considerations

Loads.   Loads and load combinations for strength design are stipulated by the ACI Code (commonly referred to as ACI 318-83, revised

TABLE 4-10 Typical Safety Factors in Foundation Design

Failure type	Item	Safety factor*
Shearing	Earthworks	1.3–1.5
	Earth retaining structures, excavations	1.5–2.0
	Foundations	2.0–3.0
Seepage	Uplift, heave	1.5–2.0
	Exit gradient, piping	2.0–3.0

From Meyerhof, 1984.
*The lower values are used when uncertainty in design is small and consequences of failure are minor; higher values are used when uncertainty in design is large and consequences of failure are major.

1986); the 1986 AISC LRFD specifications that provide for factored load combinations; and the current AASHTO specifications supplemented by the proposed LRFD specification. Among the loads that are essential to this discussion are the following:

Permanent loads: DD = downdrag

DC = dead load of structural components

EA = earth pressure

EW = water pressure

ES = earth surcharge load

Transient loads: LL = live load T = temperature

WL = wind load S = shrinkage

EQ = earthquake SE = settlement

Note also that other causes of lateral loads may relate to ice formation, swelling pressures, and thermal expansion of the bracing. These effects may be considered if applicable and where they increase the design requirements.

Load combinations. Relevant specifications and codes stipulate possible combinations of loads for substructure and foundation design. These groups include dead load, live load, lateral earth pressure, water pressure, uplift, wind load, earthquake load, ice load, and strain-related effects such as creep and shrinkage in the concrete.

The primary function of diaphragm walls is to resist lateral pressures and also carry certain vertical loads. A relevant load group for ultimate and serviceability limit state may be expressed in the following format:

$$\text{Group } N = \gamma(\beta_{DC}DC + \beta_L LL + \beta_E EA + \beta_{ES}ES + \beta_W EW$$
$$+ \beta_{EQ}EQ + \beta_{DD}DD) \quad (4\text{-}40)$$

where γ = overall load factor, β = load coefficient, and the rest of the symbols correspond to the previous notation.

In some cases, the inclusion of certain loads (for example, dead load, live load, and downdrag) may tend to decrease overall load effects and thus underestimate the design requirements. This can be true where bending stresses control the design and extra wall thickness relegates concrete compressive stress to secondary importance. In these instances, these loads may be omitted. A further factor to be considered is that vertical loads may be absorbed at the interface by shear resistance so that the section for maximum moment does not coincide with the section for maximum compressive load.

Load factors. In order to fit the limit state approach into the design of diaphragm walls, the following considerations must be recognized: (1) several different types of loads may act on the wall; (2) the actual values of permanent loads may be less than or far exceed the specified nominal values; (3) although limited data are available on the variability of permanent loads, it has been established that the negative variability of these loads is less than the positive one (implying that minimum load factors are not necessary); (4) load combinations that include the entire range of loads in Eq. (4-40), and also strain-related load effects, and furthermore relate to very high dead load to transient load ratios may have a minimal reduction in the value of γ; however, where this ratio is very low, the load factor γ may be reduced further; (5) where the number of types of loads to be considered is reduced (for example, approaches 2 or even 1), load factor analysis approaches ASD merely by calibrating load and resistance factors to be compatible with safety factors; and (6) load factors for lateral earth stresses should recognize the fact that soil used as backfill behind a diaphragm wall is original soil in natural state subject to changes because of construction events.

Equation (4-40) represents an "extreme event" limit state since it includes effects due to seismic activity. Omitting the component EQ from Eq. (4-40) yields the normal strength limit state. Load coefficients β are shown in Table 4-11 for the most common types of loads included in Eq. (4-40). Where the lateral earth pressures control design in conjunction with water pressure (effective stress analysis), the

TABLE 4-11 Load Coefficient β, Limit States

Type of load	Coefficient β
DC = dead load of structural components	1.00
DD = downdrag	1.80
EA = earth pressure:	
Lateral	1.20–1.70
Vertical	1.00
ES = earth surcharges	1.50–1.70
EW = water pressure	1.00
LL = live load	1.70
EQ = earthquake	1.00

coefficient β for the EW load may be increased to reflect dynamic effects (broken water mains, etc.).

The load factor γ is suggested as follows:

- If the earthquake force is not included in Eq. (4-40), $\gamma = 1.30$
- If the earthquake force is included in Eq. (4-40), $\gamma = 1.20$

Performance (resistance) factors ϕ. Performance factors are introduced to modify and reduce the resistance level of components and materials for uncertainties in structural properties, soil characteristics, variability in workmanship and construction limitations, and inaccuracies in the design and results therefrom because of implicit assumptions in estimating system capacity. Performance factors ϕ are used solely for design at the ultimate (strength) limit state and are not applied to serviceability states. For the purpose of this discussion, performance factors are stipulated for three basic system components: concrete wall, anchorages, and part of soil mobilizing passive resistance.

Code ϕ factors for concrete. The idealized or nominal strength is typically multiplied by a resistance factor $\phi < 1$ to obtain a reasonably dependable strength. The nominal strength is based on ideal material properties, exact calculations, and analyses based on pragmatic assumptions. The factored resistance reflects imperfection in the strength of the member "as built," and possible variations in the foregoing factors. Thus real strength can only be determined by probability theory and has also a basis on consideration of relatively limited test results. The performance factors ϕ are considered, therefore, interim provisions until further results and studies become available.

Factored resistance is the product of nominal resistance R_n and the performance factor ϕ. The ACI Code specifies the following values for ϕ:

	ϕ
Flexure without axial load	0.90
Axial tension and axial tension with flexure	0.90

Axial compression and axial compression with flexure:
Members with spiral reinforcement (Sec. 10.9.3)	0.75
Other reinforced members	0.70
Shear and torsion	0.85
Bearing on concrete	0.70

In addition the ACI Code includes provisions for the gradual increase of the ϕ values to 0.90 as the axial compression drops below $\phi P_n = 0.10 f'_c A_g$.

The ϕ values are largest for flexure because the variability of steel is less than that of concrete. Flexural members are specified to be designed to fail in tension, i.e., by steel failure; these members should therefore have large ductility. The ϕ values for columns are lowest (with a favor of spiral columns over tied columns) because columns fail in compression where concrete strength is critical and ductility limited. Where heavy vertical loads are involved and the load transfer is by base bearing, the analysis should investigate the worst possible combination of axial load and moment. For shear and torsion, the factor ϕ is intermediate because it depends on $\sqrt{f'_c}$ rather than on f'_c.

Interestingly, the proposed LRFD specifications for highway bridges give the following summary of the resistance factor:

	ϕ
Flexure and tension (conventional concrete)	0.90
Flexure and tension (prestressed concrete)	1.00
Shear and torsion (conventional or prestressed)	0.90
Axial compression (spiral or tied)	0.75
Bearings on concrete	0.70
Compression in anchorage zones (nominal weight concrete)	0.80

Performance factors for anchorages. Ground anchors may fail by (1) excessive yielding or fracture of the tendon, (2) failure of the grout-tendon bond, and (3) failure of the ground-grout bond. These mechanisms are reviewed by Xanthakos (1991). In this discussion, we briefly present failure criteria of the ground-grout interaction merely to summarize methods for estimating anchor pullout resistance.

For straight-shaft anchors in rock, the bond strength and length can be estimated from direct pullout tests (Xanthakos, 1991). Theoretical data are provided by Coates and Yu (1970) and are confirmed by Berardi (1967). Where shear strength tests are performed on representative rock samples, Littlejohn (1980) recommends maximum average working bond stress (based on uniform bond distribution) obtained from the measured shear strength divided by a factor of safety ($\geqslant 2$ and probably ≈ 3). This approach is valid for soft rocks with uniaxial compressive strength less than 7 N/mm^2 (1000 lb/in^2), and where the holes have been drilled using rotary-percussive techniques. If shear

TABLE 4-12 Rock-Grout Bond Values Recommended for Design

Rock type	Working bond, N/mm^2	Ultimate bond, N/mm^2	Factor of safety	Source
Igneous:				
Medium hard basalt		5.73	3–4	India—Rao (1964)
Weathered granite		1.50–2.50		Japan—Suzuki et al. (1972)
Basalt	1.21–1.38	3.86	2.8–3.2	Britain—Wycliffe-Jones (1974)
Granite	1.38–1.55	4.83	3.1–3.5	Britain—Wycliffe-Jones (1974)
Serpentine	0.45–0.59	1.55	2.6–3.5	Britain—Wycliffe-Jones (1974)
Granite and basalt		1.72–3.10	1.5–2.5	USA—PCI (1974)
Metamorphic:				
Manhattan schist	0.70	2.80	4.0	USA—White (1973)
Slate and hard shale		0.83–1.38	1.5–2.5	USA—PCI (1974)
Calcareous sediments:				
Limestone	1.00	2.83	2.8	Switzerland—Losinger (1966)
Chalk—Grades I–II	0.005N	0.22–1.07	2.0	Britain—Littlejohn (1970)
(N = SPT in blows/0.3 m)		0.01N	(temporary) 3.0–4.0 (permanent)	
Tertiary limestone	0.83–0.97	2.76	2.9–3.3	Britain—Wycliffe-Jones (1974)
Chalk limestone	0.86–1.00	2.76	2.8–3.2	Britain—Wycliffe-Jones (1974)
Soft limestone		1.03–1.52	1.5–2.5	USA—PCI (1974)
Dolomitic limestone		1.38–2.07	1.5–2.5	USA—PCI (1974)

strength data and pullout tests are not available, the ultimate bond stress is often taken as one-tenth the uniaxial compressive strength of rock (100 percent recovery) up to a maximum value of 4.2 N/mn² (600 lb/in²). Recommended design and ultimate bond values are summarized in Table 4-12 for a wide range of igneous, metamorphic, and sedimentary rocks. The factor of safety correlating ultimate and working bond resistance is based on uniform bond distribution.

The ultimate resistance of anchors in sand depends on the following: (1) relative density and degree of uniformity of the soil; (2) fixed anchor geometry and dimensions (mainly the length and to a lesser degree the diameter); (3) method of grout injection and grout pressure used; (4) dilatancy in the soil that can result in higher normal stresses, hence greater friction at the grout-soil interface; and (5) to a lesser degree, the drilling method and equipment. For the two basic types (enlarged cylinder and straight shaft), field trials have provided the following empirical rule for estimating ultimate capacity:

$$T_n = LN' \tan \phi \qquad (4\text{-}41)$$

where T_n = ultimate load capacity (nominal resistance) in kN; L = fixed anchor length (m); N' = a constant factor; and ϕ = friction angle of sand. Equation (4-41) provides a simple but crude estimation of ultimate capacity. Where pressure grouting is used, the effect is to increase nominal resistance considerably. In this context, an empirical formula derived from field tests relates ultimate capacity T_n to grout pressure p' as follows:

$$T_n = p' \pi DL \tan \phi \qquad (4\text{-}42)$$

where D and L are effective anchor diameter and length in the fixed zone, respectively. A complete review of procedures for estimating ultimate capacity based on theoretical and empirical data is given by Xanthakos (1991).

Load capacity of anchors in clay depends on adhesion, and thus it can be improved by special procedures, such as the use of high-pressure grouting and the formation of bells or underreams in the fixed zone. For a tremie-grouted straight shaft, pullout capacity is derived theoretically as

$$T_n = \pi DLas_u \qquad (4\text{-}43)$$

where s_u = average undrained shear strength over fixed length and a = adhesion factor. Postgrouting appears to increase load resistance by causing hydraulic fracture in the clay locally. For clays of medium to high plasticity, tests show a linear increase in shear resistance with increasing postgrouting pressure until the latter attains values of 3

N/mm^2 (450 lb/in^2). Postgrouting pressures should be well below the values at which bursting of the grout can occur.

The foregoing highlight the complexities of load transfer at the ground-grout interface and suggest the effect of many variables. A detailed review of methodologies for estimating fixed anchor length is given by Xanthakos (1991). Taking into account all variables influencing the load transfer, the minimum factor of safety for ASD should be 2.5 and preferably close to 3.0, unless full-scale field tests confirm a lower value.

Resistance factors for ground anchors in conjunction with strength design are stipulated as follows (anchor pullout resistance):

	ϕ
Sand:	
Based on soil data	0.60
Based on pullout tests	0.65
Clay:	
Correlation with unconfined compressive strength	0.60
Using shear stress from pullout field tests	0.65
Rock:	
Presumptive value	0.50
Laboratory rock-grout bond tests	0.70–0.75

Interestingly, these values of ϕ are somewhat less than the values suggested by the proposed LRFD document (Modjeski and Masters, 1982). It is felt that at this time the available statistical information is not sufficient to warrant the application of reliability theory; hence experience and judgment were formidable supplements in deriving these performance factors.

Performance factors for passive resistance. In conjunction with Eq. (4-38), active earth pressure is considered a load and is factored according to a load factor >1. Conversely passive pressure is a load effect and is placed on the resistance side of the equation. Thus, when considering the overall equilibrium of the system a performance factor must be applied to the passive resistance.

Performance factors for passive resistance are stipulated as follows:

	ϕ
Sand:	
Semiempirical procedure using SPT data	0.45
Semiempirical procedure using CPT data	0.55
Rational method, using ϕ from SPT data	0.35
Rational method, using ϕ from CPT data	0.45
Clay:	
Semiempirical procedure using CPT data	0.50
Rational method	0.50–0.60
Rock, semiempirical procedure	0.60
Plate load test	0.55

where SPT = standard penetration test and CPT = cone penetration test. These values of ϕ have been introduced by the proposed LRFD document (Modjeski and Masters, 1992).

Commentary. It is essential to recognize that the load factor approach is applied to the combined system of soil and structure. Using the same methodology, failure is explicitly examined in the structure (in this case load effects are moments, shears, and so on), and also in the soil-structure system (anchor-ground interaction, and wall-soil interaction in the passive zone). In the same context, serviceability states are not considered since this is primarily a strength state.

For normal functions where the wall serves essentially as ground support to retain earth masses, the loads included in Eq. (4-40) are sufficient to cover all possible combinations and contingencies. As the function of the wall is expanded, the typical load group expressed by Eq. (4-40) must be amplified to include other types of loads. For example, where walls serves as piers and abutments for bridge superstructures, other loads to be introduced are those acting on bridges, such as wind, longitudinal forces, and braking forces. These cases are examined in other sections.

Alternate limit state approach, soil-structure systems

In this approach limit states are classified as either ultimate limit states where account is taken of the worst credible values that the associated variables could take, or serviceability limit states where the most probable values are used. Although in principle all limit states should be examined explicitly, in practice only one may be more critical than the others.

Ultimate limit states. These are manifested by (1) failure in the soil without failure in the structure, involving loss of stability and causing considerable rigid movement of the structure; (2) failure in the structure without failure occurring in the soil; and (3) failure occurring in the structure and the soil together.

Serviceability limit states. These are assumed to have been reached after excessive deformation and ground settlement, heave, lateral movement, structural deformation, and excessive cracking.

Loads and load effects. A load is an external action applied to the soil-structure system, for example, dead and wind loads or gravitational forces and surcharges acting on the soil mass under consideration.

Interestingly, earth pressures are not classified as loads but may be considered load effects. The latter are necessarily internal to the soil-structure system. In this context, internal forces and moments are considered load effects. In considering the overall stability, the total disturbing moment or force is load effect.

Characteristic values. These are not intended to have direct design significance. The term is merely a convenient reference item that may have a specified minimum value, a statutory value, or an average value based on testing.

Characteristic loads. For dead, imposed, and wind loads, the characteristic values are defined by relevant codes and specifications.

Characteristic material properties. These are strength, stiffness, unit weight, etc. For concrete and steel, they are defined in the specifications. For soils, the characteristic value of any material property is the best estimate of in situ value. The assessment of test results relates to the variability and number of tests in relation to the variability of in situ conditions. If sufficient reliable results are available, the characteristic value may be taken as the mean of the results. This is justified since failure in the soil requires the development of limiting states of stress over a significantly large area over which the assumption of average values is reasonable.

Characteristic in situ values. Establishing the initial pore water pressure is often the first requirement. This should be the best estimate of pressures considering all available information, and seasonal or other variations. Characteristic initial vertical stresses may be derived from the characteristic unit weight and pore water pressure. It may also be necessary to establish the characteristic initial lateral stresses, particularly if the expected deformations are not sufficient for the limiting states of stress to be attained.

Most probable values. These are defined as follows: (1) for variables that are constant with time, for example, dead loads and certain material properties, the most probable values are the best estimates of in situ values; (2) for variables that change with time (for example, live and wind load or soil strength and stiffness) the most probable values are the best estimates of the extreme values that will occur during the life of the structure.

The most probable values of the different variables are obtained by applying partial factors to the characteristic values. In many instances, these factors are close to unity. Exceptions are structural material strengths, for which the characteristic values are defined in terms of specified minimum strength rather than mean values.

Worst credible values. For loads and material properties these have an accepted very small probability of being encountered. As a criterion, this probability should notionally be set at 0.1 percent. The worst credible value of any variable will be either the maximum or the minimum value depending on whether the effect is beneficial or adverse.

The worst credible load effects will be the worst credible combinations of the effects of different variables, but allowance can be made for the reduced probability of the worst credible values of the individual variables occurring together.

For variables such as dead, live, and wind loads and structural material strengths, the worst credible value may be obtained by applying partial safety factors to the characteristic values, but for soil strengths this approach is not always appropriate. This methodology suggests that for variables such as pore water pressure, material stiffness, and initial stresses, the partial factor approach is impractical. When partial factors are not to be applied, worst credible values should be evaluated directly from the available information.

Partial safety factors. These are intended to reflect the effect of various uncertainties inherent in the design and construction.

Load factors γ_{f1} and γ_{f2}. The load variation factor γ_{f1} takes into account the possibility of unfavorable deviations of loads from their characteristic values. The load combination factor γ_{f2} takes into account the reduced probability of loads, which are stochastically independent, occurring at the same time.

Structural performance factor γ_p. This factor reflects the following effects: (1) Inaccurate assessment of loading effects and unforeseen stress redistribution within a system; (2) variations in construction accuracy; (3) the importance of the limit state under consideration; and (4) some systems may provide a warning of approaching a limit state, while others may reach it suddenly.

Partial material factor γ_m. This factor reflects the effect of the following: (1) materials in the system may have a strength lower than indicated by samples; and (2) the structure may be weakened from construction imperfections.

From ultimate limit states the factors γ_{f1} and γ_{f2} should be applied to the characteristic values of the loads, and the resulting values taken as the worst credible loads or load combinations. The worst credible material strengths can be obtained in the same manner by dividing characteristic strengths by γ_m.

Ultimate limit state requirements. These requirements are satisfied if

$$\frac{\text{Worst credible resistance } R}{\text{Worst credible load effects } S} \geq \gamma_p \qquad (4\text{-}44)$$

where R and S are calculated using the worst credible values and combinations of loads and material strengths. The term γ_p is the structural performance factor.

Serviceability limit state requirements. These requirements are satisfied if it can be demonstrated that movement, distortion, and cracking of the structure is acceptable. The most probable values would normally be assumed, except where the consequences can be serious and the associated effects particularly sensitive to variations, in which case most conservative values may be introduced.

Where structural elements are considered, the limit state for service conditions will usually be deemed to be satisfied once ultimate limit state checks have been made.

For movements in the soil, two approaches are suggested, and in case of uncertainty the assessment of the design may be based on both results: (1) calculate most probable settlement, heave, or other movement from conventional theories; and (2) demonstrate that stability can be maintained with stresses in the soil known from experience with similar problems or on the basis of a theoretical investigation consistent with tolerable deformations. Occasionally it may be necessary to carry out separate checks for the ultimate limit state.

4-14 Design Examples

Design Example 4-1 Figure 4-105 shows a diaphragm wall section for a waterfront installation. In the permanent state the wall will resist lateral earth pres-

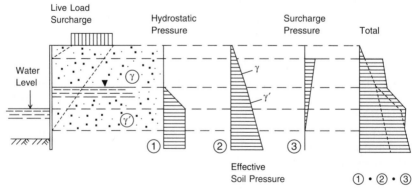

Figure 4-105 Diaphragm wall for a waterfront installation, example 4-1.

sure (probably close to the K_0 condition), hydrostatic pressure, and surcharge loads due to traffic moving alongside the structure. The wall is braced near the top by ground anchors (not shown) and at the bottom by embedment into dense soil.

Three separate pressure diagrams are drawn. Diagram 1 is for hydrostatic water pressure, and its shape is self-explanatory. Diagram 2 is for earth pressures; note that below the design groundwater level, the diagram is based on effective weight. Diagram 3 represents lateral effects from the live load surcharge at the surface. For strength design, moments and shears due to loads 1, 2, and 3 are computed separately and entered into Eq. (4-40) with appropriate load coefficients and load factors. These factored loads are then compared with the factored resistance of the system. Note that two computations are necessary; one is to check the ultimate structural capacity of the wall in moment and shear, and the other to check the stability of the wall-soil-anchor system.

For allowable stress design (ASD), the composite diagram of pressures shown in Fig. 4-105 may be used since the variability of loads is not differentiated.

Design Example 4-2   For the wall shown in Fig. 4-106, a preliminary analysis will be carried out merely for system optimization. The support is a diaphragm wall braced by two rows of anchors and by embedment below excavation level. The soil to be retained is sand with $\phi = 30°$, $\gamma = 110$ lb/ft³, $K_a = \frac{1}{3}$, $K_0 = 1 - \sin \phi = 0.50$. The height of the excavation is 33 ft. We choose the ASD method.

Total horizontal earth thrust is estimated for the K_0 condition as follows: $P_e = \frac{1}{2}\gamma K_0 H^2 = \frac{1}{2}(110 \times 0.5)(33)^2 = 29,950$ lb/ft of wall, say 30,000 lb/ft. With these data, a preliminary design can be carried out according to the following steps:

$Step\ 1.$ Determine anchor vertical spacing. Initially we assume two rows of anchors, and locate each row at the $\frac{1}{4}$ point from the top and bottom, as

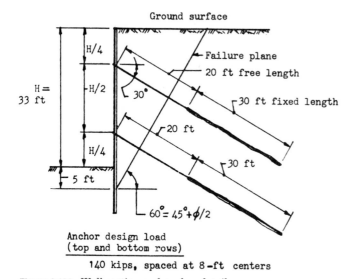

Anchor design load
(top and bottom rows)

140 kips, spaced at 8-ft centers

Figure 4-106 Wall section and anchor details.

shown in Fig. 4-106. This gives a cantilever height of about 9 ft, assumed to be consistent with the intent to limit lateral wall movement. Each anchor can now be assumed to take a load component from the top or bottom of the wall to midheight.

Step 2.   Anchor horizontal force. We select anchor loads based on uniform horizontal pressure distribution with a resultant 30,000 lb. The horizontal reaction per anchor is therefore 15,000 lb/ft.

Step 3.   Anchor inclination. Because suitable anchoring strata are available, a very steep angle is not necessary. Considering the influence of adjacent utilities, foundations, and wall drawdown by the vertical anchor component, we select an angle of 30° with the horizontal.

Step 4.   Determine anchor load. Given the anchor inclination of 30°, the anchor load is 15/cos 30° = 17.3 kips/ft for both rows. For a wall panel 24 ft long supported by three vertical rows of anchors, anchor spacing is 8 ft horizontally, giving a design anchor load of 17.3 × 8 = 139 kips (say 140 kips). The vertical anchor component is 140 × sin 30° = 70 kips, which induces an external vertical load 70/8 = 9 kips/ft in addition to the weight of the wall. The wall embedment must now be estimated to accommodate the transfer of the vertical load. This may be considered by shear resistance at the wall-soil interface below excavation level and by base bearing (see also Chap. 5).

Step 5.   Determine fixed anchor length. Since the sand is fine-grained but dense, we can assume that cement grout injected under pressure will produce an anchor zone with essentially nonuniform diameter. For an effective hole diameter of 9 in, we estimate next $p' = 2 \times 25 = 50$, where 25 ft is the height (assumed) of overburden above the top of fixed anchor. From Eq. (4-42), and using a factor of safety of 2, the fixed anchor length is

$$L = \frac{2 \times 140,000}{50 \times 3.14 \times 9 \times \tan 30°} = 343 \text{ in} = 29 \text{ ft}   \text{(use 30 ft)}$$

Step 6.   Determine failure plane and anchor free length. Using $\phi = 30°$, the failure plane is assumed to begin 5 ft below excavation level and extend at $45 + \phi/2 = 60°$ as shown in Fig. 4-106. The length from upper anchor entry point to failure plane is 29.75 × sin 30° = 14.9 ft. Allowing 5 ft of penetration, the free length in the upper row is 20 ft, and the same free length is used in the lower row to provide the minimum stressing length.

Step 7.   Select tendon steel for a design load of 140 kips. We select 0.6-in-diameter 270-ksi strand, and an anchor tendon consisting of 5 strands. For a factor of safety of 2, the required area is 2 × 140,000/270,000 = 1.04 in². Each strand has a cross-sectional area of 0.215 in, giving a total tendon area of 5 × 0.215 = 1.07 in².

Step 8.   Compute moments and shears in a diaphragm wall. This stage is demonstrated in subsequent design examples.

Design Example 4-3   Figure 4-107 shows a typical section of a diaphragm wall anchored at the top by a single row of anchors and at the bottom by embedment below excavation level. The soil is cohesionless material with strength parameters as shown. The wall is assumed to penetrate an impervious formation so that the ground inside the excavation is assumed to be dry with $\phi = 32°$. The stability of the wall of the base will be checked for fixed earth support to compare allowable stress and load factor design.

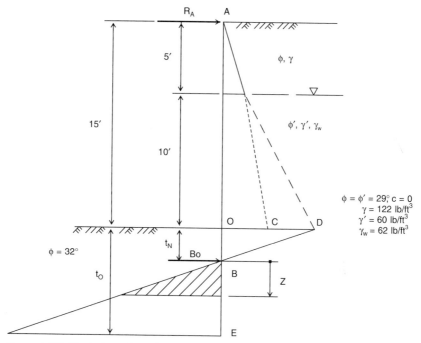

Figure 4-107 Typical section of a diaphragm wall and soil data for Design Example 4-3.

The importance of friction at the wall-soil interface has been emphasized in the foregoing sections. In this example, friction will be considered below excavation level on the passive side. For the soil conditions of the problem a friction angle $\delta = 20°$ is assumed. On the active side the wall must resist lateral earth stresses at rest and water pressure. The coefficient K_0 is computed from $K_0 = 1 - \sin \phi' = 0.52$.

Allowable stress design.   The total pressure at excavation level is the sum of earth pressure (OC) and water pressure (CD), or

$$(OD) = (122)(0.52)(5) + (60)(0.52)(10) + (62.50)(10)$$

$$= (317 + 312) + 625 = 629 + 625 = 1254 \text{ lb/ft}^2$$

The coefficient of passive pressure K_p is estimated according to the Coulomb method for $\phi = 32°$ and $\delta = 20°$, or $K_p = 6.89$. Below excavation the active pressure (at rest pressure plus water) increases by $(60)(0.52) + 62.5 = 94$ lb/ft, and the passive pressure by $(122)(6.89) = 840$ lb/ft. The point of zero load is located at distance x such that $840x = 1254 + 94x$, or $x = t_N = 1.68$ ft. The reaction B_0 is computed for the load diagram ABD and for the equivalent beam AB, or $B_0 = 6400$ lb.

For beam BE, pinned at B and fixed at some point below, the moment M at depth z is due to the reaction and the shaded pressure diagram, or

$$M_z = (6400) z - \frac{(1254)}{1.68} \cdot \frac{z^3}{6}$$

and setting $M_z = 0$ gives $z = \sqrt{6400/124} = 7.2$ ft.

For a factor of safety of 2, the wall embedment is $t_0 = t_N + 2z = 1.68 + 2(7.20) = 16.1$ ft.

Load factor design. We assumed that the K_0 obtained from $1 - \sin \phi'$ is a fairly good representation of in situ value so that we can select the lower range of load factor coefficient 1.2 (from Table 4-11). Therefore, the factored pressure OD at the base is (AASHTO criteria)

$$OD = 1.3(629 \times 1.2 + 625) = 1795 \ \text{lb/ft}^2$$

For a performance factor $\phi_p = 0.55$, the factored passive resistance coefficient is

$$\phi_p K_p = (0.55)(6.89) = 3.80$$

The point of zero load is now

$$(122)(3.80)x = 1795 + 130x \qquad \text{or} \qquad x = t_N = 5.37 \ \text{ft}$$

The reaction B_0 is computed for the load diagram with $OD = 1795$ lb and $AB = 15 + 5.37 = 20.37$ ft, or $B_0 = 10,400$ lb.
    Likewise

$$M_z = (10,400)z - \frac{(1795)}{5.37} \cdot \frac{z^3}{6}$$

and for $M_z = 0$,

$$z = \sqrt{\frac{10,400}{55.7}} = 13.6 \ \text{ft}$$

or total embedment $t_0 = 5.37 + 13.6 = 19.0$ ft.
    We should note that both the safety factor in allowable stress design and the load and performance factors in strength design may be modified at the discretion of the designer depending on the level of uncertainty in design and the consequences of failure. A smaller passive resistance than K_p values may also be dictated by limitations to lateral movement. Passive resistance may be absent, for example, close to the base of excavation because of soil deterioration due to scour, freeze-thaw, or other disturbances. These effects are reflected in the safety and resistance factors. Some designers may also choose a reduced friction angle to compensate for uncertainties in design parameters.
    The same problem may be solved by finite-element methods using general computer programs. These solutions have the advantage of parametric studies, and include iterations necessary to optimize the results. Nonetheless they require a substantial output that is impractical for this text.

Design Example 4-4 Figure 4-108 shows a typical section of a single-anchored wall in loose and dense sand, with water level on either side as indicated. The wall will be analyzed according to the alternate limit approach discussed in Sec. 4-13. The load variation factor is 1.25, to be applied to the surface surcharge and earth pressure loads (increase for active and decrease for passive) to obtain the worst credible values. Table 4-13 summarizes relevant material properties and soil parameters including more probable and worst credible values. Free earth support is assumed for wall embedment.

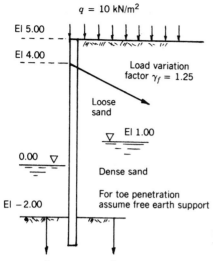

Figure 4-108 Typical cross section; anchored wall.

Step 1.   Calculate total pressures

	Most probable values	Worst credible values
Active pressure:		
At level +5 10 × 0.26	2.6	3.2
At level +1 (10 + 4 × 17.2) × 0.26	20.5	25.6
At level +1 (10 + 4 × 17.2) × 0.23	18.1	22.6
At level 0 [10 + 4 × 17.2) + (20.6 −		
9.8)] × 0.23 + 9.8	30.4	37.6
Below −2	55.0 + 12.3x	63.9 + 13.2x
Passive pressure:		
At level −2	19.6	19.6
Below −2 x(20.6 − 9.8)(6.3) +		
9.8(2 + x)	19.6 + 77.8x	19.6 + 54.0x
where x is measured from level −2		

Step 2.   Design for ultimate limit state. First we calculate forces using worst credible resistance and worst credible load effects, and then take moments about level +4 (anchor level). The dimension x is measured downward from level −2.00.

$$\text{Active force} = 189.9 + 63.9x + 6.55x^2 \quad \text{(kN/m)}$$

$$\text{Moment} = 713.4 + 63.9x(6 + x/2) + 6.55x^2(6 + \tfrac{2}{3}x)$$

$$\text{Passive force} = 19.6 + 19.6x + 26.9x^2 \quad \text{(kN/m)}$$

$$\text{Moment} = 104.5 + 19.6x(6 + x/2) + 26.9x^2(6 + \tfrac{2}{3}x)$$

TABLE 4-13 Soil Data, Most Probable Values, and Worst Credible Values; Wall of Fig. 4-108

Material property		Most probable values	Worst credible values
Steel strength		255 MN/m²	γ_m = 1.15
Steel modulus		207 × 10³ MN/m²	γ_m = 1.00
Loose sand	γ_L	17.2 kN/m³	18.5 max
			15.7 min
	ϕ	33°	29°
	δ	0.5ϕ	0.5ϕ
	K_a	0.26	0.305
	K_p	5.5	4.3
Dense sand	γ_d	20.6 kN/m³	21.5 max
			19.1 min
	ϕ	35°	31°
	δ	0.5ϕ	0.5ϕ
	K_a	0.23	0.29
	K_p	6.3	4.75
Water	γ_w	9.8 kN/m³	9.8

For equilibrium active moment = passive moment, which gives x = 3.2 m below level −2.00. However, Eq. (4-44) applies. For a performance factor γ_p = 1.25, M_p = 1.25M_A, giving x = 3.9 m.

Interestingly, for this example the strength reduction for the passive resistance is reflected by a smaller value of the friction angle (from 33° to 29°), and a corresponding decrease in the K_p value (from 6.30 to 4.75) or a strength reduction factor of 4.75/6.30 = 0.75.

Commentary

The foregoing examples show how to apply routine analysis to solve problems that involve active and passive pressures. They also show the importance of selecting load and resistance factors that reflect the statistically possible maximum deviation of loads and resistances from the assumed design values.

At rest pressure. The Jaky (1944) expression [Eq. (4-14)] generally applies to normally consolidated soils where ϕ' = drained friction angle of soil. This is a simplified form of the expression

$$K_0 = (1 + \tfrac{2}{3} \sin \phi')K_a \tag{4-45}$$

For granular materials another expression for a modified at rest coefficient K_{01} is proposed by Pruska (1972) as

$$K_{01} = \tan (45 - \phi'/2) \tag{4-46}$$

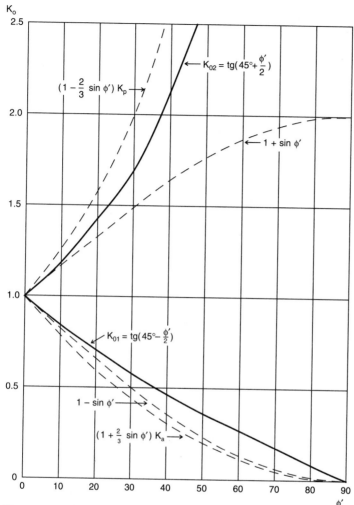

Figure 4-109 Coefficient of earth pressure at rest K_0 as a function of the drained friction angle ϕ'.

Eqs. (4-14), (4-45), and (4-46) are plotted in Fig. 4-109, and evidently Jaky's formulas define the lower limit of the at rest pressure coefficient.

For overconsolidated soils the current practice is to estimate the coefficient K_{0u} using empirical relationships as suggested by Mayne and Kulhawy (1982). In this case the pressure coefficient K_{0u} is a function of K_0 (coefficient at rest for normally consolidated soils), the drained friction angle ϕ', and the factor OCR = overconsolidation ratio (maximum previous vertical pressure divided by current effective

TABLE 4-14   Typical Coefficients of Lateral Earth Pressure At Rest

Soil type	ϕ_f	OCR = 1	OCR = 2	OCR = 5	OCR = 10
		Coefficient of lateral earth pressure			
Loose sand	33.5°	0.45	0.65	1.10	1.50
Medium sand	36.5°	0.40	0.60	1.05	1.55
Dense sand	40.5°	0.35	0.55	1.00	1.50
Silt	29.5°	0.50	0.70	1.10	1.60
Lean clay, CL	23.5°	0.60	0.80	1.20	1.65
Highly plastic clay, CH	20.5°	0.65	0.80	1.10	1.40

vertical pressure). Typical values of K_{0u} corresponding to various values of OCR are given in Table 4-14 (Clough and Duncan, 1991). A brief review of this procedure is given in Sec. 10-4.

These considerations show the load variability for various soil types and stress histories, and should judge the selection of the load coefficient β for earth pressure shown in Table 4-11.

Passive resistance.   Likewise, the variability of the passive earth pressure coefficient K_p obtained from the Coulomb theory is shown in Table 4-15 as a function of the soil friction angle ϕ and the wall-soil friction angle δ. The performance factors introduced in Sec. 4-13 reflect uncertainties in soil characteristics, overexcavation, soil deterioration near the base, and inaccuracies in design. Although they do not apply to serviceability states, a reduction in passive pressure may also be dictated by the desire to limit movement of the wall.

These considerations should likewise judge the selection of performance factors for passive resistance, and if conditions warrant, the factors shown in Sec. 4-13 may be increased.

4-15   Further Topics for Analysis in Soil with Cohesion

Tension zone.   Neither the Coulomb nor the Rankine theory explicitly incorporates cohesion as a relevant parameter in equation form for computing lateral earth stresses. Equations (4-19) and (4-19a) were developed by Bell (1915) and obtained directly from Mohr's circle.

According to Eq. (4-19a), and with cohesion not zero, we should expect a tension zone to develop. The depth at which $\sigma_h = 0$ can be found directly from Eq. (4-19a) and is

$$h_t = \frac{2c}{\gamma\sqrt{K_a}} \tag{4-47}$$

As mentioned, the tension zone h_t should not be relied on to reduce lateral earth stresses. Instead, a usual assumption is that the crack can form and will probably fill with water, causing a hydrostatic force $\gamma_w h_t$. Hence the pressure diagram is as shown in Fig. 4-110. Either of the two alternatives may be used together with the water pressure profile if the assumption is made that the tension crack is filled with water. However, treating the tension block as a surcharge is considered the more correct approach and gives a more conservative solution (larger force and overturning moment).

Wall embedment with top support. An assumed pressure diagram for soil with cohesion is shown in Fig. 4-66b for a free earth support at the bottom. The analysis is for $\phi = 0°$, or undrained conditions below the dredge line. Taking moments about the anchor point and rearranging, an expression is obtained for the embedment D as

$$D^2 + 2Dh_3 - \frac{2\bar{y}R_a}{4c - \bar{q}} = 0 \qquad (4\text{-}48)$$

where all symbols correspond to the notation of Fig. 4-66b. From inspection, the system is unstable if the passive pressure $\sigma_p \leq 0$, and this occurs if

$$\frac{\gamma H}{c} \geq 4 \qquad (4\text{-}49)$$

Wall embedment with cantilever walls ($\phi = 0$). This case is treated similarly to granular soils, but with some additional requirements. These may involve consolidation in the passive zones, tension cracks as before, shrinking of the clay that may thus pull away from the wall, and associated increases in lateral pressures. Interestingly, wall adhesion may be included in the foregoing analysis or may be ignored to allow for the soil-wall separation.

A generalized pressure diagram for a cantilever wall is shown in Fig. 4-111. From a consideration of the equilibrium conditions and from Eqs. (4-19) and (4-19a), an expression for the embedment D is derived as

$$D^2(4c - \bar{q}) - 2DR_a - \frac{R_a(12c\bar{y} + R_a)}{2c + \bar{q}} = 0 \qquad (4\text{-}50)$$

where all terms are as shown in Fig. 4-111.

Long-term conditions. In cohesive soil, because of the load decrease caused by excavation, the ground in the passive zone just below the

TABLE 4-15 Coulomb Passive Earth Pressure Coefficients K_p

						Alpha = 90, Beta = −10			
δ	$\phi = 26$	28	30	32	34	36	38	40	42
0	1.914	2.053	2.204	2.369	2.547	2.743	2.957	3.193	3.452
16	2.693	2.956	3.247	3.571	3.934	4.344	4.807	5.335	5.940
17	2.760	3.034	3.339	3.679	4.062	4.493	4.983	5.543	6.187
20	2.980	3.294	3.645	4.041	4.488	4.997	5.581	6.255	7.039
22	3.145	3.490	3.878	4.317	4.814	5.389	6.050	6.819	7.720

						Alpha = 90, Beta = −5			
δ	$\phi = 26$	28	30	32	34	36	38	40	42
0	2.223	2.392	2.577	2.781	3.004	3.250	3.523	3.826	4.163
16	3.367	3.709	4.094	4.529	5.024	5.591	6.243	7.000	7.883
17	3.469	3.828	4.234	4.694	5.218	5.820	6.516	7.326	8.277
20	3.806	4.226	4.704	5.250	5.879	6.609	7.462	8.468	9.665
22	4.064	4.532	5.067	5.684	6.399	7.236	8.222	9.397	10.809

						Alpha = 90, Beta = 0			
δ	$\phi = 26$	28	30	32	34	36	38	40	42
0	2.561	2.770	3.000	3.255	3.537	3.852	4.204	4.599	5.045
16	4.195	4.652	5.174	5.775	6.469	7.279	8.229	9.356	10.704
17	4.346	4.830	5.385	6.025	6.767	7.636	8.661	9.882	11.351
20	4.857	5.436	6.105	6.886	7.804	8.892	10.194	11.771	13.705
22	5.253	5.910	6.675	7.574	8.641	9.919	11.466	13.364	15.726

Alpha = 90, Beta = 5

δ	φ = 26	28	30	32	34	36	38	40	42
0	2.943	3.203	3.492	3.815	4.177	4.585	5.046	5.572	6.173
16	5.250	5.878	6.609	7.464	8.474	9.678	11.128	12.894	15.076
17	5.475	6.146	6.929	7.850	8.942	10.251	11.836	13.781	16.201
20	6.249	7.074	8.049	9.212	10.613	12.321	14.433	17.083	20.468
22	6.864	7.820	8.960	10.334	12.011	14.083	16.685	20.011	24.352

Alpha = 90, Beta = 10

δ	φ = 26	28	30	32	34	36	38	40	42
0	3.385	3.712	4.080	4.496	4.968	5.507	6.125	6.840	7.673
16	6.652	7.545	8.605	9.876	11.417	13.309	15.665	18.647	22.497
17	6.992	7.956	9.105	10.492	12.183	14.274	16.899	20.254	24.633
20	8.186	9.414	10.903	12.733	15.014	17.903	21.636	26.569	33.270
22	9.164	10.625	12.421	14.659	17.497	21.164	26.012	32.601	41.863

Alpha = 90, Beta = 15

δ	φ = 26	28	30	32	34	36	38	40	42
0	3.913	4.331	4.807	5.352	5.980	6.710	7.563	8.570	9.768
16	8.611	9.936	11.555	13.557	16.073	19.291	23.494	29.123	36.894
17	9.139	10.590	12.373	14.595	17.413	21.054	25.867	32.409	41.603
20	11.049	12.984	15.422	18.541	22.617	28.080	35.629	46.458	62.759
22	12.676	15.047	18.130	22.136	27.506	34.930	45.584	61.626	87.354

δ = angle of friction between wall and soil.
φ = friction angle of soil.
Alpha = angle of inclination of wall, normally 90°.
Beta = angle of inclination of backfill or finished ground behind wall.

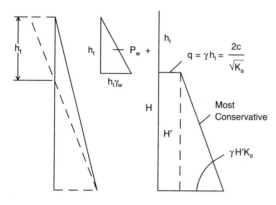

Suggested pressure diagrams (solid) in
cohesive soil.

Figure 4-110 Tension cracks and critical depth of unbraced excavation. Tension cracks are often readily
visible adjacent to excavations.

excavation will initially experience a decrease of pore pressure, which
may even become negative. With time the pore pressure will rise
again. In the immediate condition the pore pressures generated by
unloading and strain have no time to dissipate so that the analysis
can be based on the undrained shear strength ($c = s_u$) at natural
water content. For the long-term condition the pore pressures gener-

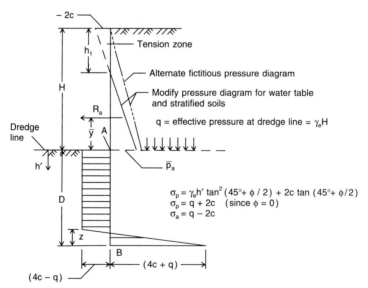

Figure 4-111 Walls in cohesive soil. The undrained shear strength ($\phi =$
0) case shown is conservative. Assumptions shown are for "classical
method" analysis.

ated by unloading will dissipate by drainage, and hence an effective stress analysis will in this case be appropriate based on static water level. Interestingly, it is not possible to conclude which method of analysis (total or effective stress) will yield more conservative results unless the computations are completed. In most instances the difference between the two methods will be small.

ASD vs. load factor. For allowable stress design, the embedment depth computed from Eqs. (4-48) and (4-50) may be increased 30 to 40 percent. Alternatively the cohesion c used in these equations may be divided by an appropriate safety factor, usually 1.5 to 2.0. When applying the safety factor concept we may arrive at the erroneous conclusion that the wall cannot be built if

$$\frac{4c}{SF} \leq \bar{q} \tag{4-51}$$

With load factor design, the factor $\bar{q}$ is not increased since this is the vertical earth pressure and from Table 4-11 the load factor is 1. An appropriate load factor $\gamma > 1$ is applied to the lateral earth pressure that produces the parameter R_a in Eqs. (4-48) and (4-50). With cohesive soil this factor should reflect the effects of anisotropic, nonhomogeneous, and time-dependent behavior of the soil where these characteristics are present, as well as the problem identified in this section. On the passive side a performance factor is applied to the cohesion c. No attempts should be made to establish structural compatibility between the two methods by recalibrating the safety factors in conjunction with the load and performance factors.

References

Aas, G., 1976: Stability of Slurry Trench Excavation in Soft Clay, *Proc. 6th Eur. Conf. Soil Mech. Found. Eng.*, Vienna, vol. 1.1, pp. 103–110. Also published in Norwegian Geotechn. Inst., Oslo, *Publ.* 111.

AASHTO, 1989: Standard Specifications for Highway Bridges.

ACI 318-83, 1983: Building Code Requirements for Reinforced Concrete, American Concrete Institute, Detroit.

AISC, 1986: Load and Resistance Factor Design Specifications for Structural Steel Buildings, Chicago, Ill., September.

Alberro, J., 1969: "Contribution to Discussion," *Proc. 7th Int. Conf. Soil Mech. Found. Eng.*, vol. 3, pp. 349–357.

Armento, W. J., 1973: "Cofferdam for BARTD Embarcadero Subway Station," presented at the ASCE National Struct. Eng. Meet., Apr. 9–13, San Francisco (Preprint 1926).

Bara, J. P., 1976: "Collapsible Soils," presented at the ASCE Annual Convention and Exposition, Philadelphia, Pa., September.

Barden, L., A. McGown, and K. Collins, 1973: "The Collapse Mechanism in Partly Saturated Soil," *Engineering Geology*, Amsterdam, The Netherlands, pp. 49–60.

Barker, R. M., et al., 1991: Manuals for the Design of Bridge Foundations, NCHRP 343, TRB, National Research Council, Washington, D.C.

Barla, G., and C. Mascardi, 1974: High Anchored Wall in Genoa, Proc. Diaphragm Walls Anchorages, *Inst. Civ. Eng.,* London.

Becker, James M., 1990: "Up/Down Construction—Decision Making and Performance," Design and Performance of Earth Retaining Structures, *Proc. ASCE Spec. Conf.,* Ithaca, N.Y., June, pp. 170–189.

Bell, A. L., 1915: "The Lateral Pressure and Resistance of Clay, and the Supporting Power of Clay Foundations," in *A Century of Soil Mech.,* ICE, London, pp. 93–134.

Berardi, G., 1967: "Sul Comportamento Deglic Ancoraggi Immersi in Terreni Diversi," Univ. Genoa, Inst. Constr. Sc. Series III, no. 60, 18 pp.

Bishop, A. W., 1958: "Test Requirements for Measuring the Coefficient of Earth Pressure at Rest," *Proc. Brussels Conf. Earth Pressure Probl.,* vol. 1, pp. 2–14.

Bjerrum, L., 1963: *Discuss. Eur. Conf. Soil Mech. Found. Eng.,* Wiesbaden, vol. 2.

Bjerrum, L., and K. H. Andersen, 1972: In-Situ Measurement of Lateral Pressures in Clay, *Proc. 5th Eur. Conf. Soil Mech. Found. Eng.,* Madrid, vol. 1.

Bjerrum, L., C. J. F. Clausen, and J. M. Duncan, 1972: Earth Pressures on Flexible Structures: A State of the Art Report, *Proc. 5th Eur. Conf. Soil Mech. Found. Eng.,* Madrid, vol. 1.

Bjerrum, L., and O. Eide, 1956: Stability of Strutted Excavations in Clay, *Geotechnique,* vol. 6, no. 1, pp. 32–47.

Bjerrum, L., 1973: "Problems of Soil Mechanics and Construction of Soft Clays and Structurally Unstable Soils," General Report, Session 4, Proc. 8th ICSMFE, vol. 3, pp. 111–159.

Bowles, J. E., 1988: *Foundation Analysis and Design,* McGraw-Hill, New York.

Breth, H., and D. Stroh, 1976: "Ursachen der Verformung im Boden beim Aushub tiefer Baugruben und konstruktive Moglichkeiten zur Verminderung der Verformung von verankerten Baugruben," *Die Bautechnik,* vol. 51, no. 3, pp. 81–88.

Breth, H., and H. R. Wanoschek, 1972: "The Influence of Foundation Weights upon Earth Pressure Acting on Flexible Strutted Walls," *Proc. 5th Eur. Conf. Soil Mech., Found. Eng.,* Madrid, vol. 1.

Broms, B., and H. Stille, 1976: "Failure of Anchored Sheet Pile Walls," *J. Geotechn. Eng. Div., ASCE,* vol. 102, no. GT3, March, pp. 225–254.

Brooker, E. W., and H. O. Ireland, 1965: "Earth Pressures as Rest Related to Stress History," *Can. Geotech. J.,* vol. 2, pp. 1–15.

Clausen, C. J. F., and S. Johansen, 1972: "Earth Pressures Measured against a Section of a Basement Wall," *Proc. 5th Eur. Conf. SMFE,* Madrid, pp. 515–516.

Clemence, S. P., and A. O. Finbarr, 1981: "Design Considerations in Collapsible Soils," *ASCE Geot. J.,* vol. 107, no. GT3, March, pp. 305–317.

Clough, R. W., 1960: "The Finite Element Method in Plane Stress Analysis," *Proc. ASCE,* 2nd Conf. Electronic Computation, Pittsburgh, Pa., September, pp. 345–378.

Clough, R. W., 1970: "Earthquake Response of Structure," in *Earthquake Engineering,* Prentice-Hall, Englewood Cliffs, N.J.

Clough, G. W., 1973: "Analytical Problems in Modeling Slurry Wall Construction," FCP Res. Rev. Conf., Fed. Hyw. Admin., San Francisco, September.

Clough, G. W., 1975: "Deep Excavations and Retaining Structures," Stanford University Press, Stanford, Calif.

Clough, G. W., 1979: "Deformations and Earth Pressures—Excavating Wall Systems," *Proc., Slurry Walls for Underground Transp. Systems,* FHWA, Cambridge, Aug. 30–31, pp. 114–136.

Clough, G. W., and G. M. Derby, 1977: "Stabilizing Berm Design for Temporary Walls in Clay," *J. Geotechn. Eng. Div., ASCE,* vol. 103, no. GT2, February, pp. 75–90.

Clough, G. W., and G. M. Derby, 1975: *Temporary Berms in Supported Excavations,* Stanford University Press, Stanford, Calif.

Clough, G. W., and J. M. Duncan, 1971: "Finite Element Analyses of Retaining Wall Behavior," *J. Soil Mech. Found. Div., ASCE,* 97 (SM12, December).

Clough, G. W., and J. M. Duncan, 1991: *"Foundation Engineering Handbook,"* 2d ed., edited by H. Y. Fang, Van Nostrand Reinhold, New York, pp. 223–235.

Clough, G. W., and L. A. Hansen, 1981: "Clay Anisotropy and Braced Wall Behavior," *J. Geot. Div., ASCE,* vol. 107, no. GT7, July, pp. 893–913.

Clough, G. W., L. A. Hansen, and A. I. Mana, 1980: "Prediction of Behavior of Supported Excavations under Marginal Stability Conditions," vol. IV, *Proc. 3d Intern. Conf. Numerical Methods in Geomechanics*, pp. 1485–1502.

Clough, G. W., and T. D. O'Rourke, 1990: "Construction Induced Movement of in situ Walls," Design and Performance of Earth Retaining Structures, *Proc. ASCE Spec. Conf.*, Ithaca, N.Y., pp. 439–470.

Clough, G. W., and B. Schmidt, 1977: "Design and Performance of Excavations and Tunnels in Soft Clay, A State-of-the-Art," *Proc. Int. Symp. Soft Clays*, Bangkok.

Clough, G. W., and Y. Tsui, 1974a: "Finite Element Analyses of Cut-and-Cover Tunnel Constructed with Slurry Trench Walls," Duke University, Durham, N.C., Soil Mech. Series no. 29.

Clough, G. W., and Y. Tsui, 1974b: "Performance of Tied-Back Walls in Clay," *ASCE J. Geotech. Div.*, 100 (December).

Clough, G. W., P. R. Weber, and J. Lamont, 1974: "Design and Observations of a Tied-Back Wall," *Proc. Spec. Conf. Performance of Earth and Earth-Supported Structures, ASCE*, Purdue University, Lafayette, Ind., vol. 1 (June), Pt. 2, pp. 1367–1389.

Coates, D. F., and Y. S. Yu, 1970: "Three Dimensional Stress Distribution around a Cylindrical Hole and Anchor," *Proc. 2d Int. Conf. Rock Mech.*, Belgrade, pp. 175–182.

Cole, K. W., and J. B. Burland, 1972: "Observations of Retaining Wall Movement Associated with Large Excavations," *Proc. 5th Eur. Conf. Soil Mech. Found. Eng.*, Madrid, vol. 1.

Cunningham, J. A., and L. D. Carpenter, 1975: Monitoring of Two Braced Excavations in Chicago, ASTM Repr. Spec. Tech. Publ. 584.

D'Appolonia, D. J., 1971: Effects of Foundation Construction on Nearby Structures, *Proc. 4th Pan-Am Conf. Soil Mech. Found. Eng.*, San Juan, Puerto Rico, State-of-the-Art Volume.

D'Appolonia, D. J., 1973: Cut-and-Cover Tunneling, U.S. Dept. Transp., Fed. Hwy. Admin. San Francisco Proj. Rev. Meet., September.

DiBiagio, E. L., 1966: "Stresses and Deformations around an Unbraced Rectangular Excavation in an Elastic Medium," Ph.D. Thesis, University of Illinois, Urbana.

DiBiagio, E., and J. A. Roti, 1972: Earth Pressure Measurements on a Braced Slurry Trench Wall in Soft Clay, *Proc. 5th Eur. Conf. Soil Mech. Found. Eng.*, Madrid.

Dudley, John H., 1970: "Review of Collapsing Soils," *J. Soil Mech. Found. Div., ASCE*, vol. 96, no. SM3, Proc. Paper 7278, May, pp. 925–947.

Duncan, J. M., and C. Y. Chang, 1970: "Nonlinear Analysis of Stress and Strain in Soils," *J. Soil Mech. Found. Div., ASCE*, vol. 96, no. SM5, Proc. Paper 7513, September, pp. 1629–1653.

Duncan, J. M., G. W. Clough, and R. M. Eberling, 1990: "Behavior and Design of Gravity Earth Retaining Structures," *Proc. Conf. Design and Performance of Earth Retaining Structures*, ASCE, Cornell University, Ithaca, N.Y., June, pp. 251–277.

Egger, P., 1972: "Influence of Wall Stiffness and Anchor Prestressing on Earth Pressure Distribution," *Proc. 5th Eur. Conf. Soil Mech. Found. Eng.*, Madrid, vol. 1.

Eide, O., G. Aas, and T. Josang, 1972: Special Application of Cast-in-Place Walls for Tunnels in Soft Clay in Oslo, *Proc. 5th Eur. Conf. Soil Mech. Found. Eng.*, Madrid, vol. 1.

Elms, D. G., and G. R. Martin, 1979: "Factors Involved in the Seismic Design of Bridge Abutments," Applied Technology Council Workshop on Earthquake Resistance of Highway Bridges, ATC-6-1, January, pp. 230–252.

Flaate, K., and R. B. Peck, 1973: "Braced Cuts in Sand and Clay," *Norw. Geotech. Inst. Publ.* 96, Oslo.

Goldberg, D. T., W. E. Jaworski, and M. D. Gordon, 1976: "Lateral Support Systems and Underpinning," vols. 1, 2, 3, 4, Reports FHWA-RD-75-130, Fed. Hwy. Admin., April.

Gould, J. P., 1970: Lateral Pressures on Rigid Permanent Structures, *Proc. ASCE Spec. Conf.*, Lateral Earth Stresses Earth Retain. Struct. Cornell University, June.

Grant, R., J. T. Christian, and E. H. Vanmarcke, 1972: Differential Settlement of Buildings, *ASCE J. Geotech. Div.*, September, pp. 973–991.

Harr, M. E., 1966: *Foundations of Theoretical Soil Mechanics*, McGraw-Hill, New York.

Henkel, D. J., 1971: "Geotechnical Considerations of Lateral Stress," *Proc. Spec. Conf. Lateral Stresses in the Ground and Design of Earth-Retaining Structures,* June, pp. 1–49.

Huder, J., 1965: "The Calculation of Ground Anchors and How They Operate," *Proc. Conf. Swiss Soc. Soil Mech.,* May.

Huder, J., 1969: Deep Braced Excavations with High Ground Water Level, *Proc. 7th Int. Conf. Soil Mech. Found. Eng.,* Mexico City.

Jaky, J., 1944: "The Coefficient of Earth Pressure At-Rest," *J. Society of Hungarian Architects and Engineers,* Budapest, Hungary, October, pp. 355–358.

James, E. L., and B. J. Jack, 1974: Design Study of Diaphragm Walls, *Proc. Diaphragm Walls Anchorages, Inst. Civ. Eng.,* London.

Janbu, N., 1957: "Earth Pressure and Bearing Capacity Calculations by Generalized Procedure of Slices," *Proc. 4th Int. Conf. Soil Mech. Found. Eng.,* (ISSMFE), vol. 2, pp. 207–212.

Janbu, N., 1971: "Jordtrykk (Earth Pressure)," Extension Course, Techn. Univ., Norway, Trondheim.

Janbu, N., 1972: "Earth Pressure Computations in Theory and Practice," *Proc. 5th Eur. Conf. Soil Mech. Found. Eng.,* Madrid, vol. 1.

Jaworski, W. E., 1973: "An Evaluation of the Performance of a Braced Excavation," Thesis presented to M.I.T., in Cambridge, Mass., in partial fulfillment of the requirements for the degree of Doctor of Philosophy.

Jennings, J. E., and K. Knight, 1975: "A Guide to Construction on or with Materials Exhibiting Additional Settlement Due to 'Collapse' of Grain Structure," *6th Regional Conf. Africa Soil Mech. Found. Eng.,* September, pp. 99–105.

Johnson, E. G., D. G. Gifford, and M. X. Haley, 1977: "Behavior of Shallow Footings Near a Diaphragm Wall," Paper presented at ASCE National Meet., San Francisco, October.

Karlsrud, K., 1975: "Practical Experience from the Excavation of Slurry Trenches in Oslo Clay," Norwegian Geotechn. Inst. Oslo, *Publ.* 110, 1976. First published in Norwegian in Nordisk geoteknikermode, Copenhagen 1975. Foredrag, Copenhaven Polyteknisk Forlag, pp. 529–542.

Karlsrud, K., E. DiBiagio, and G. Aas, 1980: "Experience with Slurry Walls in Soft Clay," Symp., Slurry Walls for Underground Transp. Systems, FHWA, Cambridge, March, pp. 383–408.

Kastner, R., and P. Lareal, 1974: Experimental Excavation 50 m Long Supported by Strutted Cast Diaphragm Walls: An Analysis of Stress Distribution in the Struts, *Proc. Diaphragm Walls Anchorages,* Inst. Civ. Eng., London.

Kavazanjian, E., and J. K. Mitchell, 1980: "Time-Dependent Deformation Behavior of Clays," *ASCE Geot. J.,* vol. 106, no. GT6, June, pp. 611–630.

Kavazanjian, E., Jr., and J. K. Mitchell, 1977: "A General Stress-Strain-Time Formulation for Soils," *Proc. Spec. Session no. 9, 9th Intern. Conf. Soil Mech. Found. Eng.,* Tokyo, Japan.

Kranz, E., 1953: "Uber die Verankerung von Spundwanden, 2 Auflage," Mitteilungen aus dem Gebiete des Wasserbaues und der Baugrundforschung, vol. 11, Ernst & Sohn, Berlin.

Kuesel, T. R., 1969: Discussion presented at Spec. Session, 7th Int. Conf. Soil Mech. Found. Eng., Mexico.

Ladd, C. C., R. Foot, K. Ishihara, F. Schlosser, and H. G. Poulos, 1977: "Stress Deformation and Strength Characteristics," State-of-the-Art Report, *Proc. 9th Int. Conf. Soil Mech. Found. Eng.,* vol. 2, JSSMFE, Tokyo, pp. 421–494.

Lambe, T. W., 1970: "Braced Excavations," Spec. Conf. Lateral Stresses and Earth Ret. Structures, ASCE, Cornell University, June 22–24.

Lambe, T. W., and R. V. Whitman, 1969: *Soil Mechanics,* Wiley, New York.

Leonards, G. A., and B. K. Ramiah, 1960: "Time Effects in the Consolidation of Clays," *ASTM Spec. Tech. Publ.* 254, pp. 116–130.

Littlejohn, G. S., 1980: "Design Estimation of the Ultimate Load-Holding Capacity of Ground Anchors," *Ground Eng., Found. Publ.* (November), Essex, England.

Littlejohn, G. S., 1982: "Design of Cement Based Grouts," *Proc. Grouting Geotechnical Eng., ASCE,* New Orleans.

Littlejohn, G. S., and D. A. Bruce, 1977: "Rock Anchors—State of the Art," Found. Publ., Essex, England.

Littlejohn, G. S., D. A. Bruce, and W. Deppner, 1978: "Anchor Field Tests in Carboniferous Strata," *Revue Française de Geotechnique,* vol. 3, pp. 82–86.

Littlejohn, G. S., et al., 1971: Anchored Diaphragm Walls in Sand, *Ground Eng.,* September, pp. 14–17, November, pp. 18–21.

Littlejohn, G. S., and I. M. MacFarlane, 1974: A Case History of Multi-tied Diaphragm Walls, *Proc. Diaphragm Walls Anchorages, Inst. Civ. Eng.,* London.

Locher, H. G., 1969: Anchored Retaining Walls and Cut-Off Walls, Losinger and Co., Bern, pp. 1–23.

Lysmer, J., M. Tabatabaie, F. Tajirian, S. Vahdani, and F. Ostadan, 1981: "SASSI—A System for Analysis of Soil-Structure Interaction," Report UCB/GT/81-02, Dept. of Civ. Eng., Univ. of California, Berkeley, April.

Lysmer, J., T. Udaka, C-F. Tsai, and H. B. Seed, 1975: "FLUSH, A Computer Model for Approximate 3-D Analysis of Soil-Structure Interaction Problems," Report no. EERC75-30*, University of California, November.

Malijain, P. A., and J. L. Van Beveren, 1974: "Tied-back Excavations in Los Angeles Area," *Proc. ASCE* 100, (C03), pp. 337–356.

Mana, A. I., and G. W. Clough, 1981: "Prediction of Movements for Braced Cuts in Clay," *ASCE J. Geot. Div.,* vol. 107, no. GT6, June, pp. 759–777.

Mayne, P. W., and F. H. Kulhawy, 1982: "K_0-OCR Relationships in Soils," *J. Geotechn. Eng., ASCE,* vol. 108, no. GT6, June, pp. 851–872.

Meyerhof, G. G., 1984: "Safety Factors and Limit States Analysis in Geotechnical Engineering," *Canadian Geotechnical Journal,* Toronto, Ontario, Canada, vol. 21, pp. 1–7.

Mitchell, J. K., 1976: *Fundamentals of Soil Behavior,* Wiley, New York.

Modjeski and Masters, 1982: "Development of Comprehensive Bridge Specifications, LRFD," NCHRP 12-33, TRB, Washington, D.C., April.

Morgenstern, N. R., and Z. Eisenstein, 1970: "Methods of Estimating Lateral Loads and Deformations," *Proc. ASCE Spec. Conf. Lateral Stresses,* Cornell University, Ithaca, N.Y. (June), pp. 51–102.

Northen, R. D., 1969: "Engineering Properties of Loess and Other Collapsible Soils," *Proc. 7th Int. Conf. Soil Mech. Found. Eng.,* pp. 445–452.

O'Rourke, T. D., 1981: "Ground Movement Caused by Braced Excavations," *ASCE Geot. J.,* September, pp. 1159–1177.

O'Rourke, T. D., 1989: "Predicting Displacements of Lateral Support Systems," Design, Construction and Performance of Deep Excavations in Urban Areas, *Proc. BSCES / ASCE Seminar,* Boston, Mass., pp. 1–35.

O'Rourke, T. D., E. J. Cording, and M. Boscardin, 1976: "The Ground Movements Related to Braced Excavations and Their Influence on Adjacent Buildings," Report no. DOT-TST 76T-23, U.S. Dept. of Transp., August.

Osaimi, A. F., and G. W. Clough, 1979: "Pore Pressure Dissipation During Excavation," *ASCE J. Geot. Div.,* vol. 105, no. GT4, April, pp. 481–498.

Otta, L., M. Pantucek, and P. R. Goughnour, 1981: Permanent Ground Anchors, Stump Design Criteria, FHWA, *Rept.* PB83-165985, September, Washington, D.C.

Palmer, J. H. L., and T. C. Kenney, 1972: "Analytical Study of a Braced Excavation in Weak Clay," *Canadian Geotech. J.,* vol. 9, pp. 145–164.

Peck, R. B., 1943: "Earth Pressure Measurements in Open Cuts, Chicago Subway," *ASCE Trans.*

Peck, R. B., 1969: "Deep Excavations and Tunneling in Soft Ground," *State-of-the-Art Report, 7th ICSMFE,* Mexico City, State-of-the-Art vol., pp. 225–290.

Peck, R. B., 1970: "Observation and Instrumentation, Some Elementary Consideration," Lecture Notes, Met. Section ASCE Seminar on Field Observations in Found. Design and Construction, New York, April (reprinted in *Hwy. Focus,* U.S. Dept. Transp. F.H.W.A., vol. 4, no. 2, pp. 1–5, June 1972).

Peck, R. B., W. E. Hanson, and T. H. Thornburn, 1974: *Foundation Engineering,* 2d ed., Wiley, New York.

Peck, R. B., A. J. Hendron, Jr., and B. Mohraz, 1972: "State of the Art of Soft Ground Tunneling," *Proc. 1st Rapid Excavation and Tunneling Conf.* (AIME), vol. 1, pp. 259–286.

Pfister, P., G. Evers, M. Guillaud, and R. Davidson, 1982: "Permanent Ground Anchors, Soletanche Design Criteria," Office of Research and Development, Fed. Hwy. Admin., U.S. Dept. Transp., Washington, D.C.

Pruska, L., 1972: "Basic Equations of Pressure at Rest of Granular Materials," *Proc. 5th Eur. Conf. Soil Mech. Found. Eng.,* Madrid.

Ranke, A., and H. Ostermayer, 1968: "Beitrag zur Stabilitats-Untersuchung mehrfach verankerter Baugrubenumschliessungen" (A Contribution to the Stability Calculations of Multiple Tied-Back Walls), *Die Bautechnik,* vol. 45, no. 10, pp. 341–349.

Rehnman, S. E., and B. B. Broms, 1972: "Lateral Pressures on Basement Wall: Results from Full-Scale Tests," Proc. 5th European Conf. SMFE, vol. 1, pp. 189–197.

St. John, H. D., 1975: Recent Research into the Movement of Ground around Deep Excavations, *Build. Res. Establish Bull.* D2/F/1.

Saxena, S. K., 1974: "Measured Performance of Rigid Concrete Wall at the World Trade Center," *Proc. Diaphragm Walls Anchorages,* Inst. Civ. Eng., London.

Scott, J. D., N. E. Wilson, and G. E. Bauer, 1972: "Analysis and Performance of a Braced Cut in Sand with Large Deformations," *Canadian Geotechn. J.,* vol. 9, no. 4, pp. 384–406.

Seed, H. B., and R. V. Whitman, 1970: "Design of Earth Retaining Structures for Dynamic Loads," ASCE Spec. Conf. on Lateral Stresses in the Ground and Earth Retaining Structures, Cornell University, pp. 103–147.

Sherif, M. A., I. Ishibashi, and C. D. Lee, 1982: "Earth Pressures against Rigid Retaining Walls," *J. Geotechn. Eng. Div.,* ASCE, vol. 108, GT5, pp. 679–695.

Simpson, B., N. J. O'Riordan, and D. D. Croft, 1979: "A Computer Model for the Analysis of Ground Movements in London Clay," *Geotechnique* (England), vol. 29, no. 2, pp. 149–175.

Skempton, A. W., 1951: "The Bearing Capacity of Clays," Build. Res. Congr. London. pap. Div. L., pp. 180–189.

Skempton, A. W., 1961: "Horizontal Stresses in an Overconsolidated Eocene Clay," *Proc. 5th Int. Conf. Soil Mech. Found. Eng.,* vol. 1, pp. 351–357.

Skempton, A. W., and D. H. MacDonald, 1956: "The Allowable Settlement of Buildings," *Proc. Inst. Civ. Eng., London,* vol. 5, pt. III.

Snyder, R., and F. Moses, 1978: "Load Factor Design for Substructures and Retaining Walls," *FHWA Report* no. 79-S0862, November.

Sokolovich, V. E., 1971: "New Developments in the Chemical Strengthening of Ground," *Osnovaniya Fundamenty i Mekhanika Gruntov,* no. 2, March–April, pp. 23–25.

Sokolovski, J., 1944: *Statics of Granular Media,* Pergamon, London.

Sokolovski, V. V., 1965: *Statics of Granular Media,* Pergamon, New York.

Sowers, G. F., 1962: *Shallow Foundations,* McGraw-Hill, New York.

Spangler, M. G., 1951: *Soil Engineering,* art. 21.18, International Textbook, Scranton, Pa.

Spangler, M. G., and J. Mickle, 1956: Lateral Pressure on Retaining Walls Due to Backfill Surface Loads, HRB Bull. no. 141, pp. 1–18.

Stille, H., and A. Fredricksson, 1979: "Field Measurements of an Anchored Sheet Pile Wall in Clay," *Proc. 7th Eur. Conf. Soil Mech. Found. Eng.,* Brighton, Sussex, U.K., vol. 3, pp. 285–290.

Sultan, H. A., 1969: "Collapsing Soils, State-of-the-Art," *7th Int. Conf. Soil Mech. Found. Eng.,* no. 5.

Terzaghi, K., 1934: "Retaining Wall Design for Fifteen-Mile Falls Dam," *Eng. News-Rec.,* May, pp. 632–636.

Terzaghi, K., 1934: "Large Retaining Wall Tests," *Eng. News-Rec.*

Terzaghi, K. 1943: *Theoretical Soil Mechanics,* Wiley, New York.

Terzaghi, K. 1954: "Anchored Bulkheads," *Trans. ASCE,* vol. 119.

Terzaghi, K., 1955: "Evaluation of Coefficient of Subgrade Reaction," *Geotechnique,* vol. 5, no. 4, pp. 297–326.

Terzaghi, K., and R. B. Peck, 1967: *Soil Mechanics in Engineering Practice,* 2d ed., Wiley, New York.

Thon, J. G., and R. C. Harlan, 1971: Slurry Walls for BART Civic Center Subway Station, *ASCE J. Soil Mech. Found. Div.,* September.

Tschebotarioff, G. P., 1973: *Foundations, Retaining and Earth Structures,* McGraw-Hill, New York.

Tsui, Y., 1973: "A Fundamental Study of Tied-Back Wall Behavior," Ph.D. Thesis, Duke University, Durham, N.C., Dissertation Abstr. Int. Order no. 752435.

Tsui, Y., and G. W. Clough, 1974: "Plane Strain Approximations in Finite Element Analyses of Temporary Walls," *Proc. ASCE Geotechn. Conf.* Austin, Tex.

Turabi, D. A., and A. Balla, 1968: Distribution of Earth Pressure on Sheet-Pile Walls, *ASCE Soil Mech. Found. Div.,* vol. SM 6, November.

U.S. Department of the Navy, 1974: Design Manual—Civil Engineering, NAVFAC DM-5, Naval Facilities Engineering Command, Alexandria, Va., April.

Ward, W. H., 1972: "Remarks on Performance of Braced Excavations in London Clay," *Proc. Conf. Performance Earth Earth-Supported Struct.,* Purdue University, Lafayette, Ind.

Wong, I. H., 1971: "Analysis of Braced Excavations," Ph.D. Thesis, MIT, Cambridge, Mass.

Xanthakos, P. P., 1974: "Underground Construction in Fluid Trenches," Colleges of Engineering, University of Illinois, Chicago.

Xanthakos, P. P., 1979: *Slurry Walls,* McGraw-Hill, New York.

Xanthakos, P. P., 1991: *Ground Anchors and Anchored Structures,* Wiley, New York.

Chapter

5

Load-Bearing
Panels and
Foundation Elements

5-1   The Use of Slurries in Drilled Shafts

Background.   Chronologically, the first significant applications of slurries were in connection with rotary drilling for large-diameter piles (McKinney and Gray, 1963). Initially the slurry was used to remove sand and cuttings from the excavation, but it became evident that it could also lubricate the tools and thus prevent stuck-pipe problems, inhibit formation fluids from entering the excavation, keep the cuttings in suspension if pumping was stopped, and enhance face stability. With an expansion of the foundation market, slurries were used in large-diameter holes, mine and access shafts, visual exploration holes, and eventually in the construction of load-bearing elements of prismatic and linear shapes.

In stable soils and where the drilling is confined to the zone above the groundwater table, the shaft can be drilled in the dry. Examples of such soils are homogeneous stiff clays, and sands with some apparent cohesion. The dry method is also feasible in soils below the water table if the permeability is low and results in seepage of a controllable rate.

Advancing the hole with conventional tools and casing.   Typical methods of construction with casing are described by Reese and O'Neill (1988). When the hole has been sufficiently excavated (usually under slurry protection), a casing is introduced and properly sealed as shown in Fig. 5-1a involving an underream shaft through a caving formation

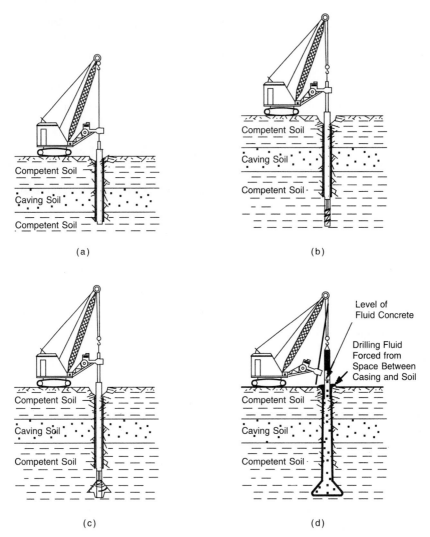

Figure 5-1 Advancing the hole with casing: (a) Introducing the casing and removing the slurry. (b) Drilling below the casing in competent soil. (c) Forming the underream. (d) Removing the casing and concreting the hole. (*From Reese and O'Neill, 1988.*)

sandwiched between two competent soil layers. In this case, once the casing is in place the slurry from inside the casing is bailed out using a suitable bucket, and the excavation continues using a smaller drill that can pass through as shown in Fig. 5-1b. A belling tool forms the underream as shown in Fig. 5-1c, the reinforcing cage is inserted, and the hole is concreted as shown in Fig. 5-1d.

The seal at the bottom of the casing where it penetrates the lower impermeable stratum should remain until the hydrostatic pressure of the fresh concrete mix is sufficient to displace the slurry trapped behind the casing. As the casing is withdrawn, concrete flows around the base and displaces the slurry in the annular space. The withdrawal of the casing is therefore a critical operation. If the concrete sets prematurely, it will move up with the casing as one body forming cracks into which slurry can flow, a situation that can be attained also with unworkable concrete. If the casing is pulled too soon, slurry is likely to flow in and mix with the fresh concrete.

Advancing the hole with slurry. In this case the slurry is introduced as soon as an unstable formation is reached and remains in the hole until the excavation is completed. The drilling equipment usually has a hollow stem or is provided with a suitable pressure relief device to allow the slurry to flow through. Since the slurry fulfills a multiple function, stability controls are essential regarding viscosity, pH, and density, and must be specified accordingly (Xanthakos, 1979; Stebbins and Williams, 1986). Very useful is the use of special circular drills equipped with reverse circulation to remove excavated materials.

Alternatively, building codes may require the hole to be drilled under slurry protection for the reasons mentioned in the construction of bored pile walls. In these cases, the slurry control limits are established according to the requirements of tremie concrete.

For the usual hole diameter (6 to 12 ft) one tremie pipe located at the center ensures good flow and complete displacement of bentonite. Occasionally, contractors use a concrete pump of the piston-displacement type coupled to a 3-in flexible rubber hose of sufficient length attached to a rigid pipe. After the pipe and the hose are inserted into the hole so that the end touches the bottom, a plastic plug is inserted in the line to separate the initial batch of concrete from the slurry, as is done in a tremie pipe. As the fresh concrete is discharged, it pushes the plug down and out of the pipe and begins to fill the hole; the plug is recovered as it flows to the top.

5-2 The Use of Slurries in Prismatic and Linear Elements

The development of machines that can perform slot excavations has led to the adaptation of special-shape foundation elements, thus expanding the range of foundation options. These may provide structural solutions that are not always feasible with circular shafts. Typical configurations are shown in Fig. 5-2. Variations from these sections can be worked out for unusual combinations and loads or for special classes of structures. In projects implemented with diaphragm walls

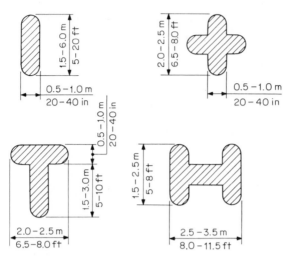

Figure 5-2 Cross sections of typical load-bearing elements.

the adaptation of prismatic foundations is a logical choice since it requires the same equipment and construction capability.

Linear or prismatic elements can replace a group of cast-in-place piles or shafts. This is particularly advantageous where heavy loads require unusually large monolithic structures, where the foundation is exceptionally deep or the installation is in difficult ground, and where the foundation elements must also resist bending moments and lateral thrusts. The flexibility inherent in prismatic panels regarding size, shape, and plan makes them suitable for almost any type and magnitude of loads.

Preparing the base. If an element is intended for base bearing, the bottom of the excavation must be checked and cleaned before concrete placement. Since visual inspection is excluded, special care is necessary to ensure a clean bottom and thus provide a firm foundation. Invariably, the design methods are based on the assumption that the construction is completed under competent supervision and with adequate quality control, and that the finished element has high structural integrity.

The shape of the base depends largely on the equipment performing the excavation. The bottom may be nearly flat and level in every direction, but it may have the irregular or rounded profile shown in Fig. 5-3. There has been no evidence to indicate that the shape of the bottom influences the transfer of load, at least from the theoretical standpoint; hence there should be no objection to the use of machines that do not give flat or square bottoms. A smooth square base is, however,

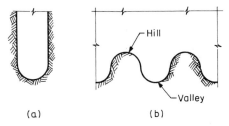

Figure 5-3 Different bottom shapes: (*a*) Round cross section cut by a round-end clamshell. (*b*) Irregular bottom excavated by a rotary long drill.

better cleaned at the end of excavation using a square-end clamshell or by shifting the long drill to level the hills.

Soft materials tend to accumulate at the base or are kept in suspension near the base in a viscous environment. Their presence is detected by taking samples of bentonite (Xanthakos, 1979). If these have unusually high density, the slurry must be recycled or replaced by a fresh solution.

There should be no compromise in the matter of bottom cleanliness. In most instances it will be possible to obtain a satisfactory base by passing an airlift. A small amount of dry or plastic cuttings left at the bottom is not likely to affect the bearing capacity, but if 1 in (2.5 cm) or more of soft mud is accumulated at the base it can influence the transfer of load by base bearing. This mud is unlikely to be displaced by the fresh mix, and usually it is partially consolidated by the weight of the concrete, resulting in some form of unacceptable settlement under load. Thus any soft material left at the bottom will constitute a zone of postconstruction settlement.

In some instances bottom softening may be caused by seepage and soil impregnation by slurry of the zone just below the excavation level. This penetration is stopped with rheological blocking but may reoccur with the passage of tools to clean or level the bottom. It can raise the moisture level of the soil just below the base but has no real influence on the compressibility or bearing capacity of the foundation.

Concreting. The requirements of concrete placement in a prepared prismatic trench are essentially the same as in conventional diaphragm walls. In addition, the shape and configuration of the trench may dictate the location and number of tremie pipes. A T section of nominal dimensions can be filled using one tremie pipe placed at the junction of the stem and the flange. An I or square section will probably require one tremie pipe at each opposite corner. Fresh concrete will flow in any direction from the discharge point but should not be restrained by stationary barriers.

An important advantage is the elimination of construction joints, round-end tubes, casings, and the associated appurtenances. The result is a simplified construction and more efficient scheduling. A single element can be excavated and cleaned in one day, and reinforced and concreted the following day. If an airlift must be applied, it should be done just before concrete placement to prevent recurrence of cavitation and sloughing while the panel is open. As in conventional walls, the concrete pour should not be interrupted.

5-3   Construction Problems and Repairs

Usual defects. For either drilled shafts or prismatic and linear elements, possible defects of the finished structure and the conditions under which they occur can be summarized as follows: (1) overstressing of soil beneath the foundation due to insufficient bearing area or because of unconsolidated materials left at the bottom; (2) deformation or collapse of soil invading the space of the foundation element; (3) improperly tremied concrete, resulting in voids and cavities within the set structure; (4) structural discontinuities and deviations from the true vertical line, causing local overstressing; (5) excessive mixing with bentonite, affecting the development of concrete strength; and (6) defects associated with restricted flow of concrete because of a thick reinforcing cage or because of torsional buckling of the steel cage during concreting.

Unlike belled drilled shafts, where bearing capacity failure is unlikely or rare, insufficient load transfer at the base of prismatic elements is a possible cause of settlement, particularly where the load transfer is primarily through direct bearing. This problem can exist with limited foundation area or with the presence of soft materials at the bottom. The cross-sectional area of the shaft usually is sufficient for the required structural capacity, and therefore concrete overstressing is unlikely.

Methods of checking and repairing defective elements. For settlement-sensitive structures and where heavy loads are expected, a postconstruction investigation may be specified to check the continuity and integrity of the finished structure. Usually, however, it is customary to require tests that can confirm the assumed load transfer, either by base bearing or by shaft resistance.

If there is indication that the set concrete is defective in one of the ways mentioned, a good check on its quality and soundness is by means of diamond coring (Baker and Khan, 1971). The larger the core diameter the more reliable the test results but the more expensive the procedure. This check can be supplemented by other test techniques such as caliper logging, seismic-wave and velocity measurements, and three-dimensional logging. Grouting can be used to repair the damaged zones, but the result is often achieved on a speculative basis. For prismatic elements structural discontinuities are less critical because of the larger than necessary cross-sectional area of the member.

Load tests. A usual procedure for confirming the design load capacity (base bearing and shaft resistance) is by means of a load test. If this test suggests the possibility of unacceptable settlement, a common remedy is to construct a second adjacent element and provide a top concrete cap to connect the two members.

The following are useful guidelines to prevent the problems associated with the load transfer: (1) require exploration to a depth several feet below the bottom of the excavation; (2) detail the steel cage with ample reference to the flow motion of tremie concrete; (3) specify the tremie placement requirements of the fresh concrete; (4) monitor the final stages of the excavation, particularly the rate of drilling and the type of excavated materials in the last few feet of penetration; (5) clean the bottom as specified; and (6) request a test panel excavated and concreted in situ and use the results thus obtained as a basis for a semiempirical design.

Advantages and disadvantages. It appears from the foregoing remarks that circular or prismatic shafts built under slurry are a form of deep foundations. As such, they must be able to support axial loads, lateral thrusts, uplift, and occasionally limit settlement to tolerable values.

The advantages associated with this type of work are as follows:

1. Cost savings where a single element can replace a group of piles.

2. Excavation that can be extended to greater depths, and through boulders, rocks, and hard strata (conditions that often inhibit the installation of a pile foundation by driving).

3. Less disturbance to adjoining ground and foundations because the excavation and installation of the element result in less displacement of the soils, and therefore minimize heave and settlement.

4. Elimination of vibrations and noise associated with pile-driving operations.

5. Flexibility in plan geometry and shape of the element to accommodate changes where required because of site conditions.

6. Ability to provide rock sockets to transfer heavier loads by base bearing.

Disadvantages associated with the operation stem from the following:

1. This type of work requires experience and specialist contractors, and adherence to strict slurry controls.
2. The action of pile driving in certain soils results in soil densification with associated strength improvement. Conversely, slurry trench or shaft excavation may result in stress relief with possible expansion.
3. The stability of the hole or trench must be maintained throughout the excavation. Poor soils under artesian conditions tend therefore to inhibit this method of construction.
4. A single shaft or prismatic element used in lieu of a group of piles does not provide the redundancy associated with a multiple path system.
5. The operation may cause a change in the shear strength of the soil, although in most cases inconsequential because of the greater contact area at the soil-element interface.

5-4 Basic Concepts of Load Transfer

For foundation elements (prismatic or round) built by the slurry method the transfer of load involves base bearing and side resistance (friction or adhesion), as in dry elements. This discussion pertains primarily to the transfer of direct vertical loads.

Base bearing

The transfer of load by direct base bearing of an axially loaded compressible element is influenced by the depth and size of the element, the soil characteristics, disturbance of the base, and the contact between the concrete and the soil underneath.

Loosening of the base, sometimes occurring with piles drilled by casing in saturated soils, is limited and unlikely in prismatic panels excavated under slurry. Care is, however, essential to prevent accumulation of sedimented soil particles and bentonite mud at the base. Chadeisson (1961) has compared the base resistance of piles built with and without slurry and found larger initial settlement for the latter. This surprising result was reconciled after compaction of the loosened soil by the first loading, and both piles behaved similarly during the second load test. Reese et al. (1973) tested piles drilled under slurry, and found that in some instances the base resistance was lower than predicted; this was explained by the presence of soft materials left at the bottom because of poor cleaning methods. The general conclusion is that for well-supervised and well-constructed projects the method of excavation and concrete placement causes minor disturbance to the soil, and conditions are satisfactory for the development of base resistance.

Shaft resistance

In the usual range of working loads, the transfer of load for round or prismatic elements generally begins with skin friction or side adhesion and is completed by base bearing when sufficient displacement has occurred vertically. Even the best methods for analyzing this mechanism are semiempirical, and relate shaft resistance to a friction factor for sands and to the undrained shear strength for clays. With the slurry process, the presence of bentonite at the interface (left there as filter cake or not displaced by the rising concrete) can influence the shaft resistance. The questions are therefore: (1) when and how the bentonite mud is completely swept or absorbed by the rising fresh mix; and (2) to what extent any bentonite left at the interface will inhibit the development of side shear.

The suspicion that slurries may adversely affect the shear resistance stems from their use as lubricants in caisson and tunnel construction. Simm (1974) comments on the results of pullout tests carried out by the Norwegian Geotechnical Institute in soft marine clay. These involved 250-mm-diameter piles cast 12 to 18 m in the ground. Two piles were cast in pure water, two in bentonite slurry, two in clay slurry, and two in a special slurry of microsoil powder. Casting piles under bentonite caused in this case a considerable decrease in shear resistance. On extraction, all piles had a lime stabilized layer of clay attached to them, except the bentonite piles.

Other engineers (Simm, 1974) commented that during concreting some cementitious material may diffuse into or mix with any filter cake on the walls of the excavation. This will produce a mix similar to a clay cement grout with a strength depending on the type of clay and cement. If the cake is from residual native clay slurry, it will produce a weak mix. With a bentonite cake the mix should be much stronger. If the cement penetrates the cake, shear resistance will depend on the shear strength of the mix, the soil, or their interface. If part of the thickness of the cake remains unaffected by cement penetration, its shear strength will probably control shear resistance. With time the filter cake will tend to consolidate, so that its strength should be estimated from tests at the appropriate overburden pressure. Results by Jefferies (Simm, 1974) on two types of bentonite produced the following undrained angle of shear resistance:

English, converted sodium, bentonite, ϕ_{cu} = 12 to 18°.

Wyoming, natural sodium, bentonite, ϕ_{cu} = 6°.

These results suggest that skin friction for excavation with Wyoming bentonite may be one-half to one-third that for English bentonite. The latter is partially flocculated by chemicals added during the conversion whereas Wyoming is used in a natural state and gives a deflocculated slurry.

It appears from these comments that in practice, the type, porosity, and permeability of the soil around the shaft will determine the associated interaction in the final position. For example, in impervious clays neither filtration nor soil impregnation will occur, and during the concrete placement all bentonite should be expected to be swept from the interface. Sand and gravel formations are prone to deep filtration or rheological blocking according to the void size and distribution, the hydraulic gradient, and the shear strength of the slurry. Although all free bentonite is swept by the rising concrete mix, the sweeping action does not extend beyond this zone. Despite the presence of colloid matter between the bulk of the vertical earth face and the hardened concrete in the final position, experience and field tests confirm that substantial friction still is available.

A hole in clay is thus equivalent to a cased hole, whereas a slurry hole in pervious granular soil enhances a slurry-soil interaction. The practical significance of these phenomena is confirmed by the performance of round and prismatic elements built under slurry and tested in both cohesive and cohesionless soils, and results from these tests provide the basis for establishing design criteria.

Effect of general excavation

Where a diaphragm wall built as lateral ground support must also carry considerable vertical loads, two basic factors should be considered in predicting the side resistance. The first is the installation of the wall before general excavation, creating load transfer conditions similar to those for a bored pile. However, during and after general excavation significant stress changes are conceivable beneath and around the wall, and they are likely to continue until equilibrium is established for the final loading, geometry, and groundwater conditions (Henkel, 1970). An analysis based on undrained shear does not include the effect of these changes, and many engineers choose to predict the load-carrying capacity in terms of effective stress. This problem remains complex, and a rational procedure is yet to be developed. The effective stress approach explains the effects of excavation on wall friction only partially, and thus considerable judgment is necessary to assess the applicability and limitations of this analysis.

For the diaphragm wall of the basement at Kensington and Chelsea Town Hall, London (discussed in the following sections), an analysis based on the foregoing principles indicated that probable wall friction at the time of final load application was unlikely to be less than that available before excavation, but this should not lead to general conclusions (Corbett et al., 1974).

Mechanism of load transfer

In predicting the mechanism of load transfer it is necessary to consider the following factors:

1. The development of shaft resistance and base bearing as a function of the vertical displacement
2. Dimensions of the element (length, width, or diameter), shape, and relative confinement, i.e., whether a single element or group action
3. The stiffness of the concrete in relation to the compressibility of the supporting soil
4. The soil characteristics and mainly its shear strength

Although it is desirable to provide a structure free of settlement, some downward displacement will take place irrespective of the method of excavation, face support, cleaning technique, and concrete placement. This displacement helps to initiate the load transfer, by mobilizing first the shaft resistance and then the base bearing. Shaft shear is mobilized at much smaller vertical displacement; hence appreciable shaft resistance (sometimes the entire) is developed before any load is resisted by base bearing.

Among the experimental and field records confirming these facts, we mention instrumented tests on bored piles with and without bells in stiff London clay (Whitaker and Cooke, 1965). These show that the ultimate load (considered the sum of shaft resistance and base bearing) was reached at a vertical displacement sometimes of the order of 10 percent of the base diameter, although the shaft resistance was fully mobilized at a vertical displacement of 0.5 to 1.0 percent of the shaft diameter.

Tests in stiff Beaumont clay by Reese and O'Neill (1969) show that a vertical displacement of 5 mm (0.2 in) is enough to mobilize shear resistance, but more displacement is generally needed to develop this resistance in sand. Vesic (1967) reports displacements of the order of 10 mm (0.4 in) for bored piles in granular soils. These displacements usually are assumed to be independent of the shaft diameter, so that the movement corresponding to full shaft resistance is considered merely a shear displacement.

The amount of displacement necessary before base bearing is available depends first on the conditions, type, and confinement of the bearing materials, and then on the size of the base; the larger the base the smaller the displacement.

Effect of shape, dimensions, and stiffness. The load-bearing elements of Fig. 5-4 demonstrate how the shape and geometry can influence the load transfer. The round element in Fig. 5-4a will develop full shear along the entire perimeter, and this is true for the elongated I section in Fig. 5-4c. The I section in Fig. 5-4b will most likely develop its shear resistance along a modified "effective" perimeter as shown, representing the shortest path of shear failure. In this case, the weight of the soil fillet between flanges should be added to the external load.

The length-to-diameter or length-to-width ratio can influence the division of load between shaft and base, but this is not explicitly defined. From a theoretical investigation of piers with enlarged bases, Poulos and Davis (1968) concluded that underreamed piers may not offer appreciable advantages over straight shaft piers of the same diameter and length when the length-to-diameter ratio exceeds about 25 unless the stratum at the base is much stiffer than the overlying materials. In general, a higher modulus of the base materials compared with the modulus of the shaft materials and a smaller length-to-diameter or length-to-width ratio should indicate that a greater portion of the load is resisted by base bearing.

Likewise the entire shaft length may not be effective in developing shear resistance. For example, in clays Reese Wright (1977) suggest that a portion of the soil near the top and the base of the shaft should be ignored, giving an effective shaft length less than the actual.

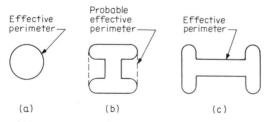

Figure 5-4 Influence of shape of load-bearing elements on effective perimeter.

5-5   Design Considerations

The initial uses of slurry wall panels as protection walls, quay walls, subway tunnel walls, and retaining perimeter walls have demonstrated their high capacity to function as reinforced concrete foundation elements. The range of applications discussed in this chapter is for load-bearing foundations as an alternative to other forms of foundation elements. The unconventional shapes shown in Fig. 5-2 offer possibilities beyond the scope of cylindrical shafts drilled by casing. The cost for site installation and diaphragm wall construction is frequently 10 to 15 percent less than for large bored piles, and may be even less than the cost of long precast prestressed piles. Since the difference in the design for the superstructure may reduce cost by another 10 to 15 percent, it is essential to investigate the load transfer by slurry wall elements.

Design methods

Many engineers have suggested that advances in the field of foundation engineering have evolved from the ability of practical designers to devise new ways of construction and from observations on how the new systems behave under field conditions. The new advances are supplemented by studies of physical models. In this context there seems to be broad agreement that the choice of a particular method of analysis may be of secondary importance compared with a competent site investigation and proper appreciation of the influence of the construction technique and the variability of the associated parameters. Computer usage can provide a rapid indication of these effects and is indicated where the cost is not prohibitive.

Limit states.   In order to make foundation design compatible with the general approach in structural design, a limit state methodology is introduced. Limit states must apply to the foundation support and the soil. Thus deep foundations must transfer the loads to the soil without reaching a limit state. This condition is said to have been reached when the foundation no longer fulfills the design requirements. Essentially, there are two limit states: (1) ultimate limit state, corresponding to the maximum load-carrying capacity of the foundation that can be provided either by the structural member or by the soil; and (2) a serviceability limit state corresponding to loss of serviceability and function. An ultimate limit state corresponds to complete collapse, whereas a serviceability limit state occurs before collapse and may involve unacceptable deformations or undesirable damage levels. For example, excessive differential or total foundation settlement, ex-

cessive lateral displacement or severe structural deterioration constitute serviceability limit states.

It is evident that the philosophy of limit state design differs essentially from the traditional way of foundation design by limiting
stresses (working stress method). In limit states, the first consideration is of the foundation at failure. Partial factors are then applied,
one for material resistance and the other for load and load effects, to
determine the structural sections and size of the member. With the
working stress method, the design is based on safe stresses and deformations, and the analytical process works in reverse. Beginning
with a design that is conservative, the components are reduced in size
to the acceptable level.

Load and resistance factors.   In principle, this design is based on a
probabilistic approach and involves procedures producing an interrelated combination of load, load factor, resistance (foundation element
and soil), resistance factor, and statistical reliability. The resistance
procedures must, however, be used in conjunction with locally accepted methods, particularly if the statistical nature of the problem is
considered through reliability theory and meets regional criteria.

According to the procedure presented in the foregoing sections, load
components are amplified by a load factor, and the factored loads are
compared with the design strength or resistance. The design resistance is obtained by applying a reduction factor to the nominal resistance. The foundation must be proportioned so that the factored resistance is not less than the effects of the factored loads. This yields
a relationship already presented in the foregoing section as

$$\phi R_n \geq \Sigma \gamma_i Q_i \tag{5-1}$$

where ϕ = performance (reduction) factor; R_n = nominal resistance
(soil or element) at the limit state considered; Q_i = load effect due to
component i; and γ_i = load factor for load component i.

In selecting proper resistance factors ϕ for a foundation, the following factors must be considered: (1) the method used to obtain soil properties and design parameters; (2) variations in the behavior of sands
and clays; (3) the procedure used to predict displacement (settlement)
and to calculate capacity; (4) the failure mode under investigation; and
(5) the type of foundation. Resistance factors are suggested for
strength and service limit states, and for various foundation schemes.
These are extracted or combined with data obtained for axially loaded
piles, and axially loaded drilled shafts. Statistical information is used
when available, combined with reliability theory and judgment in
cases where the information is not sufficient for calibration.

Structural and functional requirements

Round or prismatic elements may be subjected to both axial and lateral loads. The design requirements relate to (1) the ultimate load capacity, determined by either the member or the soil, and (2) the anticipated settlement.

It is unlikely that prismatic elements will fail in compression or by buckling. Buckling is, however, possible in members extended above the ground or through water, especially with long and slender shafts. Interestingly, the largest compression stresses are in the upper sections of the element, and more often near the top. Below this level the axial load begins to dissipate as a portion is absorbed by the ground through direct shear transfer at the interface. The load capacity of the shaft is usually greater than the ultimate capacity of the soil, except when the element is on sound rock. Where heavy uplift loads are expected, the tensile capacity of the elements should be checked.

The prismatic elements shown in Fig. 5-2 have a large flexural capacity and are therefore indicated also where lateral loads are expected. Members under combined bending and axial load should be checked for the actual stress conditions.

The ultimate soil capacity is obtained by adding the base bearing and shaft resistance. During failure, the shear stress at the interface reaches a limiting value, under either compressive or upward load. The ultimate capacity normally is not the controlling factor when the elements must resist lateral loads. The governing factor in this case is either structural capacity of the member or maximum tolerable lateral movement.

Movement. Where the foundation elements support building loads, lateral movement is induced by wind, earth pressures, and seismic action. In bridge piers and abutments horizontal movement may be caused by wind loads, stream action, braking forces, and earthquakes.

Excessive movement of foundations supporting buildings can cause functional distress and structural damage. Excessive movement of foundations supporting bridges can lead to serviceability and utility damage or even structural failure. Criteria regarding the maximum tolerable settlement and lateral movement are normally stipulated by applicable standards and codes, and will not be reviewed here.

Certain soils tend to undergo volume changes caused by variations in moisture content (also called expansive soils). A quantitative expression of this phenomenon is the coefficient of linear extensibility (COLE) that gives an estimate of the vertical component of swelling of the soil. Expansivity is defined as low, moderate, and high (Krohn and Slosson, 1980).

Where expansive soils are encountered, the following steps must be taken in selecting a suitable foundation (Reese and O'Neill, 1988): (1) estimate the depth of the expansive soil layer, and determine the amount of swell; (2) estimate the probable uplift force; and (3) select appropriate construction alternatives. One way to separate the swelling soil from the shaft is by means of a permanent surface casing. With prismatic or linear elements uplift forces can be effectively resisted by the vertical reinforcement that counteracts tensile stresses induced in this manner.

5-6   Load Tests and Experimental Data

Bored piles installed under slurry

Figure 5-5 shows soil profiles and sketches for three bored piles subjected to instrumented load tests (Reese et al., 1973). The piles were installed according to the following sequence: (1) the hole was augered without slurry until a caving layer was encountered when slurry was

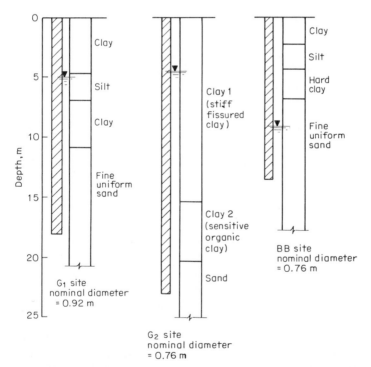

Figure 5-5 Soil profiles and sketches of shaft location; instrumented load tests. (*From Reese et al., 1973.*)

introduced in the hole while drilling continued; (2) drilling was completed with an auger or with a special drilling bucket cleaning the bottom before inserting the steel cage; and (3) concrete was placed using a 10-in-diameter tremie pipe. On extraction, visual inspection of the pile tips disclosed the presence of soft materials at the bottom. The accumulation of mud at the bottom was greater for piles G_1 and G_2 where the hole was completed with the auger, whereas pile BB had much less soft material at its tip apprently because of a better cleanout technique afforded by the drilling bucket. A hard coating of mud, clay, and sand was observed for most of the extracted length for all three piles. Examination of the concrete-soil interface showed that the failure surface was in the soil mass rather than along the interface, except for the hard clay layer of pile BB, where failure occurred at the interface.

Test results. Figures 5-6 to 5-8 show load-distribution curves obtained by plotting the measured load at various depths. For example, pile G_1 carries a load up to 3000 kN (675,000 lb) almost entirely by shaft resistance. For the same pile, at greater loads the ultimate shaft resistance is exceeded and the additional load is resisted by base bearing, as shown by the nearly parallel curves. The load transferred at the tip is estimated either directly or by extrapolation, and the corresponding settlement at the base is found by subtracting the computed elastic deflection from the observed displacement at the top of

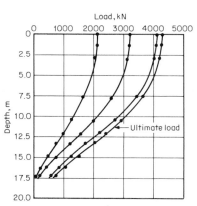

Figure 5-6 Load-distribution curves from instrumented load tests; pile G_1. (*From Reese et al., 1973.*)

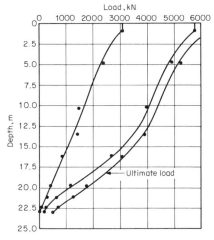

Figure 5-7 Load-distribution curves from instrumented load test; pile G_2. (*From Reese et al., 1973.*)

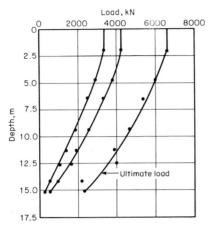

Figure 5-8 Load-distribution curves from instrumented load tests; pile *BB*. (*From Reese et al., 1973.*)

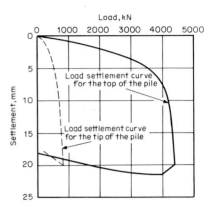

Figure 5-9 Load-settlement curves from instrumented load curves; pile G_1. (*From Reese et al., 1973.*)

the pile. Load-settlement curves for top and the tip of each pile are shown in Figs. 5-9 to 5-11.

The load-transfer curves shown in Figs. 5-12 to 5-14 are obtained at various depths by plotting the shear stress (calculated by differentiating and load-distribution curves) vs. the displacement of the same point with respect to its original position. A relationship between shear (shaft) resistance at a point at a specific depth and shaft movement is thus obtained.

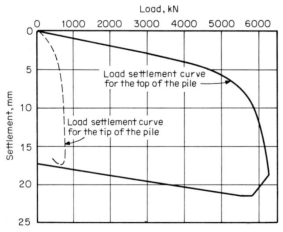

Figure 5-10 Load-settlement curves from instrumented load tests; pile G_2. (*From Reese et al., 1973.*)

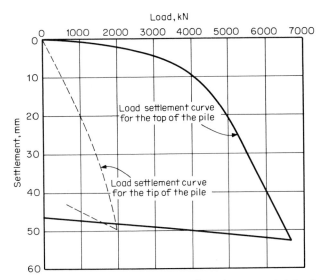

Figure 5-11 Load-settlement curves from instrumented load tests; pile *BB*. (*From Reese et al., 1973.*)

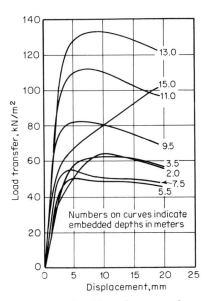

Figure 5-12 Load-transfer curves from instrumented load tests; pile G_1. (*From Reese et al., 1973.*)

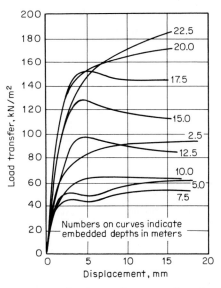

Figure 5-13 Load-transfer curves from instrumented load tests; pile G_2. (*From Reese et al., 1973.*)

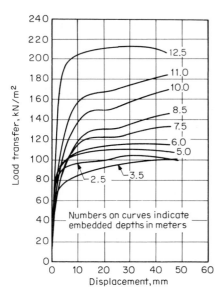

Figure 5-14 Load-transfer curves from instrumented load tests; pile *BB*. (*From Reese et al., 1973.*)

The load transfer by shaft resistance can be related to the shear strength of the soil by a reduction or adhesion factor α, which is the ratio of the average unit load transfer in a stratum to the average shear strength of the stratum. The α factor concept is extended to sands, where α expresses the portion of drained strength actually mobilized by skin friction so that the effect of the earth stress coefficient and the adhesion between concrete and sand are lumped into the same factor. Values of α for the three piles are summarized in Table 5-1

TABLE 5-1 Summary of Results from Instrumented Load Tests

Pile	Soil	Average peak load transfer, kN/m²	α_{av}	Ultimate tip resistance, kN/m²
G_1	Clay	52	0.65	
	Sand	103	0.70	1140
G_2	Clay 1	74	0.75	
	Clay 2	159	1.08	
	Sand	176	0.67	1450
BB	Clay	92	0.25	
	Sand	150	0.75	4000
$S_1 T_1^*$	Clay	49	0.44	1090
$S_2 T_1^*$	Clay	59	0.53	970
$S_3 T_1^*$	Clay	62	0.54	935

From Reese et al., 1973.
*Bored piles case in stiff fissured clay without slurry or casing.

that includes also data from other tests on bored piles cast in stiff fissured clay without slurry or casing (Reese and O'Neill, 1969). The latter piles are identified by an asterisk.

Interpretation of results. The load-settlement curves for piles G_1 and G_2 (Figs. 5-9 and 5-10, respectively) show a sudden vertical displacement when the ultimate load is reached, meaning lack of high base resistance (attributed to incomplete bottom cleaning), and indicating the high degree of sensitivity of the clay. For pile BB (Fig. 5-11) the load continues to increase with displacement (normally expected for a pile tip in very dense sand), but in reality the curve reflects the better cleanout procedure for this pile.

Irrespective of the method of installation and bottom cleanout, the important conclusion is that peak load transfer in stiff clays is reached at a relative shaft movement of the order of 4 to 5 mm (0.16 to 0.2 in), but for sands this relative displacement is higher and varies from 5 to 10 mm (0.2 to 0.4 in).

From Table 5-1 the factor α appears to be higher for piles with slurry than without. Considering, however, the uncertainties of measurements and the relative reliability of shear strength tests, we do not recommend higher α values for slurry piles.

For pile G_2 the soil layer shown as clay 2 in Fig. 5-5 is sensitive organic clay and has a much higher α value than clay 1 (stiff fissured clay). Visual examination of the soil-concrete interface in clay 2 showed that shear failure occurred in the natural soil (the weakest shear plane) about 1 cm (0.4 in) from the concrete surface. This would mean that in such clays α approaches unity and the load transfer is substantially equivalent to the undisturbed shear strength.

The very low value of α in the hard clay around pile BB is consistent with results from other tests, and shows that in hard clay the shear resistance along the shaft is less dependent on the soil strength and is determined mainly by the soil-slurry interaction. In this case the weakest shear plane is along the filter cake or along a thin fillet of earth mixed with some bentonite. For pile BB this strength is 92 kN/m^2 (about 1900 lb/ft^2).

Tests on diaphragm wall panels

UNO building in Vienna. Figure 5-15 shows load-settlement curves of test elements (circular and linear slurry panels) for the UNO Building in Vienna (Kienberger, 1974). Panels I and II have the same depth, but a direct comparison of load transfer is not practical because of differences in the shape and cross section (see pertinent data in Table

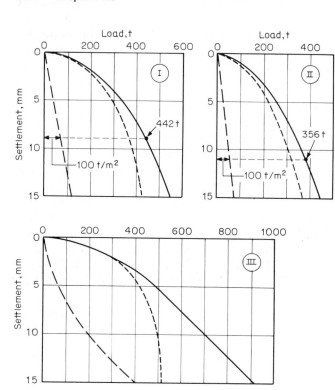

Figure 5-15 Load-settlement behavior of test elements for the UNO Building in Vienna. (*From Kienberger, 1974.*)

5-2). The ground at the site consists of gravel, silty clay, and fine sand, generally stiff or dense.

The load transfer characteristics of panels I and II can be correlated, however, noting that in both cases the base bearing is about 10 kg/cm²(100 t/m²). The total load carried by the circular element is 356 t. Of this load, 293 t is resisted by skin friction and 63 t by base bearing,

TABLE 5-2   Test Elements for the UNO Building in Vienna

Element	Dimensions and shape	Test load, t	Depth, m
I	50- by 150-cm diaphragm-wall panel	500	13
II	90-cm-diameter pile	500	13
III	50- by 150-cm diaphragm-wall panel	1000	24

From Kienberger, 1974.

giving an average shear stress of about 7.9 t/m^2 at the interface. For the linear panel I the total load is 442 t, and skin friction amounts to 372 t, giving an average shear 8.0 t/m^2 at the interface, i.e., the same as in the circular panel. The corresponding vertical displacements are 9 mm (0.36 in) and 11.4 mm (0.45 in) for the linear and circular panel, respectively. The small difference in settlement reflects differences in the methods of installation and cleaning. For the linear panel the bentonite was premixed and consistently controlled, whereas for the circular panel bentonite and water were mixed and added as the hole was advanced. The base of the hole was cleaned before concreting, but some sedimentation probably occurred, leaving loose material at the bottom.

Pullout tests confirmed the same skin friction for elements I and II at the same top displacement. For the two linear panels a displacement of 15 mm (0.6 in) mobilized a shear resistance 4.2 t/m^2 in the zone of silty clay and fine sand. The shear resistance was rather uncertain in the gravel and fill layers.

Surface deformation between and around the panels was uniform. The three elements were placed far enough apart (15 m, or 50 ft) to prevent overlapping of the influence zones, but the latter diminished within a smaller cone. This cone covered an area radially from the face about 1½ times the pile diameter or the diameter of a corresponding circle for the wall panels. The two linear panels had the same zone of influence, despite the difference in depth.

Tests in Boston clay.   These tests were carried out for the MBTA Red Line Extension (Goldberg, 1979) in typical Boston blue clay of high sensitivity (considerable loss of strength upon disturbance). They involved two slurry wall panels, 18 and 6.5 ft long, respectively. Both panels were 3 ft wide and 60 ft deep, and the shorter panel was loaded to failure.

Results from these tests indicated that base bearing was negligible and should be ignored in the design. The load-carrying capacity of the panels was essentially derived from shaft resistance. A design side shear (adhesion) of 670 lb/ft^2 was recommended in the soft sensitive clay with a factor of safety 1.8. This corresponds to an ultimate shear value of 1200 lb/ft^2. Based on the foregoing design shear, a wall element 60 ft deep could accommodate a design load of 80 kips/lin ft of wall. This load would include, however, the dead weight of the wall, estimated at 27 kips/lin ft.

Test panels in London clay.   Tests of diahragm wall panels in London clay are reported by Corbett et al. (1974). The test panels measure 1.2 by 0.5 m in plan and are 14.4 m deep. The excavation was completed with a cable-operated grab, and before placing the concrete the slurry was replaced with a fresh solution. On completion of the pour an overbreak of 8.5 percent was observed, indicating some cavitation and overexcavation in the granular layers. The soil profile is typical for London, consisting of successive layers of sandy clay (brick earth), sand and gravel, and stiff fissured clay.

Using an adhesion factor 0.5 for clay, a friction factor 0.7 for sand, and a bearing capacity factor 9.0, the ultimate shaft resistance is estimated as 2190 kN and the ultimate base bearing as 740 kN, giving a total ultimate capacity of 2930 kN.

The panels were subjected to six cycles of loading, the first five being incremental and the sixth consisting of a constant-rate load application. For the last cycle a maximum reaction of 4000 kN was sustained. At this load level the shaft carried 3650 kN, leaving only 350 kN for base bearing, or about one-half the estimated base bearing.

The actual ultimate shaft resistance in this case is 67 percent higher than estimated. It is therefore conceivable that the factor α (based on dry conditions and smooth interface) was underestimated and that favorable construction procedures (overbreak and face irregularities) contributed to the increased ultimate capacity.

5-7   General Guidelines for the Selection of Load-Bearing Elements

Choice of type and section.   The selection of size, shape, and group arrangement is normally dictated by the type and magnitude of the applied loads, the site and ground conditions, and the structural features of the superstructure. In addition, local availability of equipment and regional construction trends will influence the design.

Round cross sections are suitable where vertical loads are combined with lateral forces in varying directions, i.e., wind effects, and where the zone of influence of individual members is limited by site constraints or by the geometry of the foundation. A single slot section resists vertical loads and bending moments in one direction, and for nominal dimensions (usually one equipment pass) it can replace an equivalent row of piles, giving a monolithic structure that is independent of fixed tolerances (for example, pile spacing). A T section behaves as a T beam and offers compatible solutions along the perimeter of a foundation. Shapes of I and H configuration are suitable to stress reversal, whereas an X section is indicated where vertical loads are the predominant load effects.

Definition of failure and ultimate load.   There is no commonly accepted method as to what constitutes the failure load for an element subjected to direct vertical load effects. One way is to define failure in terms of a certain amount of gross settlement of the foundation, and another is to use a graphical interpretation of the load-settlement curve, but many investigators suggest that no single method of interpreting such a curve is satisfactory for the definition of failure. Where structural failure is involved, it means collapse. Thus the concept of failure and by analogy the ultimate resistance should be considered from the interaction of the foundation and the superstructure. In this case, different interpretations of a load-settlement curve could be valid depending on the tolerance of the superstructure to differential settlement.

Reese et al. (1977) introduce the concept of the "plunging" load, defined as the load at which the element continues to settle without additional load application. This may accommodate the ultimate limit state. However, a procedure is necessary in the criteria to ensure that settlement is not excessive and thus accommodate the serviceability limit state. The plunging load may also be used to indicate maximum strength or resistance where a working stress method is used.

For drilled foundations with their tips in clay, most investigators have found that the Skempton (1951) recommendations for bearing capacity represent a reasonable lower bound. For foundations in sand, two loads may be considered: (1) the plunging load, arbitrarily defined as the load at 5 percent relative settlement (settlement of tip divided by the equivalent diameter); and (2) the failure load, defined as the load causing a gross settlement of 1 in.

Distribution of load. The results of tests show that drilled shafts or prismatic elements carry a significant portion of the applied load in side resistance. Data on load-settlement relationships confirm that far less settlement is required to develop the ultimate side resistance than is required to develop the ultimate base bearing. Therefore, in most instances these elements under working loads will transfer practically the entire applied load to the soil by side shear.

The usual approach to the load-distribution problem involves the application of limit theory in conjunction with a semiempirical choice of parameters based on regional experience and on how well the construction conditions are controlled. There is considerable variance in how this experience is expressed. In Europe, for example, Sliwinski and Fleming (1974) recommend no reduction in the normal adhesion factor α for impervious clays but suggest a reduction of 10 to 30 percent for the friction factor of granular soils. Farmer et al. (1971) recommend a reduction in the coefficient of wall friction $\tan \delta$ in sand with increasing confining stress, and this approach agrees with results obtained for various interfaces of sand-concrete materials. Reese et al.

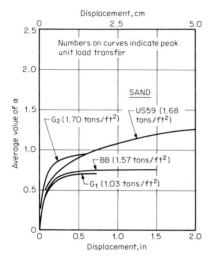

Figure 5-16 Curves of load transfer vs. displacement. (*From Reese et al., 1973.*)

(1973) have correlated the average load transfer to the drained shear strength of sands $\tau = \sigma_v' K \tan \phi'$, where σ_v' is the effective overburden stress and ϕ' is the effective friction angle. The ratio α of the actual load transfer to the average τ is plotted in Fig. 5-16 vs. the average pile settlement for the tests of Fig. 5-5. The apparent difference between the ultimate α values for the three elements is due to the varying influence of the upper clay layer on the load transfer. The minimum value of α is 0.7, recommended if the penetration is 25 ft or less. For greater penetrations the factor α could conceivably decrease (Touma and Reese, 1974).

Interestingly, in some instances building codes stipulate that shaft resistance should be ignored if the foundation bears on a stratum that is relatively rigid compared with the overburden materials. The usual practice is to design the distribution of load for both shaft resistance and base support. Alternatively, load-bearing elements of uniform section built in clays and shales should sometimes be checked for shaft resistance alone, considering base bearing an added safety margin.

Useful guidelines. The procedures outlined in this chapter are based on a combination of empirical data and theoretical investigations and reflect site conditions that are controllable in the context of design. Engineers should also take into account the actual construction procedure and the large number of variables discussed in the foregoing sections. The design recommendations should not be used indiscriminately but should be useful for most situations.

For a semiempirical design the following guidelines are useful.

1. It is advantageous to excavate the panel, place the reinforcing cage, clean the bottom, and pour the concrete as soon as possible. The shorter the time a panel is open, the less the soil disturbance, cavitation, sloughing, and other related effects.

2. The method of excavation and bottom cleaning will affect the development of base bearing and side resistance. Open panel exposure, conditions of base, roughness of the concrete-soil interface, moisture sensitivity of the supporting earth materials, slurry displacement conditions, and changes in the earth stresses are some of the factors influencing the load transfer. These are commonly lumped into a single parameter.

3. Excavating machines that produce a smooth face are no better than those that give a rough interface, but in practice it is difficult to express the difference quantitatively. Machines that remove excavated soil (such as reverse circulation) should be preferred to those that do not.

4. The load transfer characteristics of slurry panels (circular or prismatic) are essentially the same as in dry construction, but certain parameters are different.

5-8 Design for Axial Loading, Limit State

Structural capacity

An axially loaded element may fail in compression or by buckling. The latter need not be considered for shafts and prismatic elements, but buckling analysis is warranted for long slender members laterally unbraced.

Axial compression. The axial load should not exceed the factored axial structural capacity. This is expressed as follows:

$$\gamma_D P_D + \gamma_L P_L \leq \phi_a P_n \tag{5-2}$$

where ϕ_a = performance factor for the nominal structural capacity P_n; P_b, P_L = axial dead and live loads, respectively; and γ_D, γ_L = dead and live load factors, respectively. Where other types of loads are present, the design criterion may be expressed in the form

$$\Sigma \gamma_i P_i \leq \phi_a P_n \tag{5-3}$$

where P_i and γ_i denote load and load factors, respectively.

The factored nominal structural capacity of the concrete element is

$$\phi_a P_n = r\phi_a(0.85f'_c A_c + f_y A_y) \tag{5-4}$$

where f'_c = concrete strength, A_c = cross-sectional area of element, f_y = yield stress of steel reinforcement, and A_y = cross-sectional area of steel reinforcement. The capacity reduction factor ϕ_a may be taken as 0.70 for either round or prismatic sections. The parameter r is an eccentricity factor and may be taken as 0.80 for round and prismatic elements.

For a group of elements supporting a load eccentrically applied, the factored axial load on any element must include the effect of eccentricity.

Buckling of partially embedded elements.   Where buckling may control, the analysis may be carried out in terms of an equivalent free-standing length. This is the sum of the unsupported length of the shaft above ground and an additional length to the depth of full fixity. The depth to fixity depends on the flexural stiffness $E_p I_p$ of the shaft and the soil stiffness expressed as soil modulus E_s. Solutions are presented by Davisson and Robinson (1965).

Ultimate soil (bearing) capacity

Considering the absence of sufficient data to justify a rational approach, the estimation of the ultimate soil capacity may be based on presumptive capacities. The data extracted from test results are useful in establishing working range values.

The ultimate capacity is the sum of side and base resistance, expressed as

$$Q_{\text{ult}} = Q_s + Q_b \tag{5-5}$$

where Q_{ult} = total ultimate capacity, Q_s = ultimate load carried by side resistance, and Q_b = ultimate load carried by the base.

The load factor design criterion is expressed as

$$\gamma_D P_D + \gamma_L P_L \le \phi_q Q_{\text{ult}} \tag{5-6}$$

and where more types of loads are involved, as in Eq. (5-3).

Design procedure for clays.   The design in this case is normally governed by the conditions at the end of construction and is based on the total stress approach. Caution must be exercised where strength reduction is possible after construction (for example, in expansive clays) or when consolidation of the soil around the element can result in a downward movement with a downdrag force. In these cases, effective stress analysis may be indicated.

Shaft resistance. If S denotes the effective perimeter of an element, the ultimate shaft resistance is expressed in terms of the undrained shear strength s_u and the reduction factor α. For a length of shaft ΔL, this leads to the expression

$$Q_s = \Sigma S \Delta L \alpha s_u \qquad (5\text{-}7)$$

Reese and O'Neill (1988) give values of α for drilled shafts in overconsolidated clays intended primarily for dry construction. Thus this author still recommends the α values presented in the first edition of this book (Xanthakos, 1979) summarized as follows:

1. For soft clays ($q_u < 0.5$ ton/ft²) the factor α can be taken as 1, since failure should be expected to occur in the soil some distance away from the face.

2. For stiff clays (q_u from 1.0 to 2.0 tons/ft²) α can be expected to vary from 0.45 to about 0.60. The value 0.45 is commonly taken for the stiff London clay and is close to the average shear strength obtained in triaxial tests. The value 0.6 is appropriate for the lower limit of this strength range.

3. For hard clays ($q_u > 4$ tons/ft²) the shaft resistance is roughly equal to the shear strength of a hard coating at the interface. This can be taken as 2000 lb/ft² (96 kN/m²).

Some investigators recommend that a portion of the shaft near the top and near the bottom should not be considered to contribute to shaft adhesion. For simplicity, this portion covers the top 5 ft and a bottom length equivalent to one diameter.

Base bearing. The analysis of base bearing foundations is based largely on the work of Terzaghi (1943), Meyerhoff (1951), Skempton (1951), and Berezantsev et al. (1961).

If A_b denotes the area of the base, the ultimate base resistance Q_b is expressed in terms of a bearing capacity factor N_c. This leads to the expression

$$Q_b = A_b N_c s_u \qquad (5\text{-}8)$$

Whitaker and Cooke (1965) recommend N_c values of the order of 6.5 when s_u is taken as the average shear strength from soil tests, and this is intended to compensate for sample disturbance and other incidental effects. N_c may be taken as 9 for the $\phi = 0$ condition. The value 9 is also consistent with fairly undisturbed samples of nonfissured clays. According to Skempton (1951), $N_c s_u \leq 40$ tons/ft^2, and

$$N_c = 6(1 + 0.2Z/D_p) \leq 9 \qquad (5\text{-}9)$$

where Z = shaft embedment and D_p = diameter (equivalent) of the base of the shaft. The undrained shear strength s_u is taken as the average value over a depth of one to two diameters below the base. In soft clays, N_c should be used with a reduction factor $\frac{2}{3}$ to account for large displacements prior to bearing capacity failure. Caution is necessary in interpreting the validity of the bearing capacity theory where some softening of the base is unavoidable because of construction procedures.

Effective stress analysis. For shaft resistance, the ultimate unit side resistance q_s (drilled shafts) under long-term sustained loading may be estimated as proposed by Stas and Kulhawy (1984). Accordingly

$$q_s = \frac{K}{K_0}\left\{\sigma_v' K_0 \tan\left[\phi'\left(\frac{\delta}{\varphi'}\right)\right] + c'\right\} \qquad (5\text{-}10)$$

where K/K_0 = ratio of horizontal earth stress coefficient to the in situ value; K_0 = in situ earth stress coefficient before construction; σ_v' = vertical effective stress; ϕ' = effective friction angle; c' = effective cohesion; δ = friction angle at the interface. Potyondy (1961) has determined that δ/φ' is 0.50 for clay-steel interface and 0.68 to 0.95 for clay-concrete interface, with the lower value being for a smooth surface finish. The ratio K/K_0 is about $\frac{2}{3}$ for slurry construction and 1 for dry construction.

For base bearing, the drained ultimate unit base resistance q_p is approximated as proposed by Kulhawy et al. (1983). Accordingly

$$q_p = \sigma_v' N_q' \qquad (5\text{-}11)$$

where N_q' = modified bearing capacity factor obtained with the help of the graphs of Fig. 5-17. In this case N_q' depends on the rigidity index I_r that may be estimated from the following expression (Vesic, 1975)

$$I_r = \frac{E_s}{2(1 + \mu)\sigma_v' \tan\phi'} \qquad (5\text{-}12)$$

where E_s = soil modulus, μ = Poisson's ratio, ϕ' = effective friction angle of the soil, and σ_v' = vertical effective stress measured at a depth of $D/2$ below the base of the shaft, where D is the shaft (equivalent) diameter.

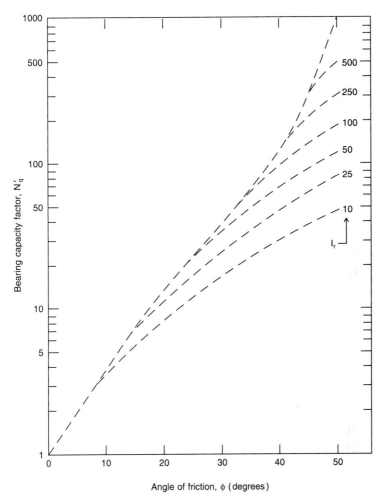

Figure 5-17 Modified N_q' bearing capacity factor for deep foundations in drained loading. (*From Kulhawy et al., 1983.*)

Design procedure for sands.   **Shaft resistance.** On the Continent, ultimate shaft resistance is expressed in terms of the effective overburden stress σ_v', the friction δ between concrete and sand, and the coefficient K (ratio of horizontal to vertical effective stress, usually taken as K_0). For a shaft length ΔL, the load transfer is expressed as

$$Q_s = \Sigma S \Delta L K \sigma_v' \tan \delta \qquad (5\text{-}13)$$

Touma and Reese (1974) suggest the expression

$$Q_s = \Sigma S \Delta L \alpha \sigma_v' \tan \phi' \qquad (5\text{-}14)$$

In conjunction with Eq. (5-14) an upper limit for the term $\alpha\sigma'_v \tan \phi'$ is 2.5 tons/ft². The reduction factor α is based on the experimental data presented in the foregoing sections, and is as follows:

$\alpha = 0.7$ for depths ≤ 25 ft

$\alpha = 0.6$ for 25 ft $<$ depths ≤ 40 ft

$\alpha = 0.5$ for depths > 40 ft

Equations (5-13) and (5-14) are compatible as long as the terms $K \tan \delta$ and $\alpha \tan \phi'$ are equivalent. For concrete-soil interfaces and dry elements ϕ' approaches δ closely (Potyondy, 1961), and for most practical purposes the same assumption can be made for slurry panels. Reduction in the coefficient α with depth (suggested in conjunction with the Touma-Reese approach) is consistent with a smaller K_0 associated with a greater friction angle as the depth increases.

Another expression suggested by Reese and O'Neill (1988) gives the ultimate unit side resistance as $q_s = \beta\sigma'_v \leq 2$ tons/ft² for $0.25 \leq \beta \leq 1.2$, where $\beta = 1.5 - 0.135\sqrt{z}$ (z = depth below ground surface). The suggestion to limit the unit side resistance to 2 tons/ft² relates to the fact that this is the maximum value ever measured.

Base bearing. Likewise, the ultimate base resistance Q_b is expressed as

$$Q_b = A_b N_q \sigma'_v \qquad (5\text{-}15)$$

where the bearing capacity factor N_q is estimated as a function of the effective friction angle ϕ' and the σ'_v term is not necessarily always equal to the overburden pressure.

Correlation of settlement with base resistance. The practical significance in the observed vertical displacement at which ultimate side resistance is mobilized (5 mm, or 0.2 in, for clays and 10 mm, or 0.4 in, for sands) is that it is normally expedient to consider the full shaft resistance in the design.

The much larger and often uncertain settlement associated with ultimate base bearing makes this contribution only a small supplement to the load-carrying capacity of the foundation. Since large settlements are not tolerable for most cases, the practice has been to define ultimate base bearing as the resistance corresponding to 1 in (25 mm) of vertical tip movement.

Bearing in sand. Touma and Reese (1974), dealing primarily with bored piles, relate the ultimate unit base resistance q_b corresponding to a tip movement 1 in as follows:

Loose sand: $q_b = 0$

Medium dense: $q_b = 16/k$ (tons/ft²)   (5-16)

Very dense: $q_b = 40/k$ (tons/ft²)

For loose and medium dense sand, $k = 1$ for $D_p < 1.67$ ft, and $k = 0.6D_p$ for $D_p \geqslant 1.67$ ft. The expression of q_b for very dense sand is applicable only if the embedment exceeds 10 times the diameter D_p. In this case D_p is the base diameter (ft) or the equivalent diameter of prismatic elements. The foregoing expressions represent refinements of formulas that appeared in the first edition (Xanthakos, 1979).

Reese and O'Neill (1988) have also recommended an alternate procedure for estimating the base resistance q_b corresponding to a specific downward movement.

$$q_b = 0.6N \text{ (tons/ft}^2) \qquad \text{for } N \leqslant 75$$

$$q_b = 45 \text{ (tons/ft}^2) \qquad \text{for } N > 75 \qquad (5\text{-}17)$$

where N is the uncorrected SPT blow count. This procedure is based on a vertical movement of 5 percent of the base diameter. For base diameters exceeding 50 in, q_b should be reduced to q_{br} such that

$$q_{br} = \frac{50}{D_p} q_b \qquad (5\text{-}18)$$

where q_{br} = reduced base resistance and q_b = ultimate unit base bearing computed from Eq. (5-17).

Bearing in clay. Similar reduction guidelines are appropriate for cohesive soils. For soft clays it is good practice to ignore base bearing completely. For stiff and hard clays, results from field tests indicate that at a tip movement of 1 in, the base resistance actually mobilized is 0.5 to 0.7 times the ultimate capacity expressed by Eq. (5-8). Hence, and in view of other available data, this author suggests a base resistance of

$$Q_b = 0.6A_bN_cs_u \qquad (5\text{-}19)$$

Performance factors

The foregoing analysis suggests the variability of predictions in estimating the load-carrying capacity of foundation elements of round or prismatic cross section using drilling techniques and excavation under slurry. Normally, and where statistical information is available, reliability theory combined in some instances with judgment is used to derive resistance factors. For the cases under study, however, the available information is considered insufficient for calibration using reliability theory. Thus values of resistance factors ϕ must be chosen based primarily on judgment so that the design using the limit state approach is consistent with that using the allowable stress method.

A consensus is that there is greater inherent variability of the capacity of foundation elements excavated in sand than in clay. This suggests that values of performance factors for elements in sand should be smaller than for shafts in clay. For the strength limit state, these factors are as shown in Table 5-3 and can be modified where regionally more specific values are available. Serviceability limit states should be carried out with unfactored loads and unfactored resistance.

TABLE 5-3   Interim Resistance (Performance) Factors for Strength Limit States in Foundation Elements Built under Slurry

Procedure—soil condition		Resistance factor ϕ
Ultimate bearing resistance of single element		
Side resistance in clay	Undrained shear strength	0.65
Base bearing in clay	Bearing capacity number	0.55
Side resistance in clay	Effective stress	0.50
Base bearing in clay	Effective stress	0.45
Side resistance in sand		See discussion this section
Base bearing in sand		See discussion this section
Side resistance in rock	Carter and Kulhawy	0.55
	Horvath and Kenney	0.65
Base resistance in rock	Canadian Geotechnical Soc.	0.50
	Pressuremeter method	0.50
Side shear and base bearing	Load test	0.80
Uplift capacity of single element		
Clay	Undrained shear strength	0.55
	Effective stress	0.40
Sand		See discussion this section
Rock	Carter and Kulhawy	0.45
	Horvath and Kenney	0.55
All soil types	Load test	0.80

Bearing capacity of elements socketed in rock

A socket in rock can be formed in two ways (Xanthakos, 1979), with the choice depending on the desired extent of penetration and the hardness of rock material. Shallow sockets in soft to medium-hard rock can be formed with lightweight chisels dropped from a clamshell or from a percussive rig. If deep sockets must be provided, or if the rock material is medium hard to hard, the most suitable tool usually is a rotary drill or a churn drill.

For design purposes the following assumptions are made: (1) the rock quality will not be degraded as a result of construction and the use of drilling fluids; (2) the bentonite mud will not lubricate the sides of the excavation; and (3) the bottom is thoroughly cleaned.

A procedure suggested by Reese and O'Neill (1988) assumes that the load is carried entirely by side resistance if the computed settlement is less than 0.4 in, and entirely by base bearing if it exceeds this value. Since no allowance is made for a combination of side resistance and base bearing, the results thus obtained are on the conservative side. The procedure involves the following steps.

1. Estimate the settlement of the portion socketed in rock. This consists of the elastic shortening and settlement of the base.

2. If the sum is less than 0.4 in, compute the ultimate load-carrying capacity based on shaft resistance (step 3). If the sum exceeds 0.4 in, calculate the ultimate load based on base bearing only (step 4).

3. Estimate the side resistance as follows: if the uniaxial compressive strength q_u of the rock does not exceed 280 lb/in², the ultimate unit side resistance is (Carter and Kulhawy, 1988)

$$q_s = 0.15q_u \tag{5-20}$$

If $q_u > 280$ lb/in², q_s may be computed as proposed by Horvath and Kenney (1979) as

$$q_s = 2.5\sqrt{q_u} \tag{5-21}$$

where both parameters are expressed in lb/in².

4. Estimate the base resistance q_b from the uniaxial compressive strength (Canadian Geotechnical Society, 1985) as follows:

$$q_b = 3q_u K_{sp} d \tag{5-22}$$

where q_u = average uniaxial compressive strength of the rock core, K_{sp} = dimensionless bearing capacity coefficient, and d = dimensionless depth factor. Procedures for estimating the parameters K_{sp} and d are given by the Canadian Geotechnical Society (1985). Alternatively,

TABLE 5-4   Dimensionless Coefficient K_b as a Function of Ratio H_s/D_s

H_s/D_s	0	1	2	3	5	7
K_b	0.8	2.8	3.6	4.2	4.9	5.2

From Canadian Geotechnical Society, 1985.

the base resistance may be estimated from pressuremeter tests as follows (Canadian Geotechnical Society, 1985):

$$q_b = K_b(p_1 - p_0) + \sigma_v \tag{5-23}$$

where p_1 = limit pressure determined from pressuremeter tests averaged over a distance of two diameters above and below the base, p_0 = at rest horizontal stress measured at the base elevation, σ_v = total vertical stress at the base elevation, and K_b = dimensionless coefficient depending on the socket diameter D_s to socket depth H_s ratio (see Table 5-4). For prismatic elements, an equivalent diameter may be used.

Groups of foundation elements

Cohesive soil. The behavior of a group of elements is largely influenced by the cap. If this is in contact with the ground, the group may fail as a unit consisting of the elements and a block of soil contained within the element geometry. The ultimate load-carrying capacity of the group should be checked for the minimum of two values: (1) the sum of individual capacities of the elements, and (2) the bearing capacity of the block defined by the element geometry.

If the cap is not in firm contact with the ground and the clay is normally consolidated or slightly overconsolidated or is sensitive, the individual capacity should be multiplied by an efficiency factor η. Its value may be taken as 0.7 for element spacing $3D$ and as 1.0 for spacing $6D$ (Reese and O'Neill, 1988). Values of η are linearly interpolated for intermediate spacing. If the cap is not in firm contact with the ground and the clay is heavily overconsolidated and insensitive, the ground capacity may be estimated as in the case of full contact with the ground.

Installations in sand. Likewise a group efficiency factor, defined as the ratio of the ultimate load capacity of the group to the sum of the ultimate capacities of the individual elements, can be taken as 0.7 and 1.0 for $3D$ and $6D$ spacing with linear interpolation for intermediate spacings (Reese and O'Neill, 1988). Note that this procedure does not make a distinction of the cap condition, and the evaluation is the same whether the cap is or is not in firm contact with the ground.

However, the contribution of pile caps to the load-carrying capacity of a group has been investigated by Garg (1979) in field tests of bored pile groups in sand. In these tests, the performance of pile groups under free-standing and resting pile cap conditions is compared. The results show that the load carried by the group under pile resting condition is more than under free-standing condition for any settlement value. This effect is shown in Fig. 5-18 together with the influence of pile spacing, expressed in terms of the underreamed pile diameter.

The two-, four-, and six-pile groups display increasing contribution from the pile cap with increasing pile spacing. This contribution is not fixed in quantitative terms but depends on the number of units and their spacing in the group as well as on the load and displacement level of the group. From these observations, Garg (1979) concludes

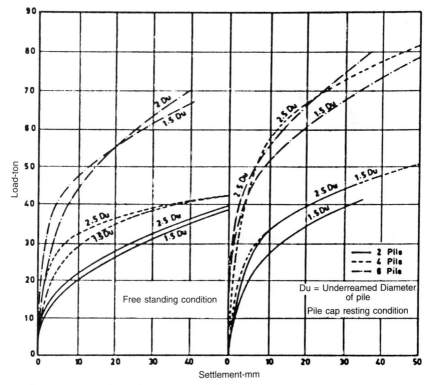

Figure 5-18 Influence of pile spacing and cap condition on the load-carrying capacity of pile groups (*From Garg, 1979.*)

that it may be erroneous to assign a fixed efficiency factor without considering all contributing parameters.

5-9 Design Procedure, Working Stress Method

For the general case this involves a semiempirical prediction of the peak-load transfer, i.e., the ultimate load discussed in Sec. 5-8. A working load is then obtained by dividing the ultimate resistance by an appropriate factor of safety.

The ultimate capacity is estimated by reference to Eq. (5-5). Since the ultimate shaft and base resistance are reached at different vertical displacements, two different factors of safety must be introduced. Accordingly, the working load P_w is

$$P_w = \frac{Q_s}{F_s} + \frac{Q_b}{F_b} \tag{5-24}$$

where Q_s and Q_b are as previously, and F_s and F_b are the factors of safety for shaft and base resistance, respectively. If F is the factor of safety relating P_w and Q_{ult} ($P_w = Q_{ult}/F$), combining Eqs. (5-5) and (5-24) yields

$$F = \frac{F_s F_b (1 + R)}{F_s + F_b R} \tag{5-25}$$

where $R = Q_s / Q_b$

Although it is customary to omit the weight of the element and the overburden term from the bearing capacity calculations (assuming that they balance approximately), for retaining diaphragm walls functioning also as load-bearing elements it is good practice to consider the weight of the wall as part of the load.

Loading conditions and safety factors.   For buildings and structures the loads stipulated in most building codes are dead load, live load, snow load acting on roofs, wind load acting on exposed parts of the building, earthquake, and occasionally hydrostatic pressure and earth pressure. For bridges, the range of loads is covered by the AASHTO specifications.

It is customary to use a bearing capacity with a safety factor of 3 for the design load. For foundations supporting buildings, design load = dead load + K_L(live load) + K_w(wind load) + K_s(snow load) where K_L, K_w, K_s are code reduction factors for the particular loading conditions. If the design load is not the maximum load believed to act on the foundation, the maximum load should be estimated. For the maximum load the safety factor should be at least 2.

5-10   Settlement Considerations

The loading conditions for settlement considerations will largely depend on the type of soil. If the soil is saturated cohesive material, the design load may be used with satisfactory results since the settlement is a function of time. If the soil is in nonsaturated condition, or it is granular, or it is a $\phi - c$ soil, the settlement will occur in a relatively short time after load application so that the maximum load conditions may control. The settlement of a soil for which consolidation theory does not apply may be very different. In this case there may be a gradual buildup of dead load as the structure is constructed, and this may result in a more dense soil condition when the live load is applied.

For the limit state approach, consideration must likewise be given to the fact that settlement of elements in sand and rock is usually small and occurs fairly rapidly. However, shafts in clay may settle over a longer period. Thus, when estimating settlement in clay, only unfactored permanent loads should be considered. Unfactored live loads must, however, be added to the permanent loads when considering settlement in granular soils.

Estimation of settlement.   With the exception of long-term consolidation effects, the initial settlement is influenced by the elastic shortening, the load-transfer characteristics, and the resistance to penetration at the tip. Since the last factor depends largely on the construction methods, a settlement analysis servers only approximate predictions.

According to some theories, the influence of shaft resistance on tip movement is considered by dividing the shaft load into a series of segmental loads. In the simplest form this procedure is carried out as suggested by Farmer et al. (1971).

Useful data on settlement (applied mainly to single drilled shafts) have been summarized by Reese and O'Neill (1988) in dimensionless form. They provide useful guidelines for predicting short-term settlement. In general, Q_s is fully mobilized at displacements of 0.2 to 0.8 percent of the shaft diameter in cohesive soil. For shafts in cohesionless soil, this range is 0.1 to 1.0 percent.

Settlement at full base bearing is different for sand and clay. Assuming controllable base conditions, Q_b may be fully mobilized at displacements of 2 to 5 percent of the base diameter in clay. For sands, there may not be a well-defined failure at any displacement, and some investigators defined Q_b as the load causing a settlement equal to 5 percent of the base diameter.

Factors of safety related to settlement. If a working load is based on the ultimate shaft resistance Q_s and base bearing Q_b corresponding to a 1-in movement, the safety factors F_s and F_b may be selected arbitrarily, or the selection may have a displacement-compatibility basis if data from load tests are available. In this case F_b may be taken the same as F_s, but they should be at least 2 and preferably 2.5.

5-11   Design Example 1

The basement at Kensington and Chelsea Town Hall (Great Britain) mentioned in the foregoing sections (Corbett et al., 1974) contains a three-level underground parking garage. The basement is approximately 13 m deep and measures 140 m × 65 m in plan.

Fairly substantial loads are carried around the periphery of the basement. A diaphragm wall provides the ground support along the periphery and is extended below the lower level to act as foundation for these loads.

An effective stress analysis was carried out as proposed by Chandler (1966, 1968) and Burland (1973), while the stress change occurring during excavation were considered as suggested by Henkel (1970). Although these methods do not lead to design parameters, they serve to enhance engineering judgment in assessing semiempirical design methods. For the particular conditions of this site, an effective stress analysis showed that the probable shaft resistance at the time of load application was unlikely to be less than that available prior to excavation, but this should not be taken as a general conclusion.

Test panel. A test panel was excavated using a 500-mm cable-operated grab. The panel is 1.2 m by 0.5 m in plan, and is 14.4 m deep. The soil profile is shown in Fig. 5-19 together with pertinent soil properties. The bentonite slurry was replaced just prior to concreting, and after concrete placement an overbreak of 8.5 percent was recorded. Prior to load testing, the concrete was allowed to cure for 5 weeks.

A preliminary estimate of the ultimate load can be made based on the theory presented in Sec. 5-8. The ultimate load Q_{ult} carried by the panel is the sum of Q_s and Q_b. Evidently

$$Q_s = A_1\alpha_1 s_{u1} + A_2\sigma_v'K \tan \delta + A_3\alpha_3 s_{u3}$$

where A = panel section area in contact with soil; α = reduction factor; σ_v' = average effective overburden pressure in the sand and gravel layer; K = ratio of horizontal to vertical stress [according to Eq. (5-13)]; and δ = ultimate angle of friction developed between panel and sand-gravel layer. Likewise

$$Q_b = A_b N_c s_u$$

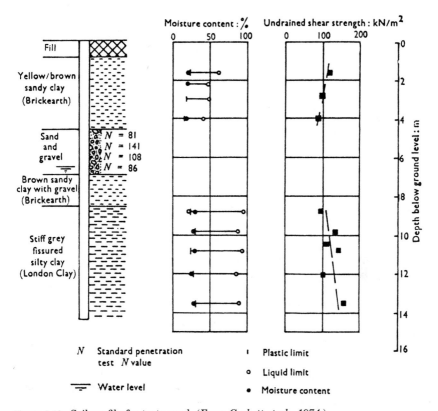

Figure 5-19 Soil profile for test panel. (*From Corbett et al., 1974.*)

where N_c = bearing capacity factor. Note that the suffixes 1, 2, and 3 refer to the three representative layers, namely, brick earth, sand and gravel, and London clay. The reduction factors α are selected to represent regional experience.

Using α_1 = 0.35, α_3 = 0.5, $K \tan \delta$ = 0.7, N_c = 9, and s_u = 1.42 tons/ft² = 137 kN/m² (at the base), we calculate, neglecting overbreak,

$$Q_s = 570 + 480 + 1140 = 2190 \text{ kN}$$

$$Q_b = 740 \text{ kN}$$

or $$Q_{\text{ult}} = 2190 + 740 = 2930 \text{ kN}$$

The test panel was subjected to six cycles of loading, the first five cycles being incremental to maxima of 1000, 1250, 1500, 1750, and 2000 kN, with the maximum load of each cycle maintained until the rate of settlement was less than 0.05 mm over a period of ½ h. On

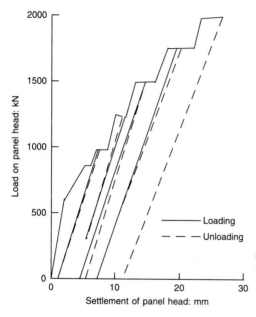

Figure 5-20 Load-settlement diagram of test panel (incremental loading). (*From Corbett et al., 1974.*)

the sixth cycle, the panel was loaded at a constant penetration rate until a maximum safe reaction 4000 kN was reached.

The load-settlement behavior for the incremental loading cycle is shown in Fig. 5-20, and the load-settlement curve for the standard penetration test is shown in Fig. 5-21. The load-distribution curve is shown in Fig. 5-22 for all six cycles. The following conclusions can be drawn.

1. The ultimate load is clearly more than calculated, and probably in excess of 4000 kN.

2. Up to a load of 2000 kN, the entire capacity is developed by side shear with the base carrying practically no load at all.

3. At a load of 4000 kN, the base carries only 350 kN, or just under half the ultimate load calculated theoretically. At the same load level, side resistance is about 3650 kN, or 67 percent higher than calculated.

5-12   Examples from Applications

Foundations for bridges.   The development of high-performance equipment (heavy self-guiding twin cable grabs) has led to expanded use of prismatic elements (also referred to as barrettes) in foundations for heavy structures. Currently, the deepest foundation for bridges is for

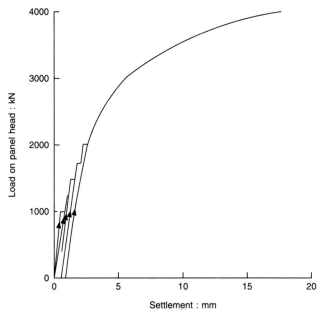

Figure 5-21 Load-settlement curve for test panel (constant-penetration rate test).

the Millefontes bridge in Portugal. The barrettes for this structure have a maximum depth of 73 m (240 ft).

The new foundation for the Galveston (Texas) Causeway consists of 468 new elements constructed under a headroom of 18 ft from the

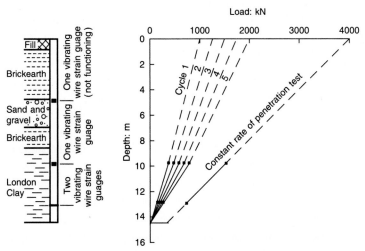

Figure 5-22 Load-distribution diagram, test panel. (*From Corbett et al., 1974.*)

existing bridge. Round elements were drilled under slurry using a 20-ft casing in the upper section of the hole. Two new columns were installed adjacent to each existing column, connected with a capping beam that intercepts also the existing column and transfers the load to the new foundations.

Statistically, successful foundations using prismatic and linear elements have been completed and tested to a depth of 100 m (330 ft) for an industrial installation in Japan, consisting of underground reservoirs for liquid gas storage.

Waterfront installations. An example of the use of barrettes for waterfront installation is the quay complex for the port of Le Havre in France. The rear running rail is founded on linear panels 2.20 m × 0.5 m in plan, and 24 m deep. These panels are designed to resist loads from the gantries and are spaced perpendicular to the quayside at 6-m centers.

A second example is the new Bristol harbor (England). The lock is 424 m long and 43 m wide. The walls of the lock are constructed using panels 80 cm thick and 20 to 23 m deep, consisting of successive T- and H-shaped elements. The dimensions of the panels were selected not to exceed a maximum weight of 20 tons for each steel reinforcing cage, inserted in a single assembly to eliminate in situ welding. A plan view of the dock with typical sections is shown in Fig. 5-23.

Foundations for buildings. Linear foundation elements (strip piles) were used for the Maine-Montparnasse Tower in Paris, a 60-story building 210 m high. The tower is built above subway line 6 of the Paris metro. This construction required underpinning by lateral protection, provided by intermittent panels tied together with four levels of anchors (Xanthakos, 1991). These are installed along the subway line and contain the entire structure.

A plan of the foundation and the underpinning scheme is shown in Fig. 5-24. The construction involved the following steps.

1. Grout and zone immediately beneath the tunnel structure to impart to the old quarries zone a minimum of cohesion. Grouting was made from the ground level.

2. Construct the two intermittent lateral retaining walls using linear panels. These walls provide the lateral underpinning and extend to just below the basement level of the tower.

3. Excavate on either side of the tunnel to about 18 m below ground level and install sequentially the four tieback bracing levels.

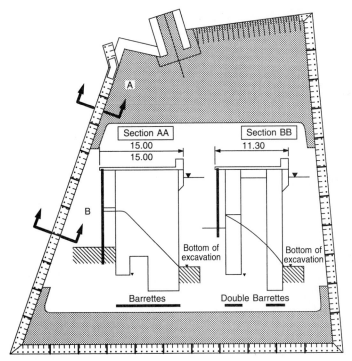

Figure 5-23 Plan view and sections of dock; port of Bristol (England).

4. From the permanent basement level construct the foundations for the tower. These foundations consist of linear elements (strip piles), 50 m deep. The dimensions vary from 2.20 × 1.20 m to 5.0 × 1.5 m, depending on the loads to be supported.

The upper part of the elements is located in a hard coarse limestone layer, and the excavation was carried out using pneumatic drills. This layer is approximately 12 m thick from the basement level and is underlain by a deep layer of clay with lenses of sand. When the sandy clays were reached, the excavation was continued under slurry using high-capacity buckets.

Referring to the plan of Fig. 5-24, it appears that the versatility of shape and configuration allows the foundation to conform to the pattern of the load-bearing elements of the superstructure, so that for a pillar or one bearing wall there is a single bearing strip pile. This allowed a reduction in connecting elements, and in some cases these were completely eliminated.

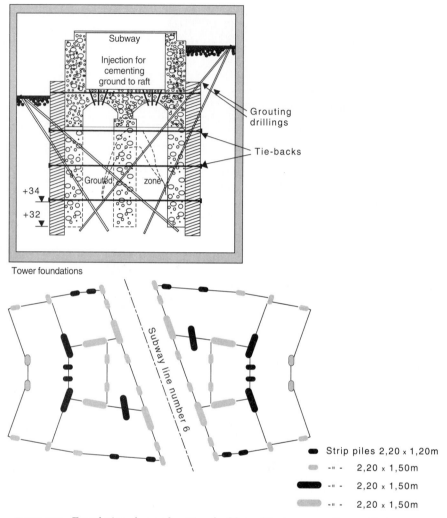

Figure 5-24 Foundation plan and section for Maine-Montparnasse Tower, Paris.

5-13   Negative Skin Friction and Uplift

Negative skin friction.   This is a downdrag force induced in end-bearing elements due to consolidation and settlement of the surrounding soil. This may involve placement of fill, groundwater lowering, and other causes (Poulos and Davis, 1975, 1980). In estimating the potential downdrag forces, it is usually assumed that full slip will occur between the element and the soil, and several field observations on piles in soft clay tend to support this assumption. Situations can conceivably arise, however, where full slip does not occur, i.e., with relatively stiff clays, or where only small settlements are expected, or where the consolidating layer may be overlain by other soils.

Although there has not been a sufficient number of field cases that cover the full range of critical situations to confirm the applicability of theory, the assumption that significant downdrag forces are accompanied by full slip between soil and element is justified among engineers. Under practical situations, involving relatively small settlements, a more accurate estimate of downdrag force should be obtained from an elastic-slip theory (Poulos and Davis, 1975). In a group of elements, downdrag forces and deflections are generally smaller than in a single element, so that solutions obtained for a single member will normally overpredict forces and deflections in a group.

Downdrag forces can increase settlement but they are unlikely to cause capacity problems. The settlement should be checked combining downdrag loads (unfactored) with dead loads. Temporary live loads do not act together with downdrag loads since they compress the element elastically and reduce the downdrag component. When the load is removed, the element rebounds elastically and restores the downdrag load.

If the downdrag load exceeds the live load, the structural and soil capacities should be checked for the combination (dead load + downdrag). In this case, the load factor for the downdrag load is the reciprocal of the performance factor for the ultimate side resistance of the shaft. This is expressed as

$$\gamma_D P_D + \frac{1}{\phi_{qs}} P_{sn} \geq \phi R \qquad (5\text{-}26)$$

where ϕ = performance factor for the limit state considered; R = resistance; ϕ_{qs} = performance factor for the ultimate side resistance; and P_{sn} = downdrag load.

Neutral plane and settlement. The neutral plane is the elevation where the settlement of the drilled element and the settlement of the soil are the same, as shown in Fig. 5-25. Above the neutral plane the soil causes negative skin friction, but below the neutral plane the shaft derives support capacity from the soil. Figure 5-25a shows the distribution of load and resistance. The dead load P_D acts at the top but increases with depth because of the negative side shear so that the new total load is $P_D + P_{sn}$. The resistance of the element is the tip capacity at the base Q_p and increases upward as the side resistance Q_s increases, giving the curve ($Q_p + Q_s$). The two curves intersect at the neutral plane, and this is the location of the maximum load on the shaft.

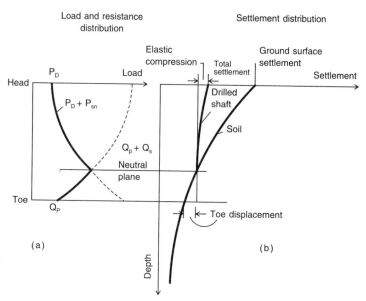

Figure 5-25 Neutral axis and settlement: (*a*) Calculation of the location of the neutral axis. (*b*) Settlement pattern of a shaft or a group of shafts. (*From Canadian Geotechnical Society, 1985.*)

Figure 5-25*b* illustrates the procedure for estimating the settlement at the top. This is the sum of the settlement at the neutral plane and the elastic shortening of the shaft above that plane. Unfactored loads are used to compute the settlement.

Uplift.   The cause of uplift in deep foundations may be related to swelling soils, frost heave, buoyancy, lateral loads, and upward loads. The latter are particularly critical in certain classes of structures such as transmission towers. Uplift must be checked vs. the tensile stresses in the concrete member and pullout from the soil.

Soil capacity.   Pullout resistance is usually adequate for long shafts but may have to be checked for shallow elements and where the load capacity is derived primarily from bearing on rock. A number of models have been proposed for predicting the uplift capacity. Basically these models fall in the three categories shown in Fig. 5-26. In the truncated cone model the uplift force is resisted by the weight of the concrete and the soil in the cone. In the curved surface model, the uplift force must be balanced by the weight of concrete and soil above the curved surface, and by cohesive or frictional stresses along that surface. The third model assumes that shear failure occurs on a cylindrical surface along the shaft so that uplift is resisted by the weight of the concrete and the shear strength along the shaft.

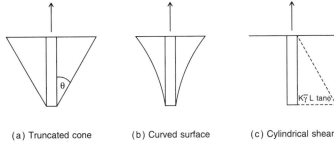

(a) Truncated cone   (b) Curved surface   (c) Cylindrical shear

Figure 5-26   Uplift capacity models: (a) Truncated cone. (b) Curved surface. (c) Cylindrical shear.

Alternatively the uplift capacity should be checked at the concrete-soil interface in a manner similar to the procedure used in estimating ultimate side resistance for an element in compression. Likewise, the weight of the element contributes to uplift resistance. The performance factors for axial compression and uplift are, however, different for two reasons: (1) the diameter (and thus the area of the shaft) decreases under tension owing to the Poisson effect, and this makes uplift capacity smaller than compression load capacity; and (2) elements in tension tend to unload the soil. Performance factors for uplift are shown in Table 5-3.

Structural capacity.   The majority of investigators agree that uplift tensile loads should be resisted by the steel reinforcement, neglecting the concrete strength. This yields the expression at ultimate limit state

$$\phi_t f_u A_y \geq P_{x,y} \tag{5-27}$$

where f_u = tensile strength of steel reinforcement (in this case yield strength); A_y = total area of steel reinforcement; ϕ_t = 0.9; and $P_{x,y}$ = uplift load.

5-14   Design Example 2

Figure 5-27 shows different schemes for the foundation of an 18-span highway bridge. Piers 1 through 11 support a narrower roadway, whereas piers 12 through 17 are sized to accommodate a wider superstructure. Scheme A consists of 3-ft-diameter precast prestressed concrete piles, and is the conventional design. Scheme B is similar to A except that the elements are caissons drilled under slurry protection. Scheme C, the alternative design, consists of 7 ft × 2 ft or 8 ft × 2 ft linear panels installed by the slurry method. Competent soil is established at elevation 725.00 for all schemes. Below this level the ground consists of stiff clay, with q_u = 2.50 tons/ft^2.

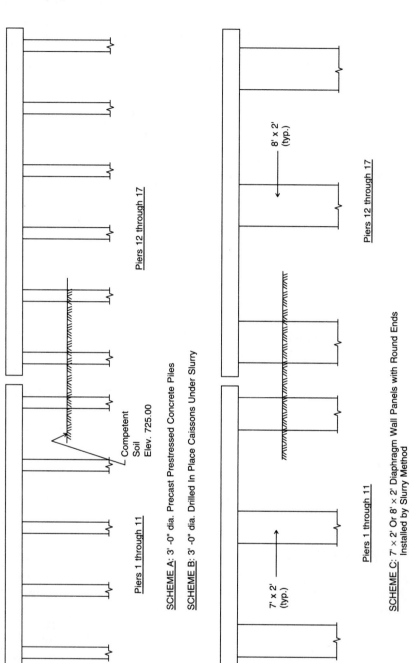

Piers 1 through 11

Piers 12 through 17

Competent
Soil
Elev. 725.00

SCHEME A: 3'-0" dia. Precast Prestressed Concrete Piles

SCHEME B: 3'-0" dia. Drilled In Place Caissons Under Slurry

7' x 2'
(typ.)

8' x 2'
(typ.)

Piers 1 through 11

Piers 12 through 17

SCHEME C: 7' x 2' Or 8' x 2' Diaphragm Wall Panels with Round Ends
Installed by Slurry Method

Figure 5-27 Elevation of substructure and foundation elements, bridge of design example 2.

Piers 1 through 11. The conventional design (scheme A) indicates bottom of pile elevation 658.00, and a working load of 240 tons per pile. From a back analysis, the design of the piles is traced as follows:

Pile embedment $= 725 - 658 = 67$ ft

Effective perimeter $S = 3.14 \times 3 = 9.42$ ft

Area $A_b = 3.14 \times 1.5^2 = 7.06$ ft²

Using $s_u = \frac{1}{2}q_u = 2.5$ kips/ft², $\alpha = 0.5$, and $N_c = 9$, we compute the following:

$Q_s = 9.42 \times 67 \times 0.5 \times 2.5 = 789$ kips

$Q_b = 7.06 \times 9 \times 2.5 \qquad = \underline{159}$ kips

$\qquad\qquad\qquad Q_{ult} = 948$ kips $= 474$ tons

Using a factor of safety of 2 for both side resistance and base bearing, the working load on the piles is $^{474}\!/_2 = 237$ tons, used 240 tons   OK.

Scheme C. Note that for this scheme, five piles are replaced by three linear panels with a plan as shown in Fig. 5-27. The design load per panel is therefore $240 \times \frac{5}{3} = 400$ tons. Likewise we compute the following:

Effective perimeter $S = 10 + 6.28 = 16.3$ ft

Area $A_b = 5 \times 2 + 3.14 \times 1 = 13.1$ ft²

Using the same parameters, we calculate now the side resistance and base bearing

$Q_s = 16.3 \times 67 \times 0.5 \times 2.5 = 1365$ kips

(using the same depth $= 67$ ft)

$Q_b = 13.1 \times 9 \times 2.5 \qquad = \underline{295}$ kips

$\qquad\qquad\qquad Q_{ult} = 1660$ kips $= 830$ tons

Using again a factor of safety of 2 for both shaft resistance and base bearing, the working load on one element is $^{830}\!/_2 = 415$ tons, used 400 tons   OK.

Piers 12 through 17. For these piers, three linear panels, 8 ft × 2 ft, will replace six piles. For a pile design load of 240 tons, each panel must have a working load of $6 \times {}^{240}\!/_3 = 480$ tons. For scheme C, we compute the following:

Effective perimeters $S = 12 + 6.28 = 18.3$ ft

Area $A_b = 6 \times 2 + 3.14 \times 1 = 15.1$ ft^2

Using the same parameters, the side resistance and base bearing are

$Q_s = 18.3 \times 67 \times 0.5 \times 2.5 = 1532$ kips

$Q_b = 15.1 \times 9 \times 2.5 \qquad = \underline{340}$ kips

$Q_{ult} = 1872$ kips $= 936$ tons

For a factor of safety of 2 for both shaft resistance and base bearing, the working load is ${}^{1872}\!/_2 = 936$ kips $= 468$ tons, used 480 tons   say OK.

Summary of quantities.   For cost analysis, the schemes shown in Fig. 5-27 are equivalent in terms of load-carrying capacity. The quantities are summarized as follows (taken below the elevation of competent soil):

Piers 1 through 11.

Scheme A $= 5 \times 67 \times 335$ lin ft of piles

Scheme C $= 7 \times 3 \times 67 = 1407$ ft^2 of wall panels

Piers 12 through 17.

Scheme A $= 6 \times 67 \qquad = 402$ lin ft of piles

Scheme C $= 8 \times 3 \times 67 = 1608$ ft^2 of wall panels

These quantities are per pier. The cost of foundation for each scheme can be obtained if relevant unit prices are available. It is conceivable that these prices may vary regionally.

5-15   Design Example 3

A bridge foundation consists of three linear panels. Each panel must carry a dead load of 110 tons and a live load of 45 tons. The foundation is inserted in stiff clay with undrained shear strength 0.9 ton/ft^2. Use the load factor method.

Step 1.   Determine the design load. Using AASHTO specifications, the design load is

$\gamma_D P_D + \gamma_L P_L = 1.3 \times 110 + 2.17 \times 45 = 143 + 98 = 241$ tons

Step 2.   Select the size of the element, dimensions, and depth. Normally this step requires optimization in terms of soil-structure interaction and must demonstrate an efficient load transfer for the minimum possible excavation and material cost. Since in this example the soil strength does not change with depth, the most efficient shape and element size is the one that gives maximum interface area with minimum volume. Other factors to be considered are the geometry of the substructure, the local availability of excavating machines, and their length-width excavating capability. From a preliminary analysis we select a linear element 7 ft long and 2 ft wide with round ends with the same configuration as in Fig. 5-27. The estimated depth of the element is 35 ft.

Step 3.   Check the capacity of the element. First we check the structural capacity of the member from Eq. (5-4). Because of the large cross-sectional area, this check is not necessary but is however mandatory. Because of the excess structural capacity of the concrete, the reinforcement may be ignored. The concrete strength f'_c is taken as 2.5 kips/in^2. The structural capacity is therefore

$$\phi_a P_n = (0.8)(0.7)(0.85 f'_c A_c)$$

We compute $A_c = A_b = 5 \times 2 + 3.14 = 13.1$ ft^2 = 1886 in^2, or $\phi_a P_n = (0.8)(0.7)(0.85 \times 2.5 \times 1886) = 2244$ kips $= 1122$ tons > 241 tons.

Next the bearing capacity is computed for side and base resistance. Note that two different performance factors are used according to Table 5-3. For base bearing, the performance factor is taken as 0.55, so that the factored base resistance is

$$\phi_b Q_b = 0.55 \times 13.1 \times 9 \times 0.9 = 58 \text{ tons}$$

Recalling that the effective perimeter is 16.3 ft, and using a performance factor of $\phi_s = 0.65$, the factored side resistance is (for $\alpha = 0.55$)

$$\phi_s Q_s = 0.65 \times 16.3 \times 35 \times 0.9 \times 0.55 = 184 \text{ tons}$$

The total factored ultimate capacity of the element is now

$$\phi_q Q_{\text{ult}} = 58 + 184 = 242 \text{ tons} > 241 \text{ tons}$$

Step 4.   Check the design for working load conditions. The unfactored total load is $110 + 45 = 155$ tons. Likewise, the unfactored ultimate resistance is computed as $(184/0.65) + (58/0.55) = 283 + 105 = 388$ tons. For working load analysis, the factor of safety is therefore $FS = 388/155 = 2.50$. Interestingly, side shear constitutes the larger fraction of the total load capacity of the member; hence a factor of safety of 2.5 for combined shaft and base load is satisfactory, and both methods are thus compatible.

Comments on the factor of safety. A more rational approach to this problem is possible if the shaft and base deformation compatibility is known (Whitaker and Cooke, 1965). An example of an experimentally derived relationship between shaft and base settlement is shown in Fig. 5-28. The mean curves of F_b and F_s are obtained from load-settlement curves and are plotted vs. the percentage settlement expressed in terms of the shaft and base diameter. The two curves are so far apart because ultimate shaft resistance is reached at much smaller displacements. For example, for s_c/d greater than 0.7 percent F_s approaches unity, indicating that ultimate shaft resistance is exceeded. This does not mean that the shaft becomes now inoperative, but it implies that further settlement is governed by the response of the base.

In order to use similar curves in design, estimates are made first of the ultimate shaft and base resistance. Assuming that the settlements of the cap (top) and the base do not exceed the allowable, a value of F_s and an approximate value of F_b are found from the curves. Working values of shaft and base load are then determined, the shaft compression is calculated, and the base settlement is thus corrected, leading to a second value of F_b from the curve. By successive approximations a more accurate value of F_b is obtained and allows estimation of the base working load.

Since the foregoing procedure requires an empirical relationship that applies to the test site only and reflects the actual duration of the test, it does not include long-term consolidation effects. Evidently, a displacement-compatibility determination of the working load results in a greater factor of safety for base resistance than for shaft resistance.

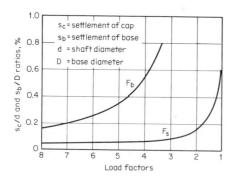

Figure 5-28 Examples of curves relating load factors with s_c/d and s_b/d for use in design. (*From Whitaker and Cooke, 1965.*)

It appears from these comments that a more consistent approach leading to a more uniform margin of safety for different types and components of foundations under different loading conditions may be obtained using the partial safety factors used in limit state design. The consistency in the structural analysis is enhanced by the fact that (1) specified loads and forces are multiplied by load factors, generally greater than unity, but different for different classes of loads; and (2) resistance of material such as shear strength soil parameters is multiplied by resistance factors less than unity but different for different types of soil.

5-16   Design for Lateral Loading

Lateral loads may originate from wind action, earthquake, water pressures, earth pressures, and live load effects. Linear and prismatic elements are frequently used to resist lateral loads. Since these elements cannot be battered, they must resist the lateral effects by developing passive resistance without undergoing large displacements. Indeed, one of the design objectives is to ensure that the lateral deflection does not exceed the tolerable limits. A factor of safety derived in this manner is therefore a deformation control value.

Several methods are available for predicting lateral load behavior of drilled shafts, and useful references are listed in the bibliography of this chapter. Essentially these involve (1) elastic analysis; (2) subgrade reaction evaluation; and (3) p-y analysis. Elastic analysis and subgrade reaction evaluation are based on the assumption that the soil behaves linearly (straight-line stress-strain relationship). The p-y analysis follows nonlinear model behavior and thus requires computer use.

Among the configurations shown in Fig. 5-2, the T and I sections are most suitable for resisting bending moments. However, the restraint against rotation provided at the top can influence the magnitude and pattern of lateral deflection under load. When this restraint is considerable (for example, embedment in heavy reinforced concrete caps), the element will deflect laterally with little rotation at the top.

Ultimate lateral resistance.   A suggested mechanism of mobilization of lateral resistance for a rigid element with free top is shown in Fig. 5-29. Considering the equilibrium conditions, and setting $\Sigma F y = 0$, we obtain

$$Q_{\text{ult}} = -\int_{x=0}^{x=x_r} p_{xu}B \; dx + \int_{x=x_r}^{x=L} p_{xu}B \; dx = 0 \qquad (5\text{-}28)$$

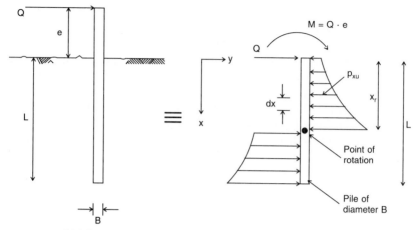

Figure 5-29 Mobilization of lateral resistance for a laterally loaded element with free top.

Also setting $\Sigma(M) = 0$ yields

$$Q_{\text{ult}}e + \int_{x=0}^{x=x_r} p_{xu}Bx \ dx - \int_{x=x_r}^{x=L} p_{xu}Bx \ dx = 0 \qquad (5\text{-}29)$$

where B = width of element and x_r = depth point of variation. If the distribution of ultimate unit soil resistance p_{xu} with depth x is known, the value of x_r and Q_{ult} can be obtained from Eqs. (5-28) and (5-29).

This basic concept has been used by Broms (1964a, b). The following simplifying assumptions are made:

1. The soil is either purely cohesionless ($c = 0$) or purely cohesive ($\phi = 0$). Elements in each soil type must be analyzed separately.

2. Short rigid and long flexible elements are considered separately. The criteria for short rigid shafts are $L/T \leqslant 2$ or $L/R \leqslant 2$, where

$$T = \left(\frac{EI}{n_h}\right)^{1/5} \qquad R = \left(\frac{EI}{k_h}\right)^{1/4} \qquad (5\text{-}30)$$

E = elastic modulus of element; I = moment of inertia of section; $k_h = n_h x$ for linearly increasing soil modulus k_h with depth x; n_h = constant of modulus of subgrade reaction; and k = modulus value in cohesive soil that is constant with depth.

The criteria for long flexible shafts are $L/T \geqslant 4$ or $L/R \geqslant 3.5$.

3. Free-head short shafts are expected to rotate around a center of rotation while fixed-head shafts will move laterally in translation (see Fig. 5-30a, b).

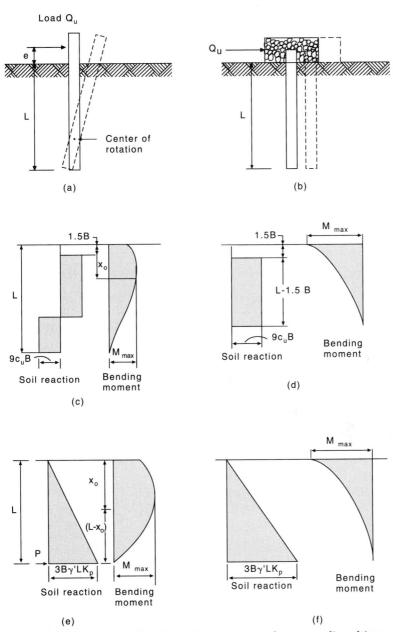

Figure 5-30   Rotational and translational movements and corresponding ultimate soil resistances for short shafts under lateral loads. Deformation modes: (*a*) free head; (*b*) fixed head. Soil reactions and bending moment in cohesive soils: (*c*) free head; (*d*) fixed head. Soil reactions and bending moments in cohesionless soils: (*e*) free head; (*f*) fixed head. (*From Broms, 1964a and b.*)

4. Distribution of ultimate soil resistance along the shaft for different end conditions is shown in Fig. 5-30 for short members.

This section deals mainly with short shafts since most of the linear and prismatic elements discussed in this chapter fall within this category.

Short shafts in cohesionless soil. The active earth pressure on the back of the shaft is neglected. The distribution of passive resistance along the front of the shaft is (at any depth) as shown in Fig. 5-30e, f, or

$$p = 3B\sigma'_v K_p = 3\gamma' LBK_p \tag{5-31}$$

where p = unit soil pressure (resistance); σ'_v = effective overburden stress; γ' = effective unit weight of soil; L = embedded length; B = width of element; $K_p = (1 + \sin \phi)/(1 - \sin \phi)$ = passive earth pressure coefficient; and ϕ' = effective angle of friction. This pressure is independent of the shape of the element section. Full lateral resistance is mobilized at the movement considered.

Short shafts in cohesive soils. The ultimate resistance is assumed to be zero at ground surface to a depth of 1.5B, and then it has a constant value $9c_u B$ below this depth, as shown in Fig. 5-30c and d.

Acceptable deflection at working lateral load. Where an element is subjected to lateral loads, the acceptable lateral deflection is likely to control the design. The two basic approaches for calculating lateral deflections are (1) subgrade reaction approach (Reese and Matlock, 1956; Matlock and Reese, 1962); and (2) elastic continuum approach (Poulos, 1971a and b; Poulos and Davis, 1980).

5-17 Load-Bearing Capacity of Prefabricated Panels

The use of a self-hardening coulis in the lower part of a prefabricated wall panel (mentioned in other sections) allows considerable economy. In addition, the coulis can also transfer appreciable load since it has a compressive strength that is usually adequate for this purpose. However, where the transfer of load is contemplated, the coulis should be checked for a probable elastic shortening; if the depth of the wall is appreciable, elastic settlement due to the low modulus of elasticity can exceed the value that can be tolerated.

If the loads are greater than can be transferred by a coulis, the wall can be made with beam and slab sections in order to make the load transfer at a lower level. Supporting a prefabricated wall on cast-in-place stilts has been tried and often found impracticable. One of the

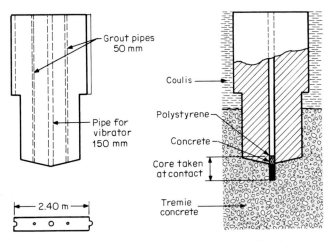

Figure 5-31 Device used to grout the contact surface between cast-in-place concrete and precast panels.

difficulties is how to secure firm contact between the cast-in-place and precast portions of the wall for full bearing. For a precast panel to bear on tremied concrete it is necessary to grout the contact surface between the two materials using a suitable device such as the one shown in Fig. 5-31. Three vertical pipes are inserted into the panel before precasting, and one of them is a central tube large enough to allow a concrete vibrator to be lowered to the level of tremied concrete. The others are two side tubes for future grouting of the contact area. Grouting can be avoided if the prefabricated panel is placed while the tremied concrete is still fresh, and in this case good bearing is obtained if its tip penetrates the fresh mix.

The transfer of load by side shear should not be based on the theoretical approach presented in the foregoing sections. The validity of this theory is questionable because of the complex interaction at the grout-soil and wall-grout interface, and also because of the considerable variability in the construction procedures. Instead, the transfer of load by side resistance should have its basis on field tests where installation methods and materials are adequately reproduced.

5-18   Case Studies from U.S. Practice

Deep foundation elements

Figure 5-32 shows soil data and details for load-bearing elements and prefounded columns for the 23-story office tower at 125 Summer Street in Boston (Johnson et al., 1991). This building has five levels

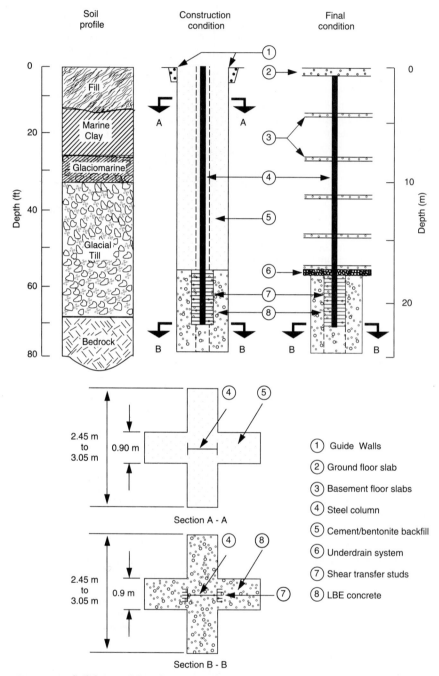

Figure 5-32 Soil data and foundation details, 125 Summer Street, Boston. (*From Johnson et al., 1991.*)

of underground parking inside a basic perimeter diaphragm wall, built using the downward construction method and prefounded columns. Load-bearing elements are combined in different shapes to form the foundations. This project is believed to be the first in the United States to utilize load-bearing elements in conjunction with prefounded columns and the downward construction method.

Construction details and installation procedures are described by Johnson et al. (1991). In general, they included thorough bottom cleaning and desanding operations, the passage of an airlift, and slurry tests for quality control. The concrete was tremied to the required level, and the panel backfilled above that level for the prefounded columns.

Table 5-5 gives design data applied to cross-shaped or linear elements. Column loads at the building perimeter are supported by the perimeter diaphragm wall, but some exterior columns are founded on T-shaped elements. The deep foundations bear on glacial till or rock

TABLE 5-5 Design Data, Load-Bearing Elements for 125 Summer Street Building, Boston

Column loads	2300 to 27,300 kN		
Recommended allowable design values	Skin friction	Glacial till	170 kPa
		Bedrock	620 kPa
	End bearing	Glacial till	1900 kPa
		Bedrock	2850 kPa
LBE sizes	Cross	0.90 m × 2.45 m and 0.90 m × 3.05 m	
	Linear	0.90 m × 2.45 m, 0.90 m × 3.05 m and 0.90 m × 6.50 m	
Bearing strata	Glacial till	Very stiff (dense), gray clayey *silt,* some to little fine *sand,* some to little *gravel,* trace coarse to medium *sand,* trace *clay* (well bonded in situ)	
	Bedrock	Very soft to moderately hard, completely to moderately weathered, extremely to slightly fractured, gray *aphanitic argillite,* joints close, open to tight, smooth to rough, planar to irregular with occasional clay seams	

From Johnson et al., 1991.
1 m = 3.28 ft, 1 kN = 0.22 kip, 1 kPa = 0.021 kip/ft^2.

at depths ranging from 16.5 to 21 m below ground surface. Typical sections are shown in Fig. 5-32. As shown in Table 5-5, column loads ranged from 2300 to 27,300 kN (500 to 6000 kips). Load-bearing elements carrying loads greater than about 18,000 kN (3960 kips) are socketed into rock for a depth of 1 to 3 m (3.3 to 10 ft) below the top of rock. Load-bearing elements with a load less than 18,000 kN are terminated in the glacial till but with a minimum of 4.5 m below the lowest floor level.

The transfer of load is based on side resistance and base bearing. Thus the elements are designed to transfer about 65 percent of the load by side shear and 35 percent by direct bearing. Assigning a greater load to side shear benefits the serviceability requirements since it gives a greater factor of safety against excessive settlement because of incomplete bottom cleaning and the presence of weathered rock at the base.

The design values given in Table 5-5 were confirmed by static load tests performed on smaller circular augered units in similar conditions. The measured settlement of the units was less than 1 cm (0.4 in) under about 80 percent of the design load.

Commentary. The theory of the bearing capacity of elements socketed in rock is based on the fact that typically the axial compression load is carried solely in side resistance until a total shaft settlement of the order of 0.4 in (1 cm) occurs. At this displacement, the ultimate side resistance Q_s is mobilized and exceeded, and slip occurs between the concrete and rock. As a result, the load is now transferred to the base, and this approach is combined with the assumption that side resistance reduces to zero. The resulting design is conservative because a considerable portion of the side shear still is present after the bond is broken. Alternative procedures are available and can be used to proportion the load between side and base resistance (Carter and Kulhawy, 1988).

If the rock socket capacity is based on side resistance, the displacements in the socket will be small. If this capacity is derived from base bearing, the settlements may be large and should be checked. Invariably, all methods assume that (1) the socket is constructed in sound rock that does not degrade upon excavation or exposure to air and water; (2) the rock strength will not deteriorate during construction; (3) the drilling fluid will not act as a lubricant along the contact surfaces; and (4) the bottom is properly cleaned out.

The procedure presented in Sec. 5-8 is suggested by Barker et al. (1991) and by the AASHTO-LRFD specification, and requires the initial estimation of the settlement of the portion of the foundation element that is socketed in rock. As mentioned, this consists of two components: the elastic shortening of the socketed portion p_e and the settlement of the base p_b. If the sum $p_e + p_b$ is less than 0.4 in, the load capacity is based on shaft resistance. If $p_e + p_b$ exceeds 0.4 in, the design considers base bearing only. A procedure for estimating p_e and p_b is discussed in Design Example 4.

As an example, if a portion of a design load P is assigned to shaft resistance and one-third to base bearing, and the estimated settlement is less than 0.4 in, the entire load will be carried by side resistance regardless. If this portion in $\frac{2}{3}P$ and the factor of safety in side shear is at least 2, the side capacity of the element is $2 \times (\frac{2}{3})P = 1.33P$; i.e., the side resistance of the element will continue to carry all the load until it exceeds a value of $1.33P$.

Post office square garage

A second example presented by Johnson et al. (1991) is for the Post Office Square garage in downtown Boston that provides seven underground parking levels. A public park was constructed above the roof at ground level, covering about 6700 m² of public space. Likewise, this structure was built using the downward method and required 101 load-bearing elements from 24 to 29 m deep. Soil data, sections, and details are shown in Fig. 5-33. The recommended design parameters (ASD) are shown in Table 5-6 and were obtained from pressuremeter tests combined with presumptive values from local experience.

The decision to use linear load-bearing elements as foundations was made during the construction phase. The initial design stipulated caissons installed in the dry, but some concern was raised regarding potential disturbance and loss of ground, resulting in excessive wall movement, because of the close proximity of some caissons to the slurry wall. A second factor that favored the conversion from caissons to linear wall elements was related to the availability of equipment combined with better production rates for the overall construction.

A cement-bentonite backfill was placed above the concrete to fill the linear trenches, the objective being to provide an impervious material but of low strength that could be readily excavated from around the columns during general excavation. This backfill served also to impede any upward groundwater seepage along the columns that might accumulate at subgrade levels during excavation.

During the main construction phase wall movement was monitored with inclinometers. At wall locations close to the foundation elements the movement was about 20 to 25 percent higher than in other locations.

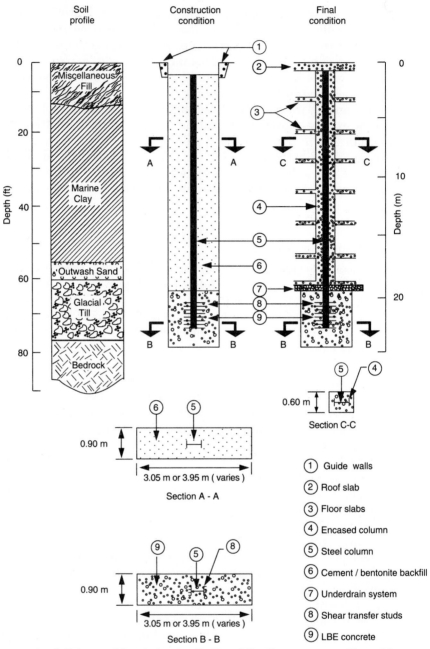

Figure 5-33 Soil data and foundation details, Post Office Square garage. (*From Johnson et al., 1991.*)

TABLE 5-6   Design Data, Load-Bearing Elements for Post Office Square Garage

Column loads	6200 to 13,800 kN		
Recommended allowable	Skin friction	Glacial till	190 kPa
designs values		Bedrock	190 kPa, upper 4.5 m
			290 kPa, lower 4.5 m
	End bearing	Glacial till	765 kPa
		Bedrock	1435 kPa
LBE sizes	Linear	0.90 m × 3.05 m and 0.90 m ×	
		3.95 m	
Bearing strata	Glacial till	Hard gray clayey to gravelly *silt* to a very dense gray-brown silty coarse to fine *sand; N* values ranged from 40 to 200+	
	Bedrock	Fine-grained *argillite* and coarse to fine-grained *sandstone.* Weathering varied from complete to slight. Recoveries ranged from 0 to 100%. RQD values ranged from 0 to 35%. Split spoon samples were able to be recovered in several borings	

From Johnson et al., 1991.
1 m = 3.28 ft, 1 kN = 0.22 kip, 1 kPa = 0.021 kip/ft^2.

5-19   Design Example 4

The linear load-bearing element of Fig. 5-34 is socketed 10 ft into basalt to support a dead load of 410 kips and a live load of 250 kips. The compressive strength of the basalt is 1.0 kip/in^2 and the RQD is 70 percent. Check the adequacy of the element assuming that this is a bridge structure.

Step 1.   Estimate the required load capacity. Using AASHTO criteria the factored loads are 1.3(410) + 2.17(250) = 533 + 542 = 1075 kips.

Step 2.   Check the structural axial capacity, assuming that the element is reinforced with 16 No. 11 bars with a yield stress of 60 kips/

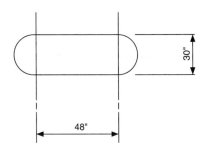

Figure 5-34 Cross section of linear element, Design Example 4.

in². Use a compressive concrete strength of 3000 lb/in². The factored nominal structural capacity is computed from Eq. (5-4).

$$A_y = 16(1.56) = 25 \text{ in}^2$$

$$A_g = 3.14(30)^2/4 + 30(48) = 707 + 1440 = 2147 \text{ in}^2$$

or

$$A_c = 2147 - 25 = 2122 \text{ in}^2$$

Therefore, $\phi_a P_n = (0.8)(0.7)[(0.85)(3)(2122) + (60)(25)] = 3870$ kips > 1075 kips   OK.

Step 3.   Estimate the bearing capacity. As mentioned, this requires an estimate of the settlement of the portion socketed in the rock.

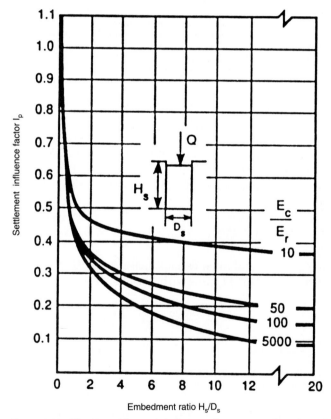

Figure 5-35 Elastic settlement influence factor as a function of embedment ratio and modular ratio, as developed by (*a*) Donald, Sloan, and Chiu, 1980; and (*b*) Reese and O'Neill, 1988. (*From Barker et al., 1991.*)

The elastic shortening p_e may be computed as follows:

$$p_e = \frac{\Sigma(P_i)H_s}{A_{soc}E_c} \quad (5\text{-}32)$$

where H_s = depth of socket; ΣP_i = working load at the top of the socket; A_{soc} = cross-sectional area of the socket; and E_c = concrete modulus considering the stiffness of any steel reinforcement.

The settlement of the base p_b may be computed from the expression

$$p_b = \frac{\Sigma(P_i)I_p}{D_s E_r} \quad (5\text{-}33)$$

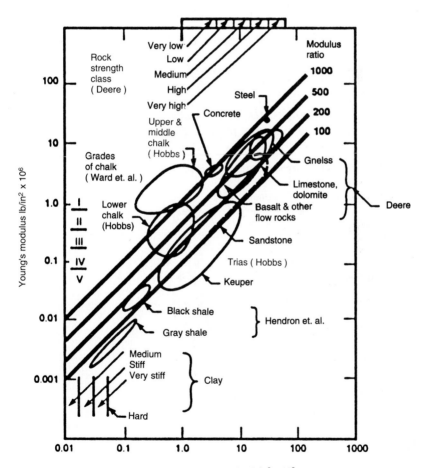

Figure 5-36 Engineering classification of intact rock, as developed by Deere (1968) and Peck (1976), and as presented by Reese and O'Neill (1988). (*From Barker et al., 1991.*)

where I_p = influence coefficient obtained from the graphs of Fig. 5-35; D_s = equivalent diameter of the element; and E_r = in situ modulus of rock considering the joints and their spacing. The parameter E_r is computed as

$$E_r = K_E E_i \qquad (5\text{-}34)$$

where E_i = intact rock modulus obtained either by tests or by reference to Fig. 5-36; and K_E = modulus modification ratio, related to the RQD as shown in Fig. 5-37.

From Fig. 5-36, the Young's modulus of intact basalt is 5×10^2 kips/in^2 and the modulus ratio is 500. From Fig. 5-37, the modulus of in situ rock mass for RQD = 70 percent is 20 percent of the intact modulus, so that $E_r = 0.2 \times 5 \times 10^2 = 100$ kips/in^2.

With these parameters we compute the following:

$$p_e = \frac{(660)(1000)(10)(12)}{(2147)(3)(10)^6} = 0.012 \text{ in}$$

The equivalent diameter D_s is $(3.14)D_s^2/4 = 2147$ or $D_s = 52$ in. Next, we compute the embedment ratio $H_s/D_s = (10 \times 12)/52 = 2.3$,

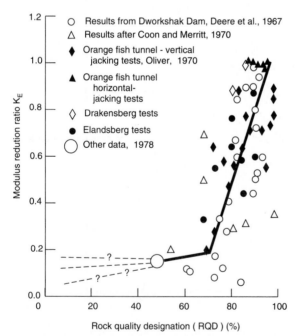

Figure 5-37 Modulus reduction ratio as a function of RQD, as developed by Bieniawski (1984), and as presented by Reese and O'Neill (1988). (*From Barker et al., 1991.*)

and $E_c/E_r = 30$. From Fig. 5-35, $I_p = 0.38$ (approximately). From Eq. (5-33)

$$p_b = \frac{(660)(1000)(0.38)}{(52)(1000)(10)^3} = 0.048 \text{ in}$$

or $p_e + p_b = 0.012 + 0.048 = 0.06$ in < 0.4 in, or the capacity of the element is derived mainly from side resistance. Since $q_u > 280$ lb/in^2, Eq. (5-21) is used. Then $q_s = 2.5\sqrt{q_u} = 2.5\sqrt{1000} = 79$ lb/in^2 and $Q_s = (79)[(3.14)(30) + 96](10)(12)/1000 = 1800$ kips. The factored capacity is $(0.65)(1800) = 1170$ kips > 1075 kips   OK.

References

Baker, C. W., and F. Khan, 1971: Caisson Construction Problems and Corrections in Chicago, *J. ASCE Soil Mech. Found. Div.*, February, pp. 417–439.

Barker, R. M., et al., 1991: "Manuals for the Design of Bridge Foundations," *NCHRP Report* 343, TRB, National Research Council, Washington, D.C.

Barker, W. R., and L. C. Reese, 1970: "Load-Carrying Characteristics of Drilled Shaft Constructed with the Aid of Drilling Fluids," *Research Report* 89-9, Center for Highway Research, University of Texas at Austin, Austin, Tex.

Berezantsev, V. G., et al., 1961: Load Bearing Capacity and Deformation of Pile Foundations, *Proc. 5th Int. Conf. Soil Mech. Found. Eng.*, Paris, vol. 2.

Bienawski, Z. T., 1984: *Rock Mechanics Design in Mining and Tunneling*, A. A. Balkema, Rotterdam/Boston, 1984, 272 pp.

Broms, B., 1964a: "The Lateral Resistance of Piles in Cohesive Soils," *J. Soil Mech. Found. Div., ASCE*, vol. 90, no. SM2, March, pp. 27–63.

Broms, B. 1964b: "The Lateral Resistance of Piles in Cohesionless Soils," *J. Soil Mech. Found. Div., ASCE*, vol. 90, no. SM3, pp. 123–156.

Burland, J. B., 1973: Shaft Friction of Piles in Clay—A Simple Fundamental Approach, *Ground Eng.*, 6.3.

Canadian Geotechnical Society, 1985: *Canadian Foundation Engineering Manual*, 2d ed., Bitech Publ. Ltd., 460 pp.

Carter, J. P., and F. H. Kulhawy, 1988: "Analysis and Design of Foundations Socketed into Rock," *EPRI Report* no. EL-5918, New York, 158 pp.

Chadeisson, R., 1961: Influence of the Boring Methods on the Behavior of Cast-in-Place Bored Piles, *Proc. 5th Int. Conf. Soil Mech. Found. Eng.*, Paris, vol. 2.

Chandler, R. J., 1966: Discussion. Large bored piles. Inst. Civ. Eng., London, 95.

Chandler, R. J., 1968: The Shaft Friction of Piles in Cohesive Soils in Terms of Effective Stress, *Civ. Eng. Publ. Wks. Rev.*, vol. 63, p. 48.

Corbett, B. O., et al., 1974: A Load Bearing Wall at Kensington and Charles Town Hall, London, *Proc. Diaphragm Walls Anchorages, Inst. Civ. Eng.*, London.

Czerniak, E., 1957: "Resistance to Overturning of Single, Short Piles," *J. Struct. Div., ASCE*, vol. 83, no. ST2, Proc. Paper 1188, March, pp. 1–25.

Davisson, M. T., 1970: "Lateral Load Capacity of Piles," Highway Research Record no. 333, pp. 104–112.

Davisson, M. T., and K. E. Robinson, 1965: "Bending and Buckling of Partially Embedded Piles," *Proc. 6th Int. Conf. Soil Mech. Found. Eng.*, Montreal, Canada, pp. 243–246.

Deere, D. V., 1968: "Geological Considerations," chap. 1 in K. G. Stagg and O. C. Zienkiewicz, *Roc Mechanics in Engineering Practice*, Wiley, New York, pp. 1–20.

Donald, I. B., S. W. Sloan, and H. K. Chiu, 1980: "Theoretical Analysis of Rock Socketed Piles," *Proc. Int. Conf. on Structural Found. on Rock*, Sydney, Balkema, Rotterdam.

Farmer, I. W., et al., 1971: "The Effect of Bentonite on the Skin Friction of Cast-in-Place Piles," *Proc. Behavior Piles, Inst. Civ. Eng.,* London.

Garg, R. G., 1979: "Bored Pile Groups under Vertical Load in Sand," *J. Geot. Div. ASCE,* vol. 105, no. GT8, August, pp. 933–956.

Goldberg, D. T., 1979: "Geotechnical Aspects of Slurry Walls," Symp. Slurry Walls for Underground Transp. Systems, U.S. DOT, FHWA, Cambridge, Mass., Aug. 30–31.

Henkel, D. J., 1970: "Geotechnical Considerations of Lateral Stress," *Proc. ASCE Spec. Conf.,* Lateral Earth Stresses Design Earth Retaining Struct., Cornell University, June.

Horvath, R. G., and T. C. Kenney, 1979: "Shaft Resistance of Rock Socketed Drilled Piers," *Proc. Symp. Deep Found., ASCE,* Atlanta, Ga., pp. 182–214.

Johnson, E. G., and K. E. Johnson, 1990: "Foundation Piers," Notes from MIT Geot. Construction Course, Session no. 5, Spring.

Johnson, E. G., K. E. Johnson, and C. M. Erikson, 1991: "Deep Foundation Elements Installed by Slurry Wall Technique," ASTM Conf. on Slurry Walls, Atlantic City.

Kienberger, H., 1974: "Diaphragm Walls as Load Bearing Foundations," *Proc. Diaphragm Walls Anchorages, Inst. Civ. Eng.,* London.

Krohn, J. P., and J. E. Slosson, 1980: "Assessment of Expansive Soils in the United States," *Proc. 4th Int. Conf. Expansive Soils, ASCE,* vol. 1, Denver, Colo., June, pp. 596–608.

Kulhawy, F. H., C. H. Trautmann, J. F. Beech, T. D. O'Rourke, and W. McGuire, 1983: "Transmission Line Structure Foundations for Uplift—Compression Loading," *EPRI Rept.* EL-2870, Electric Power Institute.

Matlock, H., and L. C. Reese, 1961: "Foundation Analysis of Offshore Pile Supported Structures," *Proc. 5th Int. Conf. Soil Mech. Found. Eng.,* Paris, vol. 2, pp. 91–97.

Matlock, H., and L. C. Reese, 1962: "Generalized Solutions for Laterally Loaded Piles," *Transactions ASCE,* vol. 127, part 1, pp. 1220–1247.

McClelland, B., and J. A. Focht, Jr., 1956: "Soil Modulus for Laterally Loaded Piles," *J. Soil Mech. Found. Div., ASCE,* vol. 82, no. SM4, Proc. Paper 1081, October, pp. 1–22.

McKinney, J. R., and G. R. Gray, 1963: "The Use of Drilling Mud in Large Diameter Construction Borings," in *Grouts and Drilling Muds in Engineering Practice,* Butterworths, London.

Meyerhof, G. G., 1951: "The Ultimate Bearing Capacity of Foundations," *Geotechnique,* vol. 2, no. 4.

Peck, R. B., 1976: "Rock Foundations for Structures," *Proc. ASCE Spec. Conf. on Rock Engineering for Found. and Slopes,* Boulder, Colo.

Pells, P. J. N., and R. N. Turner, 1979: "Elastic Solutions for the Design and Analysis of Rock-Socketed Piles," *Canadian Geotechnical J.,* vol. 16, no. 3.

Potyondy, J. G., 1961: "Skin Friction between Various Soils and Construction Materials," *Geotechnique,* vol. XI, no. 4, pp. 339–353.

Poulos, H. G., 1971a: "Behavior of Laterally Loaded Piles, I—Single Piles," *J. Soil Mech. Found. Div., ASCE,* vol. 97, no. SM5, pp. 711–731.

Poulos, H. G., 1971b: "Behavior of Laterally Loaded Piles, II—Pile Groups," *J. Soil Mech. Found. Div., ASCE,* vol. 97, no. SM5, pp. 733–751.

Poulos, H. G., 1974: "Analysis of Pile Groups Subjected to Vertical and Horizontal Loads," *Aust. Geomechanics J.,* vol. G4, no. 1, pp. 26–32.

Poulos, H. G., and E. H. Davis, 1968: "The Settlement Behavior of Single Axially-Loaded Piles and Piers," *Geotech.,* vol. 18.

Poulos, H. G., 1973: "Load-Deflection Prediction for Laterally Loaded Piles," Research Report no. R208, School of Eng., The University of Sydney, Sydney, Australia, March, pp. 1–28.

Poulos, H. G., and E. H. Davis, 1980: *Pile Foundation Design and Analysis,* Wiley, New York, 397 pp.

Poulos, H. G., and E. H. Davis, 1975: "Prediction of Downdrag Forces in End Bearing Piles," *J. Geot. Div., ASCE,* vol. 101, no. GT2, February, pp. 189–204.

Ramasuamy, F., and E. M. Pertusier, 1984: "Construction of Barrettes for High-Rise Foundations," Int. Conf. of Tall Buildings, Singapore, pp. 455–462.

Reese, L. C., and H. Matlock, 1956: "Non-dimensional Solutions for Laterally Loaded Piles with Soil Modulus Assumed Proportional to Depth," *Proc. 8th Int. Texas Conf. Soil Mech Found. Eng.,* Austin, Tex., pp. 1–41.

Reese, L. C., et al., 1968: "Instrumentation for Measurements of Lateral Earth Pressures in Drilled Shafts," University of Texas, Res. Rep. 89-2, Austin.

Reese, L. C., and M. W. O'Neill, 1988: "Drilled Shafts: Construction Procedures and Design Methods," FHWA Publ. no. FHWA-HI-88-042, or ADSC Publ. no. ADSC-TL-4, August, 564 pp.

Reese, L. C., and M. W. O'Neill, 1969: "Field Tests on Bored Piles in Beaumont Clay," ASCE Annu. Meet. Chicago, Repr. 1008.

Reese, L. C., and F. T. Touma, 1973: "Bored Piles Installed by Slurry Displacement," *Proc. 8th Int. Conf. Soil Mech. Found. Eng.,* Moscow.

Reese, L. C., and K. L. Tucker, 1985: "Bentonite Slurry in Constructing Drilled Piers," Drilled Piers and Caissons II, *Proc. Geotechn. Eng. Div. ASCE,* ASCE Convention, Denver, Colo.

Reese, L. C., and S. J. Wright, 1977: "Drilled Shaft Manual-Construction Procedures and Design for Axial Loading," vol. 1, U.S. Dept. of Transportation, Implementation Div., HDV-22, Implementation Package 77–21, July, 140 pp.

Simm, K. F., 1974: "Discussion Report," *Proc. Diaphragm Walls Anchorages, Inst. Civ. Eng.,* London.

Skempton, A. W., 1951: "The Bearing Capacity of Clays," *Proc. Building Research Congress,* London, vol. 1, pp. 180–189.

Sliwinski, Z., and W. G. K. Fleming, 1974: "Practical Considerations Affecting the Construction of Diaphragm Walls," *Proc. Diaphragm Walls Anchorages, Inst. Civ. Eng.,* London.

Stas, C. V., and F. H. Kulhawy, 1984: "Critical Evaluation of Design Methods for Foundations under Axial Uplift, and Comparison Loading," EPRI Report no. EL-3771, November, 198 pp.

Stebbins, E. E., and R. C. Williams, 1986: "Wet-Hole Drilled Shaft Construction," *Proc. Drilled Foundation Seminar,* Auburn University, February.

Terzaghi, K., 1943: *Theoretical Soil Mechanics,* Wiley, New York.

Touma, F. T., and L. C. Reese, 1974: "Behavior of Bored Piles in Sand," *ASCE JGED,* vol. 100, no. GT7, July, pp. 749–761.

Vesic, A. S., 1975: "Bearing Capacity of Shallow Foundations," chap. 3 in H. Winterkorn and H. Y. Fang (eds.), *Foundation Engineering Handbook,* Van Nostrand Reinhold Co., New York, pp. 121–147.

Vesic, A. S., 1967: Ultimate Loads and Settlement of Deep Foundations in Sand, *Proc. Symp. Bearing Capacity Settlement Found.,* Duke University, Durham, N.C.

Vesic, A. S., 1968: "Load Transfer, Lateral Loads and Group Action of Deep Foundations," *ASTM Spec. Tech. Publ.* 444.

Walker, J. N., and E. H. Cox, 1964: "Design of Pier Foundations for Lateral Loads," Paper no. 64-405, American Society of Agricultural Engineers, Fort Collins, Colo., June, pp. 417–427.

Whitaker, T., and R. W. Cooke, 1965: Bored Piles with Enlarged Bases in London Clay, *Proc. 6th Int. Conf. Soil Mech. Found. Eng.,* Montreal.

Whitaker, T., and R. W. Cooke, 1966: "An Investigation of the Shaft and Base Resistance of Large Bored Piles in London Clay," *Proc. Symp. Large Bored Piles, Inst. Civ. Eng.,* London, February.

Xanthakos, P. P., 1979: *Slurry Walls,* McGraw-Hill, New York, 622 pp.

Xanthakos, P. P., 1991: *Ground Anchors and Anchored Structures,* Wiley, New York, 686 pp.

6

Concrete Technology and Design

6-1 Factors Influencing Mix Design

The requirements for plain or reinforced concrete placed in slurry trenches are different from conventional construction. During placement and curing the fresh mix is exposed to conditions that can markedly affect its properties. Yet the set concrete must provide strength and durability, and since the wall is built below grade, watertightness is equally important.

Unlike ordinary structural work where the fresh mix is vibrated and mechanically compacted, fresh concrete in slurry trenches is placed through tremie pipes and displaces the slurry by gravity action only. For a complete displacement of slurry, this action largely depends on the difference in density between the two materials, usually having a ratio of 1.7 to 1.8.

Experience shows that the displacement is complete if it occurs with an upward motion of the fluid concrete. This particular motion also provides a gentle sweeping action on the face of the trench and on the reinforcement bars and incidental inserts. This action presumably cleans and removes any bentonite coating from these surfaces, and promotes bond by ensuring direct contact.

As a matter of practical convenience contractors may often choose to use one tremie pipe, even for panels unusually long. This is likely to result in incomplete displacement of the slurry, particularly near the ends of the panel.

It appears from these brief remarks that the method of placement of fresh concrete is an important phase because of the wide effects that bentonite not displaced can have on final properties of set concrete. The process is helped by a mix that is flowable and workable. Thus it is common to design a mix that, besides strength, provides the necessary workability. Experience shows that faults, reversed "hanging up," and "whirls" in which contaminated concrete is trapped can be avoided by a mix that if flowable and yet not subject to segregation. Carefully selected aggregate, a suitable aggregate-cement ratio, and a retarder to delay initial set are desirable features of the mix.

Lack of attention to these details can produce walls with distinct structural deficiencies. Interestingly, even if a direct basis is available for providing quality control and securing suitable construction procedures, the condition of the final structure may not be confirmed until after the wall is exposed and visually inspected.

For a complete concrete placement, the fresh material must satisfy the following conditions:

1. The mix must be flowable and have a plastic consistency. If the initial shear is too high, the flow is likely to be restrained, resulting in bentonite trapped in areas not reached by the mix.

2. However, the mix must be cohesive enough to prevent segregation and bleeding. Concrete that bleeds or disintegrates under the pressure of its own weight can block the tremie pipe or accept bentonite.

3. The mix should not set or stiffen too quickly but should remain workable until the pour is completed. The setting time must be extended to avoid adverse effects on concrete already delivered but not placed or on sections placed but not completed because of delays.

The consistency of concrete that satisfies these requirements is largely governed by the quantity of water and its relation to fines, including cement. For a mix to be workable the water must be trapped in the fines fraction, and since the particles opposing water flow are generally below the 0.5 mm size, they must be present in sufficient quantity. Whereas the consistency of concrete is primarily a matter of design, the field controls have immediate practical significance. Besides routine slump tests, fresh concrete should be examined before placement, since segregation and bleeding are usually noticeable to the trained eye.

6-2   Proportioning Concrete Mixes

Mix design and details are governed by current ACI manuals and codes. Among the many comprehensive reviews available on the composition and properties of fresh and hardened concrete, Troxell et al. (1968) and Neville (1973) discuss the details of the various types of concrete and describe the effects of component materials such as air-entraining agents and other admixtures. They also review curing methods, the manufacture of concrete, and concrete requirements for special uses.

The discussion presented in this section focuses, therefore, on the special aspects of concrete placed in slurry trenches and used in the ground, with the intent to show how simple adjustments in proportioning the basic mix can produce workable concrete without sacrificing strength and durability.

Workability. Workability is a relative characteristic; concrete that is flowable and workable under some conditions may not necessarily be the same under other conditions. Workability relates mainly to the shear resistance of force required to start flow, the mass mobility after flow has started, cohesiveness or resistance to segregation, and the sticky limit of the material. In practice, workability is affected by the quantity and characteristics of cement, gradation and shape of aggregates, quantity of water, presence of entrained air, and the type of admixtures.

In general, for concrete in slurry trenches the slump test is accepted as a measure of workability. Other procedures for assessing workability include the flow and ball penetration tests, but these methods do not take account of all the inherent variables. A crude indication of workability can be obtained by tapping the side of the slumped pile with a tamping rod; cohesive concrete will not break apart or crumble. If slump is used to determine the mass mobility of fresh concrete, it should be in the range of 7 to 9 in (18 to 22 cm). As shown in Fig. 6-1, the slump is considerably affected by the temperature of concrete, and the higher this temperature the lower the slump. Where conditions warrant, this variation should be taken into consideration.

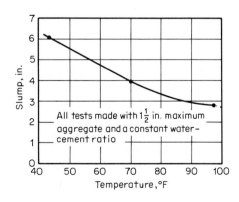

Figure 6-1 Variation in the slump of concrete with temperature. (*U.S. Bureau of Reclamation, 1963.*)

An alternate procedure is the compacting factor test, which is related to the reciprocal of workability. The degree of compaction achieved by a certain work is determined by the density ratio (ratio of the density actually achieved in the test to the density of the same concrete fully compacted). This test differs from the slump test in that variations in workability are reflected by a substantial change in the compacting factor; however, the test is more sensitive at low workability levels. The recommended compacting factor for the required workability of tremied concrete is 0.95 to 0.96.

Water quantity.   Neither strength nor durability should determine the water content of tremied concrete. Although a loss of strength of set concrete should be expected if the water-cement ratio is increased, the quantity of water should be enough to produce a mix that is workable and flowable. For a 7½-in slump and a maximum aggregate size of ¾ in, the quantity of water may be from 42 to 44 gal per cubic yard of mix for non-air-entrained concrete, and from 37 to 39 gal per cubic yard of mix for air-entrained concrete.

The water requirements can be further reduced through the use of plasticizers of an acceptable type. Finely divided workability agents are added to the fresh mix, allowing a reduction in the water content by more than 10 percent, and this increases the concrete strength, providing also an antibleed action. Furthermore, they raise the specific gravity of the mix, thereby improving its displacing ability during the pour.

Grading of aggregate.   A flowable consistency is obtained if the water actually is trapped within the aggregate. In this respect smaller aggregate will oppose movement of water within a mix more effectively. Before considering the use of plasticizers to offset deficiencies in grading that tend to produce harshness, a simple redesign of the mix with emphasis on the ratio of fine to coarse aggregate and also on the grading of the fine aggregate can produce good results and a satisfactory mix.

The tendency for the mix to segregate is reduced by limiting the maximum size of aggregate to ¾ in (2 cm). The shape of the grading curve should show evenly graded aggregate since gap-graded concrete is prone to segregation.

Cement quantity.   Because of the higher than normal quantity of water and fines the cement content must also be higher to satisfy the strength requirements. For average conditions, maintaining a water-cement ratio about 0.5 by weight will yield concrete in the 3000 to 4000 lb/in^2 range (210 to 280 kg/cm^2) for 28-day standard moist-cured compressive strength. In addition, the cement particles in rich mixes combine with the fines to produce cohesion and flowability. Higher than average cement quantity is also useful in reducing some tendency for partial segregation when concrete is poured through tremie pipes.

Retarders. These are used to prevent premature stiffening of some cements or to delay stiffening under difficult placing conditions. The setting time must be checked against the time necessary to complete the pour. Concrete that sets too quickly is difficult to tremie, especially at high temperatures. In such cases retarders are advisable to offset the accelerating and damaging effects of quick setting and keep concrete workable for the entire pour. However, some of the chemicals and admixtures alledged to retard the setting time are likely to have variable and uncertain action. A reduction in strength usually accompanies the use of organic retarders, and creep in concrete is also influenced by the setting time.

Despite these incidental effects, retarders selected carefully and in certain proportions offset the effects of disruption during placement and may even have a beneficial influence on concrete strength. The admixtures most commonly used are lignosulfonic acids, hydroxylated carboxylic acids and their salts, and derivatives of these chemicals. In general, they should be used under competent technical advice and after adequate testing under conditions similar to those in the trench.

Air entraining. Concrete made from air-entraining admixtures has lower strength than non-air-entrained concrete but shows greater plasticity even at lower water content, relative freedom from bleeding and segregation, and improved durability against freezing and thawing. Air entrainment contributes to the fluidity of the plastic mass, much as added water does. Without loss of workability it is possible to reduce the quantity of mixing water and use a higher ratio of coarse to fine aggregate. Each 1 percent of entrained air generally permits a reduction of water of about 3 percent and a reduction in sand content by an amount about equal to the volume of entrained air.

The tendency for strength to decrease is partially offset and compensated for by the use of additional cement. The decision to use air entrainment or how much air to entrain depends therefore on the degree to which strength can be satisfied in the interest of improved workability.

In most practical applications, the theoretical concrete strength does not govern the selection of wall thickness. In these cases a slight reduction in strength is acceptable if it improves workability. A slight excess of water is less harmful than a quantity that produces stiff

TABLE 6-1   Compressive Strength of Concrete for Various
Water-Cement Ratios

Water-cement ratio		Probable average compressive strength at 28 days, lb/in^2	
Gal/sack of cement	By weight	Non-air-entrained concrete	Air-entrained concrete
4	0.35	6000	4800
5	0.44	5000	4000
6	0.53	4000	3200
7	0.62	3200	2600
8	0.71	2500	2000
9	0.80	2000	1600

From ACI, 1954.

concrete. Likewise excess of fines is less detrimental than a mix behaving like a stony mass.

These considerations suggest the use of entrained air, which should
be 4 percent minimum and 5 percent desired average by volume in
conjunction with maximum aggregate size of ¾ in (2 cm). For a given
compressive strength, the probable water-cement ratio can be estimated from Table 6-1 for both non-air-entrained and air-entrained
concrete. For constant water-cement ratio the concrete strength is reduced as the air content is increased from the usually entrapped to
the usually entrained amount.

6-3   Strength Considerations of Reinforced Concrete for Diaphragm Walls

Compressive strength.   Depending on the mix (especially the water-
cement ratio) and the time and quality of curing, compressive
strengths of concrete for diaphragm walls may achieve the 3000 to
5000 lb/in^2 theoretical range. This is based on commercial production
with ordinary aggregates. For precast and prestressed panels the
range of strength is considerably expanded with 6500 to 7000 lb/in^2 a
probable upper limit. Because of the difference in aggregate and to a
lesser degree in cements, the same mix proportions can result in considerably lower strengths.

The ACI Code stipulates that the strength level of an individual
class of concrete should be considered satisfactory if both of the following requirements are met: (1) Average of all sets of three consecutive strength tests equals or exceeds f_c'; and (2) no individual strength
test (average of two cylinders) falls below by more than 500 lb/in^2.

The average concrete strength for which a concrete mix should be
designed must exceed f_c' by an amount that depends on the uniformity

of plant production. Thus the code specifies that the mix must be designed for an average strength f'_{cr} that is greater than f'_c, using the larger values of

$$f'_{cr} = f'_c + 1.34s \qquad (6\text{-}1a)$$

or

$$f'_{cr} = f'_c + 2.33s - 500 \qquad (6\text{-}1b)$$

where the standard deviation s is established according to Code Section 4.3.1. It should be noted that f'_c for design is not to be considered the average strength of job cylinder tests. The design f'_c is nearer a minimum than an average, but it is not an absolute minimum. An individual test (average of two cylinders) may be almost 500 lb/in² low and still be acceptable if all averages of three consecutive tests are satisfactory.

Tensile strength. Conceivable situations where the design must rely on the tensile strength of concrete are unlikely to arise, with some exceptions. An example is a diaphragm wall, serving as a cutoff, subjected to deformations but not under the direct action of loads. In this case, bending associated with ground deformation can induce tensile stresses, and if the wall is unreinforced these stresses must be resisted by the concrete.

In general, concrete has low tensile strength, usually 10 to 15 percent of the compression strength, and occasionally 20 percent. The modulus of rupture measured from standard 6-in square beams appears to exceed the real tensile strength. Both the ACI and AASHTO use the value of $7.5\sqrt{f'_c}$ as the modulus of rupture.

The significance of low tensile strength can be demonstrated by considering a homogeneous elastic beam subjected to bending. In this case, the bending stress is $f = Mc/I$. Consider now $f'_c = 3500$ lb/in², so that $f_r = 7.5\sqrt{3500} = 445$ lb/in². Using the AASHTO specifications, the allowable tensile stress is $f_t = 0.21f_r = 0.21 \times 445 = 93$ lb/in². If this stress is accepted as a limit on diaphragm wall strength, and considering a wall 36 in thick ($I = 1 \times 3^3/12 = 2.25$ ft⁴), the maximum resisting moment is $M = 13.3 \times 2.25/1.50 = 19.9$ ft-kips.

Modulus of elasticity. Both the ACI and AASHTO give the secant modulus as

$$E_c = w_c^{1.5}33\sqrt{f'_c} \qquad (6\text{-}2)$$

where w_c = weight of concrete (lb/ft^3) for values between 90 and 155, and f_c' is given in lb/in^2. For normal weight concrete (w_c = 145 lb/ft^3), Eq. (6-2) leads to

$$E_c = 57,000\sqrt{f_c'} \qquad (6\text{-}3)$$

Poisson's ratio may be assumed as 0.2.

Shear strength.   Reported shear strength of concrete ranges from 35 to 80 percent of the compression strength. The broad variation is explained by the difficulty in separating shear from other stresses in testing.

A special case is diaphragm walls braced with anchors or interior struts but without waling beams. The allowable shear stress to be carried by the concrete may be taken as $0.95\sqrt{f_c'}$.

Creep and shrinkage.   Factors tending to increase creep include loading at an early age, using concrete with a high water-cement ratio, and exposing the concrete to drying conditions. Completely wet concrete or completely dried sections will creep moderately, and in general creep decreases with the age of the concrete.

Shrinkage occurs as concrete loses moisture by evaporation. Because moisture is seldom uniformly withdrawn from the concrete, the differential moisture changes cause differential shrinkage and internal stresses. These stresses can be quite large, and this shows the importance of moist curing conditions. With reinforced concrete, the internal restraint caused by the reinforcement that does not shrink can result in large stresses; these are compression in the steel and tension in the concrete.

Reinforcing steel.   The two common grades used in diaphragm wall construction are Grade 40 and Grade 60, although the ACI Code permits bars up to Grade 80 provided that they meet the 0.35 percent yield strain requirement and the ASTM bend test provisions. The modulus of elasticity usually is taken as 29×10^6 lb/in^2 (ACI and AASHTO). For allowable stress design the tensile stress in the reinforcement f_s should not exceed 20,000 lb/in^2 and 24,000 lb/in^2 for Grade, 40 and 60, respectively.

Where conditions warrant, corrosion protection of reinforcing bars merits attention. The bars may be ordered with galvanized coating under ASTM Specification A679–79 or with epoxy coating under ASTM Specification A775-84.

6-4   Concrete Placement

As a general rule, the concrete should be placed soon after the reinforcing cage is inserted into the panel. Once a pour is started, it should be continued and completed in the shortest possible time without interruptions to avoid embedment of stop-end tubes, blockage in the tremie pipes, and cage flotation caused by the upward drag of rising mix. Ready-mixed concrete is commonly used for better quality control and because it can accommodate high pouring rates, sometimes close to 35 yd^3/h (27 m^3/h) or even higher.

Tremie pipes. The most common method of placement is by means of tremie pipes, withdrawn gradually as the concrete level rises. The fresh mix is directly conveyed into the hopper of the pipe. Before depositing concrete, the bottom of the trench should be cleaned with an air lift. When a hopper is used, a pipe for the air duct should be inserted in it.

Tremie pipes suitable for concreting are 6- to 10-in-diameter (15- to 25-cm) steel pipes, but the general preference is to use the largest diameter possible compatible with the discharge rate from the delivery truck. A rule of thumb is to select a diameter at least 8 times the maximum aggregate size, in order to prevent pipe blockage. The pipes should be clean and inspected prior to use.

The required length is obtained by suitable splices, but special care should be taken to ensure the watertightness of the joints. There is no standard pipe length between splices, but for simple adjustments 6-ft (2-m) lengths are practical. The splices should be easily disconnected and have no projecting flanges that could interfere with the steel cage. Threaded pipe joints are often used, and in relatively narrow panels elliptical pipes may offer advantages by allowing easier handling between steel bars.

Tremie concrete placement is based on simple rules, the disadvantage being that it cannot be checked visually. When concrete is tremied in water or slurry, a common source of dilution or segregation is water or slurry in the pipe before starting the pour. Initially the pipe should be empty except for air. The assembly is lowered through the slurry and its tip is allowed to rest firmly on the base of the trench. After the hopper is in place, a plug is inserted and allowed to float; this accessory serves to separate the initial batch of fresh concrete from the slurry in the pipe. As concrete is conveyed, the plug travels down under the weight of the fresh mix and reaches the bottom. At this stage the tremie pipe is slowly lifted, allowing the concrete to force the plug out. Concrete begins to discharge and fill the panel while the pipe is submerged and continuously filled.

Once the placement begins, the operation requires routine checking of the concrete level around the pipe and at the panel ends to check and verify the flow motion of the rising concrete. The initial plug is recovered by floating out.

General guidelines. The usual defects of diaphragm walls are cold joints, zones of segregated or contaminated concrete, trappings of bentonite mud, and cavities at the ends of panels not reached by the fresh concrete.

The first two types of defects result from interruptions in the concrete placement or premature withdrawing of the tremie pipe either partially or completely above the concrete-slurry interface. Mud trappings are caused by impediment to the flow of concrete because of closely spaced bars, poorly designed and placed boxing out, and concrete of low workability. In the worst case the fresh mix may be prevented from filling the panel completely and tightly at the joints, resulting in continuous cavities at these locations.

The fluid concrete will first flow laterally from the discharge point and then upward. The thrust available for this movement decreases with increasing distance from the outlet. As the concrete level rises, the energy gradient is reduced because the pressure head between the concrete in the hopper and the trench decreases. Trappings and faults of bentonite are therefore most often found at panel joints and in the upper portion (usually the upper third) of the panel. Shorter panels are less prone to these defects than longer panels for the same number of tremie pipes.

The nature of mud trappings and inclusions varies considerably. They may appear as a mix of soil, bentonite, and concrete in incidental proportions. Although they are squeezed and eventually compressed under the weight of overlying concrete, they fail to develop significant strength and they are not acceptable structurally, although they are fairly impermeable. If they occur locally, they can be left in place provided they are not located at critical strength sections. If they must be removed and replaced with grout, the area behind the wall should be sealed to improve watertightness.

Tremie-pipe spacing. A single tremie pipe has practical advantages but should be used only for short panels. In general, pipe spacing should be limited to 14 ft (4 m) and should give an end distance not to exceed 7 ft (2 m). Experience suggests that the average panel length that can be poured with one tremie pipe is about 15 ft, but it may reach 20 ft with the use of large-diameter pipes, workable mix, and details that do not impede flow. Where two or more pipes are used, the pouring should be simultaneous if possible or in close alternating sequence.

Other useful guidelines are: (1) always keep the tremie pipe submerged into the fresh concrete at least 5 ft (1.5 m); (2) if the concrete is not deposited easliy, the tremie pipe may be moved up and down, but the movement should not exceed 1 ft (30 cm); and (3) tremie pipes should not be moved horizontally.

Contaminated concrete. The uppermost layer of the fresh mix (usually 1 to 2 ft) will generally become intermixed with bentonite slurry, and this intermixing will have an adverse effect on concrete strength and durability. The usual practice therefore is to overpour or terminate the pour 2 ft above the finish wall line, and then remove lean concrete toppings after hardening.

Face stability during concreting. This condition is expressed by Eq. (3-32) in Sec. 3-8. The validity of this analysis has been checked by DiBiagio and Roti (1972) for a trench 18 m (59 ft) deep. Tests showed that at the end of the pour the pressure exerted by the fresh concrete was hydrostatic only in the upper 5 m of the panel. Below 5 m the lateral pressure on the face gradually became less than the overburden pressure. Specifically, at a depth of 10 m (33 ft) or more the pressure was 0.6 to 0.8 times the overburden pressure.

It is conceivable that in this case the flow motion produced a bottom concrete section that remained undisturbed and began to set as the pour continued in the upper panel. This situation is analogous to the effects caused by concrete placed in conventional forms. For a column, the pressure of fresh concrete depends on the pouring rate, concrete temperature, and height of column but is mainly influenced by the flow motion of the fresh mix. Although this relationship cannot be directly delineated to slurry trenches, a certain stiffening of parts of placed concrete before the pour is complete is accompanied by some shrinkage that relieves somewhat the initial pressure.

Using Eq. (3-32) for an approximate analysis, we may consider the case of a concreted panel in soft clay. Using $\gamma_c = 150$ lb/ft^3, $\gamma = 110$ lb/ft^3, $N = 6$, $K = 1$, and a moderate trench depth (50 to 60 ft), it appears that the undrained shear strength s_u must be at least 400 lb/ft^2 for the face to sustain the fresh concrete.

Whereas wedge failure in this case is extremely unlikely, more important is the prediction of trench enlargement or widening until passive resistance offsets the concrete thrust. Situations have been reported where face movement in soft silt resulted in a 1-ft increase in final wall thickness and required 50 percent more concrete to fill the panel. This suggests the need to monitor the volume of deposited concrete and its level, and compare it with the theoretical value.

6-5   Flow Motion of Tremied Concrete

The tremie process in slurry wall construction is the generally accepted method for placing concrete because it allows a faster operation and ensures better quality control. The finished product has high compressive strength and is sufficient for structural functions.

The importance of the flow motion of tremied concrete has been recognized and studied in a variety of conditions. Considering the effects of incidental factors, tests on prototype panels show that the flow motion is controlled mainly by panel dimensions, number and position of tremie pipes, and the workability and flowability of the fresh mix. These aspects have been investigated by Ikuta et al. (1971), using activable tracers in bentonite. The procedure and results of these investigations are briefly discussed in this section.

Procedure for activable-tracer analysis.   Table 6-2 provides pertinent information about the prototype structures. The activable tracers are readily dissolved in water and eventually absorbed by the bentonite slurry; this traces infiltration of concrete by bentonite. Among the highly activable elements gold (Au), samarium (Sm), scandium (Sc), and antimony (Sb) have been found suitable.

Samarium was the activable tracer for bentonite-slurry medium; i.e., for concrete tremied in bentonite slurry this element can be seen in bentonite-slurry spectrum, meaning that it is absorbed by bentonite and is not elutriated by water.

The activable tracers consisted of nuclides that can be measured separately by nondestructive procedures under the actual irradiation conditions. The four elements were added to the concrete and activated, and the spectra were then measured. In the final process it was possible to measure each photoelectric peak separately. Samarium was the activable tracer for checking the introduction of bentonite into concrete, but all four elements were used to observe the flow motion and mixing of fresh concrete during tremie placement.

Table 6-3 shows the quantity and type of tracer for each specimen. These quantities are several times greater than the minimum detection limits and are more than adequate for the minimum amount of bentonite that must be detected, which in this case was set at 0.5 percent.

Approximately 10 samples were obtained from the prototypes by coring, activated, and then tested in compression. A breakdown into components showed a near constant cement ratio. After subjecting the samples to irradiation and a 5-day cooling period, gamma-ray spectrometry was performed. The quantity of samarium was estimated from the ratio of area of the photoelectric peak, and this gave a measurement of bentonite in the concrete. For the conditions of flow mo-

TABLE 6-2 Specimens and Materials for Activable Tracer Tests

	III	I	IV	II	V
			Specimen		
Dimensions, m	2.1 × 6.0 × 0.6	2.1 × 6.0 × 0.6	4.1 × 6.0 × 0.6	2.1 × 6.0 × 0.6	2.1 × 6.0 × 0.6
Activable tracer	Au, Sc, Sm, Sb	Sm	Sm	Sm	Sm
Tracer medium	Concrete	Slurry	Slurry	Slurry	Slurry
Slurry composition:					
Bentonite concentration, %	0	5.0	5.0	10.0	10.0
CMC, %	0	0.05	0.05	0.05	0.05
Sodium humic acid, %	0	0.10	0.10	0.10	0.10
Slurry properties:					
Specific gravity	····	1.03	1.03	1.05	1.05
Funnel viscosity, 500/500 cm^3	····	26.0	26.0	32.5	32.5
Apparent viscosity, cP	····	9.0	9.0	15.5	15.5
Filtration film thickness, mm	····	1.0	1.0	1.5	1.5
pH	····	8	8	8	8
Concrete quantity, m^3	7.2	7.2	14.4	7.2	7.2
Placing time, min/m^3	10	9	8	14	4
Mix ratio,* kg/m^3 — Cement		330			
Water		185			
Sand		843			
Gravel		938			
Mix properties:* Design strength, kg/cm^3 (28-day)		225			
Water-cement ratio		0.56			
Slump, cm		20			
in		8			

From Ikuta et al., 1971.
*All specimens.

TABLE 6-3 Quantity and Type of Activable Tracer

Specimen	Concrete volume, m³	Nuclide-activable tracer	Quantity added, g
I	7.2	Samarium	80
II	7.2	Samarium	160
III	7.2	Gold	15
		Scandium	25
		Samarium	65
		Antimony	25
IV	14.4	Samarium	160
V	7.2	Samarium	160

From Ikuta et al., 1971.

tion and mixing of concrete during placement, different energies of photoelectric peak were used for the four different elements.

Test results. Figure 6-2a gives the content of each nuclide in various locations of specimen III of Table 6-3. Assuming that the 15 g of gold added to the initial mix was uniformly mixed with the mass of concrete, the weight of gold in the cement is 13.8 μg per sample. In Fig. 6-2a detection quantities one-tenth or less this amount are omitted. Evidently the introduction of two or more nuclides occurs at all locations of sample collection. Figure 6-2b shows the distribution of the various concrete batches.

Irradiation results of samples obtained from specimens I to V gave estimations of the bentonite-cement ratio. In addition, 28-day compressive strengths were obtained from standard tests. The intermixing of bentonite with concrete is evident in Fig. 6-3a to d, but the bentonite-cement ratio is greater at or near the wall surface, where the infiltration of concrete by bentonite is more pronounced, and almost negligible away from the face.

Method of placement. The foregoing results become meaningful if they are correlated to the method of placement. Panel V was concreted by smooth flow from a pump truck through a tremie pipe at uniform speed. Intermixing is considerably lower than in other specimens, but the mixing ratio is essentially the same near the face and in the interior of the wall. For specimens I, II, and IV the concrete was conveyed to the tremie pipe from buckets; hence the flow was considerably less uniform.

Patterns of flow motion of fresh concrete. When concrete is tremied, it usually is assumed that flow occurs in two ways, first laterally at the bottom of the panel and then upward. In this manner the initial batch

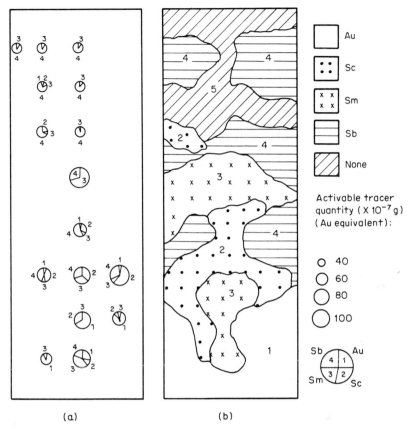

(a)   (b)

Figure 6-2 Estimated diagram of set concrete (specimen III of activable-tracer test). Numbers in *b* indicate the sequence of concrete batches. (*Data from Ikuta et al., 1971.*)

reaching the entire panel laterally is thereafter forced upward by the batches that follow so that it stays on top of the pour. This flow motion is assumed to continue until the pour is completed. Accordingly, bentonite and slime from the slurry are intermixed with fresh concrete at greater proportions near the top of the pour where contact occurs. However, the random arrangement of nuclides and the flow pattern shown in Fig. 6-2a and b, respectively, suggest a different pattern. The position of set concrete is in this case inferred from the detection of activable tracers, their relative proportions in the samples, and observations during placement. The sequence of concrete batches is gold, scandium, samarium, antimony, and no nuclides. The discharge tip of the pipe was held 40 cm (16 in) from the bottom until the block containing antimony was poured.

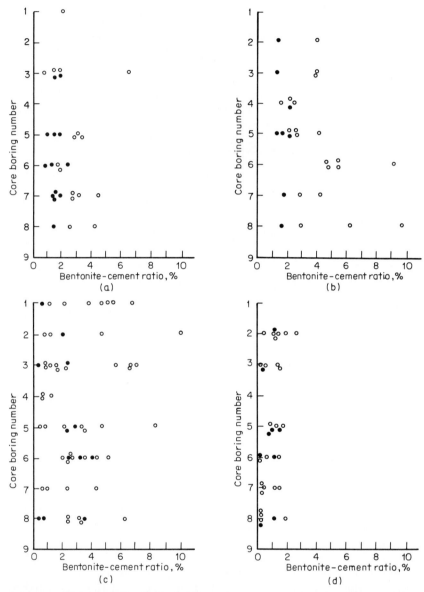

Figure 6-3 Mixing and distribution of bentonite in concrete samples of the activable-tracer test: (*a*) Specimen I. (*b*) Specimen II. (*c*) Specimen IV. (*d*) Specimen V. ● = sample from interior of wall; ○ = sample from near face. (*From Ikuta et al., 1971.*)

This example shows that concrete placed through tremie pipes can rise in different patterns: like a well around the pipe, in a lateral motion, by pushing from the bottom up like a plug (where the first batch is always on top of the pour), or by a combination of these patterns. In this process intermixing of bentonite and concrete is conceivable but occurs to a lesser degree with plug flow.

The flow motion of fresh concrete through a tremie pipe in a relatively long panel is shown in Fig. 6-4. As the initial batch is placed, it assumes an angle of repose according to the concrete slump, and around the pipe the material moves faster than it does away from the pipe. Because in this case the panel is too long for one tremie pipe, more lateral movement must occur for the concrete to fill the ends of the trench. As batch 2 is poured, it displaces batch 1 laterally and toward the ends as shown in Fig. 6-4b, rather than upward. The same pattern of flow continues as shown in Fig. 6-4e and d; each batch thus forms a block gradually squeezed to a thin column around the pipe, causing the level of concrete to rise. The initial block is pushed to the ends and the last block occupies the center.

Although general conclusions cannot be drawn, the following points are appropriate:

1. Plug motion (initial batch always on top) is preferred because (a) it minimizes mud trappings and inclusions, and (b) it provides a sweeping action that cleans and removes bentonite from around the reinforcing bars and other vertical surfaces.

2. For short panels plug flow will occur if the pipe is sufficiently submerged in the concrete. Most contractors keep the tip of the pipe 3 m (10 ft) or more below the concrete level.

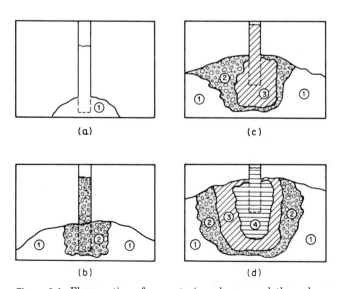

Figure 6-4 Flow motion of concrete in a long panel through a single tremie pipe: (a) Batch 1 being placed. (b) Batch 2 being placed. (c) Batch 3 being placed. (d) Batch 4 being placed.

3. Lateral flow causes the concrete at the top to be exchanged for new concrete. This may trap impurities that eventually are mixed with the concrete.

4. For long panels the desired flow motion cannot be produced unless several tremie pipes are used, and if practicable they should be located near the construction joints.

5. The flow motion depends also on the energy available to displace the fresh mix. This is the difference between the gravity thrust and the resistance to motion offered by the fresh concrete. Relevant factors are therefore the size of the tremie pipe and the panel dimensions. Larger tremie pipes are preferred, especially if the concrete is conveyed at uniform speed, but toward the end of the pour the rate of placement is reduced considerably. Resistance to motion is increased as the fresh mix becomes stiffer.

6-6   Attainable Concrete Strength

The main factors influencing strength for concrete tremied in slurry trenches are as follows:

1. Flow motion during placement. It appears from the foregoing that the initial batches are moved and displaced, and they may not come to final rest until the pour is completed. For deep or long panels this may take several hours, and premature setting in this case can influence strength.

2. Changes in the water-cement ratio. Mixing of slurry with fresh concrete may increase the water content in the latter accompanied by loss of strength.

3. Introduction of bentonite and slime. The final strength may be less than the theoretical if intermixing with bentonite and slime occurs. The finished wall may also have entrapped inclusions and soft pockets of nonconcrete materials.

4. Curing conditions. Curing time, moisture, and temperature affect the development of strength, because of their influence on the hydration of cement. Because these conditions are favorable and the period of moist storage is longer and uninterrupted, the strength is greater. The curing temperature of concrete cast underground is also a favorable factor for the development of strength unless it is much lower than the temperature during casting. In these conditions creep and shrinkage effects should be minimal.

Selection of strength. As mentioned, concrete of any specified cube strength to standard requirements can be produced. Besides the theoretical considerations affecting the selection of strength, economy and practical aspects should also govern. The requirements of excavation and concrete placement must be considered first, and it is advantageous to establish a practical wall thickness before selecting strength. For the usual wall thickness of 24 to 30 in (60 to 75 cm), the design strength (nominal values) will be between 3000 and 5000 lb/in² (210 and 350 kg/cm²). In the lower range the use of entrained air is more justified, and the water-cement ratio is more compatible with the requirements of high slump. Higher strength may be specified subject to special considerations and for unusual classes of structures.

Measured strength

Construction records show that cores obtained from exposed walls several weeks after pouring often have produced strengths higher by as much as 1000 lb/in² (70 kg/cm²) than the theoretical strength. This is due mainly to the fact that concrete undergoes curing within damp soil and is not exposed to outside detrimental conditions.

Strength will be affected if changes in the water-cement ratio can occur. For concrete intermixed with bentonite the probable maximum increase in the water-cement ratio is shown in Fig. 6-5 as a function of the bentonite-cement ratio. The diagrams are based on the assumption that the slurry infiltrates the concrete and is mixed with it. For example, for a bentonite-cement ratio of 0.1 (10 percent) about 33 kg of bentonite is mixed with 1 m³ of mix. For a 10 percent slurry this means that about 330 kg of water will be taken by the fresh mix as slurry, and this will raise the initial quantity of water to 515 kg for 1 m³ (total volume adjusted) so that the new water-cement ratio is now 1.56.

Data from activable-tracer test. If the foregoing assumption is valid, a serious reduction in the strength of set concrete could be expected.

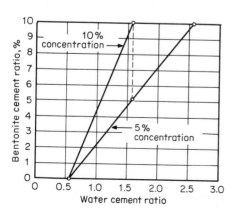

Figure 6-5 Change in water-cement ratio for varying bentonite-cement ratios for the concrete mixes of Table 6-2. (*From Ikuta et al., 1971.*)

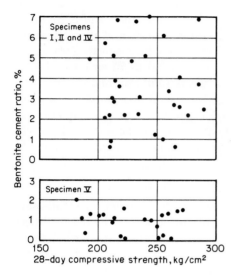

Figure 6-6 Relationship between bentonite-cement ratio and compressive strength. Samples obtained from the specimens of the activable-tracer test. (*From Ikuta et al., 1971.*)

However, the measured strength of core samples shown in Fig. 6-6 clearly shows no definite relationship between the bentonite-cement ratio and strength. The results are quite scattered and show no specific trend in the development of strength. This supports the conclusion that intermixing of bentonite with fresh concrete does not mean that the latter absorbs water.

However, the presence of bentonite in the concrete mix influences the elastic modulus and its relationship to compressive strength. At some specific region both clean and bentonite concrete have the same modulus, but the elasticity-strength curve for the latter is considerably steeper, meaning that bentonite concrete has a lower modulus at the same strength and therefore behaves more like a plastic material. These effects are clearly shown in Fig. 6-7, where the elastic modulus is plotted vs. the compressive concrete strength.

Results from laboratory tests. Table 6-4 shows data from three concrete mixes. The prototype bentonite mix was tremied into four prototype panels containing 4, 7, 10, and 13 percent bentonite slurry, respectively (Japanese grade); the prototype dry mix was poured into an empty panel. All panels were identical in size and shape (5 m deep, 1.8 m long, and 0.45 m wide). The trench mix was tremied into a trench panel 12 m deep, 2 m long, and 0.6 m wide filled with 5 percent bentonite slurry. Before testing, all concrete was cured for 8 weeks. The prototype concrete was moist-cured under standard conditions, and the trench concrete was field-cured as nearly as practicable.

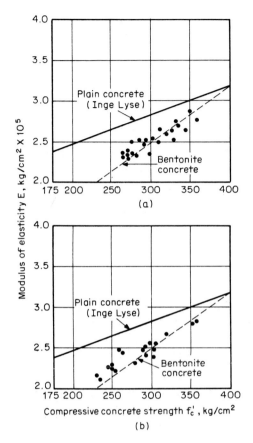

Figure 6-7 Modulus of elasticity as a function of strength for plain and betonite concrete: (*a*) Specimen IV. (*b*) Specimen V, activable-tracer test. (*From Ikuta et al., 1971.*)

Compression tests on standard cylinders from the prototype concrete produced an average compressive strength of 360 kg/cm² (5140 lb/in²). These results are shown in Fig. 6-8, and evidently the strength is moderately influenced by the presence of bentonite while it shows a single tendency to decrease with bentonite concentration higher than 7 percent. Core samples from the trench concrete produced average strength of 400 kg/cm² for the upper half of the panel and 450 kg/cm² for the lower half.

Table 6-5 shows the mix composition for concrete used in another series of tests. This mix was placed in panels filled either with plain water or with bentonite slurry, as shown in Table 6-6. Compression tests on standard cylinders show again that the 28-day strength is not significantly influenced by the presence of bentonite in the slurry.

Results from field tests.   Table 6-7 shows data for concrete used in actual structural work at six different building sites. Tests on standard

TABLE 6-4 Quantity of Materials and Properties of Mixes per Cubic Meter

Mix conditions*	Cement, kg	Water, kg	Sand, kg	Gravel, kg	Entrained air, %	Water-cement ratio	Slump, cm
Protype dry	332	186	766	1032	3–4	0.56	20
Prototype bentonite	365	200	809	927	3–4	0.56	20
Trench	363	187	738	1048	3–4	0.515	20

*Prototype tests from *Jap. Concr. J.*, vol. 9, no. 6, 1966.

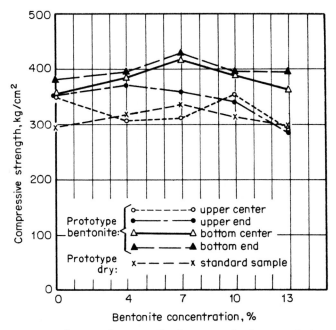

Figure 6-8 Compressive strength of core samples for concrete tremied into bentonite-slurry prototype panels and dry panels. (*From
Jap. Conc. J., vol. 9, no. 6, 1966.*)

cylinders from site A showed a 28-day strength of 284 kg/cm² near
the top and 336 kg/cm² near the bottom of the structure; standard-
cured samples of the same concrete at site A showed a 28-day strength
of 315 kg/cm². Samples at site B tested in compression showed a 28-
day strength of 325 and 366 kg/cm² near the top and bottom, respectively, compared with an average strength of 251 kg/cm² for standard-
cured samples. For site C the results of 15 compression tests showed
a compensated strength (measured strength multiplied by a correction
factor) of 210 kg/cm², compared with a theoretical value of 200 kg/
cm². The results of tests on samples obtained at sites D, E, and F are
shown in Fig. 6-9. These indicate a moderate variation in strength

TABLE 6-5 Quantity of Materials and Properties of Mix* (per Cubic Meter)

Cement, kg	Water, kg	Sand, kg	Gravel, kg	Entrained air, %	Water-cement ratio	Slump, cm
350	191	710	1033	4	0.545	20

From Nippon Co., 1975*a*.
*Used in compression and bond tests.

TABLE 6-6 Composition of Bentonite Slurry and Strength of Core Samples (Mix of Table 6-5)

| Sample | Materials used | Proportions, % | | | | | 28-day strength, kg/cm^2 |
		Bentonite	CMC	Telnite	FCL	Telmarch	
A	Air (dry)	0	0	0	0	0	333
B	City water	0	0	0	0	0	286
C	Bentonite	8	...	...	...	...	311
D	Bentonite, CMC, Telnite	6	0.05	0.5	...	...	310
E	Bentonite, CMC, FCL	6	0.05	...	0.5	...	310
F	Bentonite, CMC	6	0.05	...	...	...	310
G	Telmarch	...	...	...	...	1.0	310

TABLE 6-7 Proportions and Properties of Concrete from Field Sites per Cubic Meter*

Site	Cement, kg	Water, kg	Sand, kg	Gravel, kg	Air-entraining agent, kg	Water-cement ratio	Slump, cm
A (building)	350	162	1073	754	4.3	0.46	19
B (building)	284	182	702	1191	...	0.64	20
C (subway)	320	176	775	1023	1.3	0.55	20
D–F (buildings)	340	170	†	†	†	0.50	19

*From *Jap. Concr. J.*, vol. 9, no. 6, 1966.
†Not given.

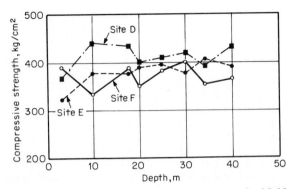

Figure 6-9 Twenty-eight-day compressive strength of field samples. Sites D, E, and F of Table 6-7. (*From Jap. Conc. J., vol. 9, no. 6, 1966.*)

and a tendency for strength to improve with depth. The tendency for in situ strength to increase with depth is also shown in Fig. 6-10 (Ikuta et al., 1973). These results should be interpreted in conjunction with plug flow and can be attributed to better consolidation in the lower part of the panel as large quantities of concrete are placed.

Recommended strength

From the existing record and reported test results of field-cured structural concrete placed in slurry trenches it appears that the attained

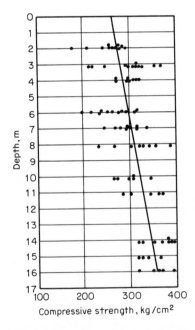

Figure 6-10 Variation of in situ concrete strength with depth for diaphragm walls. (*From Ikuta et al., 1973.*)

strength is adequate provided the placement is carried out smoothly and within the procedures suggested for the tremie process. A favorable consideration is that the development of strength is enhanced by the moist curing conditions at the site that tend to compensate for unfavorable effects. Nonetheless, interpretation of this record should take into account the actual influence of the average construction conditions, the observed variation in strength, and the fact that quality controls may not be always implemented to the extent desired.

Thus, until the matter of strength is reviewed further in conjunction with statistical reliability analyses and procedures for ensuring specified strength, engineers should continue to take a conservative approach in choosing the design strength. Irrespective of whether the design is based on allowable stress or on load factor, the recommendation is to adjust the nominal strength by an appropriate factor to reduce the initially accepted resistance level of concrete, and before the performance factor ϕ or the factor of safety FS is applied. The recommended adjustment factor is 0.90, and is based solely on experience and judgment. Thus the recommended adjusted design strength f'_{ca} is

$$f'_{ca} = 0.90 f'_c \qquad (6\text{-}4)$$

which is rounded off as shown in Table 6-8 for the most commonly used values of strength. A working stress or factored resistance may be obtained by applying a factor of safety or performance factor to the values of f'_{ca} in conjunction with the applicable code or specification.

6-7 Bond Strength and Bond Stress

Plain bars. For plain smooth bars bond resistance is caused by a maximum bond stress over a short length where adhesion is about to fail and a lower friction drag over the length where adhesion has failed. Thus the bond strength depends largely on adhesion, but even after adhesion is broken, friction between the steel and concrete continues to provide bond resistance.

Bond stress is the longitudinal shear stress per unit of bar surface, transferred from the concrete, and varies along the bar. The development length l_d is based on experimental evidence that the average stress is critical, and not the higher peak bond stress that is usually

TABLE 6-8 Recommended Values of Adjusted Stresses

f'_c, lb/in^2	2500	3000	3500	3750	4000	4500	5000
f'_{ca}, lb/in^2	2250	2700	3200	3400	3600	4000	4500

adjacent to cracks. Considering the average ultimate bond stress u, equilibrium leads to the following expression for l_d:

$$l_d = \frac{f_y}{4u} d_b \tag{6-5}$$

where f_y = yield strength of reinforcing steel and d_b = bar diameter. The minimum development length computed from Eq. (6-5) is not any better than the values of bond strength used to derive it.

Deformed bars. In this case the behavioral pattern is changed. Adhesion and friction still assist the interaction of steel bars and concrete, but most of the bond resistance is provided by the interlocks of the bars. The bond strength now depends mainly on the bearing of lugs on the concrete and the shear strength of concrete between lugs.

Tests on deformed bars show a systematic internal crack pattern, with cracks starting just behind each lug and progressing diagonally a limited distance toward the nearest transverse crack. The loaded end of the bar breaks adhesion of the concrete close to the end, and resistance is provided by friction and some bearing on the nearest bar lug. Further loading may produce crushing against the lug or shearing of the concrete to form a cylinder with diameter matching the bar out-to-out of lugs. For large bars or small cover the cylinder usually splits lengthwise, and this splitting is now the key to anchorage behavior since it is the most visible sign of approaching bond failure.

Current understanding of bond addresses the behavior of tension splices, bars in compression, development length, and mixed bar sizes and bundled bars.

Effects of slurry. The immersion of steel bars in bentonite slurry can influence the development of bond resistance in the following ways: (1) the slurry may coat the steel surface with a slippery film, partially or wholly destroying the adhesion and friction between the two materials; (2) bentonite and other impurities may be trapped between and under the lugs; and (3) the fresh mix may fail to surround the bars completely.

Experience shows that the slurry is unlikely to deposit a cake on the steel surfaces of the cage since this would require a filtration process. Instead, any adhesion between steel and a bentonite coating should be equivalent to the gel strength of slurry, which is relatively low compared with the shear stress induced by the rising concrete. The latter, as it moves upward, performs a sweeping action owing to its granular composition and internal friction, and this tends to absorb any bentonite coating from around the bars. In normal hydration this coating is replaced by cement particles to create normal adhesion.

In a mixed or random flow it is possible for some bentonite to remain and continue to envelop the steel bars. If the slurry contains too much slime, some impurities are likely to be squeezed and remain trapped between the lugs. If the tremied concrete does not replace all residual materials, their presence in the final structure will influence the development of bond. Although deformed bars are more vulnerable than plain ones because they collect more impurities, this factor should not be the only basis for comparing bond performance.

Bond tests

Results of tests on bond have been presented by CIRIA (1967), simulating diaphragm wall construction. The tests involved reinforced-concrete beams loaded in bending to produce bond failure along a 6-in bar length at the lower end. Figure 6-11 shows data for mild steel plain and deformed bars. For the plain bars the bond stress–bar slip curve shows no significant differences between the conditions of injection. Bond stresses are higher for the hand-punned concrete but within the basic range of results. For all conditions and specimens there is little increase in bond stress between 0.001 and 0.01 in bar slip (0.025 and 0.25 mm), and for practical purposes the maximum bond is reached at a bar slip of 0.002 in (0.05 mm).

For the deformed bars the bond stress is reduced with bentonite or bentonite-clay-sand slurry. However, there is also considerable increase in bond resistance with bar slip, and this holds for bar slip 0.01 in or higher (0.25 mm). For 0.001-in bar slip the average bond stress of plain and deformed bars in bentonite is nearly the same, but this stress is much higher for deformed bars as bar slip approaches or exceeds 0.005 in.

Pullout tests.   Results from pullout tests according to ASTM C234 are shown in Fig. 6-12. These tests are for the concrete mix of Table 6-5 in conjunction with the slurry of Table 6-6. The bars are deformed, 19 mm diameter (similar to ASTM No. 6 bars), and were immersed in the slurry for 24 h. Subsequently the concrete was tremied and allowed to cure for 28 days. During pullout the loading was continued until slippage of 0.25 mm (0.01 in) occurred at the loaded end.

Tests are also reported by the Japanese Highway Public Authority (1975) on deformed bars for concrete cast in conditions simulating plug flow. The concrete was placed in dry panels, panels containing plain water, and panels containing bentonite slurry at 2, 8, and 12 percent concentrations. The tests were carried out 8 days after placement, with the concrete having attained an average compressive strength of 277 kg/cm^2. Results are shown in Fig. 6-13.

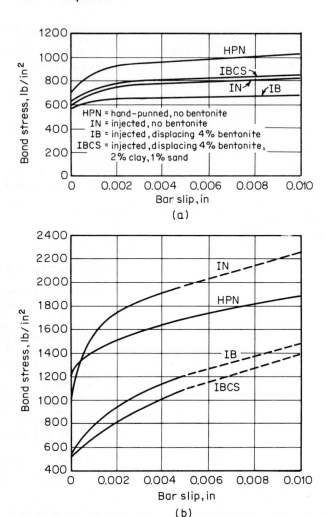

Figure 6-11 Results of bond tests: (*a*) ⅞-in-diameter mild-steel round bars. (*b*) ⅞-in-diameter high-tensile-steel deformed bars. (*CIRIA, 1967.*)

The conclusion from the results of Figs. 6-12 and 6-13 is that tremied concrete in bentonite slurry causes some loss of bond strength, especially with higher bentonite concentrations. Peptizers appear to moderate these effects.

The bond was also shown to vary considerably with the colloid content in tests conducted on the prototype dry and bentonite concrete of Table 6-4. In this case vertical and horizontal bars were tested for slip and ultimate bond resistance for both plain and deformed types; the results for the horizontal bars are shown in Fig. 6-14, and evidently

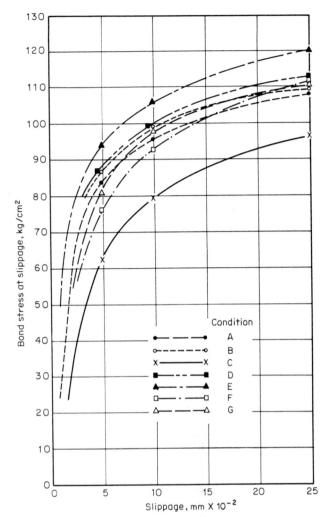

Figure 6-12 Results of bond pullout tests (ASTM C234) for dry concrete and for concrete placed in bentonite slurry. Conditions A to G correspond to notation of Table 6-6. (*Nippon Co., 1975a.*)

the bond strength decreases with increasing bentonite concentrations whereas deformed bars perform better in bond. The results also provide the average range of bond stress for both vertical and horizontal bars for the standard slippage 0.25 mm (0.01 in) summarized in Table 6-9, showing again the higher effectiveness of deformed bars.

The concrete is better consolidated above the horizontal bars than below them. For conventional cast-in-place concrete the rule is that the more concrete below a bar the greater the resulting loss of bond

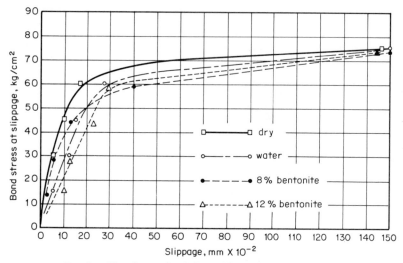

Figure 6-13 Results of bond tests for deformed bars (19 mm diameter); dry concrete and concrete placed in plain water and bentonite slurry. (*From Japanese Highway Public Authority, 1975.*)

strength, and any bleeding of the mix will tend to accumulate water and air beneath the bar with loss of contact. According to this rule, the bond should improve somewhat for bars away from the top, and this is demonstrated in Fig. 6-15, giving a crude approximation of this variation for horizontal bars.

The effect of bentonite slurry on bond strength is also demonstrated in a report by Ikuta et al. (1973), giving results of tests conducted to simulate field conditions. The results are consistent and show that in certain situations the loss of bond strength can be significant for plain bars but within a tolerable range for deformed types. These investigators present also a relationship between bond strength and concrete strength f_c' shown in Fig. 6-16 for deformed bars, and recommend an allowable bond stress 20 percent less than in conventional reinforced concrete. The same report discourages the use of plain bars, particularly for horizontal reinforcement.

Recommended bond stress.   On the basis of these data, general criteria for an acceptable bond distribution are not available. The foregoing sampling of results warrants basic guidelines but does not permit a specific procedure to be formulated. Bond analysis should therefore be based on a conservative approach. The following guidelines are recommended:

1. Use only deformed bars of an approved type.
2. Avoid splices to the extent possible, especially at points of maximum stress.

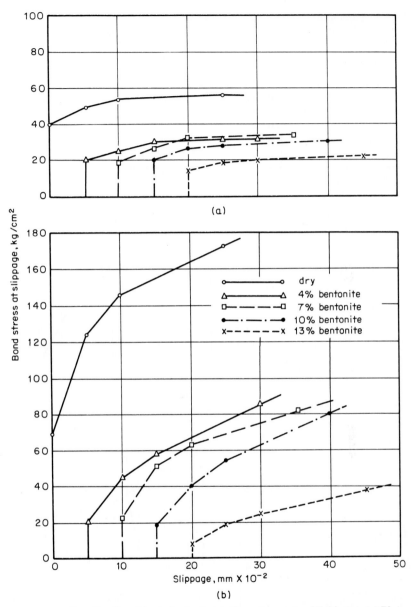

Figure 6-14 Results of bond tests for horizontal bars (concrete of Table 6-4: (*a*) Plain smooth bars. (*b*) Deformed bars. (*From Jap. Conc. J., vol. 9, no. 6, 1966.*)

TABLE 6-9 **Bond Stress for Slippage of 0.25 mm (0.01 in),
Deformed and Plain Bars**

Concrete sample	u	
---	Deformed bars	Round plain bars, kg/cm^2
Dry	$0.35f'_c$–$0.50f'_c$	45–55
Bentonite, 4%	$0.17f'_c$–$0.20f'_c$	21–22
7%	$0.13f'_c$–$0.18f'_c$	16–43
10%	$0.09f'_c$–$0.19f'_c$	20–33
13%	$0.07f'_c$–$0.18f'_c$	11–18

$f' = 300$ kg/cm^2; vertical and horizontal bars, concrete of Table 6-4.

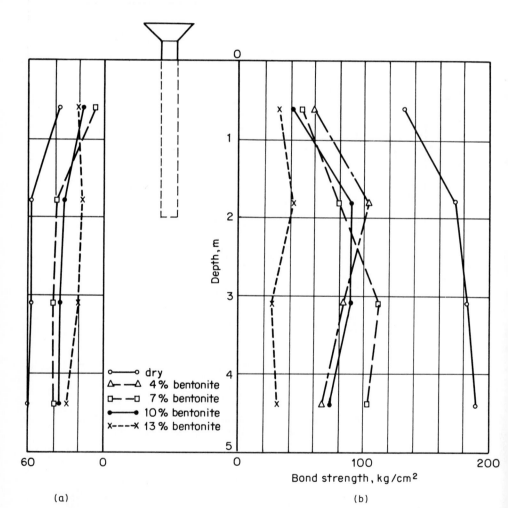

(a)   (b)

Figure 6-15 Variation in bond strength of horizontal bars with depth: (a) Plain round
bars. (b) Deformed bars. (*From Jap. Conc. J., vol. 9, no. 6, 1966.*)

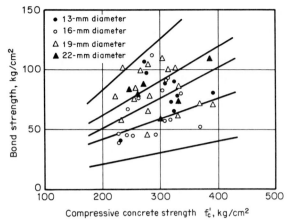

Figure 6-16 Relationship of bond strength (0.25 mm slippage) and concrete strength. (*From Ikuta et al., 1973.*)

3. Use an allowable bond stress of 80 percent of the ACI Code.

4. If splices must be used, provide generous laps (1.5 to 2 times the normal splice length).

Example of tension splice design

In the formulation of required development and lap splice lengths, protection against a brittle type of failure should be considered. Normally, the design should aim at walls that are sufficiently ductile in flexure; hence they should not be allowed to fail suddenly in bond splitting at the yield stress. This means that reserve strength in l_d above f_y is essential to maintain ductility.

For No. 3 to No. 11 bars (other than top bars) with an ultimate bond stress $u = 9.5\sqrt{f'_c}/d_b$, and using a 20 percent increase to assure flexural ductility, we obtain from Eq. (6-5) the required development length as

$$\left. \begin{array}{c} l_d = 1.2f_y d_b/4u = 1.2f_y d_b/(4 \times 9.5\sqrt{f'_c}/d_b) \\ \\ \text{or} \\ \\ l_d = 0.04f_y A_b/\sqrt{f'_c} \end{array} \right\} \qquad (6\text{-}6)$$

where A_b = bar cross-sectional area

In practice it may be necessary to splice tension bars, partly because of the limited (usually 60 ft) length of commercial bars, and partly because of handling problems. Splicing may be by welding, by mechanical connectors, or by bar laps (see also the following sections).

The lapped bars are usually tied in contact with each other but may be spaced up to 6 in apart with an upper limit of one-fifth the lap length.

The splice lap in tension is calculated from l_d (obtained from Eq. 6-6) by applying appropriate factors from 1.3 to 1.7 according to the ACI Code. The code has broken splices into three classes in increasing order of severity of conditions as follows:

- For stress less than $f_y/2$
  Class A if not over 75 percent of bars are spliced within one lap length: Use $1.0l_d$
  Class B if more than 75 percent are spliced within one lap length: Use $1.3l_d$

- For stress exceeding $f_y/2$
  Class B if not over half the bars are spliced within one lap length: Use $1.3l_d$
  Class C for more than half the bars spliced within one bar length: Use $1.7l_d$

As an example, consider a diaphragm wall controlled by bending and some axial load, reinforced with No. 8 vertical bars, and with $f'_c = 4000$ lb/in². Because the stress in the steel in the tension face of the wall will reach yield for the combination of bending and axial load, the lap is a class C splice since it is in a region where more than 50 percent of f_y in tension will be reached and all bars are spliced at the same point. Applying Eq. (6-6) we calculate

$$l_d = 0.04 \times 0.79 \times 60{,}000/\sqrt{4000} = 30 \text{ in}$$

For a class C splice and conventional concrete

$$l_s = 1.7l_d = 1.70 \times 30 = 51 \text{ in}$$

Because this is a wall cast in slurry, the ultimate bond is reduced by 20 percent, which means that the lap length is increased by 25 percent or adjusted $l_s = 51 \times 1.25 = 62$ in.

If the splices are staggered so that only half the bars are spliced at the same point or the loads are such that the tensile stresses in the bars do not exceed $f_y/2$, the splice length is now

$$l_s = 1.3 \times 30 \times 1.25 = 49 \text{ in}$$

6-8 Flexural Analysis and Compression Failure

The principles of load factor design are based on ultimate-strength analysis. While elastic methods determine stresses at design loads, ultimate strength aims at calculating the collapse load or failure load of structural members.

In the elastic theory it is assumed that stresses in a beam follow a triangular distribution. It is further assumed that the beam will fail if the steel stress f_s becomes equal to the yield strength f_y, or if the concrete stress f_c approaches the concrete strength f'_c, or both. However, a typical stress-strain diagram for a concrete cylinder is a definite curve where the full strength is reached on a gradually curving line, and then the test cylinder continues to compress under nearly constant load, later gradually decreasing. In most instances the specimen fails at a strain of about 0.003 to 0.004 in/in, and at a stress considerably less than f'_c.

In beams, since originally plane sections remain plane during bending, the same stress-strain curve is a parabolic stress diagram. Thus, for strength design current codes permit any reasonable stress distribution to be assumed, as long as it is based on tests, such as the distributions shown in Fig. 6-17.

In conjunction with the foregoing brief comments, provisions for ductility should be logically considered in diaphragm walls, because of the extra concrete strength available with the usually generous wall thickness. Ductility in this case means the maintenance of strength while sizable deformations and deflections occur. If the structure fails in concrete failure, the collapse may occur suddenly, almost explosively, and without warning. By specifying a design where yielding in the steel will occur before the concrete is strained to the dangerous limit of 0.003 in, the brittle nature of the material is inhibited, while ductility will permit the stressed portion to continue to carry the load without catastrophic collapse. In this context, current codes place an upper limit on the permissible steel ratio p to ensure that the steel will yield before crushing of the concrete.

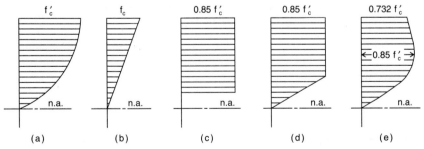

Figure 6-17 Stress distribution assumed on compression side of beam: (*a*) Simple parabola (ultimate). (*b*) Straight line (working stress). (*c*) Rectangular stress block (ultimate). (*d*) Trapezoidal stress block (ultimate). (*e*) Parabolic, with straight line (ultimate).

Compression members. Among the stress diagrams shown in Fig. 6-17, practice has moved to the rectangular stress block because of its simplicity. Researchers often use the stress distribution shown in Fig. 6-17e. The use of computers has also encouraged the development of a continuous function. Axial loads constitute practical cases for the load-bearing panels and foundation elements discussed in Chap. 5.

Tests have established the ultimate (nominal) strength P_n of a concrete element (or column), axially loaded as

$$P_n = 0.85f'_cA_c + f_yA_y \tag{6-7}$$

where A_c = cross-sectional area of element (may be refined to represent the net area of concrete) and A_y = cross-sectional area of steel reinforcement. This is the ideal or nominal strength, and Eq. (6-7) expresses the fact that when this load is reached the steel yields and the concrete likewise is stressed to the limit of its capacity in sustained loading.

Flexural behavior. The load factor equations simply state that the design strength (nominal strength or resistance multiplied by a reduction or performance factor) must exceed the required resistance (factored loads). The proportioning of a member is controlled, however, by various stages of behavior: elastic, cracked, and ultimate. The latter may have to be altered when the limiting stages are the elastic and cracked conditions for working loads, but the resistance should not be less than the ultimate state.

At the ultimate stage, load effects are resisted by the tensile yield strength of steel and by the compressive strength of concrete. Where high-strength steels are used and flexural behavior is involved, excessive crack widths and deflections may develop and thus require additional controls. Serviceability must therefore be considered in strength design and includes limitations with reference to (1) structural fitness at overload conditions, and (2) safety against excessive cracking, deflections and permanent set, and fatigue of materials.

Fatigue and crack control. AASHTO (Art. 8.15.3 1992 edition) specifies that stresses at service loads, checked to satisfy fatigue and crack control, may be based on a straight-line theory of stress and strain. Fatigue failure of beams subjected to repeated loads may occur in shear or diagonal tension, but the same beams under static load may fail in steel tension.

For crack control, criteria are provided for the distribution of flexural reinforcement if $f_y > 40,000$ lb/in². Crack control is ensured if the reinforcement bars are well distributed over the effective concrete area, and if this area has the same centroid. Furthermore, cracking is inhibited if the volume of concrete around each bar is minimum and the steel tensile stress is low.

Deflections. With diaphragm walls deflections are unlikely to control the strength and serviceability criteria.

Balanced conditions. Both the ACI Code and AASHTO specifications stipulate that balanced strain conditions exist at a flexural cross section when tension reinforcement reaches the strain corresponding to its yield strength just as the concrete in compression reaches its assumed ultimate strain of 0.003. The balanced beam in strength design is not a practical concept. Therefore, for flexural members the ratio of reinforcement $p = A_s/bd$ (also referred to as tension reinforcement index) should not exceed $0.75p_b$ (the ratio that would produce balanced strain conditions). The portion of p_b balanced by compression reinforcement need not be reduced by the 0.75 factor.

Equilibrium analysis. Referring to Fig. 6-18, equilibrium requires that $C_c = T_s$. Hence

$$0.85f'_c ab = A_s f_y \qquad (6\text{-}8)$$

Setting $p = A_s/bd$ and $m = f_y/0.85f'_c$, and solving for a gives

$$a = pmd \qquad (6\text{-}9)$$

The corresponding lever arm c of the internal forces is now

$$c = d - \frac{a}{2} = d\left(1 - \frac{pm}{2}\right) \qquad (6\text{-}10)$$

When failure is caused by yielding of the steel, the ultimate (nominal) moment is

$$M_u = M_n = A_s f_y c = pf_y\left(1 - \frac{pm}{2}\right)bd^2 \qquad (6\text{-}11)$$

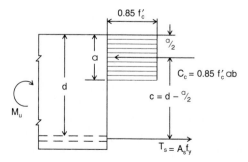

Figure 6-18 Equilibrium conditions at ultimate strength.

The ultimate moment may also be expressed as

$$M_u = M_n = A_s f_y \left(d - \frac{a}{2} \right) \tag{6-12}$$

or

$$M_u = M_n = \left[A_s f_y d \left(1 - 0.6 \frac{p f_y}{f_c'} \right) \right] \tag{6-13}$$

where $a = A_s f_y / 0.85 f_c' b$ is obtained from Eq. (6-8).

In the foregoing equations, $p \leqslant 0.75 p_b$ to avoid crushing of the concrete when the strain reaches 0.003. The value of p_b that would produce balanced strain conditions is given by

$$p_b = \frac{0.85 \beta_1 f_c'}{f_y} \left(\frac{87,000}{87,000 + f_y} \right) \tag{6-14}$$

where β_1 = ratio of depth of equivalent compression zone to depth from fiber of maximum compressive strain to the neutral axis. The factor β_1 should be taken as 0.85 for compressive strengths up to and including 4000 lb/in². For $f_c' > 4000$ lb/in², β_1 is reduced continuously at a rate of 0.05 for each 1000 lb/in² in excess of 4000, but not less than 0.65.

The foregoing analysis can be extended to beams with compression reinforcement and to members subjected to bending and axial load. It follows from this discussion that because a balanced beam will fail suddenly in compression, the usual practice is to limit the tensile reinforcement. Thus, when the steel reaches yield conditions, the concrete will still have about an added one-third reserve strength in compression. The usual ductile reinforcement will ensure member ductility, with wide cracking giving a warning of approaching capacity. However, with diaphragm walls this condition will rarely, if ever, become an operative limit because of the generous wall thickness.

6-9   Assembly and Details of Reinforcement

Reinforcing cages.   Reinforcement bars are fabricated and assembled in cages. This is rarely done in the shop because of the usually formidable panel dimensions, and it means that ample space must be available at the site to assemble, store, and handle the cages. The only practicable position for assembling a cage is the horizontal, from which it is picked up by crane and held in suspension before being inserted in the panel. During hoisting the action of its own weight can cause severe distortion of the cage. When detailing the reinforcement, it is therefore necessary to decide whether to make the cage rigid (by additional bracing or by welding the bars) or flexible. In many instances a flexible cage is favored because of economy and because it is less liable to suffer permanent distortion during handling. If the bars are large and closely spaced, it is advantageous to make the cage rigid.

A special lifting sling and two crane lines can be connected to the cage to prevent undesirable distortion. When the cage is almost vertical, the second line is disengaged since it is only used to keep the cage straight during lifting. Alternatively, for very heavy and massive cages the assembly shown in Fig. 6-19 is used. Once in the vertical position, the cage is slowly inserted into the panel and held in place by spacer blocks. A device frequently used is the concrete roller spacer, shown in Fig. 6-20, placed over the outer bars to allow the cage to roll down the trench and also ensure even cover for the reinforcement on both sides.

Bar spacing.   The usual practice is to place the main vertical reinforcement on the outside of the cage, since this will facilitate the unobstructed flow along the outer face for the concrete to surround the bars fully. The minimum spacing of vertical bars should not be less than 6 in and preferably 9 in. Horizontal bars give minimum impediment to flow if they are arranged in open spacing, preferably not less than 12 in unless the horizontal bars are the main reinforcement. A generous concrete cover should be provided, especially for the earth side of the exposed wall, with a minimum cover not less than 3 in (7.5 cm) and in spite of any bond considerations.

It is conceivable that the bond strength may be affected at bar laps, particularly where several horizontal bars in the form of distribution steel, links, or ties are in contact with each other against vertical splices and where such bars are closely spaced. In general, it is desirable to have the most open bar spacing that is practicable, and avoid bar arrangements, hooks, and shapes that could trap bentonite, cause cavitation, or otherwise impede the free flow of concrete.

Corrosion protection.   In the last decade, corrosion protection of reinforcing bars has assumed vital importance, especially where the concrete is exposed to aggressive environment. Thus, besides the generous concrete cover, reinforcing steel can be ordered with galvanized coating under ASTM specification A679-79 or with epoxy coating under ASTM specification A775-84.

Boxes and inserts.   Recesses are mandatory in a wall to accept future floors and supports. Where steel bars are to be used for future me-

(a)

(b)

Figure 6-19 Method for handling heavy cages: (a) The cage is braced to withstand handling and erection stresses. (b) The cage is suspended vertically and slowly inserted into the panel. (*Franki.*)

Figure 6-20 Concrete roller spacers placed over outer bars to guide cage during placement. (*Franki.*)

chanical connections, they usually are placed behind a recess. Shear and bentonite bars for future structural connections also require recesses, but they should be avoided at the extremities of a panel where the flow energy of the fresh mix may not be enough to displace the slurry.

Recesses are formed by using boxwork inserts attached to the reinforcing cage. The insert boxes should have nominal dimensions. If they are made too large, they are likely to restrict the flow of concrete. Where structurally possible, they should be placed on the outside of the cage. Any boxwork of a size close to the wall thickness is likely to cause inclusions of bentonite mud at the edges. Insert boxes can be easily positioned if they are robust and firmly attached to the cage as long as the latter is accurately positioned and held.

Occasionally an insert box is displaced by the force of rising concrete or lost when it is caught on the small ridge formed where the ground changes vertically. Cages are quite heavy while they are handled, and a brief resistance to motion during insertion does not always register with the operator. Hence good clearance must be provided for insert boxes after considering the width of the trench, the cage dimensions, and the tolerance of the excavation. The required degree of accuracy vertically and laterally for the cage is best maintained if the assembly is suspended from its true center of gravity. Occasionally, a cage may display a tendency to float or even be displaced upward as the fresh mix rises, and in this case it will be necessary to keep it firmly attached to the guide walls.

Materials for boxing out and recesses are usually chosen by the contractor. Long horizontal bands of wood may be inserted and tied to the cage to form continuous shear keys for floor slab connections; when the wall is exposed after excavation, the wood is removed and dowels placed behind are bent out to form the connection (see also following sections). Contractors often choose styrofoam planks to form keys and inserts.

Splices. Clearance during lifting, capacity of available equipment, panel size, and incidental construction considerations will determine the number of cage lengths. Tensile length development is a matter of design, as discussed in the foregoing sections.

When splices are necessary, the first cage length is left projecting above the guidewalls and the second cage is attached to it before the entire assembly is lowered into position. The splice connection shown in Fig. 6-21 consists of a U-bolt fastened with two nuts and a link. The bolts can carry a load of 12 tons and are a formidable substitute to welding. This splice implies that the bar lap is the development length of the bar strength.

Alternatively and where the bars are closely spaced, a field splice for cages can be executed as shown in Fig. 6-22a. The bars are shop-welded to the plates and the two cage sections are spliced in the field with bolts as shown. The bolted connection (plate size and bolts) must develop the tensile strength of the cage, and the welded connection for

Figure 6-21 U-bolt connection used to splice the upper and lower part of the reinforcing cage. (*Franki.*)

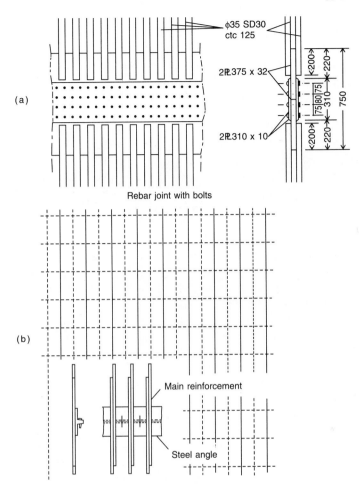

(a)

(b)

Figure 6-22 Field splices and connections: (*a*) Cage spliced using steel plates. (*b*) Cage spliced using steel angles. (Japanese standards.)

each bar must develop the tensile strength of the bar. This splice is expensive but eliminates overcrowded conditions. The detail shown in Fig. 6-22*b* uses the steel angles to connect the cage sections, whereas the splice connection between bars derives its strength from the development length. The bars are spot-welded to the angles merely to be held in place during handling.

Where a cage is wider than can be transported, it can be made of two sections as shown in Fig. 6-23. The two sections are placed flat on the ground and assembled as shown before they are picked up for insertion into the panel.

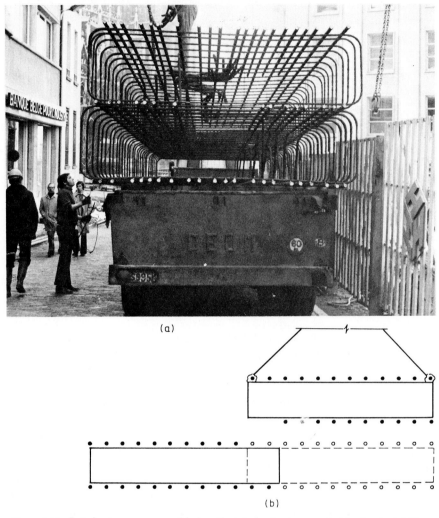

(a)

(b)

Figure 6-23 Reinforcing cage assembled so that it can be transported by truck: (*a*) The cage upon arrival at the site. (*b*) Diagram showing how the cage is spliced before it is inserted into the panel.

6-10 Common Vertical Construction Joints

Basic requirements. In general, construction joints must satisfy the following requirements:

1. Physically the joint should not disturb the previously poured panel but should also accommodate the excavation of the following panel without restricting the use of equipment.

2. While the joint is executed there should be no leakage of fresh concrete.

3. The joint forms and plates should withstand the pressure of fresh concrete without distortion.

4. Where necessary the joint should be designed and built to transfer shear and other forces, and should be fairly watertight.

5. The joint should not collect slime and bentonite.

6. The construction should be feasible using simple methods and equipment.

7. The joint should be economically feasible for the intended function of the wall.

Common types of joints

Round tube (interlocking pipe) joint. This is a common joint and fairly simple to construct (see also Fig. 1-1). It is a semicircular joint formed by means of a steel tube inserted at one end as a stop for the concrete. Some time after the pour is started (usually 2 h) the pipe is given a slight rotational movement to break any bond with the fresh concrete. When the pour is completed and the concrete begins to set, the tube is slowly extracted. Removal of the tube leaves a half-round concrete key at the end of the unformed panel, used to guide the excavating tool as construction continues with the next panel. Any deviation from the true vertical alignment of the completed panel is thus introduced to the next panel and is corrected in the next equipment pass. Theoretically, the outside tube diameter should be the trench width; hence the pipe may encounter resistance if during insertion the trench is not straight.

The round tube joint is used if the excavating tool produces round-end panels. The connection can transfer lateral shear but cannot transfer bending stresses since the steel is not continuous through the joint.

If cavitation or overwidth excavation occurs at the end, the fresh concrete can flow around the tube, as shown in Fig. 6-24. These protrusions must be broken with chisels. If these concrete rings are not detected and removed, they can force the excavating tool out of alignment.

Steel plate and vinylon sheet. This detail may be used when the horizontal bars must be extended through the joint. In this case the connection is placed away from the ends. A steel plate is attached to the cage as shown in Fig. 6-25a to provide a barrier between the concrete

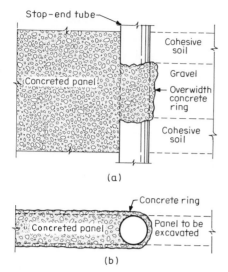

(a)

(b)

Figure 6-24 Penetration of fresh concrete beyond the stop-end tube due to overwidth excavation: (a) Partial elevation. (b) Partial section through gravel layer.

and the slurry. Suitable textile sheets (usually vinylon) surround the ends of the cage as shown in Fig. 6-25c, covering also the bottom for maximum protection against leaking concrete. The horizontal reinforcement is extended through holes in the plate and is spliced with the steel cage of the other side.

The detail is relatively simple but requires some previous experience. Potential problems may arise if the plate does not separate the two chambers completely, and if holes are accidentally punched in the sheet.

Modified round tube joint. This detail is shown in Fig. 6-26. A round steel tube and a corrugated plate are attached to the cage to prevent direct contact between the concrete and the tube so that its extraction can occur any time while stuck-pipe problems are avoided. The teeth provide interlocks for the two concrete sections as long as slime and bentonite are not collected there.

I-beam joint. This detail, shown in Fig. 6-27, is used in composite steel and concrete panels, and accommodates trenches excavated with square-end clamshells. In composite walls the beam is used to make structural connections.

RPT joint. This was developed in England for a special project by Randel, Palmer, and Tritton but can be used on a general basis. The conventional end tube is combined with sections of straight web piles attached to the cage and incorporated in the concrete panel, as shown

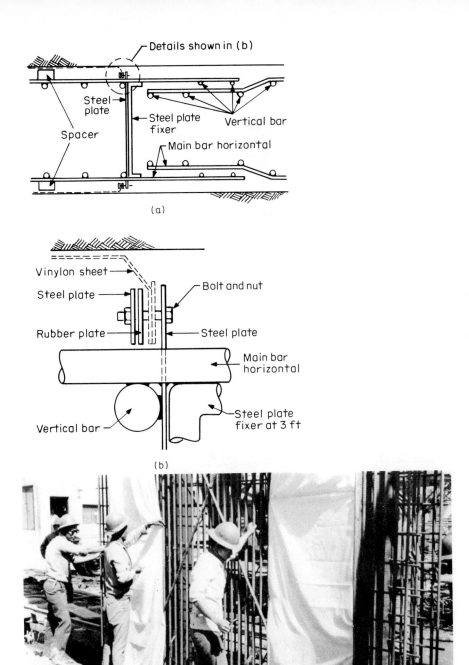

Figure 6-25 Vinylon-sheet and steel-plate joint: (*a*) General joint detail and splicing of horizontal reinforcement. Note that the interlocking pipe is not shown. Concrete is poured against the vertical steel plate. (*b*) Detail showing the attachment of vinylon sheet to the steel plate. (*c*) The reinforcement cage is lowered into the trench; vinylon sheets are extended 3 to 4 ft to prevent concrete from leaking into the next panel.

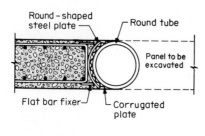

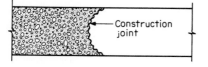

Figure 6-26 Modified round-tube joint.

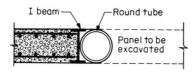

Figure 6-27 I-beam joint details.

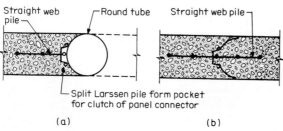

(a)   (b)

Figure 6-28 RPT joint details.

in Fig. 6-28*a*. When the concrete has set, the split pile provides a recess at the end of the section into which one of the clutches of the straight web pile protrudes. When the end pipe is extracted and the next panel is excavated, two sections of straight web pile are sunk, as shown in Fig. 6-28*b*, and linked with the web of the first panel. This connection can transfer shear and axial force.

The CWS joint. This detail is discussed in Sec. 2-10, and the underlying principle is shown diagrammatically in Fig. 2-18. Essentially, the method allows freedom from the constraints associated with concreting since extraction of the form is not controlled by the concreting operation. Since the form is left in place while the next panel is ex-

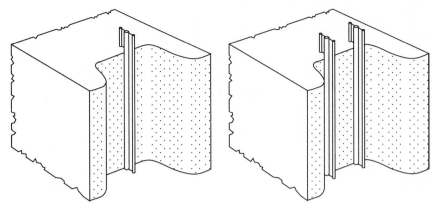

Figure 6-29 One- and two-blade systems of waterstops.

cavated, it protects the concrete surface from any aggressive action of the excavating tool. As mentioned, the joint can be executed with waterstop blades to give a watertight connection. Figure 6-29 shows the joint with one- and two-blade waterstop systems.

6-11   Special Construction Joints

With the exception of the steel plate joint shown in Fig. 6-25, the construction joints discussed in Sec. 6-10 accommodate diaphragm walls where the vertical steel is the principal reinforcement. Special joint details have been developed, mainly by specialist contractors, to allow structural continuity in the horizontal direction. Their success and effectiveness depend on how well they are executed. Thus a joint may be well designed and become defective because of poor construction workmanship. Some joints can transfer only shear, and some can transfer axial tension. A joint such as the RPT detail can resist laminar tilting of the panels. Reinforcement extended through a joint and spliced with the bars of the next panel provides all these functions.

Despite the theoretical adequacy of a joint detail, the in situ performance is a different matter. Thus engineers should be cautioned that a joint is as good as the way it is built.

Joints by BACHY

TEBA joint.   This is essentially stress transmission by jack rods. Steel bars are telescoped through the joint and anchored at both ends in the concrete. The bars can be located near the center of the wall if axial tensile loads must be transferred, or positioned near the wall face to transfer bending stresses.

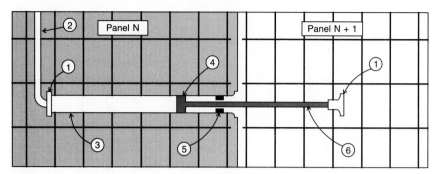

Figure 6-30 Anchoring rod while it is pushed into the reinforcing cage of next panel. 1. Anchor plate. 2. Feed pipeline. 3. Ram cylinder. 4. Ram piston. 5. Piston stop. 6. Tie bar.

The basic element is a single-action ram whose cylinder is the anchorage in a panel, and the rod extension is the anchorage in the adjacent panel. The ram has therefore the following: (1) a fixed part comprising the cylinder of the ram fitted at its end with an anchor plate and connected to a pipeline, and (2) a moving part consisting of the piston and rod. The rod is fitted at its end also with an anchor plate and is pushed out hydraulically, as shown in Fig. 6-30. The component parts of the ram are selected according to the loads to be transmitted.

The installation sequence is shown schematically in Fig. 6-31, and involves the following steps:

1. Panel n is excavated and the CWS form (see also Fig. 6-29) is installed at the end of the panel. The reinforcing cage is assembled and fitted with the rams necessary to transmit the design load. Each ram is placed in the cage facing panel $n + 1$, with the piston and rod pulled in.

2. The cage is installed in the panel against the form CWS. The anchor plates are pressed against the form by connecting the pipeline to a low-pressure source.

3. Panel n is concreted, and adjacent panel $n + 1$ is excavated while the CWS form protects the anchor plates.

4. The form is extracted and the reinforcing cage is inserted in panel $n + 1$. The cage is assembled so that it will not block the rods from extending into the panel.

5. The rams sealed in panel n are grouted with a nonshrink cement. This will ensure that each rod and another plate can be pushed into panel $n + 1$.

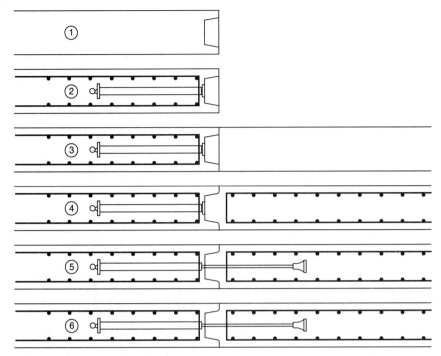

Figure 6-31 Sequence of operations for installing tie rod (see text).

6. The panel marked $n + 1$ is concreted while the rods and anchor plates provide a mechanical connection between the two successive panels.

TECA joint. This is based on the principle of providing sufficient bar lap to transfer tensile stresses. Essentially it requires a rectangular steel caisson placed at the end of the panel, and initially serving as a barrier for the fresh concrete. The caisson or box consists of the following parts: (1) a transverse web with horizontal reinforcement passing through and welded to provide resistance to the thrust of the fresh concrete; and (2) a removable shuttering of I configuration. The installation, shown in Fig. 6-32, involves the following steps:

1. Excavate panel n.
2. Install reinforcing cage with steel box at the end.
3. Place concrete in panel n, and excavate panel $n + 1$.
4. Remove the movable shuttering of the box and install cage in panel $n + 1$ to overlap with the bars of panel n.
5. Concrete panel $n + 1$.

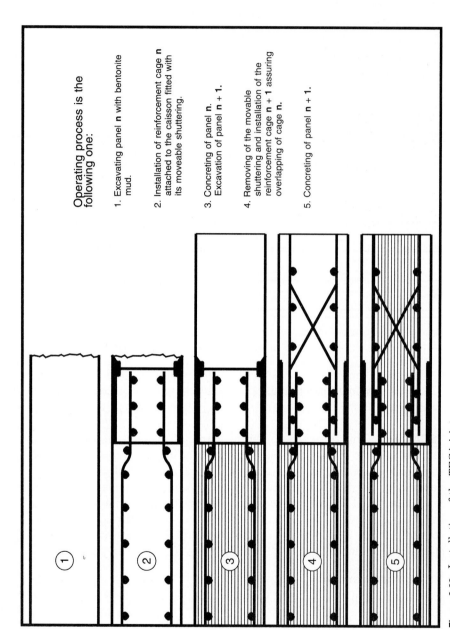

Operating process is the following one:

1. Excavating panel **n** with bentonite mud.

2. Installation of reinforcement cage **n** attached to the caisson fitted with its moveable shuttering.

3. Concreting of panel **n**.
   Excavation of panel **n + 1**.

4. Removing of the movable shuttering and installation of the reinforcement cage **n + 1** assuring overlapping of cage **n**.

5. Concreting of panel **n + 1**.

Figure 6-32 Installation of the TECA joint.

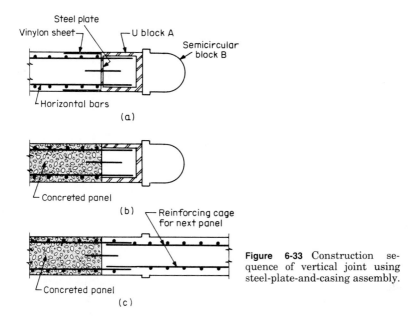

Figure 6-33 Construction sequence of vertical joint using steel-plate-and-casing assembly.

Steel-plate-and-casing joint

This joint, executed as shown in Fig. 6-33, is designed to eliminate problems sometimes caused by concrete leaking to the slurry chamber with the joint shown in Fig. 6-25. The partition steel plate and vinylon sheet are attached to the reinforcing cage as before, but in addition two specially shaped steel blocks or casings are inserted in the slurry section, as shown in Fig. 6-33a. Block A serves as barrier for concrete that tends to leak but also creates a chamber for the extension of the horizontal bars. In this context the detail is similar to the joint of Fig. 6-32. Block B is also a barrier for leaking concrete, and because it fits tight at the end, it keeps the cage in position. With the concrete poured, the panel appears as shown in Fig. 6-33b. The blocks are then extracted and the panel is completed as shown in Fig. 6-33c.

Casing joint by Franki

The special steel casing joint shown in Fig. 6-34 is used in horizontally continuous diaphragm walls (Baar, 1971), and in principle it is therefore similar to the joints presented in the foregoing sections. The joint protects the protruding bars from fresh concrete during pouring and from slime and bentonite impurities when the next panel is excavated.

The casing is made to have two deep slots, or housings, that receive the horizontal bars; the depth of the slots is determined by the re-

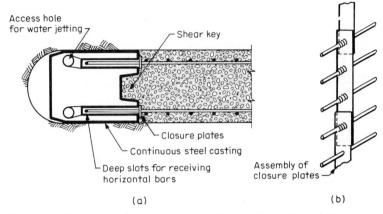

Figure 6-34   Steel-casing joint developed by Franki. (*From Barr, 1971.*)

quired bar splice length. The slots are wider at their ends than at the entry to allow a vertical spacer bar to be inserted in order to keep the horizontal bars in position. The earth end of the casing can be shaped as shown in order to reduce the contact area with the soil and facilitate extraction with less pulling force. Two holes at the ends of the slots allow water jetting to be forced in to clean the bars after concreting. The protruding bars are then kept in clean water.

The housings are separated from the fresh concrete during pouring by means of the two closure plates, perforated at intervals to match the bar spacing, and assembled as shown in Fig. 6-34b. The pressure of the rising concrete pushes the steel plates one at a time tightly against the housings, and this prevents the fresh mix from entering this area. The casing can be left in place for several days while the next panel is excavated.

The assembly can be inserted when a panel is excavated and before the reinforcing cage is inserted. After the first panel is concreted and the adjacent panel has been excavated, the casing is extracted and placed at the end of the new panel. Figure 6-35 shows a construction joint after the casing has been removed. This is a well-executed joint with a definite shear key and reinforcing bars that are clean and free of any residual material. Baar (1971) recommends a minimum width of trench of 80 cm (about 32 in) for walls of average depth, but the detail has been better executed if the wall thickness is 100 cm (40 in) or more.

Locking box by Takenaka

This detail initially appeared in the first edition of *Slurry Walls* (Xanthakos, 1979), and like the other joint types it addresses two main

Figure 6-35 Construction joint executed as shown in Fig. 6-34. The joint is seen after the casing is removed; note the shear key, the horizontal splice bars, and the vertical spacer bars. (*Franki.*)

objectives: (1) the load transfer, particularly when complex loading conditions must be considered; and (2) the prevention of concrete leakage. Although the transmission of shear, axial load, moment, and torsion is theoretically a design problem, in reality it depends on the strength and quality of the connection. Concrete leakage is often assumed to be a construction problem, but very often it relates to the initial design of the joint.

For permanent walls the unit lengths between joints should correspond closely to those established by the design. The joint connector should be placed accurately for the intended structural continuity, and detailed after considering the bar splice and development length requirements. During pouring the fresh concrete should not be allowed to leak or flow around the boxes.

The Takenaka joint is shown in Fig. 6-36 and is used in connection with the TBW system mentioned in other sections and shown in Fig. 2-24. A partitioning device (locking box) is used to form connections in continuous walls. The process shown in Fig. 6-36 is self-explanatory. The locking box is fabricated using two steel sections, usually channels placed back to back, each receiving and holding two sealing hoses. The assembly is inserted into the joint location so that the four hoses cover the entire width. When in place, the hoses are inflated to expand and give a tight fit that forms a barrier beyond the concrete line.

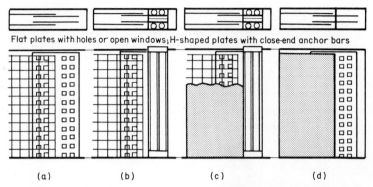

Flat plates with holes or open windows; H-shaped plates with close-end anchor bars

(a)   (b)   (c)   (d)

Figure 6-36 Locking-box joint: (*a*) Insertion of reinforcing cage and steel connection plates, which in this case are provided with holes or open windows. (*b*) Setting of the locking box and inflating the sealing hoses. (*c*) Pouring concrete. (*d*) Withdrawing the locking box.

The connection can be executed using either a perforated plate or an I section attached to the cage and perforated for the bars to pass through. Modification may be developed to handle special loading conditions.

6-12   Efficiency of Construction Joints

Usual joint defects

Three typical defects of the round tube joint are shown in Fig. 6-37. In Fig. 6-37*a* bentonite mud and impurities are trapped between panels. In part *b* the edge of the panel is not thoroughly cleaned, and slime is accumulated between concrete sections, resulting in a cavity. Similar problems cause the partial cavity shown in Fig. 6-37*c*. Similar

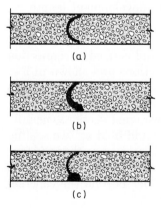

(a)

(b)

(c)

Figure 6-37 Common defects of construction joints: (*a*) Bentonite mud and impurities left between concrete. (*b*) Cavities caused by soil not completely removed from the end of the concrete. (*c*) Partial cavity due to soil trapped between concrete.

defects may appear in panels with square joints and shear keys, and constitute structural deficiencies resulting in (1) more seepage than permitted through the joint; (2) reduction in the effective cross-sectional area that resists loads and deformations; and (3) inhibited wall performance in terms of serviceability criteria.

Bentonite mud and impurities accumulated at the joint are swept by the rising concrete and better removed when they are against smooth metal surfaces. Thus any joint executed with a steel plate is likely to have less mud trappings. However, the problem shown in Fig. 6-24 can occur despite all precautions to deter leakage of fresh mix. Whenever the difference between trench width as excavated and the diameter of the end tube or casing is more than 3 in (7.5 cm), cement paste and even aggregate from the concrete will escape out and around the pipe.

Tests on the transfer of load

Although the strength of vertical construction joints, either plain or continuous, can ordinarily be analyzed by flexural and shear theory, the actual capacity often cannot be inferred because of lack of experimental data that can verify structural response. Thus properly devised and performed tests may supplement design procedures and other recommendations provided the cost is justified. Relevant tests have been carried out for various loads and stress combinations and for various joint types, and the results are suggested as an excellent supplement to design.

Transfer of vertical load. Tests (University of Osaka, 1971) on diaphragm walls used as load-bearing elements show that a plain round tube shear joint has increased ability to transfer vertical load across if it is provided with dowels. In these tests a steel ball weighing 2 t was freely dropped from a certain height on a diaphragm wall while observations were made on the dissipation of energy and shock waves through the joint to the adjoining panel. Effective joints were considered those transmitting energy as in continuous monolithic walls. Conversely, reduction in shock wave amplitude would indicate that a portion of the wave energy had dissipated and was absorbed at the joint.

Figure 6-38 shows the energy transfer through three different joints. The joint in Fig. 6-38a is open, i.e., filled with premolded material or bentonite to inhibit structural interaction. In Fig. 6-38b the joint provides full contact of the adjoining sections, and its strength is therefore the shear resistance at the common interface. The joint in Fig. 6-38c is provided with steel dowels.

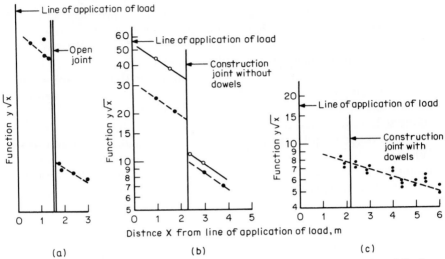

Figure 6-38 Energy transfer across construction joints. (*From University of Osaka, 1971.*)

If the wave amplitude y is multiplied by the square root of the distance x from the point of load application and then plotted on a logarithmic scale while the distance x is plotted on an arithmetic scale, the resulting function approaches a straight line. The wave transfer is discontinuous in Fig. 6-38a, and a serious drop in energy transfer occurs at the joint. In Fig. 6-38b the wave energy is partially transmitted, and a considerable fraction dissipates at the joint. In Fig. 6-38c the full energy is transferred across the joint.

Transfer of direct axial load (tension). Situations where axial tensile load may have to be resisted at a vertical joint are corners of walls where inside pressures tend to separate the panels. Connections that can transfer direct tension include plates and dowel bars. These devices also prevent sliding across the joint and thus increase resistance to laminar tilting.

Direct tension tests on concrete sections taken from diaphragm walls have been performed by Ikuta et al. (1969b). The connections consist of dowel bars, plain-steel rectangular plates, tapered plates, and plates punched to provide slits. The last two types are thought to increase the ultimate resistance of the connection by direct bearing against the slits or by forcing sliding to occur along a tapered surface. The connection devices used in the tests are shown in Table 6-10, together with the test results.

If we consider type B as the reference connection, the average bond stress on the steel plate at ultimate load is $u = 8.33/[2(10.35)(50)] =$

TABLE 6-10 Various Types of Connection Devices and Results of Tests on the Transfer of Axial Load

Type	Dimensions, mm, and shape	Average initial cracking load, t	Ultimate load, t	Comparison with A type, %
A		6.5	10.35	100
B		6.3	8.33	80.4
C		6.32	9.15	88.4
D		6.4	7.77	75
E		6.1	9.23	89.2

From Ikuta et al., 1969*b*.

8.05 kg/cm^2 = 115 lb/in^2. This can be taken as the basic stress and applied to the other types. For type C the total bond area (excluding the slits) is about 849 cm^2, and therefore the actual increase in the ultimate bond strength of the connection is 9150 − 8.05(849) = 2310 kg, or 2.31 t. If we assume that this increase is due to the single shear of concrete across the slit area, the corresponding shear stress is τ_c = $^{2310}/_{100}$ = 23.1 kg/cm^2. Likewise it can be shown that for type D the increase in the yield strength due to the single shear of concrete in the tapered zone is 1050 kg, corresponding to a shear stress τ_c = $^{1050}/_{100}$ = 10.5 kg/cm^2.

Type A has a diameter of $^{16}/_{25}$ = 0.64 in ($^5/_8$ in), giving a perimeter 3.14 × 0.64 = 2 in. For a total ultimate bond load 10.35 × 2205 = 22,820 lb, the bond stress is 22,820/40 × 2 = 280 lb/in^2, or 19.5

kg/cm². Assuming that this is a plain bar, the bond strength is consistent with the results of tests shown in Table 6-9 for bentonite concentrations ≥10 percent (Japanese bentonite).

A complete discussion of the connection types of Table 6-10 is given by Ikuta et al. (1969b). The main points are as follows:

1. With type A (dowel bars) initial cracking appeared at the center of the connection when the applied load reached about one-fifteenth the compressive strength of concrete. Cracking continued longitudinally, and eventually the bars underwent pullout failure before fracture could occur.

2. With type B cracking first occurred wide open and across the section, although the plate showed no signs of distress. This might indicate that the bond strength of the plate was reached and exceeded before yielding, and the plate was subsequently subjected to pullout.

3. For certain C types (plates with slits) rupture was observed at the ends where the smallest effective section actually occurs. The calculated ultimate load at this section is 0.35(5)(4.19) = 7.31 t. Therefore, the effect of bond and slits is to increase the load by 9.15 − 7.31 = 1.84 t.

4. For type D no visual rupture was observed on the plate, although the concrete cracked. In some specimens, however, the initial longitudinal construction cracks opened simultaneously, probably because of the tapering effect that forced the concrete to split after the plate slipped.

5. Type E underwent rupture at the smallest section. Again for a calculated ultimate load 7.31 t and an actual ultimate load 9.23 t, the contribution from plate bond, tapering, and slitting is 1.92 t, or about 20 percent.

From a series of tests Ikuta et al. (1969b) conclude that rusted or fabricated plates improve the structural capacity of these connections. Although no set relationship is developed between the size and shape of the holes, the thickness of the plates, and the effect of flanges around the holes, it is suggested that better results are achieved when the surface is rusted, the plates are relatively thick, and the number of holes is greater for the same hole area. Flanges have an effect similar to that of plate thickness.

Transfer of shear.   A shear connector used often in structural walls for deep basements is shown in Fig. 6-39, and presumably it can accommodate large lateral shear transfer across the panel. Ikuta et al. (1972) have studied the capacity of this connection in full-scale field tests on panels constructed in slurry trenches. The conclusion is that the ultimate shear strength depends largely on the bearing pressure

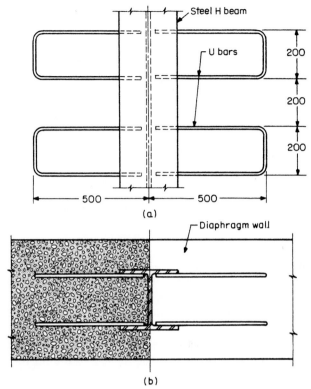

Figure 6-39 Shear connector consisting of steel H beam and U bars; dimensions in millimeters: (*a*) Elevation. (*b*) Sectional plan.

of concrete on the U-shaped bars, and therefore it can be taken as the crushing strength of concrete on the same area. This conclusion is suggested as a criterion for designing connections of this type.

6-13   Structural Capacity of Joints and Connections

General principles

The design of connections to transfer or receive loads from beams, columns, floors, slabs, and bracing is a mandatory requirement. Joints and connections have a direct effect on structural integrity and must be adequate to ensure structural integrity as a unit. This means that the structural adequacy of a structure at any stage should not be controlled by the strength of individual connections but should rather be governed by the strength of principal members including the walls.

Joints and connections can be made by welding steel bars or structural steel inserts to the main cage; by transferring tensile or compressive stress by bond or anchorage; by using steel plates and angles to prevent separation of the wall from independently supported members; by using key-type devices; or by using bonding media that affect the adherence of one member to another.

Joints and connections should preferably occur at logical connections in the walls, and when practical, at points that may be readily analyzed and easily reinforced. The design should avoid connections and details that may cause stress concentrations and result in spalling or splitting or members at contact surfaces.

It appears from these brief remarks that constructibility is the first aspect to be checked in detailing joints and connections. Constructibility refers to the placement of reinforcement, plates, angles, etc., as well as to the consolidation of concrete.

Design considerations.   Loading conditions to be considered in the design of joints and connections are service loads including effects of creep, shrinkage and temperature change, erection loads, and sequence of construction. A summary of loads acting on diaphragm walls is given in Sec. 4-13.

The classification of joints and connections involves two basic categories, based on the loading conditions and the anticipated deformations. These are:

Type 1.   This joint connects walls with other members designed to satisfy strength requirements and in which no significant inelastic deformations are anticipated.

Type 2.   This joint connects members and walls designed to have sustained strength under deformation reversals into the inelastic range.

The requirements for joints and connections are thus dependent on the deformations at the joint implied by the design loading conditions. Typical examples from each category are: (1) Type 1 is a joint in a wall-floor system designed to resist continuous moments due to lateral loads and dead loads, without considering special ductility requirements. Type 2 is a connection of wall and slab required to dissipate energy through reversals of deformation into the inelastic range arising from earthquake motions or blast effects.

Distortion of a joint will generally depend on the magnitude and sense of the moment on opposite faces. Under very high lateral loads or large differences in adjacent span lengths, the resulting moments may induce high shears through a joint. The most common occurrence of large unbalanced moments across a connection is under seismic loading. For connections in nonseismic regions, the latest ACI Committee Report 352 (1985) provides a complete design summary with recommendations. In the usual case the prime factors to be considered in the design of joints are shear, anchorage of reinforcement, and transfer of axial load.

Under load factor design, the ultimate strength capacity of joints and connections (nominal resistance) should be at least 10 percent in excess of that required of the members connected. This recommendation may be deemed to have been satisfied if the joint or connection is proportioned to provide a nominal strength 1.1 times the nominal strength of the member.

If any reasonable doubt exists with respect to the determination of the load-carrying capacity of a connection, this value should be established by tests, properly designed and performed.

Transfer of shear

The transfer of shear to a diaphragm wall can be accomplished by means of bentout bars used as dowels combined with cast-in-place concrete placed against naturally roughened wall interfaces or by such mechanical devices as embedded plates or shapes, brackets, or other similar sections.

Wall-to-slab connections. For shears from nominal spans and loads the extension of bentout bars anchored in each connecting member and with sufficient embedment to develop the full yield strength of the bar generally is adequate to transfer shear. The dowels require recesses in the wall formed either by horizontal bands of wood or by styrofoam planks. The resulting continuous shear key and roughened interface contributes to the shear capacity. If the bentout bars are horizontal, shear is resisted by bearing of the concrete on the steel bars and by the shear strength of concrete along the key. If the bentout bars are inclined, the shear resistance is a function of the tensile strength of the steel and the angle of inclination.

The allowable shear, based on extended bars or dowels, should not exceed

$$V = A_s f_s \cos \theta \qquad (6\text{-}15)$$

where A_s = cross section of bar or dowel, f_s = allowable stress in steel, and θ = angle of inclination as shown in Fig. 6-40. If the concrete cover on the dowels is more than 3 in, a second term in Eq. (6-15) may be considered based on the strength of concrete f'_c.

Shear friction. The connection shown in Fig. 6-40 involves an interface between two members that can slip relative to one another. The

Diaphragm Wall

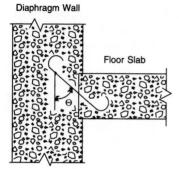

Floor Slab

Figure 6-40 Wall-slab connection
to transfer shear.

shear carrying mechanism is referred to as "interface shear transfer"
or "shear friction."

Extensive tests have been carried out by Mattock et al. (1969, 1972)
using specimens of general configuration. When a shear is applied to
an initially cracked surface, or a surface formed by placing one layer
of concrete against an existing layer of hardened concrete, relative slip
of the two concrete masses causes separation of the surfaces as shown
in Fig. 6-41a. If there is reinforcement across the separation, it is
elongated by the separation and hence is stressed in tension. For equilibrium a compressive stress is needed as shown in Fig. 6-41b. Shear
is transmitted across the separation by (1) friction resulting from the
compressive stress, and (2) interlock of aggregate protrusions on the

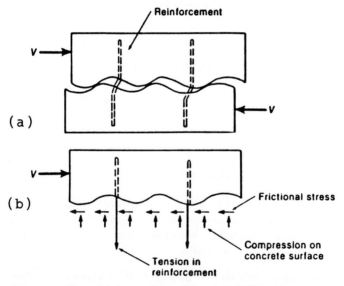

Figure 6-41 Shear friction analogy. (*From ACI-ASCE, 1973.*)

surfaces combined with dowel action of the reinforcement. If the transverse reinforcement is perpendicular to the shear plane, Mattock and Hawkins (1972) suggest that the shear strength of the surface is

$$V_n = 0.8A_{uf}f_y + A_cK_1 \qquad (6\text{-}16)$$

where V_n = nominal shear resistance, A_{uf} = area of reinforcement crossing the surface, A_c = concrete area resisting shear friction, and K_1 = 400 lb/in² for normal weight concrete. Equation (6-16) applies if $pf_y > 200$ lb/in², where $pf_y = A_{uf}f_y/A_c$.

The first term in Eq. (6-16) represents the friction, the coefficient of friction taken as 0.8 for concrete sliding on concrete. The second term represents the shear transferred by shearing off surface protrusions and by dowel action. For grade 60 bars, the pf_y limit requires a minimum reinforcement ratio $p = 0.0033$.

ACI criteria. The ACI Code presents design rules and criteria for cases where it is appropriate to consider shear transfer across an interface between two concretes cast at different times.

The factored resistance ϕV_n must exceed the factored loads. The nominal resistance V_n is related to the amount of reinforcement as follows:

$$V_n = A_{uf}f_y\mu \qquad (6\text{-}17)$$

where $\phi = 0.85$ for shear and μ is the coefficient of friction taken as (1) 1.0λ for concrete placed against hardened concrete with a surface roughened to an amplitude of about ¼ in, and (2) 0.6λ for concrete placed against hardened concrete not intentionally roughened. The factor λ may be taken as 1.0 for normal weight concrete. The upper limit of V_n from Eq. (6-17) is set as $0.2f'_cA_c$.

If a permanent net compressive force C_u acts across the joint, it can be considered a direct additive to the force $A_{uf}f_y$, so that Eq. (6-17) becomes now

$$V_n = (A_{uf}f_y + C_u)\mu \qquad (6\text{-}18)$$

The compressive force C_u is in this case the reaction from the lateral earth stresses, and for most conservative results it should be entered with the minimum probable value.

When shear friction reinforcement is inclined to the shear plane as is the dowel bar of Fig. 6-40, the shear strength becomes

$$V_n = A_{uf}f_y(\mu \sin \theta + \cos \theta) \qquad (6\text{-}19)$$

The origin of the two terms in parentheses should be explained. There are two components of $A_{uf}f_y$: a normal component $A_{uf}f_y \sin \theta$ and a parallel component $A_{uf}f_y \cos \theta$. Only the normal component is multiplied by μ since it causes friction. Only bars that are stressed in tension by the sliding motion, as in Fig. 6-40, should be considered.

Mechanical devices. Alternatively, a floor slab can be supported on a diaphragm wall as shown in Fig. 6-42*a*. The vertical connection plate may be continuous or intermittent, and for better construction it should be positioned and attached to the cage. The connection angle is welded to the plate after the wall is exposed and before the slab is placed.

The strength of this connection should be checked at three locations: initially at the wall for the capacity of the anchor bars using Eq. (6-15); second, at the junction of plate and steel angle for the strength of the weld joint; and finally at some critical section of the slab or at the direct bearing on the horizontal leg of the angle. Any bearing on the underside of the embedded plate should be ignored because of possible accumulation of bentonite mud.

In lieu of the anchor bar with hook shown in Fig. 6-42*a*, the connection plate may be embedded into the wall using studs as shown in Fig. 6-42*b*. For allowable stress design, the allowable shear as determined by the studs is

$$V = 110d^2\sqrt{f_c'} \qquad (6\text{-}20)$$

if $h/d \geqslant 4.2$ and

$$V = 27hd\sqrt{f_c'} \qquad (6\text{-}21)$$

if $h/d < 4.2$, where h and d are as shown in Fig. 6-42*b*.

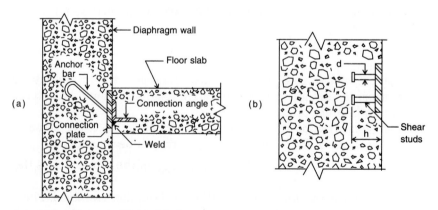

(a)

(b)

Figure 6-42 Shear connection details.

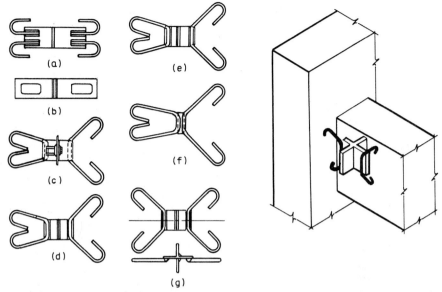

Figure 6-43 Shear connectors of beam to diaphragm wall, consisting of bearing plates, angles, and bolts. (*From Ikuta et al., 1969.*)

Transfer of shear from beams.   Brackets and corbels made by fastening suitable steel shapes to plates cast flush with the concrete face can be designed and detailed to resist and transfer shear from beam to walls. Alternatively, structural connections to beams may be developed according to the configurations shown in Fig. 6-43, by combining plates or angles with anchor bars.

Tests of these connections (Ikuta et al., 1969a) show that in the initial stage of loading slide occurs along the connection face, but as more load is applied cracking develops in the concrete panel. With more load, complex compressive cracking is generalized and leads to fracture. These investigators give also the following comments.

1. For types that have pressure-bearing plate identical in shape and size but different anchor bars the shear stiffness is the same. The ultimate strength of the connection depends, however, on the type of anchorage because flexure and tension are introduced in the final stage.

2. The ultimate strength (measured by yielding or displacement) is increased with increased bearing area of the vertical plate. For plate thickness $\geqslant 1$ cm (0.4 in) the ultimate strength of the connection is the bearing strength of concrete; hence thicker plates are more effective.

3. For the same cross-sectional (bearing) area the use of angles results in higher initial shear stiffness and also ultimate strength.

4. All connections should be shaped and dimensioned to give minimum impediment to the flow of concrete.

Transfer of moment

Commonly the transfer of moment from a slab or beam to a diaphragm wall is accomplished by reinforcing bars extended as dowels. The transfer of the corresponding tension of the bar in the protruding section is achieved by sufficient lap, by welding, or by other mechanical devices. Once the bars are bent to the right position and cleaned, the structural continuity is obtained as in conventional construction. The most critical phase is the accurate positioning of the connection bars in the cage to satisfy the construction tolerance and also to minimize the eccentricity of force during its transfer through the connection.

Couplers and other mechanical devices. For commercial mechanical devices developed by specialist contractors, performance data are available from manufacturers or from tests by users. However, judgment is necessary to determine compliance of such data with applicable codes and specifications, and to set the acceptability level in technical terms. In general, couplers must develop 125 percent of the yield strength of the bar. Sufficient data must also be available on resistance to fatigue, stress reversal, dynamic load, long-term creep, and other special conditions such as effect of bar misalignment. The use of coupling devices to splice bars for moment connection is shown in Fig. 6-44.

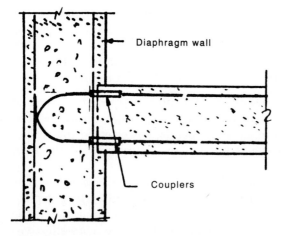

Figure 6-44 Coupling devices used to splice bars for moment connection.

Cadweld splices. This method of splicing rebars is an exothermic process (not a weldment) for butt splicing deformed bars that produces a joint with basically the same mechanical characteristics of the unspliced bar.

Tests have been carried out to study the performance of high-strength bars spliced with Cadweld couplers subjected to stress reversal (Sozen and Gamble, 1967). Two reinforced-concrete beams were subjected to 400 reversals of the yield moment of No. 18 bars spliced with Cadweld couplers. At the yield moment the bars had a calculated steel tensile stress of 55,800 lb/in², compared with the theoretical yield strength of 55,000 lb/in² (A432 steel). After the 400 reversals of the yield stress the spliced bar sustained a maximum tensile stress of 87,600 lb/in² before fracture at the end of the splice, compared with the theoretical tensile strength of 93,800 lb/in².

Tests have also been carried out to study creep effects. For No. 18 bars tested for 240 h (Siess, 1966), the conclusion is that no creep occurs at an average bar stress of 20,000 lb/in². For bars subjected to higher stresses some creep may occur. At an average stress of 30,000 lb/in² the average strain in the tests increased by 2 percent, and when the stress reached 35,000 lb/in², the average strain increased almost by 5 percent. This creep is considered insignificant, and occurs during the first hours of loading, suggesting that it is the maximum creep for an infinite duration of loading. For exposed bars such as those used in the tests, strains of this order and magnitude should not be any larger than those expected due to variations in the elastic modulus of the steel or because of variations in the cross-sectional area of the bars. However, for bars encased in concrete, the transfer of stress from the concrete to the bar would also involve creep in the concrete, tending to further increase the elastic strain in the bar. For bar sizes smaller than No. 9 there is some suspicion that creep may occur but still be structurally insignificant.

Other tests on creep in Cadweld bar splices reported by Ebert (1967) involved specimens at ambient temperatures. The conclusion is that in these conditions the couplers behave as the unspliced bar as long as adequate installation procedures are followed. The bars were tested for 260 h, considered sufficient for the occurrence of first-stage creep. Coupling devices similar to those tested above normally would not be expected to undergo strains associated with long-term creep, at least at normal temperatures and under usual stress conditions.

Tensile tests on Cadweld splices are reported by Thomas (1979). The tensile acceptance criteria from these tests agree with NRC (Nuclear Regulatory Commission) standards requiring that (1) the minimum required tensile strength is 125 percent of the minimum yield strength, and (2) the average strength of each group of 15 consecutive tests should exceed the guaranteed ultimate tensile strength of the bar. Thomas (1979) provides also guidelines for quality control and gives the requirements for splice preparation. Thus bar ends and splice sleeves are not required to be heated to an exact temperature. In fact, this may be counterproductive, especially where temperature measuring devices are used, and should be eliminated in favor of more general criteria with emphasis on removing any moisture that is present rather than achieving a specified temperature.

Bar misalignment with voids in coupling splices.   Under the normally accepted tolerance, misalignment or angular distortion can occur in any of the patterns shown in Fig. 6-45. For the Cadweld splices, the maximum cocking (angular distortion) of a bar at a splice and the maximum eccentricity are shown in Figs. 6-46 and 6-47, respectively.

Tests conducted on No. 14 and 18 bars grade 60 using T-series Cadweld splices gave strengths exceeding the 90,000 lb/in^2 ultimate load. These tests were carried out in air environment and without the effect of concrete encasements. For the same tests in concrete the performance of the splice should be improved as bending forces would be absorbed by the set concrete rather than by bar straightening, and this response would tend to offset the effect of eccentricity. The results of these tests are summarized in Tables 6-11 and 6-12, and evidently the effect of misalignment is practically absent.

Welded splices.   Codes in general permit welded splices subject to appropriate provisions and requirements. The ACI Code specifies that a fully welded splice should have the bars butted and welded to develop a tension at least 125 percent of the specific yield strength of the bar.

The decision to specify welded splices should be made with regard to steel weldability and proper field welding procedures. Reinforcement that is to be welded should be so indicated, and welding procedures should be specified. Certain steels have been developed specifically for welding, having a restricted chemistry plus maximum carbon equivalent so that supplementary provisions in this case are not necessary.

(a)   (b)   (c)   (d)

Figure 6-45 Misalignment and angular distortion of bars spliced with coupling devices: (a) Bars cocked. (b) Bars parallel but off center and on the same side of sleeve. (c) Bars parallel but one bar off center. (d) Bars parallel but both off center on either side of sleeve.

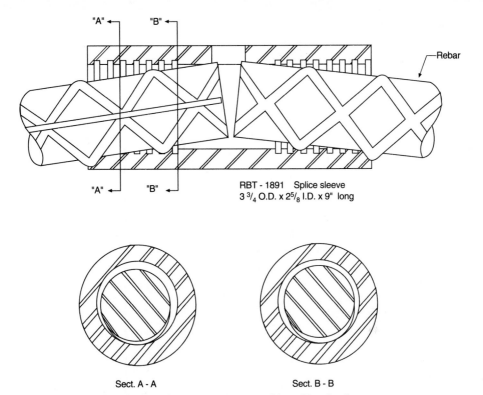

RBT - 1891 Splice sleeve
3 $\frac{3}{4}$ O.D. x 2$\frac{5}{8}$ I.D. x 9" long

Sect. A - A   Sect. B - B

Figure 6-46 Cadweld splice showing maximum cocking of bar in sleeve.

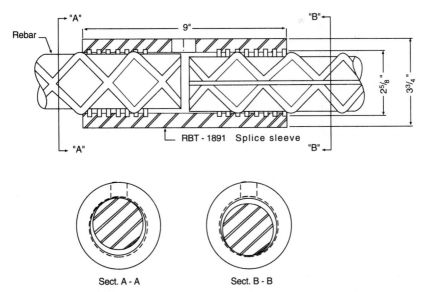

Sect. A - A   Sect. B - B

Figure 6-47 Cadweld splice showing one bar touching top of sleeve, the other touching the bottom.

TABLE 6-11 Results of Tensile Tests, Misaligned No. 18 Bars, Grade 60

Specimen No.	Sectional area, in²	Max. load, lb	Tensile strength, lb/in²	Type and description (Fig. 6-45)	Fracture pattern
1	4.00	395,000	98,750	(b) Bars in line and parallel. Off center with center of sleeve. Touching ID	Bar pulled out of sleeve
2	4.00	385,500	96,400	(d) Bars parallel, but both off center. Within ¹⁄₁₆ in of sleeve ID	Bar fracture
3	4.00	389,500	97,100	(a) Bars cocked to maximum Both touching sleeve ID. Bars in same plane	Bars pulled out of sleeve
4	4.00	402,500	100,600	(a) Bars cocked to maximum Both touching sleeve ID. Bars in same plane	Bar fracture

TABLE 6-12   Results of Tests, Misaligned No. 14 Bars, Grade 60

Specimen No.	Ultimate load, lb	Observed yield	Type and description (Fig. 6-45)	Fracture pattern
5	210,000	142,000	(b) Bars in line and parallel. Off center with center of sleeve. Within ¹⁄₁₆ in of sleeve ID	Bar fracture
6	218,500	147,500	(c) Bars parallel. One bar off center of sleeve to within ¹⁄₁₆ in of sleeve ID	Bar fracture
7	210,000	141,000	(d) Bars parallel, but both off center. One bar ⅛ in of sleeve, the other ¹⁄₁₆ in of sleeve ID	Bar fracture
8	218,000	147,000	(a) Both bars cocked. Both bars within ⅛ in of sleeve ID. Bars in same plane	Bar fracture

Welded splices have been used in diaphragm wall construction but at a cost often too high. For certain cases, such as wall-to-beam or wall-to-strut connections, welded splices may be cheaper.

Heat bents.   In practice, bars intended as dowels are initially inserted and anchored in the wall as shown in Fig. 6-48. The front area is blocked with styrofoam or other suitable material. When the wall is exposed, this material is removed and the bars are bent, usually at ambient temperatures. A lap splice is thus provided with the bars of

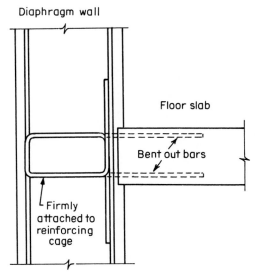

Diaphragm wall

Floor slab

Bent out bars

Firmly attached to reinforcing cage

Figure 6-48 Moment connection, diaphragm wall to floor slab.

the horizontal member. Considering, however, the considerable splice length required in most cases, this connection is often impractical and uneconomical. Alternatively, bentout bars may be used with short cantilever slab projections and wall brackets.

Bending is accomplished better if it is done after the bars are heated to an optimum temperature. The effect of heating is shown in Fig. 6-49, where the work necessary to bend the bars, expressed as bending moments, is related to bar temperature and bar diameter. The larger the bar size, the greater the effort necessary to bend the bar. For each bar size there is a suitable temperature at which the bar can be bent manually using a pipe. Heating can be applied at the initial bent of the bar as it is assembled with the cage, and then to restore the bar for the splice. Alternatively, heating may be used in one of these stages while the other is done at ambient temperature.

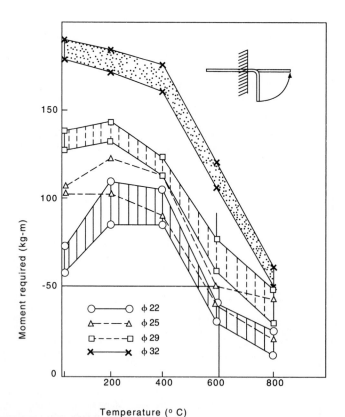

Figure 6-49 Work necessary to bend bars at various temperatures.

The effect of heating on bar strength and performance is rather complex, as is the effect of changing the point of bent along the bar. Certain results have been obtained from field tests. Results from such tests, summarized in Table 6-13, refer to Japanese standard deformed bars type 3 SD 35, 22 mm diameter (⅞ in), at a temperature of 400°C. In these results, type 1 is the basic deformed bar tested without bents at ambient temperature and then used for comparison. With the exception of types 6 and 7, the average yield and tensile strength is about the same. Comparing types 1 and 3 with types 2 and 4, the strength characteristics of the bar remain unchanged, indicating the absence of heating effects. A restoration point other than the point of original bent should be avoided. Restoring the bars without heating

TABLE 6-13   Effect of Heating on Bar Characteristics

Process type	Sample No.	Yield strength, t/cm^2	Tensile strength, t/cm^2	Elongation, %	Remarks
1	1	3.84	5.93	34 (14)	Untreated, ambient temp
	2	3.87	5.95	25 (13)	Basic type, no bents
	3	3.79	5.85	28 (15)	
	Average	3.83	5.91	28 (14)	
2	1	3.84	5.93	34 (11)	Heated but no bents
	2	3.87	5.95	37 (11)	
	3	3.87	5.85	14 (11)	
	Average	3.86	5.91	28 (11)	
3	1	3.84	5.85	14 (5.2)	Bent without heating
	2	3.69	5.85	11 (8.6)	Restored without heating
	3	3.69	5.82	13 (11)	
	Average	3.74	5.83	13 (8.3)	
4	1	3.89	5.52	17 (12)	Bent without heating
	2	3.84	5.75	32 (12)	Restored with heating
	3	3.89	5.93	34 (11)	
	Average	3.87	5.73	28 (12)	
5	1	3.81	5.85	— (14)	Bent without heating
	2	3.89	6.01	— (15)	Restored without heating
	3	3.89	6.03	— (15)	Point of bent changed
	Average	3.86	5.96	— (15)	
6	1	—	3.40	— (5.2)	Bent without heating
	2	—	3.74	— (5.6)	Restored with heating
	3	Excessive deformation. Unable to test			Point of bent changed
	Average	—	3.57	— (5.4)	
7	1		2.19	2 (1.6)	Bent with heating
	2		2.47	3 (2.2)	Restored without heating
	3		2.99	4 (1.7)	
	Average		2.55	3 (1.8)	
8	1	3.89	6.0	24 (12)	Bent with heating
	2	3.84	5.90	23 (13)	Restored with heating
	3	3.87	5.98	26 (13)	
	Average	3.87	5.96	24 (13)	

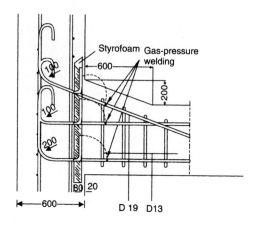

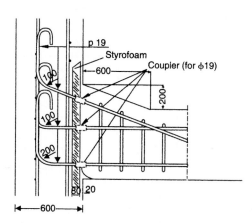

Figure 6-50 Examples of the bar arrangement for connecting a diaphragm wall and a slab.

can encounter difficulties, especially since this is not easy to do at the point of initial bent, resulting in brittle behavior. Heating, however, can cause some loss of ductility while it makes restoring easier.

Examples of bar arrangement and connection details for a diaphragm wall and a slab are shown in Fig. 6-50.

Connections for composite walls

Composite walls (discussed in other sections) are indicated where extra wall thickness and strength is required only in certain parts of the finished structure (Xanthakos, 1980).

Connection with shear studs. A composite wall can be made as shown in Fig. 6-51. The anchor bars are welded to a steel plate and the assembly is attached to the cage. When the wall is exposed, the plate is

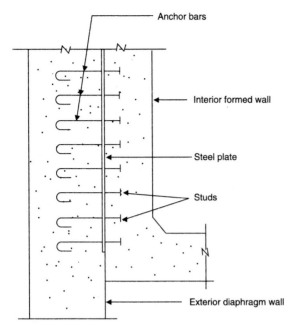

Figure 6-51   Composite wall using anchor bars and shear studs.

cleaned and shear studs are welded to it, usually one stud opposite each bar. The studs project into the formed portion of the structure. The design of the studs is according to Eqs. (6-20) and (6-21).

Connection with deck plate.   This detail, shown in Fig. 6-52, involves a plate embedded in the diaphragm wall and bent to the configuration shown in Fig. 6-52a so that anchor bars will eventually protrude into the interior formed wall.

The usual thickness of the forming plate is 1.6 mm ($\frac{1}{16}$ in). Once the walls áre compositely connected the plate has no structural function; hence its thickness is selected merely to withstand distortion during handling and concrete placement. Practical dimensions and shape are as shown. The angle θ is made 40 to 45° when the plate is set horizontally and 60 to 70° when the plate is set vertically. The bar arrangement on the recess of the plate is shown in Fig. 6-52b.

The plate is fixed to the reinforcing cage and held secured with a bracket or by welding. When the detail is set horizontally, both top and bottom ends are attached to the cage as shown in Fig. 6-52c. The anchor bars pass through holes made in the plate, to be spliced with bars of the adjoining section. On the outer side, the anchor bars protrude 7 to 7.5 cm (2 ¾ to 3 in), which is the normal clearance from

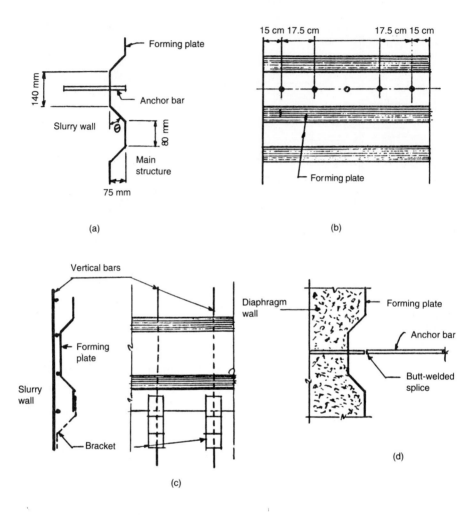

Figure 6-52 Deck plate shear connector detail for composite walls.

the face of the cage to the face of the trench. All recesses are filled with temporary material such as styrofoam. After the plate is exposed and cleaned, the bars of the interior wall are placed and butt-welded to the anchor bars.

6-14 Design Examples

Design Example 6-1 The concrete floor of a permanent structure frames into a diaphragm wall, as shown in Fig. 6-53. The unfactored reactions are 6.2 kips

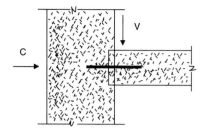

Figure 6-53 Wall-slab connection, Design Example 6-1.

dead load, and 3.5 kips live load per foot width of slab. The diaphragm wall resists lateral earth pressures. The minimum earth pressure reaction at the floor level is 4.3 kips per foot of wall. Ignore shrinkage and other restraints, and determine the total steel across the joint using $f_y = 40,000$ lb/in^2.

First we factor the loads from the service values using the expression

$$U = 1.4D + 1.7L \quad \text{(ACI Code)}$$

The factored shear is therefore

$$V_u = 1.4(6.2) + 1.7(3.5) = 8.7 + 6.0 = 14.7 \text{ kips}$$

Since this is normal weight concrete, $\lambda = 1.0$. Since the floor slab is cast against hardened concrete, we use $\mu = 1.0\lambda = 1.0$.

From Eq. (6-18),

$$V_n = A_{uf}f_y + C_u$$

where $V_u = \phi V_n$ and $C_u = 4.3$ kips. For $\phi = 0.85$ we obtain

$$0.85(A_{uf}f_y + 4.3) = 14.7$$

or

$$0.85 A_{uf}f_y = 11$$

and

$$A_{uf} = \frac{11}{0.85(40)} = 0.32 \text{ in}^2$$

which is satisfied by No. 5 bars at 12-in centers.

If the lateral earth pressure reaction is ignored, $A_{uf} = 14.7/34 = 0.43$ in^2.

Design Example 6-2 A diaphragm wall is constructed according to the method shown in Fig. 1-32b and is integrated into the permanent structure of an underground transportation facility. Beams from the interior framing are connected directly to the pillar or pile inserted between the strip panels. A beam carries an end reaction as follows: dead load, 35 kips; live load plus impact, 23 kips. Design a connection to transfer the factored shear, using load and resistance factors specified by AASHTO. Ignore any compressive thrust due to lateral earth pressure. Use grade 60 steel.

First we factor the service loads using the expression

$$V_u = 1.3(D + 1.67L)$$

The factored shear is therefore

$$V_u = 1.3(35 + 1.67 \times 23) = 45.5 + 49.9 = 95.4 \text{ kips}$$

As in the previous example, $\mu = \lambda = 1$. We select bars inclined at $45° = \theta$. The required amount of reinforcement is therefore obtained from Eq. (6-19), or

$$0.85A_{cf}f_y(\sin \theta + \cos \theta) = 95.4 \text{ kips}$$

or

$$0.85A_{cf}f_y(0.707 + 0.707) = 95.4 \text{ kips}$$

or

$$A_{cf} = 95.4/(1.20 \times 60) = 1.32 \text{ in}^2$$

Provide 2 No. 8 bars across the joint. These must be anchored on both sides. This can be done by the use of hooks at both ends.

Using allowable stress design and ignoring shear friction, the required amount of steel is computed from Eq. (6-15) as

$$A_s = V/(f_s \cos \theta) = 58/(24 \times 0.707) = 3.4 \text{ in}^2$$

Interestingly, the difference in the two methods reflects the following: (1) the effect of shear friction; (2) the factor of safety 2.5 that relates f_s and f_y for grade 60 steel; and (3) a smaller factor of safety for dead load as the analysis is shifted from allowable stress to load factor.

Design Example 6-3 A bracket or corbel is a short member that cantilevers out from the wall or pillar to receive a supporting beam. For the wall of Fig. 1-32 it is generally built monolithically with the intermediate pole. The terms are restricted to cantilevers with a shear span-to-depth ratio less than 1. The structural response can be idealized as a truss consisting of a compression strut and a tension tie, as shown in Fig. 6-54. The tension tie supports a constant tensile force between the load point and point A, which is the beginning of the anchorage in the pole.

Brackets and corbels may fail by (1) yielding of the tension tie; (2) failure of the end anchorage; (3) failure of the compression strut by crushing or shearing; and (4) local failure at the bearing area. Both the ACI and AASHTO present a design procedure based partly on the strut-and-tie truss model and partly on shear friction.

For this example, a bracket will be designed to transfer a beam reaction to a supporting pillar placed between diaphragm wall panels. The factored shear is 165 kips, and the beam to be supported is restrained against longitudinal shrinkage and expansion. Ignore lateral earth stresses. Use $f'_c = 4000 \text{ lb/in}^2$ and $f_y = 60,000 \text{ lb/in}^2$.

Step 1.   Referring to Fig. 6-55, first we compute the distance a from the pillar to the line of action of V_u. Assuming a 12-in-wide bearing plate, the allowable bearing stress is

$$\phi(0.85)f'_c = 0.70 \times 0.85 \times 4 = 2.38 \text{ kips/in}^2$$

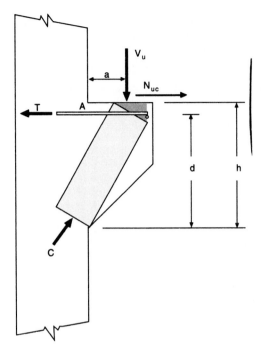

Figure 6-54 Typical truss action in a corbel.

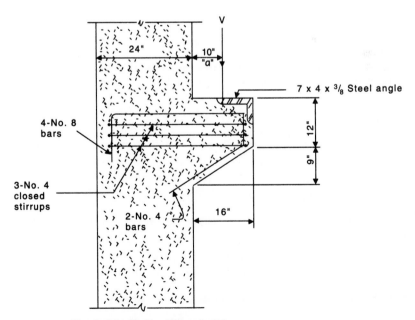

Figure 6-55 Bracket for Design Example 6-3.

so that the required width of the plate is $165/(2.38 \times 12) = 5.8$ in, use a plate 12 in $\times$ 6 in. Assuming that the beam overhangs the plate by 6 in, with a 1-in gap to the face of the pillar, the dimension a is $6 + 1 + 3 = 10$ in.

Step 2.   Compute the depth d (at the face of the pillar) assuming a bracket width $b_w = 18$ in.

For $f'_c = 4000$ lb/in², we compute $0.2f'_c = 800$ lb/in². Therefore, the factored shear strength is

$$\phi V_n = \phi(0.2)f'_c b_w d = 0.85 \times 800 \times 18d$$

The minimum d is now

$$\frac{165{,}000}{0.85 \times 800 \times 18} = 13.5 \text{ in}$$

As detailed, the actual d is $21 - 2.5 = 18.5$ in   OK.

Step 3.   Calculate the forces on the bracket. For a factored shear $V_u = 165$ kips, the tensile force representing shrinkage is

$$N_{uc} = 0.2V_u = 33 \text{ kips}   \text{(ACI and AASHTO)}$$

The factored moment is

$$M_u = V_u a + N_{uc}(h - d)$$
$$= 165 \times 10 + 33(21 - 18.5) = 1732 \text{ in-kips}$$

Step 4.   Compute the shear friction, reinforcement A_{uf} from $\phi V_n \geq V_u$ or $A_{uf} = V_u/(\phi \mu f_y)$, where $\mu = 1.4\lambda$ (bracket monolithic with pillar), and $\lambda = 1.0$ (normal weight concrete). Therefore

$$A_{uf} = \frac{165{,}000}{0.85(1.4)(60{,}000)} = 2.31 \text{ in}^2$$

Step 5.   Compute the flexural reinforcement A_f. In this case A_f is computed from Eq. (6-8), where A_s is replaced by A_f. From Eq. (6-12)

$$M_u = \phi A_f f_y \left(d - \frac{a}{2}\right)$$

where $\phi = 0.85$ and $a = A_f f_y/0.85 f'_c b$. As a first trial, we assume that $(d - a/2) = 0.9d$, so that

$$A_f = \frac{M_u}{\phi f_y(0.9d)} = \frac{1732}{0.85 \times 60 \times 0.9 \times 18.5} = 2.04 \text{ in}^2$$

The dimension a is computed as $a = (2.04)(60)/(0.85)(4)(18) = 2.0$ in, and A_f is recomputed as

$$A_f = \frac{1732}{0.85 \times 60(18.5 - 1)} = 1.94 \text{ in}^2$$

Step 6.   Compute the reinforcement A_n for direct tension.

$$A_n = N_{uc}/\phi f_y = 33/(0.85 \times 60) = 0.65 \text{ in}^2$$

Step 7. Compute the area of tension reinforcement A_s. Both the ACI and AASHTO stipulate that the area of primary tension reinforcement A_s must be the larger of

$$(A_f + A_n) = 1.94 + 0.65 = 2.59 \text{ in}^2$$

$$(\tfrac{2}{3}A_{uf} + A_n) = 1.54 + 0.65 = 2.19 \text{ in}^2$$

Check for minimum A_s:

$$A_{s(\min)} = \frac{0.04f'_c}{f_y} b_w d = \frac{0.04 \times 4000}{60,000} \times 18 \times 18.5 = 0.89 \text{ in}^2$$

Final selection: Select 4 No. 8 bars, $A_s = 3.16 \text{ in}^2$.

Step 8. Calculate the area of horizontal stirrups.

$$0.5(A_s - A_n) = 0.5(2.59 - 0.65) = 0.97 \text{ in}^2$$

Use 3 No. 4 double-leg stirrups, area $= 1.20 \text{ in}^2$.

The bracket is detailed as shown in Fig. 6-55. Note that the requirement that the depth at the outside edge of the bearing area is at least $0.5d$ is satisfied.

6-15 Watertight Joints

Typical joint defects associated with the round-tube end details were discussed in Sec. 6-12 and are shown in Fig. 6-37. For overlapping joints, or with joints that provide structural continuity, three common defects are (1) complete cavities in areas not reached by the fresh mix; (2) exposed reinforcing bars; and (3) contaminated concrete, mixed with bentonite, near the partition plate.

Defects and quality control. Lee et al. (1991) have summarized the usual joint defects, and proposed quality control measures to ensure structurally adequate and watertight joints.

Cavities, a common defect, are soft pockets filled with bentonite mud, slime, and impurities squeezed between panels. They may be partial or complete. The former will appear is isolated pockets of trapped material, while the latter transverse the entire wall thickness.

Exposed reinforcing bars result when the outside cover is bentonite and impurities rather than pure concrete. During excavation, this filter cake or impurities will simply peel off, exposing the steel bars and leaving them without protection.

Contaminated concrete results when bentonite mud and slime trapped between joints are intermixed with tremied concrete to produce a weak end zone in the panel. This material has low-strength accelerating crack formation that produces a joint prone to leakage.

Invariably, the main factors contributing to joint defects relate to slurry controls, flowability and mass mobility of concrete, method of tremie placement, and impediment to flow because of poorly designed details. Other precautions and quality control measures include the following (Lee et al., 1991).

Joint sweeping. This should be standard practice, done before concreting the secondary panel to remove accumulated slime and impurities. Usual forms of joint cleaning are the use of scraper, brush wheel, or water jets. While the complete success of joint sweeping is not always physically possible, in most instances it will prevent serious joint defects.

Excessive amount of sediments. Usually suspended particles from the excavation will settle to the bottom of the trench over a period of 1 to 2 h. They should be removed by the use of air lift, suction pump, or the passing of a suitable excavating tool.

Uneven excavation tolerance. Poor verticality and excessive deviation from the horizontal alignment often pose problems for the insertion of the steel cage. The latter tends to scratch the soil off the face of the trench and increase sedimentation.

Concrete leakage. When partition devices are used to form structural joints, concrete may leak to the dry chamber (see also preceding sections). A usual remedy is to chip off concrete protrusions in the open areas using chisels and scrapers, but a complete removal is not always possible. Panel joints in this case may show distinct defects.

Wall deflection. Structural discontinuity between panels may be the cause of differential deflection and angular distortion during extreme events such as an earthquake. In these conditions the joint tends to open more, eventually affecting the watertightness of the wall.

Joint details. Contractors have introduced specially designed joints to improve joint quality and watertightness. Such a joint is shown in Fig. 6-56, detailed to improve the bonding capacity of the partition plate and cut off groundwater leakage. It consists of a pair of metallic hooks welded to the partition plate. The hooks serve as plate stiffeners and as waterstops. In addition the L-shaped hooks can be used as ideal guide walls for joint cleaning devices.

Waterstops. Keyed and waterstop details are shown in Fig. 6-29 in conjunction with the CWS caisson beam. The intent of this joint is to ensure protection at the end of the previous panel in order to maintain the exact geometry of the joint between adjoining panels. The lateral extraction of the form allows the installation of impervious devices such as waterstop blades. In this respect the CWS form can be fitted with an additional grooved caisson that receives one or more plastic or rubber waterstop blades. These blades jam in the grooves owing to

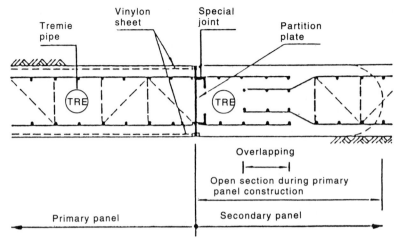

Figure 6-56 Special joint for seepage control.

the elasticity of the central duct, while their free half will be sealed in the concrete when the next panel is concreted. This half is exposed and uncovered when the form is laterally extracted. The continuity of the watertightness is restored thereafter by providing the same arrangement in the adjoining panel.

Other keyed and waterstop joints are shown in Fig. 6-57, developed to accommodate essentially a round-tube panel end. The construction

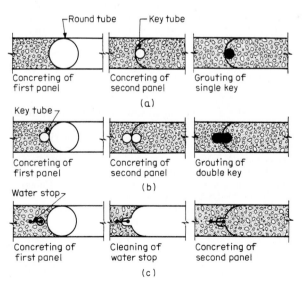

Figure 6-57 (a) Single key joint. (b) Double key joint. (c) Waterstop joint.

involves the creation of a vertical cavity in the same alignment and between adjoining panels as shown. One or two key tubes can be inserted with the main end tube. When the adjoining panels are completed and the concrete has set, the cavity formed by the key is thoroughly cleaned and grouted. A waterstop may be inserted following the sequence shown in Fig. 6-57c.

References

ACI Committee 352, 1976: "Recommendations for Design of Beam-Column Joints in Monolithic Reinforced Concrete Structures," *ACI J., Proc.*, vol. 73, no. 7, July, p. 375.

ACI Committee 352, 1985: "Recommendations for Design of Beam-Column Joints in Monolithic Reinforced Concrete Structures," *ACI J., Proc.*, vol. 82, no. 3, May–June, p. 266.

ACI 318-83, 1983: Building Code Requirements for Reinforced Concrete Am. Concrete Inst., Detroit.

ACI-ASCE Committee 426, 1973: "The Shear Strength of Reinforced Concrete Members," *Proc. ASCE, J. Struct. Div.*, vol. 99, no. ST6, June, pp. 1148–1157.

American Concrete Institute, 1954: Recommended Practice for Selecting Proportions for Concrete (ACI 613-54).

American Concrete Institute, 1963: Formwork for Concrete, Spec. Publ. 4.

American Concrete Institute, 1966: Bond Stress: The State of the Art, ACI Committee 408.

American Concrete Institute, 1971: Placing Concrete by Pumping Methods, ACI Committee 304.

Baar, M., 1971: "Continuous Reinforced Structures for Cast-in-Place Diaphragm Walls," *Proc. Franki Congr. Madrid.*

"Cadweld Rebar Splicing," *Bull.* RB5M-274, Enrico Products, Inc., Cleveland, Ohio.

CIRIA, 1967: The Effect of Bentonite on the Bond between Steel Reinforcement and Concrete, Constr. Ind. Res. Inf. Assoc., Interim Rep. 9, London.

DiBiagio, E., and J. A. Roti, 1972: "Earth Pressure Measurements on a Braced Slurry-Trench Wall in Soft Clay," *Proc. 5th Eur. Conf. Soil Mech. Found. Eng.*, Madrid, vol. 1, pp. 473–483.

Ebert, L. J., 1967: "Creep in Bar Splices," CASE Institute of Technology, Cleveland.

Fukui, S., 1980: "Diaphragm Wall Experience in Japan," *Proc. Slurry Walls for Underground Transp. Systems*, FHWA, Cambridge Mass.

Hofbeck, J. A., I. A. Ibrahim, and A. H. Mattock, 1969: "Shear Transfer in Reinforced Concrete," ACI *J., Proc.*, vol. 66, no. 2, February, pp. 119–128.

Ikuta, Y., et al., 1969a: "An Experimental Study on the Integration of Diaphragm Walls with Major Building Structures," *Trans. Jap. Concr. Inst.*, August.

Ikuta, Y., et al., 1969b: "Studies of the Vertical Joint Method for the Slurry Trench Basement Wall," *Takenaka Tech. Res. Rep.* 4, Tokyo, November.

Ikuta, Y., et al., 1972: "Studies of the Vertical Joint Method for the Slurry Trench Basement Wall," *Jap. Concr. J.*, vol. 10, no. 3, March.

Ikuta, Y., et al., 1973: "Compressive and Bond Strength Characteristics of Concrete Replacing Bentonite Slurry," *Takenaka Tech. Rep.* 10, Tokyo.

Ikuta, Y., et al., 1971: An Experimental Study on the Flow Motion of Fresh Concrete in Slurry Trench Wall by Activable Tracer, *Takenaka Tech. Rep.* 6, Tokyo.

Lee, K. H., C. O. Ou, and K. A. Tsai, 1991: "Quality Control in Construction of Diaphragm Wall Joints," ASTM Symp. on Slurry Walls, Atlantic City, June 27–28.

Mattock, A. H., and N. M. Hawkins, 1972: "Shear Transfer in Reinforced Concrete—Recent Research," *J. Prestressed Concrete Inst.*, vol. 17, no. 2, March–April, pp. 55–75.

"Mechanical Splices in Reinforcing Bars of Category I Structures," 1971: Regulatory Guide 1.10, U.S. Nuclear Regulatory Commission, Washington, D.C.

Neville, A. M., 1973: *Properties of Concrete,* 2d ed., Wiley, New York.

Nilsson, I. H. E., and A. Losberg, 1976: "Reinforced Concrete Corners and Joints Subjected to Bending Moment," *ASCE J. Struct. Div.,* ST-6, June, p. 1229.

Nippon Co., 1975a: Compression and Bond Tests, unpublished Rep., personal communication, Tokyo.

Nippon Co., 1975b: Bond Stress Test Rep. 1, unpublished, Tokyo.

Pittsburgh Testing Laboratory, 1968: "Effect of Bar Misalignment on Bar Splices," Cleveland.

Schlaich, J., and K. Schafer, 1984: "Towards a Consistent Design of Reinforced Concrete Structures," Proc. 12th Congr. IABSE, Vancouver, B.C., September.

Schlaich, J., and D. Weischede, 1982: "Detailing of Concrete Structures," Comite Euro-International du Beton, Info. Bull. no. 150, March, Paris (in German).

Siess, C. P., 1966: "Creep Testing of CADWELD Splices," Talbot Laboratory, Urbana, Ill.

Sozen, M. A., and W. L. Gamble, 1967: "A Report," University of Illinois, Urbana, Ill.

Thomas, H. R., J. H. Willenbrock, and J. L. Burati, 1978: "A Comparative Analysis of Structural Concrete Quality Assurance Practices on Nine Nuclear Power Plant Construction Projects," presented at the April 24–28 ASCE National Spring Convention and Continuing Education Program, Pittsburgh, Pa. (Preprint 3150).

Thomas, H. R., 1979: "Quality Control of Cadweld Splices," *J. Constr. Div., ASCE,* vol. 105, no. C03, September, pp. 201–216.

Troxell, G. E., et al., 1968: *Composition and Properties of Concrete,* 2d ed., McGraw-Hill, New York.

University of Osaka, 1971: "Tests on the Efficiency of Construction Joints in Diaphragm Walls," *Spec. Bull.*

U.S. Bureau of Reclamation, 1963: *Concrete Manual,* 7th ed., Denver, Colo.

Xanthakos, P. P., 1974: "Underground Construction in Fluid Trenches," Colleges of Engineering, University of Illinois, Chicago.

Xanthakos, P. P., 1979: *Slurry Walls,* McGraw-Hill, New York.

Xanthakos, P. P., 1980: "Structural Connections in Slurry Walls," *Proc. Slurry Walls for Underground Transportation Systems,* FHWA, Cambridge, Mass.

Zhang, L., and J. O. Jirsa, 1982: "A Study of Shear Behavior of Reinforced Concrete Beam-Column Joints," PMFSEL Report no. 82-1, University of Texas at Austin, February.

7

Design Principles
of Wall-Structure
Systems

7-1 Two-Way Wall Systems

Basic principles

The diaphragm wall shown in Fig. 7-1 is braced by single internal struts at predetermined points. The wall acts therefore as a two-way system and responds to the lateral loads by bending in two perpendicular directions. Shears are transmitted at the brace points or supports and must be absorbed directly by the wall.

Among the various forms that two-way walls can take (flat plates, flat slabs, waffle slabs, and two-way slabs with beams), the flat plate is feasible and practical, and hence the only system considered in this discussion. Besides the wall shown in Fig. 7-1, where the bracing is temporary and consists of steel struts, two-way walls originate from bracing with ground anchors, or with beams of the permanent structure serving also as struts. In the latter case the bracing beams are installed in a downward process as the excavation is carried out in stages. The beams may be self-supported from wall to wall where slenderness does not govern, or they may be part of a general framing system with interior columns. In the final structure the beams support also the floor slabs. Using beams in lieu of floor bracing allows ample accessibility for earth removal. A special two-way system will result if at the final excavation level the wall is braced by embedment into firm ground, allowing moment in one direction only.

Figure 7-1 Diaphragm walls for the New York City subway.

The ACI Code stipulates that two-way systems may be designed by the empirically based direct design method of Section 13.6 (ACI) or by the more analysis-based equivalent frame method of Sec. 13.7. The direct design method is simpler to use but is restricted to regular layouts. Although the equivalent frame method may be used for any two-way system, it is selected for use for cases that do not fit the direct design method limits. Flat plates are more economical for spans from 15 to 20 ft (4.5 to 6 m), which include the usual range of bracing of diaphragm walls.

The division between statical equilibrium and elastic analysis requires a consideration of the relationship between moments and wall curvatures. Commonly, walls are divided into "thick" walls with a thickness less than about one-tenth of the span, "thin" walls with a thickness less than about one-fortieth of the span, and "medium-thick" walls. Thick walls transmit a portion of the loads as a flat arch and have in-plane compressive forces, with the result that the internal resisting force C is larger than the internal tensile force T. Thin walls transmit a portion of the loads acting as a tension membrane, and hence T is larger than C. A medium-thick wall exhibits neither arch action nor membrane action and hence has $T = C$. Invariably, diaphragm walls will fall in the category of thick walls.

Direct design method

When layouts are relatively simple, a direct design procedure may be used under the following limitations.

1. A minimum of three spans each way, directly supported by struts
2. Rectangular panels with long spans not more than twice the short span
3. Successive spans not differing by more than one-third of the longer span
4. All loads uniformly distributed

Statical equilibrium. The total statical design moment for a span is determined in a strip bounded laterally by the centerline of the panel on each side of the centerline of the supports. Referring to Fig. 7-2, where all panels are loaded uniformly by unit load w, the total statical design moment M_0 is the absolute sum of the negative moment M_1 and the positive moment M_2, as computed by summing moments about line $A - A$.

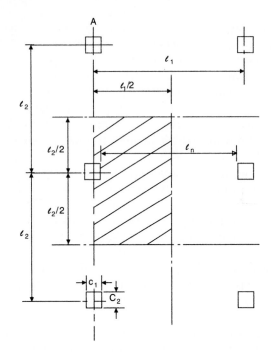

(a) Plan of slab element.

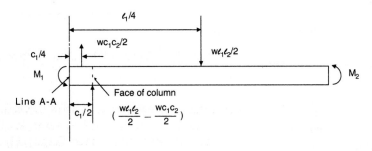

(b) Side view of slab element.

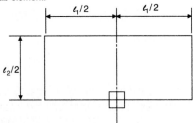

(c) Plan of second slab element.

Figure 7-2 Wall panel configuration and loading for statical moment analysis.

The ACI Code has simplified the expression for M_0 by introducing the term $l_n = l_1 - c_1$. Accordingly, M_0 is given by

$$M_0 = \frac{wl_2l_n^2}{8} \qquad (7\text{-}1)$$

where l_1 = length of span in the direction moments are determined, measured center-to-center of supports; l_2 = length of span tranverse to l_1, measured center-to-center of supports; l_n = length of clear span in the direction moments are determined, measured face-to-face of supports; and w = design load (uniform) per unit area.

The foregoing analysis applies to a rectangular, typical interior wall panel braced by rectangular beam-struts. For steel struts bearing on steel plates, the equivalent face of support is determined from AISC criteria. If the equilibrium of the element shown in Fig. 7-2a were studied, a similar equation for M_0 would result, with l_1 and l_2, and c_1 and c_2, interchanged. This indicates that the total load must satisfy moment equilibrium in both the l_1 and l_2 directions.

Distribution of moments within panels. For practical purposes the diaphragm wall is considered a slab consisting of a series of frames in two directions with the struts replaced by columns. This assembly is shown in Fig. 7-3. The spandrel beam in edge frame may represent the fixed end conditions provided by embedment below excavation level.

The frames extend to the middle of the panels on each side of the support line. In each span of these frames it is necessary to compute the total statical moment M_0

as
$$M_0 = \frac{w_u l_2 l_n^2}{8} \qquad (7\text{-}2)$$

where w_u is the factored load per unit area.

The total statical moment M_0 is divided into positive and negative moments according to ACI Code Section 13.6.3. This distribution is illustrated in Fig. 7-4. In interior spans, 65 percent of M_0 is assigned to the negative moment regions and 35 percent to the positive moment regions. This is approximately the same as a fixed-end beam where the negative moment is two-thirds of $wl^2/8$ and the positive moment is one-third.

The exterior end of the end span is the wall base that may or may not be embedded. If fixed-end conditions exist at the base, the actual fixed-end moment will govern. With free-end condition or without wall embedment the restraining negative moment may be zero or some

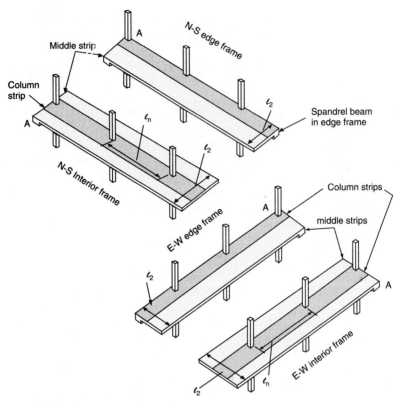

Figure 7-3 Structural idealization of diaphragm wall as slab divided into frames.

percentage of M_0. The limits shown in Fig. 7-4 (0 to 0.63 M_0) must therefore be interpreted after considering the actual wall restraint.

If the computed negative moments on two sides of a support are different, the negative moment section of the wall should be designed for the larger value, unless a moment distribution is carried out to divide the unbalanced moment.

Column strips and middle strips. The moments vary continuously across the width of the wall panel. The steel placement is approximated by averaging the design moments over the width of column strips over the columns or supports, and middle strips between the column (support) strips. The widths of these strips are defined in ACI Sections 13.2.1 and 13.2.2 and are illustrated in Fig. 7-5. The support strips in both directions extend one-fourth of the smaller span l_{min} away from the column line.

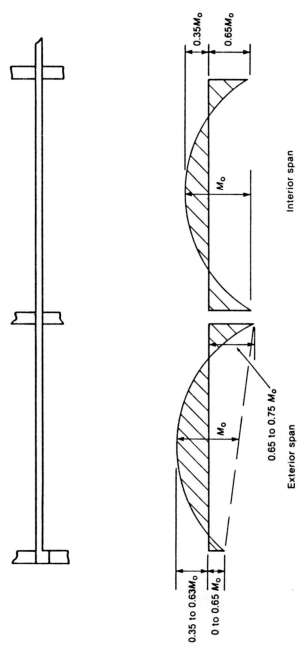

Figure 7-4 Distribution of M_0 to positive and negative moment regions.

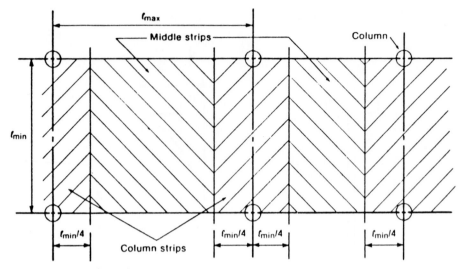

(a) Short direction of panel.

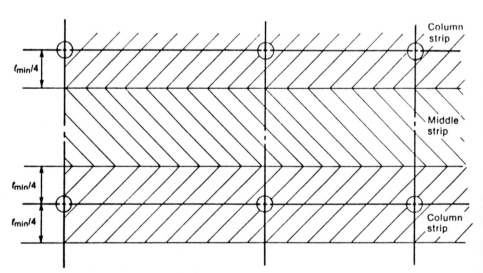

(b) Long direction of panel.

Figure 7-5 Column and middle strips, two-way systems, direct method. (*a*) Short direction of panel. (*b*) Long direction of panel.

Distribution of moments between middle strips and support strips. (ACI Section 13.6.4). The division is a function of $\alpha_1 l_2/l_1$ which depends on the aspect ratio of the panel l_2/l_1 and the relative stiffness α_1 of the beams (if any) spanning in the direction of the panel. Diaphragm walls are treated as flat plates; hence $\alpha = 0$. In this case, 75 percent of the negative moment is assigned to the column strip, and the remaining 25 percent is divided equally between the two adjacent half middle strips. Similarly, 60 percent of the positive moment is assigned to the column strip and the remaining 40 percent is divided equally between the adjacent half middle strips.

At an exterior edge, the division of the exterior end negative moment in the strip spanning perpendicular to the edge also depends on the torsional stiffness of the edge restraint. Since the support provided by wall embedment is continuous and there is no torsion, the negative moment should be distributed equally throughout the panel.

Design for shear

The interaction of struts, anchors, etc., involves the transfer of "punching shear" or two-way shear. This is similar to slab or footing behavior. The maximum moments in a uniformly loaded flat plate occur around the support (column or strut) and lead to a circular crack around it. After additional loading, the cracks necessary to form a fan yield line mechanism develop, and at about the same time inclined or shear cracks form on a truncated conical surface, as shown in Fig. 7-6.

A punching shear failure can occur suddenly with little, if any, warning. Subsequently, the shear capacity at the connection is completely lost, and as the two-way plate slides along the support the negative moment reinforcement rips out, leaving no physical connec-

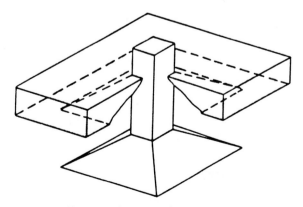

Figure 7-6 Two-way shear (punching).

tion between the two elements. Thus, although the two-way system possesses considerable ductility if it fails in flexure, it has no defense if it fails in shear.

Design considerations for punching shear. Two-way shear is assumed to be critical on a vertical section through the wall and extending around the support (strut). This section is chosen so that it is not more than $d/2$ from the face of the support and so that its length b_0 is a minimum. The intent of the ACI Code is that the critical section for rectangular supports should be rectangular. Two relevant examples related to diaphragm walls are shown in Fig. 7-7. The line shown as the edge of slab may be the edge of the wall at the top or bottom or, in case of the round-tube construction joint, the edge of wall where a cross section has the full wall thickness.

In the case of interior supports in a braced flat plate wall the worst loading case for shear generally corresponds to a negligible moment

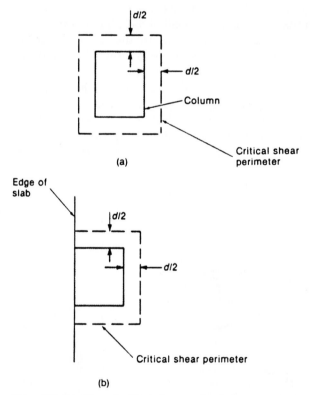

Figure 7-7 Location of critical shear perimeters.

transfer from the wall to the support and vice versa. Design for punching shear without moment transfer first considers the basic equation

$$V_u \leq \phi V_n \tag{7-3}$$

where V_u is the factored shear force due to loads and V_n is the nominal shear resistance of the wall. From previous sections, $\phi = 0.85$. The shear V_u may result from lateral earth stresses, surcharge loads, pore pressures, earthquake effects, etc.

Potential panel configurations and tributary areas used to calculate V_u are assumed to be bounded by lines of zero shear which for simplicity are taken at the centerlines of panels around a support, as shown in Fig. 7-8. However, this assumption is conservative for shear at exterior supports, where V_u is likely to be overestimated but is unconservative for shear at the first interior support.

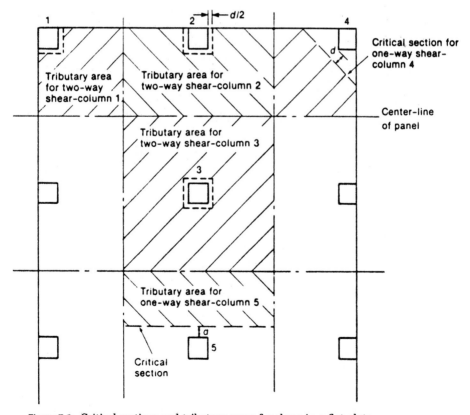

Figure 7-8 Critical sections and tributary areas for shear in a flat plate.

Ignoring shear resistance attributed to shear reinforcement,

$$V_n = V_c \qquad (7\text{-}4)$$

where V_c is the shear resistance of concrete. For two-way shear V_c is given by

For $\beta_c \leqslant 2$: $\qquad\qquad V_c = 4\sqrt{f'_c}\, b_0 d \qquad (7\text{-}5)$

For $\beta_c > 2$: $\qquad\qquad V_c = \left(2 + \dfrac{4}{\beta_c}\right)\sqrt{f'_c}\, b_0 d \qquad (7\text{-}6)$

where b_0 = length of critical perimeter and β_c = ratio of long side at support to short side.

If $\phi V_c < V_u$, the shear capacity may be increased as follows: (1) add a fillet or a capital around the support to increase b_0, or (2) increase the size of support by providing an end cone. Providing shear reinforcement in diaphragm walls is not a popular solution because of practical difficulties in detailing and executing the connection.

Representation of lateral loads

The use of the direct method of analysis is simplified considerably if the loading pattern is consolidated into a uniform unit load acting throughout the flat plate, since in this case any unbalanced moments are likely to be small. A rectangular pressure diagram from apparent pressure theories is therefore entirely compatible with the assumed two-way slab action. Where triangular pressure diagrams must be considered, the analysis is greatly simplified again if the original pressure triangle is converted into a redistributed pressure diagram, as shown in Fig. 7-9. Unbalanced moments will still result and must be redistributed before the final moments are reassigned.

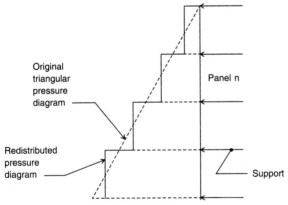

Figure 7-9 Original and redistributed pressure diagram for flat plate analysis.

Pattern loading effects may in most cases be ignored since the permanent loads are large compared with transient loads, and irrespective of the ratios β_a and α_c (load and stiffness ratio, respectively).

Design Example 7-1 Figure 7-10 shows a typical diaphragm wall panel braced with the beams of the permanent structure acting as struts during excavation, and dimensioned as shown. The panel has square ends.

The bottom beams are cast individually in separate trenches so that bottom bracing is provided before final excavation stage. The excavation is in stiff clay; hence base stability is not a problem so that the wall can be terminated just below final excavation level. The excavation pattern suggests a wall movement equivalent to rotation about its top, so that the rectangular pressure diagram shown in Fig. 7-10a is appropriate for wall analysis at the end of construction. The weight of clay is 115 lb/ft³, and in addition the design must consider a live load surcharge resulting in a uniform lateral pressure of 200 lb/ft². The wall is 24 in thick. The example will demonstrate the analysis and design of an interior panel, and the requirements for shear.

Step 1. Compute the factored loads. The lateral earth stress is $0.3\gamma H = 0.3(0.115)(33) = 1.14$ kips/ft². From Table 4-11 the β coefficient is 1.70 max. for both earth stresses and lateral live load surcharges. Also $\gamma = 1.30$ since the analysis does not consider earthquake stresses. Therefore,

$$w_u = 1.3(1.14 + 0.20)(1.7) = 2.96 \text{ kips/ft}^2$$

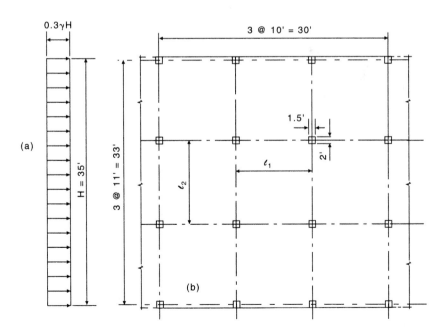

Figure 7-10 Diaphragm wall of design example: (*a*) Lateral earth pressure. (*b*) Typical wall panel treated as flat plate showing dimensions and location of struts.

Step 2.   Compute the moments in the short span of the wall. This requires calculation of l_n and l_2 as follows:

$$l_n = 10 - 1.5 = 8.5 \text{ ft}$$

$$l_2 = 11.0 \text{ ft}$$

The wall is divided into strut and middle strips. The strut strip extends the smaller of $l_2/4$ or $l_1/4$ on each side of the strut centerline. Thus the strut strip is $^{10}\!/_4 = 2.50$ ft on each side of the strut centerline, giving a total strut strip of 5.00 ft. Each half middle strip extends from the edge of the strut strip to the middle of the panel. The total width of two half middle strips is $11.00 - 5.00 = 6.00$ ft. Strut and middle strips for an interior panel are shown in Fig. 7-11.

The moment M_0 is computed next as follows [Eq. (7-2)]:

$$M_0 = \frac{w_u l_2 l_n^2}{8} = \frac{2.96 \times 11 \times 8.5^2}{8} = 294 \text{ ft-kips}$$

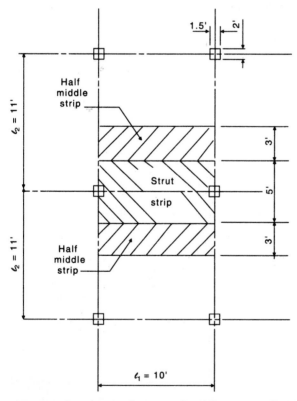

Figure 7-11   Interior panel; strut and middle strips; wall of Fig. 7-10.

This moment is divided into negative and positive moment:

$$\text{Negative moment} = 0.65 \, M_0 = -192 \text{ ft-kips}$$

$$\text{Positive moment} = 0.35 \, M_0 = 102 \text{ ft-kips}$$

These moments are now distributed to strut and middle strips.

$$\text{Strut strip negative moment} = 0.75 \times 192 \times -144 \text{ ft-kips}$$

$$\text{Middle strip negative moment} = 0.25 \times 192 = -48 \text{ ft-kips}$$

Half of the middle strip negative moment, or -24 ft-kips, goes to each adjacent half middle strip. Since the adjacent bays have the same width l_2, a similar moment is assigned to the other half so that the total middle strip negative moment is -48 ft-kips. Likewise

$$\text{Strut strip positive moment} = 0.6 \times 102 = 61 \text{ ft-kips}$$

$$\text{Middle strip positive moment} = 0.4 \times 102 = 41 \text{ ft-kips}$$

Step 3.   Compute the moments in the long span of the wall. It is obvious that the total width of the strut strip is 5.0 ft, giving a total width of the middle strip, also 5.0 ft. The span lengths are now

$$l_n = 11.0 - 2.0 = 9.0 \text{ ft}$$

$$l_1 = 10.0 \text{ ft}$$

The corresponding moment M_0 is

$$M_0 = \frac{w_u l_1 l_n^2}{8} = \frac{2.96 \times 10 \times 9^2}{8} = 299 \text{ ft-kips}$$

This moment is divided into negative and positive moment:

$$\text{Negative moment} = 0.65 \, M_0 = -194 \text{ ft-kips}$$

$$\text{Positive moment} = 0.35 \, M_0 = 105 \text{ ft-kips}$$

to be likewise distributed to strut and middle strips. This gives

$$\text{Strut strip negative moment} = 0.75 \times 194 = -146 \text{ ft-kips}$$

$$\text{Middle strip negative moment} = 0.25 \times 194 = -48 \text{ ft-kips}$$

and also

$$\text{Strut strip positive moment} = 0.6 \times 105 = 63 \text{ ft-kips}$$

$$\text{Middle strip positive moment} = 0.4 \times 105 = 42 \text{ ft-kips}$$

Step 4.   Check shear capacity (punching shear between struts and wall). The tributary area for two-way shear for an interior strut is a panel 10×11 to be increased by 10 percent to make the design shear more compatible with the actual value. Therefore

$$V_u = 1.10 \times 10 \times 11 \times 2.96 = 358 \text{ kips} = 358{,}000 \text{ lb}$$

For a wall thickness of 24 in, $d = 20$ in and $d/2 = 10$ in. The effective perimeter for shear is at distance $d/2$ from the face of the strut, or $b_0 = 2(24 + 20) + 2(18 + 20) = 164$ in. For a concrete strength $f'_c = 3500$ lb/in^2 adjusted to $f'_{ca} = 3200$ lb/in^2 (as shown in Table 6-8), we can write from Eqs. (7-4) and (7-5)

$$V_n = V_c = 4\sqrt{f'_c}\, b_0 d = 4\sqrt{3200}\,(164)(20) = 734,700\ \text{lb}$$

and the factored shear resistance is therefore $0.85 \times 734,700 = 624,500$ lb $> 358,000$.

Step 5.   Check reinforcement requirements to demonstrate the structural adequacy of the wall. This can be done by considering a specific portion acted upon by negative moment, for example, the strut strip and the middle strip of the short bays. We recall that this negative moment is

Strut strip $= -144$ ft-kips, or $^{144}/_5 = -28.8$ ft-kips/ft of wall
Middle strip $= -48$ ft-kips, or $^{48}/_6 = -8.0$ ft-kips/ft of wall

Since the procedure is the same, the reinforcement requirements will be checked at the strength limit state for the strut strip.

First we compute the balanced reinforcement ratio p_b from Eq. (6-14) using Grade 40 steel, $f_y = 40,000$ lb/in^2, or

$$p_b = \left(\frac{0.85 \times 0.85 \times 3200}{40,000}\right)\left(\frac{87,000}{87,000 + 40,000}\right) = 0.04$$

or $0.75p_b = 0.75 \times 0.04 = 0.03$, which is the ratio that cannot be exceeded. Next, we select No. 7 bars at 12 in centers, $A_s = 0.60$ in^2/ft. The reinforcement ratio is $p = 0.60/(12 \times 20) = 0.60/240 = 0.0025 < 0.03$. The value of m is $40/0.85(3.2) = 14.8$; hence the value of a is computed from Eq. (6-9) as

$$a = pmd = 0.0025 \times 14.7 \times 20 = 0.74\ \text{in} = 0.06\ \text{ft}$$

The nominal moment resistance is

$$M_n = A_s f_y \left(d - \frac{a}{2}\right) = 0.60 \times 40 \times (1.83 - 0.03) = 43.2\ \text{ft-kips}$$

and the factored resistance is obtained as $0.90 \times 43.2 = 38.8$ ft-kips > 28.8.

7-2   Posttensioned Diaphragm Walls

Section 1-4 discusses the general principles of posttensioned diaphragm walls and demonstrates the advantages of this application with certain classes of building construction. A factor favoring the application of prestressing is the apparent stiffness of the wall embedded in the ground so that a temporary overstressing may be introduced without affecting the response of the concrete.

Prestressed precast diaphragm walls have been introduced on a trial basis but they have not received general acceptability. Precast diaphragm walls can be posttensioned in situ to utilize the stiffness of embedment in restraining the associated concrete stresses, but some problems have been reported regarding the practicality of the application. Posttensioning tendons could be placed in the forms before casting the panel, but some degree of prestressing or conventional reinforcement would be necessary to resist handling stresses. Among several good references on prestressed precast units we should mention Lin and Burns (1981), PCI (1972), and Martin et al. (1977). In this section we consider only posttensioned walls.

Suitability of materials

Concrete. The use of higher-strength concrete in posttensioned diaphragm walls, although justified in terms of higher durability and resistance, is somewhat restricted and limited by general design requirements and the actual attainable in situ strength. For a strength in excess of 5000 lb/in^2 (345 kg/cm^2), it is necessary to use a water-cement ratio close to 0.45, and in this range it may be prudent to sacrifice the slump or use expensive admixtures to replace the lost workability of the fresh mix. In spite of these conflicts, experience shows that concrete for posttensioned walls can be ensured in the range of 4000 to 4500 lb/in^2 (275 to 310 kg/cm^2). This restriction is not critical, however, since any loss of structural capacity is compensated and offset by the extra wall thickness.

Consideration should be given to a lower concrete strength at transfer than its 28-day strength, in order to introduce an early transfer of posttensioning to the wall. At initial prestressing the wall is not subjected to external loads, and strength is necessary only to protect against anchorage failure and excessive creep; hence a smaller factor of safety is admissible.

Direct tensile strength may be in the range quoted in Sec. 6-3, and could be zero if cracks have developed as a result of shrinkage or other reasons. Most natural processes are, however, inhibited by the moist environment and the favorable curing conditions. As in conventional diaphragm walls, flowability and workability are essential to ensure a continuous structure without cavities and voids, especially along the path of posttensioning. Whereas early hardening may be considered necessary to hasten field construction, most contractors prefer to posttension all the panels after the entire wall is in place in order to minimize the duration of the prestressing operations. The use of admixtures to affect strength or curing should be specified with caution and after considering the effects on possible corrosion of the prestressing steel.

Prestressing steels. High-tensile steel is the most suitable for introducing prestress and supplying the tensile force in posttensioned walls. The usual approach toward the production of high-tensile steel is by alloying, which permits the manufacture of such steels under normal operations.

High-tensile steel for prestressing usually takes one of three forms: wires, strands, and bars. For posttensioning of diaphragm walls, wires and commonly used, grouped into parallel cables. Strands are fabricated by twisting wires together, thus decreasing the number of units to be handled in the tensioning operation. Methods have been proposed for defining the yield point of high-tensile steel such as the 0.1 percent set, 0.2 percent set, 0.7 percent strain, or 1.0 percent strain. Reference is made to applicable posttensioning manuals.

Steel wires. Wires for prestressing generally conform to ASTM Specifications A421 for Uncoated Stress-Relieved Wire for Prestressed Concrete. The tensile strength and minimum yield strength, measured by the 1.0 percent total elongation, are shown in Table 7-1 for the most common sizes of wires. A typical modulus of elasticity is $29,000,000$ lb/in^2, and the specified minimum elongation in 10 in is 4.0 percent while a typical elongation at rupture is more likely from 5 to 6 percent. Wires are supplied in reels or coils, and then cut to length and assembled either at the plant or in the field. Some steels may need degreasing and cleaning before placement. Handling and installation should follow applicable standards and operational instructions from relevant manuals.

In this country, wires are manufactured according to U.S. Steel Wire Gage No. 2 that has a diameter of 0.2625 in (6.668 mm) and No. 6 (diameter 0.1920 in, or 4.877 mm). Neither of these has the exact equivalent of the millimeter counterparts used in Europe. For posttensioning systems in the United States, ¼-in (6.35-mm) wires are most commonly selected.

TABLE 7-1 Properties of Uncoated Stress-Relieved Wire (ASTM A421)

Nominal diameter, in (mm)	Minimum tensile strength, lb/in^2 (N/mm^2)		Minimum stress at 1% extension, lb/in^2 (N/mm^2)	
	Type BA†	Type WA	Type BA†	Type WA
0.192 (4.88)	*	250,000 (1725)	*	200,000 (1380)
0.196 (4.98)	240,000 (1655)	250,000 (1725)	192,000 (1325)	200,000 (1380)
0.250 (6.35)	240,000 (1655)	240,000 (1655)	192,000 (1325)	192,000 (1325)
0.276 (7.01)	*	235,000 (1622)	*	188,000 (1295)

*These sizes are not commonly furnished in type BA wire.

†Type BA wire is used for applications in which cold-end deformation is used for anchoring purposes (button anchorage), and type WA is used for applications in which the ends are anchored by wedges and no cold-end deformation of the wire is involved (wedge anchorage).

Steel strands.   Generally, these conform to ASTM Specifications A416 for Uncoated Seven-Wire Stress-Relieved Strand for Prestressed Concrete. Two grades are available, 250 and 270 kips/in², where these values indicate minimum guaranteed breaking stress. These specifications are also applicable to posttensioned construction, hence to diaphragm walls, whether of the bonded or the unbonded type. Seven-wire strands commonly have a center wire slightly larger than the outer six wires that enclose it tightly in a helix with a uniform pitch.

Typical properties of seven-wire strands are listed in Table 7-2. Since 1962, the stronger steel known as the 270K grade has been produced and marketed, and is now almost universally used in the United States, in both pretensioned and posttensioned structures.

As fabricated, seven-wire strands are several thousand feet long. When unwinding strands, care must be exercised in laying them along the path to prevent kinking and permanent twisting of the strands.

Other tendon types.   High-tensile steel bars are available in lengths up to 80 ft (24.4 m), but because of difficulty in shipping this length is often limited further. Sleeve couplers are available to splice the bars to the desired length. Whereas steel bars are used in conventional prestressed construction, their practicality in diaphragm walls is in doubt.

Fiberglass tendons have not yet been commercially applied to prestressed concrete construction. Some problems still relate to the static fatigue limit and the duration of loading; the chemical stability and its reaction to the surrounding concrete, especially under wet condi-

TABLE 7-2   Properties of Uncoated Seven-Wire Stress-Relieved Strand (ASTM A416)

Nominal diameter, in (mm)	Breaking strength, lb (kN)	Nominal area of strand, in² (mm²)	Minimum load at 1% extension, lb (kN)
Grade 250			
0.250 (6.35)	9,000 (40.0)	0.036 (23.22)	7,650 (34.0)
0.313 (7.94)	14,500 (64.5)	0.058 (37.42)	12,300 (54.7)
0.375 (9.53)	20,000 (89.0)	0.080 (51.61)	17,000 (75.6)
0.438 (11.11)	27,000 (120.1)	0.108 (69.68)	23,000 (102.3)
0.500 (12.70)	36,000 (160.1)	0.144 (92.90)	30,600 (136.2)
0.600 (15.24)	54,000 (240.2)	0.216 (139.35)	45,900 (204.2)
Grade 270			
0.375 (9.53)	23,000 (102.3)	0.085 (54.84)	19,550 (87.0)
0.438 (11.11)	31,000 (137.9)	0.115 (74.19)	26,350 (117.2)
0.500 (12.70)	41,300 (183.7)	0.153 (98.71)	35,100 (156.1)
0.600 (15.24)	58,600 (260.7)	0.217 (140.00)	49,800 (221.5)

tions; and the design of suitable end anchorages since the brittle material is liable to fail in the grip under the effect of stress concentrations.

In spite of these problems, in posttensioned diaphragm walls fiberglass chords, twisted strands, and parallel fibers may offer distinct advantages because of the relative simplicity in handling, gripping, and anchoring. Besides the high ultimate tensile strength and the low modulus of elasticity, the high resistance to corrosion makes fiberglass tendons suitable to situations that involve a corrosive environment.

Grouting. Grouting may be necessary in conjunction with provisions for proper conduits for the tendons. For posttensioning there are two types of conduits, one for bonded and the other for unbonded prestressing.

Bonding usually is done by grouting, and in this case the conduits (ducts) are made of ferrous metal that may be galvanized. Suitable materials for these ducts are 22- to 28-gage galvanized or bright spirally wound or longitudinally seamed steel strips with flexible or semirigid seams. It is impractical to form a duct by withdrawing extractable rubber cores buried in the concrete.

For bonding the tendons to the concrete after posttensioning, cement grout is injected and also serves to protect the steel against corrosion. Entry of the grout into the cableway is provided by means of holes in the anchorage heads and cones. The injection is applied at one end of the loop until it emerges at the other end. For deeper walls, it can be applied at both ends until complete resistance is met. Either ordinary portland cement or high-early-strength cement may be used for the grout.

To ensure good bond, grouting under pressure is desirable, but care is necessary to prevent bursting effects of the pressure on the walls of the cable enclosure. Quoted grouting pressures range from 80 to 100 lb/in² (0.55 to 0.69 N/mm²). Guide specification for grouting are provided by the current edition of *Tentative Recommended Practices for Grouting Posttensioned Prestressed Concrete* of the Prestressed Concrete Institute.

Posttensioning assembly

An arrangement of prestressing strands in posttensioning units is shown in Fig. 1-8. The reinforcing cage serves primarily as an attachment for holding the casing ducts that contain the strands and thus must resist handling stresses. Once in place, the cage no longer has a static function except that of preventing the distortion and displacement of the ducts under the effect of differential pressure from the rising fresh concrete. Alternatively, the reinforcement in the cage can be arranged to serve also as tensile steel to ensure the absence of tension cracks in the concrete and thus allow a greater prestress force to be applied (see also subsequent sections).

Irrespective of the final function, the cage must be constructed with a fine tolerance. Gysi et al. (1975) have suggested the standard assembly details shown in Fig. 7-12. The cage is spot-welded for increased stiffness, but it may still be deformable if it is too long. The position of the ducts should therefore be checked while the cage is held vertically and before it is inserted into the trench. A cage in the upright position ready for inspection is shown in Fig. 7-13.

The market contains well over one hundred patents on various systems of prestressing. For the practicing engineer the objective is to design a posttensioned wall and to identify the characteristics of the prestressing system without becoming involved in the intrigues of patent rights. Thus the designer may leave the choice of prestress equipment to the contractor under the premise of some technical supervision and the right to approve the selection.

The most commonly used method for posttensioning is jacking. In Great Britain, for example, contractors have been able to fix and firmly hold the BBRV units within the cage. Jacks are then used to pull the steel against the hardened concrete. Problems, however, can arise when the anchoring of the heavily stressed strands is near the base of the wall. Anchor blocks and anchor heads or similar devices have been used, operating on the principle of direct bearing, such as the ones shown in Fig. 7-14. Although these systems are dependable in conventional posttensioning, their use in this case is not practical because of the possibility of yielding if contaminated concrete and bentonite mud are accumulated on the upper side of the block and remain there as residual materials. These devices should thus be avoided, and

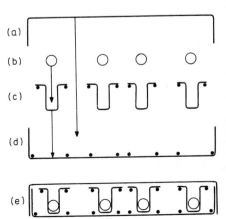

Figure 7-12 Method of detailing and assembling a reinforcing cage for posttensioned cast-in-place diaphragm walls: (*a*) Upper perimeter bar. (*b*) Cable ducts. (*c*) Cable brackets with vertical reinforcement. (*d*) Lower perimeter bar with vertical reinforcement. (*e*) Cage in the assembled position. (*From Gysi et al., 1975.*)

Figure 7-13 Reinforcing cage held in vertical position to be checked for exact location of cable ducts and possible distortion. (*ICOS, Great Britain.*)

Figure 7-14 Details of stressing anchor heads in reinforcing cage; construction of the German Embassy in London. (*ICOS, Great Britain.*)

instead the method of looping the bars in a U shape should be incorporated in the detailing of the cage (see also Figs. 1-8 and 7-13). The stress concentration resulting from the small loop radius can be resisted by special slot-tension bars placed in the loop area.

Design considerations

Elastic shortening of the wall. Besides the dependability of the prestressing method and the efficiency of the end anchorage, the application will be fully effective if the prestress force does not dissipate and is not otherwise absorbed. The prestressing normally causes the wall to shorten elastically. Because the wall is confined in the ground, one might suspect that the soil in contact at the interface will impede the elastic shortening and retard or even stop the process altogether. Comparison of the modulus of an average soil with the actual concrete modulus shows, however, that the latter may be 150 to 300 times stiffer; hence the only impediment will be provided by shear resistance at the face (friction or adhesion) acting opposite to the direction of prestress.

The existence of frictional forces along the face of a wall being prestressed is uncertain and highly indeterminate. The tensile force in the cable induces compression in the concrete as an internal reaction, and for routine jobs the response of the wall at the soil-concrete interface can be inferred merely by estimating the probable elastic shortening. For example, a wall 60 ft deep and 24 in thick acted upon by a prestressing force of 200,000 lb per foot of length is likely to have an elastic shortening of 0.16 in (0.4 cm), based on a concrete modulus $E_c = 3 \times 10^6$ lb/in^2. The resulting relative displacement at any section is unlikely to mobilize shear stresses at the interface; hence the entire prestress will remain in the concrete.

With the excavation in progress on one side, the relative soil movement with respect to the wall may result in some shear resistance at the interface. If a downdrag is introduced, it may reduce the prestressing force, but the reduction will be greater near the base of the wall where the entire prestressing is not needed. These effects can be compensated for by an appropriate inclusion in the predicted prestress loss or by delaying grouting as a provision for restressing the tendon if this loss occurs.

Effect of soil stiffness. The confinement of the wall in the ground while the posttensioning is applied results in a unique wall-soil interaction that has a distinct effect on the response of the wall to prestressing

(Gysi et al., 1975; 1977). Clearly the design concept involves two objectives:

1. The general principle is still maintained. Thus the prestressing is intended to introduce a compressive stress in the concrete that will compensate for any tensile stresses that may develop at the final load application.

2. The arrangement and position of strands and the amount of prestress in the concrete must counteract the stresses resulting from external loads acting on the wall at the end of excavation. Little or no attention can be given to boundary conditions of partial excavation or with the wall fully embedded in the ground. If the tendons are laid out and the eccentricity and amount of prestress are selected to supply the most desirable system or prestressing to the concrete for the final loads, the result can be a considerable tensile stress, as normally is the case for unrestrained posttensioned elements.

A posttensioned wall embedded in the ground is under the effect of confinement in a restraining medium. Field observations suggest a different and more favorable response of wall and surrounding soil. Tests on posttensioned diaphragm walls show that the introduction of prestress could not cause tension in the concrete, even if the prestress force was applied outside the middle third and the tendons were overstressed (Braun, 1972). The conclusion is that the surrounding soil acts as a stressing bed of infinite strength.

The amount of restraint at stress transfer depends on the nature of the soil and its deformability with an upper limit of the corresponding reaction or counterthrust approaching the passive resistance of the soil. However, the absence of full flexural deformation of the embedded wall during the eccentric application of the jacking force indicates a considerable intensity of soil response, so that considerable passive resistance is developed without the movement predicted in soil mechanics taking place. A rough model of wall-soil interaction is shown in Fig. 7-15 (Xanthakos, 1974). An important point to be considered is the fluidity and flowability of the high-slump fresh concrete resulting in a net gain in the initial stress in most soils, and this partly explains the observed high elastic soil response. This clamping effect can be expected in most soils, except for very soft or very loose materials such as turf and organic normally consolidated sea sediments. Better results will be achieved if the posttensioned wall is in relatively stiff or dense formations.

A measure of deformability of the soil is the modulus of horizontal subgrade reaction k_h defined as the ratio of stress to deformation. As a conceptual relationship between soil pressure and deflection it may be applied to the analysis of posttensioned diaphragm walls. This re-

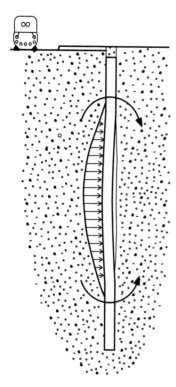

Figure 7-15 Diagrammatic soil response to posttensioning of diaphragm wall.

fined method of analysis takes into account the soil-wall interaction by employing a discrete-element or finite-element approach through the use of computers. The discrete-element approach involves analysis of the wall if it is a continuous beam resting on a bed of springs that simulate a passive soil resistance. Terzaghi (1955) has related the modulus of horizontal subgrade reaction to the values obtained from field load tests on small plates. In granular soils and normally consolidated cohesive soils, it is assumed that k_h increases linearly with depth. In overconsolidated clays, the horizontal subgrade modulus is taken constant with depth. The finite-element approach models the soil as a continuum and thus provides a better representation of the system although it is more complex to use.

Using the discrete-element approach with a spring stiffness equivalent to the subgrade modulus, and later confirmed by large-scale tests and in situ measurements, Gysi et al. (1975) derived the solution shown in graphical form in Fig. 7-16. The diaphragm wall is embedded in silty moraine with an elastic modulus $E_s = 500$ kg/cm^2 (about 6900 lb/in^2). The concrete modulus is $E_c = 200,000$ kg/cm^2 (2.75 $\times$ 10^6 lb/in^2); that is, the concrete is 400 times as stiff as the soil. The wall is 20 m (66 ft) deep and 80 cm (32 in) thick.

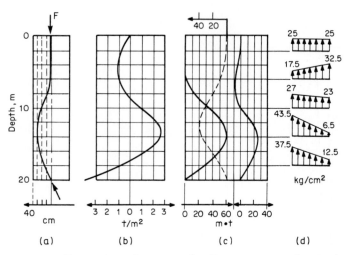

Figure 7-16 Prestress, earth pressure, bending moments, and stress in a posttensioned diaphragm wall embedded in silty moraine: (*a*) Diagram showing the eccentricity of prestress. (*b*) Earth pressure caused by the prestress. (*c*) Bending moments caused by the prestress, the earth pressure, and resultant bending moments. (*d*) Compressive stresses in the wall at various depths. (*From Gysi et al., 1975.*)

Figure 7-16*a* shows the arrangement of prestress. The axis of the tendon is a parabolic curve below 6 m and reaches a maximum eccentricity of 30 cm, or well outside the middle third. Figure 7-16*b* shows the soil pressure against the wall mobilized upon the application of the jacking forces (200 t/m of wall), computed from a consideration of the horizontal subgrade modulus. Figure 7-16*c* shows the moment due to the eccentricity of the posttensioning, the moment due to the lateral earth pressure, and the resultant bending moment. The left solid line is the moment caused by the prestressing, and refers to the bottom scale; evidently, this moment begins at about 6 m and reaches a maximum value of $200 \times 0.3 = 60$ t-m. The dashed line represents the moment caused by the mobilized earth pressure and refers to the top scale. The right solid line is the composite (resultant) moment. Without the earth effect the two solid lines would be the same.

Without the restraining effect of the soil the wall would have been stressed in tension in the zone of large eccentricities ($e > 13.3$ cm). For a maximum prestress moment 60 t-m corresponding to $e = 30$ cm, the tensile stress would have been 11 kg/cm^2 (155 lb/in^2). With the restraining effect the maximum moment is about 25 t-m, giving a tensile stress of 4.6 kg/cm^2 (65 lb/in^2).

Loss of prestress. This may be caused by (1) elastic shortening (initial) of the concrete and also due to stressing the cables in sequence (in the case of looped cables); (2) shrinkage of concrete; (3) creep in concrete before general excavation (at stress transfer), and after general excavation (at load transfer); (4) relaxation of the stressing steel; and (5) frictional loss within the prestressing cables (depending on the type of cable and cable curvature).

Elastic shortening in concrete. This causes a corresponding elastic shortening in the steel that can be written in a general form as

$$ES = \frac{E_s f_{cir}}{E_{ci}} \qquad (7\text{-}7)$$

where $E_s/E_{ci} = n =$ modular ratio at transfer, and $f_{cir} =$ stress in the concrete at center of gravity due to prestress force F_0 which is effective immediately after prestress has been applied to concrete.

In diaphragm walls the force in the posttensioning system is usually measured after the elastic shortening of the concrete has taken place, and hence it is not necessary to make an allowance for a loss of prestress because of this factor. Likewise the loss of prestress due to local yielding of weak or contaminated concrete in the loop zone occurs as soon as the jacking force is applied, and does not represent a final loss.

Time-dependent losses. Prestress loss due to creep and shrinkage of the concrete and steel relaxation are both time-dependent and interdependent. There is a tendency to track the simultaneous effects of shrinkage, creep, and steel relaxation with time, following a step-by-step procedure in which time-dependent losses are accumulated in successive time intervals.

Factors affecting creep include the volume-to-surface ratio, age of concrete at time of prestress, relative humidity, and type of concrete. Creep will be more serious if the prestress in the steel is low and the compression in the concrete is high, but the latter condition is avoided with the large cross-sectional area of the wall. On the other hand, overstressing the concrete is not desirable because of the possibility of further local yielding of weak zones. Assuming an average prestress in the concrete of 1000 lb/in² (about 70 kg/cm²) the loss of prestress due to creep may range from 6 to 7 percent.

The amount of prestress loss due to shrinkage will vary first with the proximity of the concrete to moisture during hardening and then with the time of application of prestress. The favorable curing conditions and moist environment keep the initial shrinkage low, but this is not of great importance since the posttensioning is applied much later. Usually the concrete is prestressed and then subjected to dry

TABLE 7-3 Estimate of Prestress Losses, Lb/In²

Type of prestressing steel	Total loss	
	$f'_c = 4000$	$f'_c = 5000$
Pretensioning strand	—	45,000
Posttensioning*		
Wire or strand	32,000	33,000
Bars	22,000	23,000

*Losses due to friction are excluded. Friction losses should be computed according to AASHTO Article 9.16.1.

conditions as excavation proceeds; hence further shrinkage will occur with a corresponding loss of prestress.

The loss of prestress as steel relaxation can be limited (1) by limiting the initial prestress (say to $0.70\, f_{pu}$), and (2) by specifying low-relaxation strand. Some design situations warrant this approach to reduce relaxation losses to less than 3.5 percent.

Lump-sum estimates for prestress loss. Most recommendations or relevant codes include lump-sum estimates for losses. For example, AASHTO (1992 Edition) stipulates that in lieu of the more exact methods, estimates of prestress losses may be based on Table 7-3. The Posttensioning Institute recommendations for lump-sum losses are shown in Table 7-4. Where concrete is stressed at very low strength, where it is highly prestressed, or in very dry or very wet conditions, there might be a significant variation from these values.

Although it is very difficult to interpret these guidelines in the design of diaphragm walls, it is conceivable that for the usual curing conditions, type of concrete and steel, amount and time of stress transfer, and methods of posttensioning, the loss will not exceed 15 percent. For example, using 270 kips/in² strands with initial stress $0.70 f'_s$ or

TABLE 7-4 Approximate Prestress Loss Values* for Posttensioning

Posttensioning tendon material	Prestress loss, lb/in² (N/mm²)	
	Slabs	Beams and joists
Stress-relieved 270 strand and stress-relieved 240 wire	30,000 (207 N/mm²)	35,000 (241 N/mm²)
Bar	20,000 (138 N/mm²)	25,000 (172 N/mm²)

*Losses due to friction not included. Average values of concrete strength, prestress level, and exposure conditions.

189 kips/in^2, the total predicted loss of prestress is $0.15 \times 189 =$ 28,350 lb/in^2 or in close agreement with Tables 7-3 and 7-4. Hence the recommended effective prestress is 85 percent of the initial prestress.

Walls suitable for posttensioning

Diaphragm walls suitable for the prestressing application are (1) vertical cantilevers fully restrained at the base by sufficient embedment, and (2) walls laterally restrained at the bottom (by sufficient embedment or by rigid support) and braced at or near the top. These types are shown in Fig. 7-17 with the corresponding lateral earth stress diagrams.

The walls in the first group must have adequate embedment below excavation level for lateral support and control of movement. These walls are used only in very stiff or very dense soil. Top bracing for the walls of the second group reduces moments and wall movement considerably, and also results in less embedment below excavation level.

The pattern of lateral earth stress distribution developed when the prestress is applied can be assumed to be similar to the pattern with the excavation completed. This is shown in Fig. 7-17, and with the top bracing it takes into account the preloading of the struts. Only the magnitude and at some point along the wall the sign of the stress in the diagram will change as the excavation progresses and gradually leads to the final earth pressure distribution. Thus the two conditions for which the wall must be analyzed are the initial application of prestress with the wall fully embedded and the final stage with the excavation completed. Intermediate stages with partial excavation are unlikely to govern and need not be considered.

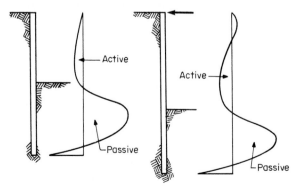

Figure 7-17 Walls suitable for posttensioning and patterns of lateral-earth-stress distribution.

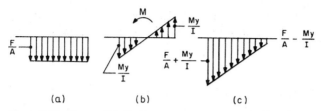

Figure 7-18 Stress distribution across a concentrically postten-sioned wall: (a) Due to prestress F. (b) Due to external moment M. (c) Due to F and M.

This conformity at various stages of excavation and loading is not possible with walls braced at several levels. At each excavation and bracing stage the corresponding combination of spans, supports, and pressure diagrams will be in some conflict with the preceding or with the following stage with respect to the eccentricity and amount of pre-stress, resulting in intricate complications. In this case the prestress and its composite action may have to be applied in stages or even delayed until the final stage. Thus diaphragm walls are suitable for eccentric prestressing only where the wall deflection remains uniform and consistent from the initial (no-excavation) to the final (full-excavation) condition.

The concept of concentric tendons for multibraced or multianchored walls may be considered if the analysis provides economic justification. The concentric application of prestress is intended to alleviate the complexities of stage excavation by introducing the simple action shown in Fig. 7-18. The prestress is chosen now to counteract the tensile stress due to the maximum moment acting at any time and anywhere in the wall. The possibilities and limitations of this concept are demonstrated in the following example.

The wall shown in Fig. 7-19 is 18 in thick and is braced at five levels. Assuming that the wall rotates about the uppermost bracing point, a

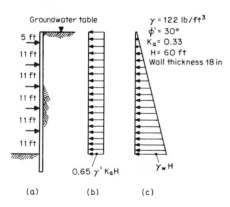

Figure 7-19 A concentrically posttensioned diaphragm wall braced at five levels: (a) Wall section showing the bracing intervals. (b) Lateral-earth-stress diagram. (c) Water-pressure diagram.

rectangular effective stress diagram is assumed as shown and is combined with full hydrostatic pressure. The maximum moment occurs with full excavation at the lower wall sections and is approximately 40 ft-kips (about 5.5 t-m). The cross-sectional area and moment of inertia per foot of length are 216 in^2 and 5832 in^4, respectively, giving a bending stress $My/I = (40 \times 12 \times 1000 \times 9)/5832 = 740$ lb/in^2 (52 kg/cm^2). Assuming 15 percent losses and no tension allowed, the required prestress force per foot of wall is F, where $0.85F = 0.74(216)$, or $F = 190$ kips (86 t). The total compressive stress in the concrete is therefore $f_c = 740 + 740 = 1480$ lb/in^2 (104 kg/cm^2). This is compatible with an allowable (working) stress based on $f'_c = 4000$ lb/in^2; hence the preliminary analysis is just right. However, the concrete will be overstressed in compression or in tension if fewer bracing levels are used or if the excavation becomes deeper unless a thicker wall is selected.

Advantages

The design advantages of posttensioned diaphragm walls can be summarized as follows:

1. The resisting moment of posttensioned walls is more than double that of a conventionally reinforced wall of the same thickness. This means that with prestressing the unsupported height can be increased by about 50 percent or, alternatively, the thickness of the wall can be reduced.
2. The design is completed based on compressive stresses only at any cross section.
3. The initially unbonded tendons are subsequently bonded with grout under a fully controlled process that ensures ultimate bond, whereas the prestressing is in itself a test of the integrity of the concrete.
4. There is considerable saving in the weight of reinforcing bars. The cage is lighter, and the larger bar spacing facilitates the flow of tremied concrete.

Extended analytical concepts

Combination of high-strength steel and concrete.   Prestressed walls may be considered a combination of steel and concrete similar to reinforced concrete, with steel taking tension and concrete taking compression, forming a resisting couple against the external moment.

In posttensioned walls high-strength steel is used and will have to be elongated before its strength is fully developed. If the high-tensile steel is simply buried in the concrete, as in ordinary concrete reinforcement, the surrounding concrete will crack considerably before the full strength of the steel is produced. Hence the solution is to prestretch the steel with respect to the concrete. By prestretching and anchoring the steel against the concrete desirable stresses are produced in both materials. The concrete is in compression and the steel is in tension, and this combination enhances safety and economic use of materials.

Stages of loading.   A consideration relevant to posttensioned walls is the plurality of stages of loading corresponding to the excavation stages. For cast-in-place walls, the posttensioned concrete is designed for two stages: the initial stage with the wall fully embedded, and the final stage with full excavation. In some instances, intermediate excavation stages may have to be checked.

Under allowable stress design (ASD), the permissible stresses in posttensioned walls are as follows:

Steel stresses.   Both the ACI Code and AASHTO Specifications allow a stress in the prestressing steel $0.70f'_s$ where f'_s is the ultimate strength (guaranteed tensile strength) of the steel.

Concrete stresses.   A distinction is made for temporary stresses and at service loads after losses have occurred.

1. Immediately after transfer of prestress, extreme fiber stress

   Compression: $0.60f'_{ci}$ (ACI), or $0.55f'_{ci}$ (AASHTO)

   Tension: $3\sqrt{f'_{ci}}$

2. At service load after allowances for all prestress losses

   Compression: $0.45f'_c$ (ACI), or $0.40f'_c$ (AASHTO)

   Tension: $6\sqrt{f'_c}$ (for members with bonded prestressed strands)

   where f'_{ci} = compressive strength of concrete at time of initial prestress and f'_c = compressive strength of concrete at 28 days.

Resistance factors.   The computed strength capacity should not be less than the factored load effects. Strength (resistance) capacity factors ϕ should be applied to the nominal strength as follows:

For flexure: $\phi = 0.90$ (ACI), or 0.95 (AASHTO)

For shear: $\phi = 0.85$ (ACI), or 0.90 (AASHTO)

Interestingly, the design of prestressed concrete members ordinarily is based on $f'_c = 5000$ lb/in^2, with provisions for increase to 6000 lb/in^2 where this strength can be provided consistently. Since controls over materials and construction procedures cannot be instituted to an extent necessary to satisfy the design requirements, the strength range recommended in the foregoing sections should be followed.

Ultimate moment, bonded tendons. Because both steel and concrete generally are stressed beyond the elastic range, relative simple procedures should be used. The analysis is limited to the following conditions.

1. The failure is primarily in flexure, without shear, bond, or anchorage failure that might decrease the strength of the section.

2. The tendons are bonded. Unbonded systems possess different ultimate strength and are not considered.

3. The walls are statically determinate, although the discussion applies equally to individual sections of continuous beams.

4. The loads are static. Impact or fatigue are not considered. Furthermore, some caution is necessary for effects of long-term loading.

The analysis is simplified by treating the section as in conventional reinforced concrete where the steel supplies a tensile force and the concrete supplies a compressive force, the two forces forming a couple with a lever arm between them. Referring to Fig. 7-20, we choose the simplest stress block for the ultimate compression in the concrete. Note that this configuration is similar to Fig. 6-18, except that T' is the prestress force, and A_{ps} and f_{ps} indicate the area and stress level of the prestress steel, respectively.

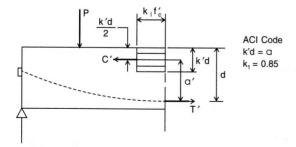

Figure 7-20 Ultimate moment.

The ultimate (nominal) moment is obtained as in Sec. 6-8, as

$$M_n = M_u = A_{ps} f_{ps} \left(d - \frac{a}{2} \right) \qquad (7\text{-}8)$$

which is similar to Eq. (6-12). The factored moment resistance is obtained from Eq. (7-8) by applying the appropriate resistance factor ϕ.

Example A wall section 24 in long is prestressed with $A_{ps} = 2.50$ in^2 of prestressing steel. Using 270 kips/in^2 strands, with 70 percent initial prestress and 15 percent losses, the effective prestress is $f_{pe} = 270 \times 0.70 \times 0.85 = 160$ kips/in^2. Find the ultimate resisting moment using $f'_c = 4500$ lb/in^2. The wall is 30 in thick, and the prestress is applied 6 in from the face ($d = 24$ in).

First we compute the steel ratio $p_p = 2.50/(24 \times 24) = 0.0043$. Next we estimate the steel stress at ultimate using the following equation:

$$f_{ps} = f_{pu} \left(1 - 0.5 p_p \frac{f_{pu}}{f'_c} \right) \qquad (7\text{-}9)$$

since $f_{pe} = 160$ kips/in$^2 > 0.5 \times 270 = 135$ kips/in^2, or $f_{ps} = 270,000[1 - (0.5)(0.0043)(270,000/4500)] = 235,000$ lb/in$^2 = 235$ kips/in^2, $T' = A_{ps} f_{ps} = 2.50 \times 235 = 588$ kips. Likewise, we compute $C' = 0.85 f'_c \times 24 \times a = 588$ or $a = 588/(0.85 \times 4.5 \times 24) = 6.4$ in. The nominal moment is now

$$M_n = T' \left(d - \frac{a}{2} \right) = 588 \left(24 - \frac{6.4}{2} \right) = 588 \times 1.73 = 1017 \text{ ft-kips}$$

This moment should be factored to obtain the design moment.

Preliminary design. For preliminary purposes the ultimate flexural strength of sections can be expressed by simple semiempirical formulations. It is usually sufficient to assume that the ultimate resisting moment of bonded wall sections is given by the ultimate strength of steel acting with a lever arm. This arm lever varies with the shape of section and generally ranges between $0.6h$ and $0.9h$, with a common value of $0.8h$, where h is the wall thickness. Hence the area of steel required is given approximately by

$$A_s = \frac{M_T m}{0.80 h f_{ps}} \qquad (7\text{-}10)$$

If the concrete on the compressive side is assumed to be stressed to $0.85 f'_c$, the required ultimate concrete area under compression is

$$A'_c = \frac{M_T m}{0.80 h (0.85) f'_c} \qquad (7\text{-}11)$$

where m in the foregoing equations is the factor of safety or load factor.

Final design. Although the preliminary design can readily be carried out using the load factor approach, the final design is more complicated because it involves a more accurate determination of stresses (and deformations) for various stages of loading. The following general procedure is suggested.

1. Select proper factors and load combinations for steel and concrete by reference to the foregoing sections and applicable codes.
2. Investigate compressive and tensile stresses in the concrete at transfer, generally using elastic theory.
3. Check factored resistance for final load stage based on an effective lever arm for the interal resisting couple accurately estimated.
4. Perform checks for excessive deflection and overstress. Where computer programs are available and reliable values of the horizontal subgrade modulus are obtainable, the analysis may consider the restraining effect of soil stiffness according to the suggested procedures. If relevant data are not available, these effects may be approximated if the wall is in stiff or dense ground, and ignored if the construction is in soft or loose strata.

There appears to be a preference for load factor (ultimate strength) design, but codes and designers still consider the allowable stress method. Stating an exact preference for one or the other is beyond the scope of this text, since they both have advantages and shortcomings. If strength is a more important consideration, the design should be based on ultimate resistance and load factor. If serviceability conditions such as cracking, creep, and deflection impose critical limits, they should be checked for service loads under elastic analysis.

Design Example 7-2 A posttensioned diaphragm wall 30 in thick is the lateral support for a 30-ft-deep transit facility. The wall is braced at the top by the permanent ground floor, and at the bottom by embedment into rock. The soil consists of loose sand with $\phi' = 28°$, and because of the close proximity of the structure to a nearby waterway, the water level is assumed at ground surface for design purposes. The wall must also resist a uniform lateral pressure of 200 lb/ft² resulting from live load surcharge at street level. The wall is shown in Fig. 7-21.

Step 1. Establish lateral pressure diagrams and appropriate design parameters. The wall will be designed for (1) effective earth pressure based on the K_0 condition; (2) full hydrostatic pressure; and (3) live load surcharge. The coefficient of the lateral earth pressure at rest is $K_0 = 1 - \sin \phi' = 0.53$, and $\gamma' = 120 - 62.5 = 57.50$ lb/ft. Lateral pressures at the base of the wall are computed as follows:

$$\text{Effective earth pressure} = (57.50)(0.53)(30) = 914 \text{ lb/ft}^2$$

$$\text{Pore pressure} = 62.50 \times 30 \qquad = 1875 \text{ lb/ft}^2$$

$$\text{Surcharge pressure} \qquad\qquad\qquad = 200 \text{ lb/ft}^2$$

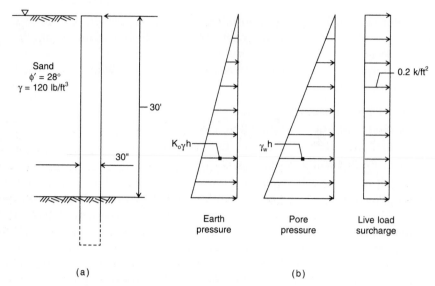

Figure 7-21   Wall of design example 7-2: (*a*) Wall configuration and soil data. (*b*) Pressure diagrams; $f'_c = 4500$ lb/in².

The total (resultant) pressures are therefore

$$\text{Earth pressure } W_e = 0.91 \times {}^{30}\!/\!_2 = 13.65 \text{ kips}$$

$$\text{Pore pressure } W_w = 1.88 \times {}^{30}\!/\!_2 = 28.20 \text{ kips}$$

$$\text{Live load surcharge } W_L = 0.20 \times 30 = 6 \text{ kips}$$

Step 2.   Compute maximum moments. From beam formulas the maximum moment for triangular load diagrams is located at distance $0.5774h$ from the top of the wall, or $0.5774 \times 30 = 17.3$ ft, and its magnitude is $0.1283Wh$ where W is total triangular load. The maximum moments are therefore

$$\text{Earth pressure } M_e = (0.1283)(13.65)(30) = 52.6 \text{ ft-kips}$$

$$\text{Pore pressure } M_w = (0.1283)(28.20)(30) = 108.6 \text{ ft-kips}$$

$$\text{Live load surcharge } M_L = 3(12.70) - 0.2 \left(\frac{12.7}{2}\right)^2 = 21.9 \text{ ft-kips}$$

$$\text{Total moment at service loads } M_s = 52.6 + 108.6 + 21.9 = 183.1 \text{ ft-kips}$$

Likewise, for ultimate strength design, the moments are factored according to the criteria stipulated in the foregoing sections. The load coefficient β is taken as 1.7 for the earth pressure and the live load surcharge, and as 1.0 for the pore pressure. The load factor γ is 1.3. Accordingly, and using AASHTO criteria

$$M_u = 1.3(74.5 \times 1.7 + 108.6) = 306 \text{ ft-kips}$$

Step 3.   Select the prestressing steel area on a preliminary basis using Eq. (7-10). Because the wall is extra thick, the design will be assumed to be controlled by tensile stresses. Note that $M_T m$ = 306 ft-kips, so that

$$A_s = \frac{(306)(12)(1000)}{(0.80)(30)(240,000)} = 0.64 \text{ in}^2/\text{ft of wall}$$

We will select, however, A_s = 0.80 in^2/ft. For 270 kips/in^2 grade the effective stress after losses is f_{se} = (270)(0.85)(0.70) = 160 kips/in^2, giving a prestressing force F = 0.80 × 160 = 128 kips/ft of wall. The strands are arranged in a parabolic profile. Note that this profile is established after an analysis is carried out at various sections (normally at each tenth point along the wall).

At the section of maximum moment the center of gravity of the tension is 7 in from the outside face, giving an eccentricity of e = 8 in (see also Fig. 7-22).

Step 4.   Check stresses at transfer. Two assumptions are made: (1) the prestressing is carried out at least 4 weeks after the wall is cast so that f'_{ci} = f'_c = 4500 lb/in^2, and (2) the restraining effect of the soil stiffness is disregarded in the initial computation but may be considered later.

The section properties of the wall are

$$A = 12 \times 30 = 360 \text{ in}^2$$

$$I = 12 \times 30^3/12 = 27,000 \text{ in}^4$$

At the section of maximum eccentricity (also maximum moment) we compute the following:

$$F/A = 128,000/360 = 356 \text{ lb/in}^2$$

$$Fey/I = (128,000)(8)(15)/(27,000) = \pm570 \text{ lb/in}^2$$

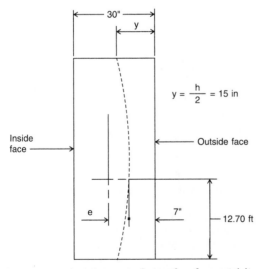

Figure 7-22   Arrangement of strand and eccentricity of section at maximum moment; Design Example 7-2.

At transfer, the stresses in the concrete are therefore, (Fig. 7-22),

$$\text{Compression } f_c = 356 + 570 = 926 \text{ lb/in}^2 \text{ (outside face)}$$

$$\text{Tension } f_t = 356 - 570 = -214 \text{ lb/in}^2 \text{ (inside face)}$$

Allowable stress (tensile) at transfer $= 3\sqrt{f_c'} = 3 \times 67 = 201$ lb/in². Although this stress is exceeded by 7 percent, it will be offset by the stiffness of the soil; hence the design is satisfactory.

Step 5.   Check stresses under service conditions, with excavation completed. Recall that $M_s = 183.1$ ft-kips. Compute

$$M_s y / I = (183,100)(12)(15)/(27,000) = 1220 \text{ lb/in}^2$$

At service loads, the stresses are therefore

$$\text{Compression} = 1220 - 214 = 1006 \text{ lb/in}^2 < 0.40 f_c'$$

$$= 1800 \text{ lb/in}^2 \text{ (inside face)}$$

$$\text{Tension} = (1220 - 926) = -294 \text{ lb/in}^2 < 6\sqrt{f_c'}$$

$$= 402 \text{ lb/in}^2 \text{ (outside face)}$$

Step 6.   Check section for ultimate moment and load factor conditions. First we compute the steel ratio

$$p_p = \frac{0.80}{12 \times 23} = 0.0029$$

Next we estimate the steel stress at ultimate using Eq. (7-9), or

$$f_{ps} = 270,000 \left[1 - (0.5)(0.0029) \left(\frac{270,000}{4500} \right) \right] = 246,000 \text{ lb/in}^2$$

Referring to the notation of Fig. 7-20, $T' = 0.80 \times 246 = 197$ kips and $C' = 0.85 f_c'(12)a = 197$, or $a = 197/(0.85 \times 4.5 \times 12) = 4.3$ in. The nominal moment M_n is computed from

$$M_n = T' \left(d - \frac{a}{2} \right) = 197 \left(23 - \frac{4.3}{2} \right) = 343 \text{ ft-kips}$$

or

$$\phi M_n = 343 \times 0.9 = 309 \text{ ft-kips} > 306 \text{ ft-kips} \quad \text{OK.}$$

The conclusions from the foregoing analysis are: (1) the compressive strength of the concrete is most unlikely to govern the design because of the normally generous wall thickness; (2) the restraining effect of the soil stiffness is a temporary benefit since it does not enter in the analysis of the final stage; (3) the prestressing force required is nominal and in the range of 100 to 150 kips per foot of wall; and (4) tension may be allowed if all the loads are not sustained loads.

7-3   Prefabricated Diaphragm Walls

General guidelines

The design of prefabricated diaphragm walls must consider, besides serviceability and ultimate strength state, the loading conditions at various stages of construction. This is particularly important when the panels must serve as temporary support and as part of the permanent structure.

The loading conditions during construction can be controlled to some extent by a proper bracing (struts, shores, or ground anchors). Stresses and deflections in the members can be altered by predetermined jacking of struts, retensioning of ground anchors, and in some instances by introducing posttensioning tendons that can be tensioned and detensioned as construction continues to produce the desired effects. For temporary loading conditions, higher unit stresses or lower factors of safety are admissible under allowable stress design.

Since prefabricated units are set in slurry trenches where the slurry is replaced or transformed into a coulis, the initial stress condition remains "built in" and forms the basis of analysis. If these units are to be used for both initial ground support and permanent structure, consideration of the construction method is an integral part of the design.

The choice between allowable stress and load factor design should be based on the same criteria as for cast-in-place walls, and the load and resistance factors should have the same basis. An advantage of the prefabricated walls is better quality control to assure the specified concrete strength, and hence concrete with $f_c' \geqslant 5000$ lb/in^2 should normally be considered.

Prestressing.   Unlike cast-in-place diaphragm walls in which the generous thickness can accommodate the structural requirement with top and bottom bracing only, prefabricated walls normally have a thickness limited by weight and handling restrictions. Hence they are most commonly used where, besides top and bottom bracing, there is one or more intermediate lateral supports. In this case moments induced by lateral earth stresses, pore pressure, and surcharge loads can vary widely, and even reverse, during the various stages of loading and construction. This complexity can be rectified if the prestress is applied concentrically, but in this case the design is more likely to be controlled by compressive stresses in the concrete (see also Sec. 7-2).

Where compressive stresses control the design, it is necessary to include the weight of the wall above the critical moment section, and any dead load transferred to the wall from the main structure.

Panels suitable for prestressing are the sections shown in Fig. 1-13 where the wall consists of identical panels, and the beam sections shown in Fig. 1-14. It is more practical to have the units pretensioned if this does not conflict with the panel position and stresses during handling, but occasionally contractors have reported prefabricated walls posttensioned after installation through ducts provided in the concrete during casting.

Slenderness. For both allowable stress or load factor design, the effects of slenderness should be considered. This can be done either by classical methods or by the use of the moment magnification concept. Slenderness effects apply to moments caused by eccentricity of the axial loads, and not by normal loads. For unsupported lengths in most applications, and for vertical members designed to carry lateral loads as well as vertical loads, slenderness effects are usually minimal.

Design Example 7-3 *Part A.*   Using elastic interaction diagrams, determine the prestressing strands (number, diameter) for the vertical prefabricated wall of Fig. 7-23a. The precast sections are rectangular shapes 48 in × 16 in. The wall is subjected to the following loads per section:

$$P_{a1} = 20 \text{ kips dead load, } 50 \text{ kips live load}$$

$$P_{a2} = 20 \text{ kips dead load, } 20 \text{ kips live load}$$

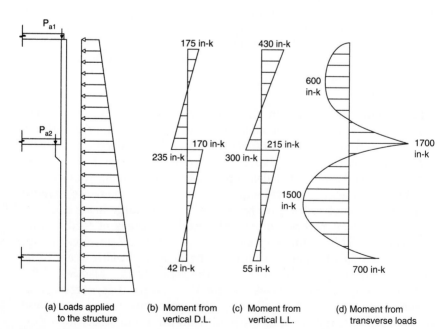

(a) Loads applied to the structure

(b) Moment from vertical D.L.

(c) Moment from vertical L.L.

(d) Moment from transverse loads

Figure 7-23 Wall configuration, loads, and moments for Design Example 7-3.

The strands are ½-in-diameter grade 270, and for design purposes the assumed loss is 35,000 lb/in². A detailed analysis results in the moment diagrams shown in Fig. 7-23b through d.

Step 1. Construct the elastic interaction diagram; use $f'_c = 5000$ lb/in², and a solid section 48 in by 16 in. Develop interaction curves for

$$f_c = 0.45f'_c = 0.45(5000) = 2250 \text{ lb/in}^2 \text{ (allowable compression)}$$

and

$$f_t = 0 \quad 3\sqrt{f'_c} = -212 \text{ lb/in}^2 \quad -6\sqrt{f'_c} = -424 \text{ lb/in}^2 \text{ (allowable tension)}$$

The section properties are computed as follows:

$$A = 48 \times 16 = 768 \text{ in}^2$$

$$I = 48(16)^3/12 = 16,384 \text{ in}^4 \quad z = 16,384/8 = 2048 \text{ in}^3$$

Point 1: $M = 0 \quad P = f_c A = 2250(768) = 1728$ kips

Point 2: Balance point $(P/A) + (M/z) = f_c \quad (P/A) - (M/z) = f_t$

For $f_t = 0$, $P = (f_c + f_t)A/2 = (2250 + 0)(768/2) = 864,000$ lb $= 864$ kips

$$M = (P/A - f_t)/z = (864/768 - 0)(2048) = 2304 \text{ in-kips}$$

For $f_t = -3\sqrt{f'_c} = -212$ lb/in², $P = (2250 - 212)(768/2) = 782,590$ lb $=$ 783 kips

$$M = (783/768 + 0.212)(2048) = 2519 \text{ in-kips}$$

For $f_t = -6\sqrt{f'_c} = -424$ lb/in, $P = (2250 - 424)(768/2) = 701,184$ lb $=$ 701 kips

$$M = (701/768 + 0.424)(2048) = 2738 \text{ in-kips}$$

Point 3: $P = 0 \quad Mz - f_t z$

For $f_t = 0$: $M = 0$

For $f_t = -212$ lb/in²: $M = 0.212(2048) = 434$ in-kips

For $f_t = -424$ lb/in²: $M = 0.424(2048) = 868$ in-kips

These data are used to construct the elastic interaction diagram shown in Fig. 7-24.

Step 2. Compute maximum combined moments. These are taken directly from the moment diagrams of Fig. 7-23.

■ Maximum negative moment, $M_a + M_t = -(170 + 1700) = -1870$ in-kips
■ Maximum positive moment, $M_a + M_t = +1500$ in-kips
  (neglecting small compensating moments from axial dead loads)

Including the axial live loads, the total moments are

■ Maximum negative moment, $M_a + M_t = -(1870 + 215) = -2085$ in-kips
■ Maximum positive moment, $M_a + M_t = +1500$ in-kips (same as before)

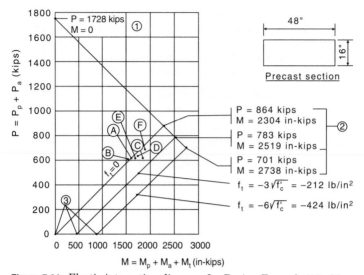

Figure 7-24 Elastic interaction diagram for Design Example 7-3; M_p = moment due to eccentricity of prestress force P_p; M_a = moment caused by eccentricity of applied vertical loads P_a; M_t = moment caused by transverse loads.

Step 3. Determine the requirements for prestressing. Criteria for this phase are: (1) for combined action of horizontal earth pressure and dead load from the structure, no tension is allowed; and (2) for total loads (dead + live + earth pressure), the allowable tension is $6\sqrt{f_c'}$.

Let P_p = total prestress force and M_p = moment caused by the eccentricity of P_p. For dead load and lateral earth pressure, the following are obtained:

$$P = P_p + P_a = P_p + 20 + 20 = P_p + 40 \text{ (kips)}$$

$$M = M_p + M_a + M_t = M_p - 1870 \quad \text{or } M = M_p + 1500 \text{ (in-kips)}$$

The prestress force may be placed eccentrically to balance the positive and negative moments. Then $M_p = (1870 - 1500)/2 = 185$ in-kips, giving a moment $M = 1870 - 185 = 1500 + 185 = 1685$, say 1700 in-kips.

From the interaction diagram, min P is about 600 kips (point A). The required prestress is therefore $P_p = P - P_a = 600 - 40 = 560$ kips, resulting in an optimum eccentricity of $^{185}\!/_{560} = 0.33$ in.

Step 4. Select the prestressing strands. Per strand = $P_p = [0.70(270) - 35](0.153) = 23.6$ kips/strand. No. of strands required = $560/23.6 = 24$. Try 11 strands in inside face and 13 strands in outside face. Assume c.g. 2 in from face or 6 in from center.

$$e = [13(6) - 11(6)]/24 = 0.50 \text{ in}$$

$$P = 24(23.6) + 40 = 566 + 40 = 606 \text{ kips}$$

$$M = 566(0.50) - 170 - 1700 = -1587 \text{ in-kips, point B}$$

or

$$566(0.50) + 1500 = 1783 \text{ in-kips, point C}$$

$$\text{Maximum allowable} = (606\!/864)(2304) = 1615 \text{ in-kips}$$

This shows that there is a small tension, so that one more strand will be added to the inside face.

$$e = [13(6) - 12(6)]/24 = 0.25 \text{ in}$$

$$P = 25(23.6) + 40 = 630 \text{ kips}$$

$$M = 590(0.25) - 170 - 1700 = 1723 \text{ in-kips, point D}$$

or

$$590(0.25) + 1500 = 147 + 1500 = 1647 \text{ in-kips, point E}$$

Check the total load condition

$$P = 630 + 50 + 20 = 700 \text{ kips}$$

$$M = M_p + M_a + M_t = +147 - 170 - 215 - 1700 = 1938 \text{ in-kips, point F}$$

Final prestress scheme:

$$13 \text{ strands outside face, } A_{ps} = 1.99 \text{ in}^2$$

$$12 \text{ strands inside face, } A_{ps} = 1.84 \text{ in}^2$$

In the foregoing analysis the weight of the wall was not included, assuming that it might dissipate through shear resistance at the interface. This weight is 0.8 kip/ft, and therefore it has little effect on the distribution of stresses.

Part B. Repeat the same problem for ultimate strength (load factor) design.

Step 1. Construct ultimate interaction curves as follows:

1. Referring to Fig. 7-25, select a value of a or c for each point on the interaction curve. Determine the corresponding a or c from the equation $a = \beta_1 c$. Note that a is the depth of equivalent rectangular stress block and β_1 is the ratio of a to the distance (depth) from fiber of maximum compressive strain to the neutral axis.

2. Determine the value of A_{comp} from the geometry of the section (shaded portion in Fig. 7-25).

3. Determine the initial strain f_{se}/E_s in the strand caused by the prestressing, where f_{se} = effective stress in the steel after losses.

4. Calculate the strain in the strand caused by external loading (from similar triangles) as shown in Fig. 7-25a. The total strain is the initial strain ± the strain caused by external loading.

5. Estimate the stress in the strand from the stress-strain curve of Fig. 7-26.

6. Calculate P_u and M_u for each point selected by statics using the basic relationships shown in Fig. 7-25.

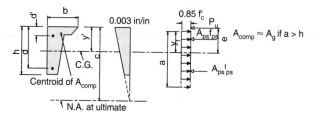

$$\epsilon_s = [f_{se}/E_s - \frac{0.003}{c}(c-d')] \leq 0.035 \text{ in/in}$$

$$\epsilon_{ps} = [f_{se}/E_s + \frac{0.003}{c}(d-c)] \leq 0.035 \text{ in/in}$$

$$P_u = (A_{comp}) \, 0.85 \, f'_c - A_{ps} f_s - A_{ps} f_{ps}$$

$$M_u = P_u e = (A_{comp}) \, (y_t - y') \, 0.85 \, f'_c - A_{ps} f_s \, (y_t - d')$$
$$+ A_{ps} f_{ps} \, (d - y_t)$$

(a) Basic relationships

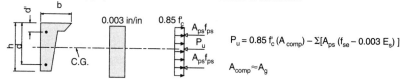

$$A_{comp} \approx A_g \text{ if } a > h$$

(b) Special case with Neutral Axis outside of the section

$$P_u = 0.85 \, f'_c \, (A_{comp}) - \Sigma[A_{ps} \, (f_{se} - 0.003 \, E_s)]$$

$$A_{comp} \approx A_g$$

(c) Special Case when $M_u = 0$

Figure 7-25   Strain compatibility relationships for prestressed concrete beam-columns.

Essentially, the foregoing procedure is a strain compatibility solution for one assumed strain distribution. The maximum compressive strain is set at 0.003 (see also other sections) and corresponds to failure of the section. For the special case shown in Fig. 7-25b, the neutral axis can be outside the section, and the same relationships are still valid. In the case of axial load only, P_u is calculated by the equation shown in Fig. 7-25c.

Step 2.   Calculate M_u and P_u for various points. All relevant parameters are as before, and since this is assumed to be factory-produced prestressed concrete, we will use $\phi = 1.0$. Likewise, $d = 14$ in, $d' = 2$ in, $f_{se} = 0.7(270) - 35 = 154$ kips/in².

Point 1: $M_u = 0$ $P_{u0} = 0.85(5)(768) - 3.83[154 - 0.003(27,000)]$

$$= 3264 - 280 = 2984 \text{ kips}$$

Point 2: $P_u = 0$ (bending only)

From Eq. (7-9)

$$f_{ps} = f_{pu} \left(1 - 0.5 p_p \frac{f_{pu}}{f'_c}\right)$$

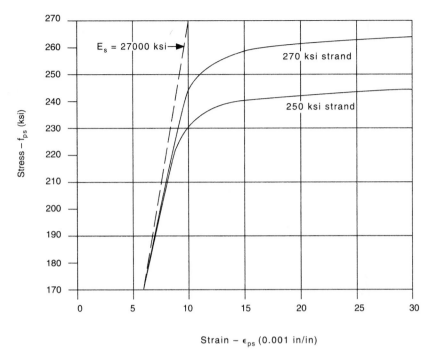

Strain – ϵ_{ps} (0.001 in/in)

Figure 7-26 Typical stress-strain curves for seven-wire prestressing strand.

where

$$p_p = 1.99/(48)(14) = 0.0030$$

or

$$f_{ps} = 270\left[1 - 0.5(0.003)\left(\frac{270}{5}\right)\right] = 248 \text{ kips/in}^2$$

The value of a is computed from

$$a = A_{ps}f_{ps}/0.85f'_cb = 1.99(248)/(0.85)(5)(48) = 2.42 \text{ in}$$

$$M_{uo} = A_{ps}f_{ps}\left(d - \frac{a}{2}\right) = 1.99(248)(14 - 1.21) = 6318 \text{ in-kips}$$

$$= 527 \text{ ft-kips}$$

Point 3, set $a = 4$ in on the inside face. The configuration of the section is shown in Fig. 7-27. The value of β_1 for 5000 lb/in^2 is (see also Sec. 6-8) 0.85 − 1(0.05) = 0.80. Thus $c = a/\beta_1 = 4/0.80 = 5.0$ in.
The ratio f_{se}/E_s is 154/27,000 = 0.0057. From Fig. 7-26

$$e_s = 0.0057 - \frac{0.003}{5.00}(5.00 - 2.00) = 0.0039$$

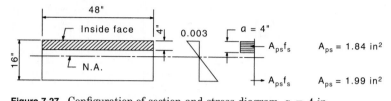

Figure 7-27 Configuration of section and stress diagram, $a = 4$ in.

and

$$f_s = 0.0039(27,000) = 105.30 \text{ kips/in}^2$$

$$e_{ps} = 0.0057 + \frac{0.003}{5.00}(14.00 - 5.00) = 0.0111$$

$f_{ps} = 250$ kips/in^2 (obtained graphically from the diagram of Fig. 7-26).

The value of P_u is calculated next from the relation

$$P_u = (A_{\text{comp}})0.85f_c' - A_{ps}f_s - A_{ps}f_{ps} \tag{7-12}$$

or

$$P_u = (4 \times 48)(0.85)(5.0) - 1.84(105.3) - 1.99(250)$$

$$= 816 - 194 - 497 = 125 \text{ kips}$$

also

$$M_u = (A_{\text{comp}})(y_t - y')0.85f_c' - A_{ps}f_s(y_t - d') + A_{ps}f_{ps}(d - y_t) \tag{7-13}$$

where y_t = distance from extreme compression fiber to c.g. of the section
y' = distance from extreme fiber to centroid

or

$$M_u = 192(8 - 2)(0.85)(5) - 1.84(105.3)(8 - 2) + 1.99(250)(14 - 8)$$

$$= 4895 - 1163 + 2982 = 6714 \text{ in-kips} = 558 \text{ ft-kips}$$

Point 4, set $a = 12$ in on the inside face, as shown in Fig. 7-28. $A_{\text{comp}} = 48 \times 12 = 576$ in^2,

$$c = a/\beta_1 = 12/0.80 = 15.00 \text{ in}$$

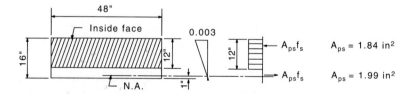

Figure 7-28 Configuration of section and stress diagrams, $a = 12$ in.

From Fig. 7-26

$$e_s = 0.0057 - \frac{0.003}{15}(15 - 2) = 0.0031$$

$$f_s = 0.0031(27{,}000) = 83.7 \text{ kips/in}^2$$

$$e_{ps} = 0.0057 - \frac{0.003}{15}(15 - 14) = 0.0055$$

$$f_{ps} = 0.0055(27{,}000) = 148.5 \text{ kips/in}^2 \qquad \text{(from Fig. 7-26)}$$

From Eq. (7-12) the value of P_u is

$$P_u = 0.85(5)(576) - 1.84(83.7) - 1.99(148.5)$$

$$= 2448 - 154 - 296 = 1998 \text{ kips}$$

$$M_u = 0.85(5)(576)(8 - 6) - 1.84(83.7)(8 - 2) + 1.99(148.5)(14 - 8)$$

$$= 4896 - 924 + 1773 = 5745 \text{ in-kips} = 479 \text{ ft-kips}$$

Point 5, set $a = 8$ in (center of section).

$$A_{\text{comp}} = 48 \times 8 = 384 \text{ in}^2 \qquad c = 8/0.80 = 10.00 \text{ in}$$

From Fig. 7-26,

$$e_s = 0.0057 - \frac{0.003}{10}(10 - 2) = 0.0033$$

$$f_s = 0.0033(27{,}000) = 89.1 \text{ kips/in}^2$$

$$e_{ps} = 0.0057 + \frac{0.003}{10}(14 - 10) = 0.0069$$

$$f_{ps} = 0.0069(27{,}000) = 186.3 \text{ kips/in}^2$$

Likewise, we compute P_u from Eq. (7-12),

$$P_u = 0.85(5)(384) - 1.84(89.1) - 1.99(186.3)$$

$$= 1632 - 164 - 371 = 1097 \text{ kips}$$

$$M_u = 0.85(5)(384)(8 - 4) - 1.84(89.1)(8 - 2) + 1.99(186.3)(14 - 8)$$

$$= 6528 - 984 + 2225 = 7769 \text{ in-kips} = 674 \text{ ft-kips}$$

The foregoing computations illustrate the method needed to establish various points of an interaction diagram using strain compatibility and mechanics. The extension of this approach is the construction of the ultimate interaction diagram shown in Fig. 7-29 using points 1 through 5. For simplicity, $\phi = 1.0$ (no reduction in strength is included).

Step 3. Check the ultimate capacity of the section for factored moments and loads. Recall: Dead load = 40 kips, Live load = 70 kips. Also, of the 1700 in-kips negative moment shown in Fig. 7-23, 900 in-kips is caused by earth

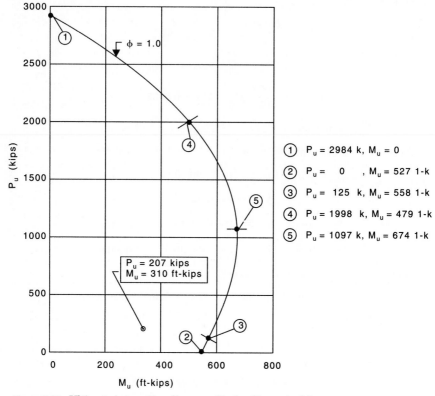

$$P_u = 2984 \text{ k}, M_u = 0$$

① $P_u = 2984 \text{ k}, M_u = 0$

② $P_u = 0 \quad, M_u = 527 \text{ 1-k}$

③ $P_u = 125 \text{ k}, M_u = 558 \text{ 1-k}$

④ $P_u = 1998 \text{ k}, M_u = 479 \text{ 1-k}$

⑤ $P_u = 1097 \text{ k}, M_u = 674 \text{ 1-k}$

Figure 7-29 Ultimate interaction diagram, Design Example 7-3.

pressure and surcharge, and 800 in-kips is due to pore pressure. Recall also $M_{DL} = 170$ in-kips, $M_{LL} = 215$ in-kips. Using the load factors stipulated in Sec. 6-12, we obtain

$$P_u = 1.3(40 + 1.70 \times 70) = 207 \text{ kips}$$

$$M_u = 1.3(170 + 800 + 1.70 \times 215 + 1.70 \times 900) = 3726 \text{ in-kips}$$

$$= 310 \text{ ft-kips}$$

The point corresponding to $P_u = 207$ kips, $M_u = 310$ ft-kips, is plotted in the diagram space of Fig. 7-29, and is well within the load-moment capacity of the member.

7-4 Composite Walls

These are essentially the systems discussed in Sec. 1-7, and encompass two major groups: (1) steel-concrete panels and (2) bored piles with concrete panels. Suitable configurations are shown in Figs. 1-25 through 1-29.

Steel and concrete panels

The wall configurations shown in Figs. 1-25 through 1-27 ordinarily are reinforced in the horizontal direction, except where the piles are spaced close enough so that reinforcement is not necessary. Walls reinforced horizontally are usually designed for maximum pressures at the controlling depth, and the resulting reinforcement requirements are carried through the entire wall depth. The design methodology is a routine problem and will not be repeated here.

Unreinforced panels spanning between vertical steel beams may be designed under the following criteria: (1) the concrete section is assumed to act in bending subject to elastic theory, and hence failure will occur in the concrete when the tensile strength is reached and exceeded; (2) for relatively short and thick panels elastic arch action may be assumed and the wall analyzed accordingly; (3) the panels may be treated as deep beams under appropriate span-width ratios; and (4) the analysis may have a semiempirical basis.

Walls in elastic bending. In Sec. 6-8 we emphasized the importance of understanding how a wall should be proportioned, and identified three stages of behavior: elastic, cracked, and ultimate. Cracks are investigated using a straight-line theory of stress and strain. Better crack control is exercised if f_y does not exceed 40,000 lb/in^2, if the reinforcement bars are well distributed over the effective concrete area, if the volume of concrete around each bar is minimum, and where the tensile stress is low.

Without reinforcement, cracks are controlled if the last criterion is complied with. From Sec. 6-3, a wall 36 in thick has a maximum bending resistance of about 19.9 ft-kips based on an allowable tensile concrete stress of 93 lb/in^2. This criterion can be applied to a specific example. Consider a composite wall of steel beams and concrete panels. The beams are spaced at 8-ft intervals, giving a clear (design) span of 7 ft. The wall supports sand with water, so that the design must consider effective stresses and pore pressure with $\phi' = 28°$. From the example of Sec. 7-2 we check the structural capacity of the wall at a depth of 30 ft. Recall that at this depth the lateral pressure is $[(57.50)(0.53) + 62.50(30)] = 2.8$ kips/ft^2.

The resulting moment at this depth is

$$M = \frac{(2.8)(7^2)}{8} = 17.2 \text{ ft-kips}$$

or below the moment capacity of the section based on allowable tensile stress.

Walls designed as deep beams. A generally accepted definition of a deep beam is "a member in which a significant amount of the load is carried to the supports by a compression thrust joining the load and the reaction." For a uniformly loaded beam this occurs with a span-to-depth ratio less than about 4 or 5. For a composite beam panel 10 ft long, this criterion is satisfied if the wall thickness is $^{10}\!/_4 = 2.5$ ft; hence most composite walls meet the qualification requirements.

Elastic analysis of deep beams in the uncracked state is only meaningful prior to cracking. In a deep beam cracking will occur at about one-third to one-half of the ultimate load. After cracks develop, a major redistribution of stresses is necessary since there can be no tension across the cracks. Elastic analysis is useful because it shows the stress distribution that causes cracking and hence gives guidance about the direction of cracking and the flow of forces after cracking.

Alternatively, a deep beam is essentially a member short enough to make shear deformations important in comparison with pure flexure. An uncracked, elastic, single-span deep beam supporting a uniform load has a distribution of horizontal stresses on vertical sections at midspan and the quarter point as shown in Fig. 7-30a. The stress trajectories can be represented by the simple truss shown in Fig. 7-30b, where the uniform load is divided into two parts, each represented by its resultant $wl/2$. The angle θ can vary from about 68° for $l/d = 1.0$ to 55° for $l/d = 2.0$, and is much smaller for $l/d > 2$. The crack pattern is shown in Fig. 7-30c.

Plane sections in deep beams do not remain essentially plane under loading. After cracking has developed as in Fig. 7-30c, the beam behaves more like a truss or tied arch, and anchorage of tension steel (bottom horizontal) becomes critical. Horizontal hooks on tension bars are suggested to avoid splitting. For the composite walls of steel and concrete, the arch is fixed at the ends by its confinement in the beam recess created by the flanges and the web, and this resists splitting until a critical load is reached.

Semiempirical analysis. Unreinforced-concrete panels inserted between steel beams fail according to a mode that should not be associated with cracking of plain concrete in bending. The panels continue to resist additional loads after initial cracking through arching action, and failure by fracture actually occurs when the stresses exceed several times the tensile strength of concrete. This behavior explains the increased structural capacity of the panels.

Semiempirical design criteria can be based on results of tests carried out by Miyoshi et al. (1976). A steel-concrete panel used in these tests is shown in Fig. 7-31. The beam spacing is 1 m (3.3 ft) and the beam depth 40 cm (16 in), giving an effective span-to-thickness ratio

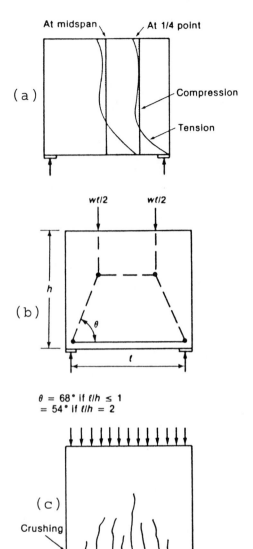

At midspan   At 1/4 point

(a)

Compression

Tension

$wl/2$ $wl/2$

h

(b)

θ

l

$\theta = 68°$ if $l/h \leq 1$
$= 54°$ if $l/h = 2$

(c)

Crushing

Figure 7-30 Deep beams: (*a*) Distribution of horizontal stress on vertical sections, midspan and quarter point. (*b*) Truss model. (*c*) Crack pattern.

of 2, which is closer to the ACI definition of deep beams. The plain concrete has a compressive strength of 250 kg/cm² (3600 lb/in²) and a tensile strength of 22 kg/cm² (315 lb/in²). Note that this is less than the modulus of rupture defined as $7.5\sqrt{f'_c} = 450$ lb/in².

The panel was subjected to beam action under the loading shown in Fig. 7-31*b* and *c* until the first tension cracks appeared as shown.

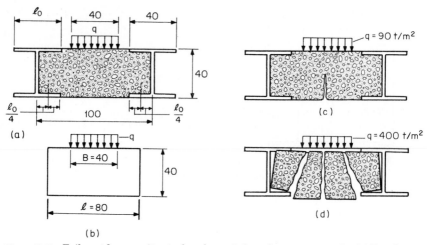

Figure 7-31 Failure of composite-steel and unreinforced-concrete panels: (*a*) Panel configuration and loading. (*b*) Span length. (*c*) Initial cracking on tension side. (*d*) Fracture by transverse and diagonal cracks. All dimensions in centimeters. (*From Miyoshi et al., 1976.*)

The load was increased further while the panel withstood the stresses satisfactorily. As the unit load q approached 400 t/m^2 (about 82,500 lb/ft^2), diagonal cracks developed at the edge of the steel flange on the tension side and spread across the section to the compression side, causing fracture, as shown in Fig. 7-31*d*.

For a beam loaded as shown in Fig. 7-31*b* and taking the effective span as shown, the maximum bending moment M and shear V are, respectively,

$$M = \left(\frac{Bl}{4} - \frac{B^2}{8}\right)q \quad \text{and} \quad V = \frac{Bq}{2}$$

For $B = 0.4$ m and $l = 0.8$ m, and expressing q in tons (metric) per square meter, we have

$$M = 0.06q \quad \text{(t-m)} \quad \text{and} \quad V = 0.2q \quad \text{(t)}$$

so that the maximum stresses in the concrete are

$$\text{Flexural stress} = f_c = 2.25q \quad \text{t/m}^2$$

$$\text{Shear stress} = u_c = 0.75q \quad \text{t/m}^2$$

The load that caused initial cracks is $q = 90$ t/m^2, so that the tensile strength is $90 \times 2.25 = 202.5$ t/m^2 = 20.3 kg/cm^2, or close to the theoretical tensile strength 22 kg/cm². The strength at cracking is 292 lb/in², or 65 percent of the modulus of rupture.

The graphs in Fig. 7-32a to c show the flexural stress plotted as a function of the distance from the neutral axis of the beam for values of q of 25, 50, and 75 t/m²; also shown are the measured stresses. All these stresses are within the precracked stage, and evidently the concrete responds elastically to flexure. The graph of Fig. 7-32d shows the maximum shear stress plotted vs. q, and again theoretical values agree with measured.

In this example the concrete did not actually fail in fracture until the load reached many times the load causing initial cracking, in this case 4.4 times.

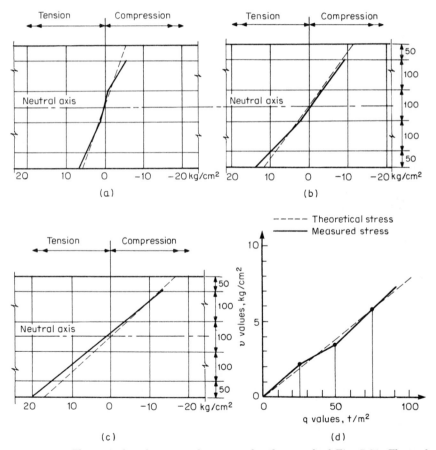

Figure 7-32 Theoretical and measured stresses for the panel of Fig. 7-31. Flexural stresses for q values of (a) 25, (b) 50, and (c) 75 t/m²; (d) maximum shear stress. (*From Miyoshi et al., 1976.*)

TABLE 7-5   Relevant Stress for Wall of Fig. 7-31

	q, t/m^2	f, lb/in^2	f, kg/cm^2	v, lb/in^2	v, kg/cm^2
1	29	95	6.6	31.2	2.18
2	90	292	20.3	97.3	6.77
3	400	1300*	90.0*	433.3	30.00

*Fictitious stresses corresponding to the q value that caused fracture.

Table 7-5 shows relevant stresses, flexural f, and shear v, for the wall of Fig. 7-31, corresponding to specific values of q. Line 1 is for the value of q corresponding to the allowable tensile stress f_{all} taken as $0.21f_r$ where f_r is the modulus of rupture $7.5\sqrt{f'_c}$. Line 2 represents the q value causing initial cracks and gives the tensile strength of the panel. Line 3 gives fictitious stresses for the q value that caused fracture. An allowable shear stress would be $v_{all} = 0.95\sqrt{f'_c} = 57$ lb/in^2.

Interestingly, the wall failed at a load that was almost 14 times the load causing a flexural stress equal to the allowable. Clearly, allowable stress design in this case is overconservative. On the other hand, these results cannot be extrapolated readily to walls with $l/d > 2$, and since the concrete is not reinforced, a truss model will consist of compression struts but with a tension chord replaced by the confinement and fixity of the panel at the ends. Since no theoretical solution is available, a conservative but more realistic approach would be to design the wall by factoring the loads and compare the resulting stresses with the modulus of rupture multiplied by a performance factor (strength reduction) $\phi = 0.50$. When the size of the project justifies the cost, a design methodology may have full-scale load tests as a basis.

Bored piles and concrete panels

The wall shown in Fig. 1-28 usually is horizontally reinforced, and its design is essentially a simple-beam problem. Occasionally, the wall is horizontally braced by permanent floors, or temporarily by rakers, berms, and ground anchors. In such cases the design must check stresses resulting from intermediate construction stages and arrange the reinforcement pattern accordingly.

Maximum panel lengths are controlled by the structural capacity of the wall in both tension and compression, but the location of the drilled shafts must also accommodate the layout of the structure and the foundation requirements.

Design Example 7-4   A steel-concrete composite wall is 50 ft deep. The vertical beams consist of 36-in steel I sections with flange width 12 in, and are spaced at 8-ft intervals. The concrete has $f'_c = 3500$ lb/in^2, or a modulus of rupture

$7.5\sqrt{f_c'} = 444$ lb/in². The wall supports soil with $K_0 = 0.6$, $\gamma = 122$ lb/ft³, and a groundwater table at the surface. Check the structural capacity of the concrete panels using ultimate strength.

At a depth of 50 ft the pressures are

$$\text{Lateral earth pressure} = 0.6 \times 60 \times 50 = 1800 \text{ lb/ft}^2$$

$$= 1.8 \text{ kips/ft}^2$$

$$\text{Pore pressure} = 62.5 \times 50 = 3125 \text{ lb/ft}^2$$

$$= 3.1 \text{ kips/ft}^2$$

Clear span = 7 ft = design span. The moments are computed as follows:

$$M_e = 1.8 \times 7^2/8 = 11.0 \text{ ft-kips}$$

$$M_w = 3.1 \times 7^2/8 = 19.0 \text{ ft-kips}$$

For a 36-in wall the section properties are

$$I = 1 \times 3^3/12 = 2.25 \text{ ft}^4 \qquad \text{S.M.} = 2.25/1.50 = 1.50 \text{ ft}^3$$

The factored moment is (AASHTO criteria)

$$M_u = 1.3(19.0 + 1.7 \times 11.0) = 49.0 \text{ ft-kips}$$

or

$$f_{cu} = 49/1.50 = 32.7 \text{ kips/ft}^2 = 32,700/144 = 227 \text{ lb/in}^2$$

The factored concrete strength at rupture is $0.50 \times 444 = 222$ lb/in²   say OK.

Design for shear.   An allowable shear stress of $0.95\sqrt{f_c'}$ is unduly restrictive for deep beams. A more reasonable alternative for allowable shear is given as $2\sqrt{f_c'}$, and the obvious first step would be to check the shear (actual) stress against this allowable before considering more complex relationships. An upper limit for shear is $6\sqrt{f_c'}$ to be used in connection with load factor analysis. In this case a strength reduction factor $\phi = 0.60$ should be applied.

For this example the shear will be checked at the edge of the steel beam, although the codes allow the shear stress to be checked at some distance from the support.

$$\text{Working shear, total } V = 4.9 \times 3.5 = 17.15 \text{ kips} = 17,150 \text{ lb}$$

$$v = \frac{17,150}{36 \times 12} = 40 \text{ lb/in}^2 \qquad v_{\text{all}} = 2\sqrt{f_c'} = 118 \text{ lb/in}^2$$

$$\text{Ultimate shear } V_u = 1.3(10.85 + 1.7 \times 6.30) = 28.0 \text{ kips}$$

$$= 28,000 \text{ lb}$$

$$v_u = \frac{28,000}{432} = 65 \text{ lb/in} \qquad \phi v_n = 0.5 \times 6\sqrt{f_c'}$$

$$= 177 \text{ lb/in}^2 \qquad \text{OK.}$$

Some designers, however, will prefer to use the multiplier 0.55 for allowable shear at working loads, or

$$v_{all} = 0.55 \times 118 = 65 \text{ lb/in}^2 > 40 \text{ lb/in}$$

7-5 Bored Pile Groups and Walls

Lateral loads on bored pile walls result from earth pressures, water pressure, live load surcharge, wind, seismic effects, etc. Loads may be classified as permanent or as transient (see also Sec. 4-13). The walls must be designed to withstand these forces without failing (i.e., without reaching the ultimate strength state), and without deflecting excessively (i.e., without reaching the serviceability limit state). Normally, the structural capacity of the members will govern the design, but in built-up areas the tolerable deflection may be the applicable criterion.

Design consideration

Continuous bored piles acting as retaining walls are members conventionally reinforced to resist bending moments and shear forces, and these considerations can dictate the pile spacing and diameter. There is greater flexibility in the choice of pile diameter in comparison with diaphragm wall thickness, but the circular pile section usually requires more main reinforcement per unit length of wall than the constant section of a diaphragm wall to produce the same moment capacity.

Consider, for example, the contiguous bored pile wall and the continuous diaphragm wall shown in Fig. 7-33. Let A = distance from

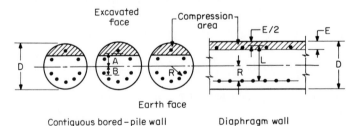

Figure 7-33 Plan sections through contiguous bored-pile and diaphragm wall. Comparison of effective section and lever arms for circular and constant section. Lever arm for bored piles = $A + B$. Lever arm for diaphragm wall = $L = D/2 + R - E/2$. Given D = 600 mm and R = 200 mm, it is estimated that the lever arm for the bored pile is 267 mm and for the diaphragm wall is 433 mm.

c.g. of compression area (shown hatched) to the center of the circular section. Then

$$A = \frac{(D \sin \theta/2)^3}{12 \text{ (hatched area)}}$$

Let also B = centroidal distance of tensile steel from center. The lever arm for the pile is $A + B$. Referring to the diaphragm wall layout, the lever arm is $L = R + D/2 - E/2$, where the notation is as shown.

The lever arms can be compared in a numerical example, for applied bending moments equal to maximum moment resistance of circular section provided by concrete in compression, assuming piles are touching. Given $D = 600$ mm (24 in); $R = 200$ mm (8 in); $f_c = 10$ N/mm^2 (1450 lb/in^2); $f_s = 210$ N/mm^2 (30,450 lb/in^2), and ignoring steel in compression.

Circular section. As a first approximation, the maximum moment due to compression is $M_r = 125.28 \times 10^6$ N-mm, Lever arm = $A + B = 267$ mm (10.7 in).

Diaphragm wall length D. For equilibrium $(D)(E)(\frac{2}{3})(10)(L) = 125.28(10^6)$. Setting $L = R + D/2 - E/2$ and solving for E, we obtain $E = 134.3$ mm (5.37 in), and lever arm $L = 432.8$ mm (17.3 in). Note also that for maximum resisting moment based on concrete in compression, $L = 375$ mm (15.0 in).

Design options. The usual practice is to increase the moment capacity of the piles based on steel tension by providing more steel on the tension side if bars are not overcrowded and if there is no stress reversal. When an unusually large number of bars are required and the congestion may hinder the flow of concrete, it is possible to use steel sections as an alternative.

From the standpoint of strength it is possible to design free-standing contiguous pile walls with an unbraced cantilever as high as 30 ft, but the resulting deflection may dictate the use of anchors or other bracing. A uniform transfer of load from the piles to the anchors is better made if a reinforced-concrete waling beam is cast in situ to serve as the anchorage point.

Lateral deflection

A general method for analyzing the behavior of foundations using lateral load is presented in Sec. 5-16, with a distinction between rigid and flexible shafts, and emphasizing short members.

In this section, the procedure for predicting lateral deflections of drilled piles is based on work by Evans and Duncan (1982). The method models nonlinear behavior of the soil but does not require computer use.

The condition of restraint against rotation at the top can affect the magnitude and pattern of lateral deflection under load. Bored pile walls may have a concrete cap at the top restraining rotation or a free end. As a rule of thumb, the lateral deflection of a fixed-head shaft is about one-fourth as large as the deflection of a free-head member subjected to the same load.

Deflection of single element. Evans and Duncan (1982) relate lateral deflections to the lateral load using a so-called characteristic load P_c that expresses the section properties (diameter, stiffness) and the soil strength (stiffness). The larger the value of P_c the higher the structural capacity of the member and the smaller the deflection. The procedure is applicable to bored piles with a length-to-diameter ratio of 10 or greater for shafts in firm soils, and 15 or greater for shafts in soft soils.

Fixed-head bored piles. Figure 7-34a and b shows charts in dimensionless form for fixed-head drilled shafts in sand and clay, respectively. These charts show the variation of P_s/P_c with Y_s/D, where P_s = unfactored lateral load, Y_s = shaft displacement, and D = shaft diameter. The chart model has the same nonlinear behavior of soil as the p-y method of analysis. The graphs can be used as follows:

1. Select the shaft diameter D, the concrete modulus E_c, and the steel reinforcement. Compute the flexural stiffness $E_p I_p$ and the ratio R_I of the moment of inertia of the bored piles to the moment of inertia of a solid, unreinforced circular section.

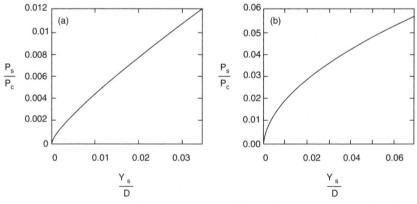

Figure 7-34 (a) Lateral load vs. deflection for fixed-head drilled shafts in sand. (b) Lateral load vs. deflection for fixed-head drilled shafts in clay. (*After Evans and Duncan, 1982.*)

2. Estimate the average undrained shear strength for clays, or the average angle of internal friction for sands. The soil behavior close to the ground is most important. The soil properties should be averaged over a depth extending about eight shaft diameters from the top of the shaft. Effective unit weight for sands should be used below the water table.

3. Determine the characteristic load P_c from the following equation:

For clay:
$$P_c = 7.34D^2(E_pR_I)(s_u/E_pR_I)^{0.683} \qquad (7\text{-}14)$$

For sand:
$$P_c = 1.57D^2(E_pR_I)(\gamma'D\phi'K_p/E_pR_I)^{0.57} \qquad (7\text{-}15)$$

where $R_I = I_p/I_{solid}$ where $I_{solid} = \pi D^4/64$, so that

$$E_pR_I = (E_pI_p)/(\pi D^4/64) \qquad (7\text{-}16)$$

K_p = Rankine passive pressure coefficient = $\tan^2(45 + \phi'/2)$ and γ' = unit weight of sand. R_I values may be estimated directly with the help of Table 7-6 for common steel ratios and diameters.

4. Calculate the load ratio P_s/P_c, where P_s = unfactored lateral load.

5. Use the graphs of Fig. 7-34 to determine the ratio Y_s/D; part a is for sand and part b for clay. From this ratio calculate Y_s.

Free-head bored piles. A lateral load P_s is resolved into two components, a lateral load acting at the base of excavation, and a bending moment $M_e = P_se$, as shown in Fig. 7-35. The lateral displacement of a free-head bored pile can be estimated using nonlinear superposition of the deflection Y_{SP} caused by the lateral load and the deflection Y_{SM} caused by the bending moment.

The component of the lateral displacement Y_{SP} due to the lateral load acting at the excavation line can be estimated using Fig. 7-36a

TABLE 7-6 R_I Values for Drilled Shafts with E_c = 3500 kips/in² E_s = 29,000 kips/in², and c = 3 in

	Diameter of drilled shaft			
A_s/A_g	18 in	24 in	30 in	36 in
0.01	1.06	1.07	1.09	1.09
0.02	1.11	1.14	1.16	1.18
0.04	1.21	1.27	1.31	1.34
0.08	1.38	1.50	1.58	1.63

where A_s = area of steel
A_g = gross cross-sectional area
of drilled shaft
From Barker et al., 1991.

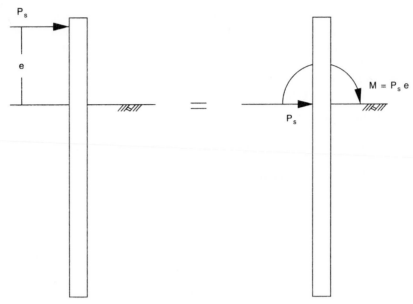

Figure 7-35 Resolution of eccentric load into a lateral load acting on the groundline and a moment.

and b, following the same procedure as in Fig. 7-34, for sand and clay, respectively.

The component Y_{SM} of the lateral displacement due to the bending moment can be estimated as follows:

1. Calculate the bending moment $M_e = P_s e$.

2. Determine the characteristic moment M_c from the following equations:

For clay: $M_c = 3.86 D^3 (E_p R_I)(s_u/E_p R_I)^{0.46}$ (7-17)

For sand: $M_c = 1.33 D^3 (E_p R_I)(\gamma' D \phi' K_p/E_p R_I)^{0.4}$ (7-18)

3. Calculate the ratio M_e/M_c directly.

4. Determine the ratio Y_{SM}/D referring to the graphs of Fig. 7-37a and b for sand and clay, respectively. From this ratio calculate Y_{SM}.

With Y_{SP} and Y_{SM} known, the total lateral deflection can be estimated using nonlinear superposition as suggested by Evans and Duncan (1982).

1. Using Y_{SM} and Fig. 7-36a and b, calculate P_M from Fig. 7-38b. This is the equivalent lateral load that would cause the deflection Y_{SM}.

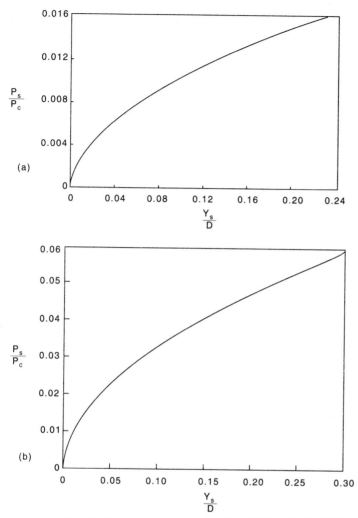

Figure 7-36 Load-deformation curves for free-head drilled shafts: (a) Sand. (b) Clay. (*From Evans and Duncan, 1982.*)

2. Using Y_{SP} and Fig. 7-37a and b, calculate M_p from Fig. 7-38e. This is the equivalent moment that would cause the deflection Y_{SP}.

3. Determine the deflection Y_{SPM} caused by the lateral combination $(P_s + P_n)$ as shown in Fig. 7-38c. Y_{SPM} is the deflection caused by the sum of the real load plus the equivalent load.

4. Determine the deflection Y_{SMP} caused by the combination $(M_s + M_p)$ as shown in Fig. 7-38f. Y_{SMP} is the deflection caused by the sum of the real moment plus the equivalent moment.

5. Calculate the total deflection Y_s from $Y_s = 0.5(Y_{SPM} + Y_{SMP})$.

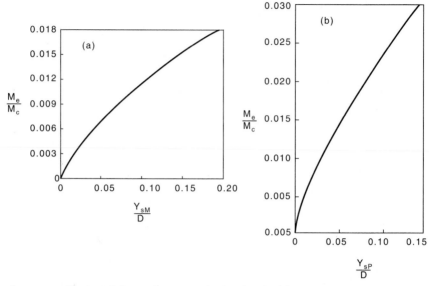

Figure 7-37 Moment deformation curves for free-head drilled shafts: (*a*) Sand. (*b*) Clay. (*From Evans and Duncan, 1982.*)

Deflection of bored pile walls.   When a single row of bored piles is constructed side by side, interaction effects can result in more deflection than in a single shaft for the same lateral load. Thus where the shafts are closer than three diameters group action must be considered.

Fixed-head bored piles.   The lateral deflection Y_g of a group may be estimated from the following semiempirical relation:

$$Y_g = \frac{A + N_{ds}}{B\sqrt{S/D} + P_s/CP_N} Y_s \tag{7-19}$$

where Y_s = lateral displacement of a single shaft subjected to lateral load P_s; N_{ds} = number of drilled shafts in group; S = average spacing of shafts; D shaft diameter; P_s = average lateral load per shaft = P_{yg}/N_{ds}; P_{yg} = lateral load on the group; and

$$P_N = K_p \gamma D^3 \quad \text{for sand} \tag{7-20}$$

$$P_N = s_u D^2 \quad \text{for clay} \tag{7-21}$$

The parameters K_p, ϕ', γ, and s_u are as before. The parameters A, B, and C are as follows: $A = 16$ for clay, $A = 9$ for sand; $B = 5.5$ for

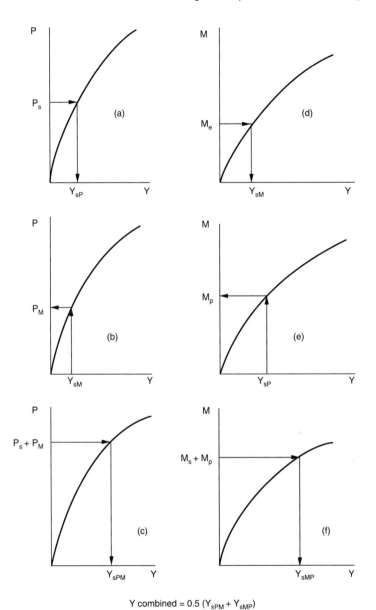

$$Y \text{ combined} = 0.5 \, (Y_{sPM} + Y_{sMP})$$

Figure 7-38 Nonlinear superposition. (*After Evans and Duncan, 1982.*)

clay, $B = 3$ for sand; and $C = 3$ for clay, $C = 16$ for sand (Barker et al., 1991).

Free-head bored piles. Likewise, the free-head condition will give rise to two components of lateral deflection: (1) the component due to the excavation level lateral load, and (2) the component due to the bending moment. The composite lateral deflection for a group of bored piles or a continuous wall may be estimated as suggested by Focht and Koch (1973).

Bending moments

Single bored piles. Procedures are available for shafts restrained at the top, and for shafts with free heads.

Fixed-head bored piles. A simple procedure has been proposed by Evans and Duncan (1982) for estimating the maximum bending moment induced by a lateral load at the top of the shaft (where full restraint exists). The procedure is fully described by Barker et al. (1991) and includes design charts for sand and clay.

Free-head bored piles. The maximum moment in a free-head pile occurs at some depth below excavation level. It is partly due to the lateral load at excavation level and partly due to the moment at this level. The magnitude and location of maximum moment may be estimated as proposed by Matlock and Reese (1961), based on the value of the ground line deflection calculated from the Evans-Duncan (1982) procedure. With Y_s known, the maximum bending moment and its location are determined as follows:

1. Calculate the lateral deflection Y_s as described in the foregoing section. If the lateral load acts above ground line (excavation line), the nonlinear superposition procedure should be used.

2. Calculate the characteristic length T of the free-head shaft from the following:

$$Y_s = \frac{2.435P_s}{E_pI_p} T^3 + \frac{1.623M_e}{E_pI_p} T^2 \tag{7-22}$$

   where all parameters are as previously defined.

3. Calculate the maximum bending moment in the shaft from the expression

$$M = k_M M_e \tag{7-23}$$

   where $M_e = P_se$ as before, and k_M is a moment multiplier obtained from

$$k_M = 1 + 0.756(T/e) \tag{7-23a}$$

4. Obtain the approximate location of the maximum moment by referring to Table 7-7.

TABLE 7-7   Approximate
Location of the
Occurrence of the
Maximum Bending
Moment in Free-Head
Drilled Shafts

T/e	z/T
0.0	0.0
0.1	0.4
0.2	0.5
0.3	0.6
0.4	0.7
0.5	0.8
0.8	0.9
1.6	1.0
3.0	1.2
14.0	1.4

From Barker et al., 1991.

Group of bored piles.   Considerable work has been done by Brown et
al. (1987, 1988). A semiempirical procedure that gives a reasonable
approximation of the maximum moment in the critical row of a group
of bored piles is suggested by Focht and Koch (1973). This can be
applied to groups with fixed-head conditions or to groups with free
heads. If in the latter case the lateral load acts eccentrically above the
ground line (excavation level), the analysis must consider the deflection components due to both the moment and the lateral load.

Structural capacity under axial load
and bending

The design of circular shafts for axial load is covered in Sec. 5-8. Under
combined axial load and bending, the structural capacity is derived
from axial load-moment interaction diagrams. These are envelopes of
possible combinations of moments and axial loads that could possibly
cause failure.

Normalized load-moment interaction diagrams for circular shafts
are presented in Figs. 7-39 and 7-40 for $f_y/f'_c = 10$ and $f_y/f'_c = 15$,
respectively. The factored axial load $\Sigma \gamma_i P_i$ has been normalized by dividing by the factored nominal axial capacity $\phi_a P_n$. All symbols correspond to the notation of Eqs. (5-2), (5-3), and (5-4). Likewise, the
factored bending moment $\gamma_m M$ is normalized by dividing by the factored nominal moment capacity $\phi_m M_n$. The factored structural capacity under axial load is computed from Eq. (5-4). The factor ϕ_a is taken
as 0.70 for tied shafts. Load-moment interaction diagrams similar to

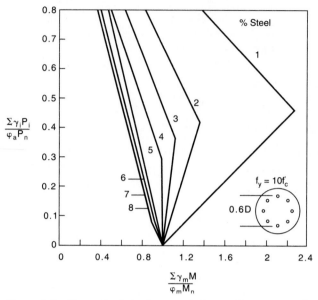

Figure 7-39 Normalized load-moment interaction curves for drilled shafts. $f_y = 10f_c'$.

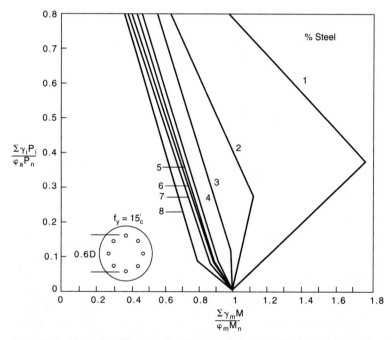

Figure 7-40 Normalized load-moment interaction curves for drilled shafts, $f_y = 15f_c'$.

those in Figs. 7-39 and 7-40 can be developed for f_y/f_c' ratios other than 10 or 15, and cage diameters other than 0.6D.

The procedure for checking the structural adequacy of a circular shaft using load-moment interaction diagrams involves the following steps:

1. Calculate all axial loads and combined load effects $\Sigma \gamma_i P_i$.

2. Calculate the factored axial capacity $\phi_a P_n$ from Eq. (5-4).

3. Compute the factored design bending moment $\gamma_m M$ using factored loads.

4. Estimate the nominal structural moment capacity M_n of the shaft from Table 7-8.

5. Compute $\phi_m M_n$ using $\phi_m = 0.90$.

6. Calculate the ratios $\Sigma \gamma_i P_i / \phi_a P_n$ and $\Sigma \gamma_m M / \phi_m M_n$ and use these as coordinates to locate a corresponding point. If this point is close to the interaction diagram on the inside area, the circular shaft is adequate. If it fails outside this region, the shaft must be redesigned.

Design Example 7-5 A 36-in-diameter circular shaft is reinforced with 20 No. 8 bars. Compute the moment of inertia I_p and the ratio R_I, using $E_c =$

TABLE 7-8 Nominal Moment Capacity M_n for Drilled Shafts

Ratio of area of steel to gross cross-sectional area	$\dfrac{M_n}{f_c' D A_g}$	
	$f_y = 10f_c'$	$f_y = 15f_c'$
0.01	0.037	0.050
0.02	0.067	0.092
0.03	0.088	0.119
0.04	0.107	0.147
0.05	0.126	0.172
0.06	0.144	0.197
0.07	0.161	0.208
0.08	0.176	0.244

f_c' = 28-day concrete cylinder strength
f_y = yield stress of steel
D = diameter of drilled shaft
A_g = gross cross-sectional area of concrete

3500 kips/in², E_s = 29,000 kips/in², and concrete cover c = 3 in. The notation is D = shaft diameter, d_s = steel bar diameter = 1 in.

$$I_c = \frac{\pi D^4}{64} - 20\frac{\pi d_s^4}{64} - \left[2 + \frac{4}{(\sqrt{2})^2}\right]\frac{\pi d_s^2}{4}\left(\frac{D}{2} - c - \frac{d_s}{2}\right)^2 = 81{,}788 \text{ in}^4$$

Moment of inertia of steel

$$I_s = 20\frac{\pi d_s^4}{64} + \left[2 + \frac{4}{(\sqrt{2})^2}\right]\frac{\pi d_s^2}{4}\left(\frac{D}{2} - c - \frac{d_s^2}{2}\right) = 660 \text{ in}^4$$

$$E_p I_p = E_c I_c + E_s I_s = 3500(81{,}788) + 2900(660) = 28.9 \times 10^7 \text{ kip-in}^2$$

For the equivalent homogeneous section, we use $E_p = E_c$. Hence

$$I_p = \frac{E_c I_c + E_s I_s}{E_c} = \frac{28.9 \times 10^7}{3500} = 82{,}570 \text{ in}^4$$

The moment of inertia ratio is $R_I = I_p/I_{\text{solid}}$ or

$$R_I = \frac{82{,}570(64)}{3.14159(36)^4} = 1.001$$

or for practical purposes ≈ 1.00.

Design Example 7-6   Bored piles may be used as load-bearing elements for bridge foundations. In this case the foundation elements must resist, besides axial loads, lateral thrusts because of wind action, longitudinal forces, etc. Such a pile is shown in Fig. 7-41. The circular shafts are reinforced with eight No. 7 bars. A wind load of 90 kips is applied 10 ft above the top of the shafts. It is necessary to estimate the lateral deflection of the system as well as the structural adequacy. The heavy footing fixes the shafts at the top against rotation.

Step 1.   Compute the percentage of steel.

$$A_y = 8\left(\frac{\pi}{4}\right)(0.875)^2 = 4.81 \text{ in}^2 \qquad A_g = \frac{\pi}{4}(18)^2 = 254 \text{ in}^2$$

Percentage of steel = $(4.81)/(254) \times 100 = 1.89$ percent.

Step 2.   Compute the lateral deflection of a single shaft. Load per shaft = $^{90}\!/_6 = 15$ kips. An SPT blow count 10 corresponds to $\phi' = 35°$. From diagrams (Barker et al., 1991), Y_s may be estimated directly:

For D = 18 in: A_y/A_g = 1 percent Y_s = 0.13 in

For D = 18 in: A_y/A_g = 2 percent Y_s = 0.12 in

Step 3.   Estimate the group deflection. Y_g is computed from Eq. (7-17). First we obtain $P_N = K_p \gamma D^3$, Eq. (7-18) or

$$P_N = \left(\frac{1 + \sin 35°}{1 - \cos 35°}\right)\left(\frac{120}{1000(12)^3}\right)(18)^3 = 1.49$$

and

$$Y_g = \frac{9 + 6}{3\sqrt{4 + \dfrac{15}{16(1.49)}}} = 0.28 \text{ in}$$

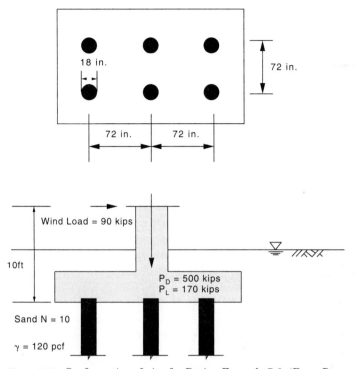

Figure 7-41   Configuration of pier for Design Example 7-6. (*From Barker et al., 1991.*)

Step 4.   Consider lateral and axial loads shown in Fig. 7-41, and establish the location of the resultant force acting on the cap. Use AASHTO load factors and load coefficients.

$$\Sigma \gamma_i P_i = (1.3)(500) + (2.17)(170) = 650 + 369 = 1019 \text{ kips}$$

$$\gamma_w P_w = (1.3)(90) = 117 \text{ kips}$$

Eccentricity e of resultant R, $e = (117)(10)/1019 = 1.15$ ft.

Step 5.   Compute the axial load for the most heavily loaded shaft.

$$P_{xy} = P_g \left(\frac{1}{N_{ds}} + \frac{e_x x}{\Sigma x^2} \right) = (1019) \left[\frac{1}{6} + \frac{(1.15)(6)}{4(6)^2} \right] = 219 \text{ kips/shaft}$$

Step 6.   Estimate maximum bending moment in a single drilled shaft using $P_5 = 15$ kips, and $\varphi' = 35°$; the maximum bending moment is estimated directly from charts (Barker et al., 1991) as $= 780$ kip-in.

Step 7.   Compute maximum moment in the most heavily loaded shaft. First compute the ratio $Y_g/Y_s = 0.28/0.12 = 2.32$. The most severely loaded shaft has a bending moment obtained from the equation

$$M_g = (Y_g/Y_s)^n M_s \tag{7-24}$$

where

$$n = \frac{\gamma_h P_s}{150 P_N} + 0.25 \qquad \text{for clay} \qquad (7\text{-}25)$$

$$n = \frac{\gamma_h P_s}{300 P_N} + 0.3 \qquad \text{for sand} \qquad (7\text{-}26)$$

where γ_h = load factor for lateral load. From Eq. (7-26).

$$n = \frac{(1.3)(15)}{(300)(1.49)} + 0.3 = 0.344$$

and

$$M_g = (2.32)^{0.34} M_s = (1.33)(780) = 1037 \text{ kip-in}$$

Step 8.   Check the structural adequacy using load-moment interaction diagrams.

The factored structural axial load capacity is obtained from Eq. (5-4) as

$$\phi_a P_n = 0.7[(0.85)(4)(254 - 4.81) + 60(4.81)] = 795 \text{ kips/shaft}$$

Moment capacity for a shaft with $f_y / f'_c = 15$ (Table 7-8)

$$\frac{M_n}{f'_c DA_g} = 0.0874 \qquad \text{or} \qquad M_n = (0.0874)(4)(18)(254) = 1598 \text{ kip-in}$$

$$\frac{P_{x,y}}{\phi_a P_n} = \frac{219}{795} = 0.28 \qquad \frac{M_g}{\phi_M M_n} = \frac{1037}{(0.9)(1589)} = 0.72$$

The point (0.72, 0.28) plots inside the load-moment interaction diagram of Fig. 7-40, and hence the structural capacity is more than adequate.

7-6   Single Walls, Built-up Walls, and Composite Sections

General principles

Diaphragm walls used as part of the permanent structure may act independently or as a composite section in a variety of geometric and structural configurations. This section presents the most common solutions emphasizing the special conditions and project requirements that dictate the choice.

Single walls.   A single-wall construction is shown in Fig. 7-42a. The diaphragm wall is the outside member of the permanent structure and also serves as ground support during excavation. The wall thickness and reinforcement are determined for the loading conditions of the final structure where the wall is part of a rigid frame. Vertical and

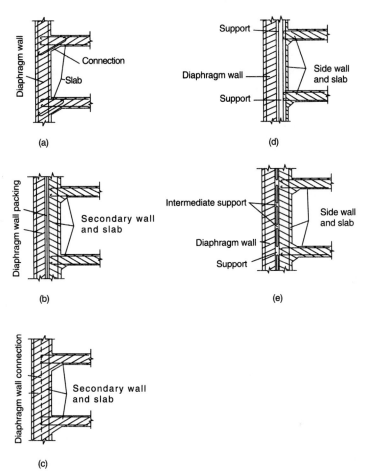

Figure 7-42 Structural configurations with diaphragm walls as part of the permanent structure: (*a*) Single wall. (*b*) Built-up wall with packings in between. (*c*) Composite wall. (*d*) Separate wall. (*e*) Separate wall with intermediate supports.

horizontal loads, temperature stresses, creep and shrinkage, moving loads, etc., must be considered. The wall must also withstand earth stresses, pore pressure, and any other temporary loads and forces that may act at any excavation stage and with the wall braced temporarily.

For this construction to be feasible, the walls must resist all the loads before any permanent floor slabs are in place, and for optimum design the wall thickness requirements should be the same for the temporary and permanent condition. Other factors to be considered are the depth of excavation and face treatment on the interior.

Because the wall is connected directly to the permanent floors (shear or rigid joint), the structural analysis is relatively simple. Structural sections, loading conditions, and bending moments on the single wall and the final structure are shown in Fig. 7-43*a* for (1) at the end of excavation with the temporary bracing in place; (2) immediately after completion; and (3) after considerable time following completion. A significant aspect of these diagrams is the redistribution of moments and shears as the bracing is changed from the temporary struts to the permanent walls and as the structure begins to act as a

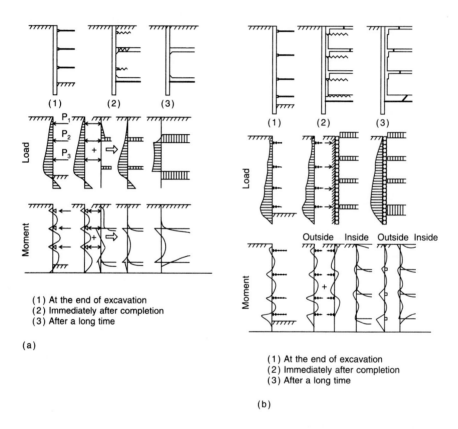

(1) At the end of excavation
(2) Immediately after completion
(3) After a long time

(a)

(1) At the end of excavation
(2) Immediately after completion
(3) After a long time

(b)

Note:

At the second stage vertical loads on rigid frame and horizontal loads on the points of removed struts are assumed to act on the unified structure, taking account of ground reaction corresponding to incremental deformation.
Lastly, apart from the second stage, the stresses at the final stage should also be examined. At the final stage the earth and water pressures are assumed to return to the rest condition.

Figure 7-43 Sections, loads, and bending moments: (*a*) Single wall. (*b*) Built-up wall. (*c*) Composite wall. (*d*) Stress on composite wall. (*e*) Separate wall.

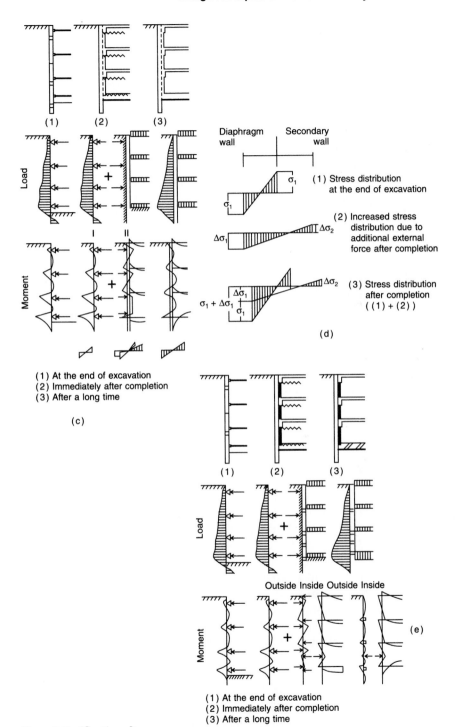

Diaphragm wall   Secondary wall

(1) Stress distribution at the end of excavation

(2) Increased stress distribution due to additional external force after completion

(3) Stress distribution after completion ((1) + (2))

(d)

(1) At the end of excavation
(2) Immediately after completion
(3) After a long time

(c)

Outside Inside Outside Inside

(e)

(1) At the end of excavation
(2) Immediately after completion
(3) After a long time

Figure 7-43 *(Continued)*

rigid frame. In stage 2 vertical loads and lateral earth stresses from the backfilled portions are superimposed on the diagrams of stage 1 to give the composite load and moment diagrams shown (see also stage construction and incremental summation of stresses discussed in other sections). In stage 3, earth stresses are assumed to return to the at rest condition.

Built-up walls. A built-up wall is shown in Fig. 7-42b. In this case a secondary wall is cast with the interior structure against the outside diaphragm wall. The latter may be treated, however, as part of the permanent structure. Because the quality of concrete at the interface is usually poor, shear between the two walls is not considered.

Normally, design calculations are carried out separately for the two walls. Since the walls are in contact, the design must consider compatibility in their flexural deformations. Thus it is customary to divide stresses, produced after the walls are in contact, between the two systems in proportion to their stiffness.

Structural sections, loading conditions, and moment diagrams are shown conceptually in Fig. 7-43b for the outside and inside walls at (1) the end of excavation; (2) immediately after completion; and (3) after considerable time. The same principles of superposition as in the single wall are applied to obtain composite results. The moments and axial forces are distributed among the two walls as follows:

$$M_1 = \frac{I_1}{I_1 + I_2} M_0 \qquad N_1 = \frac{A_1}{A_1 + A_2} N_0 \qquad (7\text{-}27)$$

$$M_2 = \frac{I_2}{I_1 + I_2} M_0 \qquad N_2 = \frac{A_2}{A_1 + A_2} N_0 \qquad (7\text{-}28)$$

where M_1, M_2 = moment distributed to diaphragm wall and secondary wall, respectively

N_1, N_2 = shear force distributed to diaphragm wall and secondary wall, respectively

M_0 = total moment

N_0 = total shear force

I_1, I_2 = moment of inertia of diaphragm wall and secondary wall, respectively

A_1, A_2 = area of diaphragm wall and secondary wall, respectively

Composite walls. Composite walls were discussed briefly in Sec. 6-13. The diaphragm wall and the secondary wall are integrated, in order to resist the shear stresses at the interface, by means of shear connectors (as shown in Fig. 6-51) or using the deck plate shown in Fig. 6-52. A composite wall section is shown in Fig. 7-42c.

A composite wall may be selected where the wall thickness in the final structure exceeds the required wall thickness during excavation and temporary bracing. Structural sections, loading conditions, and bending moments for a composite wall are shown in Fig. 7-43c for (1) the end of excavation; (2) immediately after completion; and (3) long after completion. Note that at stage 2 the moments caused by loads acting on the composite structure (floor loads, etc.) are superimposed on the moments from stage 1 and give the moment diagrams shown for stage 3, adjusted, however, as the lateral earth stresses return to the at rest condition. The stress distribution in the composite wall is shown in Fig. 7-43d and is self-explanatory.

In addition to the redistribution of moments because of changes in the bracing levels, new loads, and rigid frame action, the design should also investigate the effect of differential shrinkage strains between the two concrete layers.

Separate walls.   In this scheme the diaphragm wall and the secondary wall of the interior box are structurally and physically separated as shown in Fig. 7-42d. The diaphragm wall resists lateral earth loads and water pressure while the slabs of the permanent box serve as lateral bracing. Loads acting on the final structure are resisted internally by the interior box and have no effect on the diaphragm walls.

Where the unsupported wall height is considerable, intermediate supports can be provided as shown in Fig. 7-42e. Lateral loads may be redistributed to both walls after considering the construction sequence and incremental staging, but with explicit design assumptions. Structural sections, loading conditions, and moment diagrams are shown conceptually in Fig. 7-43e for the three main stages. Again, the effect of superposition is obvious from stage 1, at the end of excavation, to stages 2 and 3, immediately after completion and after a long time. Both walls are active in the final loading condition.

Design Example 7-7   A section of the Osaka (Japan) metro system has a double deck. A net interior width of 12.2 m (40 ft) is necessary to accommodate three lines, and has no interior columns. In addition to the normal traffic and dead loads, the structure must resist surcharges from several piers of an elevated expressway, and direct loads from a proposed new expressway acting on the top slab of the subway section.

Solution   The design considered diaphragm walls in two configurations: (1) built-up walls where the diaphragm wall and the secondary wall resist moments and axial forces according to the relative stiffness as shown in Eqs. (7-27) and (7-28); and (2) a composite section where the two walls are consolidated into a single structural unit. The two schemes are illustrated in the cross section of

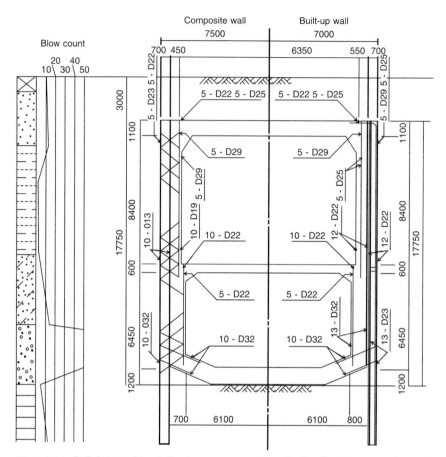

Figure 7-44 Soil data and typical subway cross section, Osaka (Japan); composite wall compared with built-up wall. All dimensions are in mm, and reinforcing bars in Japanese designation.

Fig. 7-44, and evidently the resulting advantages of the composite sections are: (1) reduction of wall thickness of the secondary wall, and (2) reduction in the reinforcement requirements of the secondary wall by using a single reinforcement layer (one face only).

Design parameters are: unit weight of soil $\gamma = 1.6$ t/m^3 above groundwater table, $\gamma' = 1.0$ t/m^3 effective weight; coefficient of earth pressure $K_0 = 0.406$.

Allowable stresses in the concrete: $f'_c = 240$ kg/cm^2 (3400 lb/in^2), $f_c = 80$ kg/cm^2 (1150 lb/in^2); allowable stress in reinforcement $f_s = 1600$ kg/cm^2 (23,000 lb/in^2).

Bond at the interface between the two concrete surfaces is not considered, and all shear forces are resisted by the diagonal steel bars as shown in Fig. 7-45. The diagonal connector bar is a deformed type 16 mm in diameter (No. 5 U.S. equivalent).

The ultimate shear resistance of the joint is

$$Q_u = P_v + \mu P_H \qquad (7\text{-}29)$$

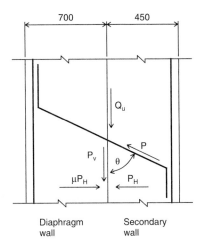

Figure 7-45 Shear resistance at joint; diaphragm and secondary wall composite section.

where $P_v = P \cos \theta$, $P_H = P \sin \theta$, $P = A_s f_y$, and μ = coefficient of friction at the interface. For allowable stress design a factor of safety of 3 is used. Coupling devices are used to connect diagonal bars, with their capacity determined from tension tests. Figure 7-46 shows the shear force diagram and the diagonal connector steel arrangement in the cross section. All bar symbols refer to Japanese designation. Note that Eq. (7-29) is similar to Eq. (6-19).

The construction sequence for this example is shown in Fig. 7-47 and is carried out in three main stages A, B, and C.

Stage A, shown in Fig. 7-47a, includes the following:

1. Construct guide walls.
2. Construct diaphragm walls.
3. Drive intermediate point bearing piles for interior support of the temporary decking. Stage B is shown in Fig. 7-47b and continues with the following operations.
4. Install temporary street decking (used also as top bracing).
5. Carry out the first stage excavation to the level of the second temporary bracing. Install temporary bracing as shown.
6. Construct upper side walls W_1 and top slab B_0 (composite construction). When the concrete has attained its full strength, transfer the pile loads to the upper slab and cut piles below that level.
7. Continue excavation to third temporary bracing level and install this bracing.
8. Complete excavation to final level (underside of bottom slab).
9. Construct bottom slab B_2, side walls W_2 and intermediate slab B_1 (composite construction).

Stage C is shown in Fig. 7-47c and includes the following restoration operations:

10. Remove temporary lateral bracing.
11. Remove temporary street decking.
12. Backfill the area above top slab.
13. Resurface street and restore all surface functions.

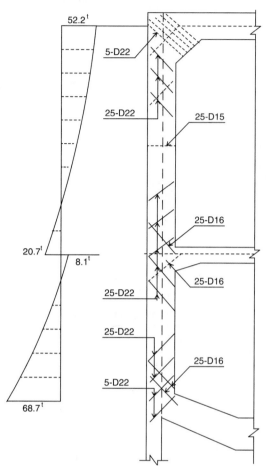

Figure 7-46 Shear force diagram and diagonal connection steel arrangement.

Design Example 7-8 Figure 7-48 shows typical cross sections of the Rio De Janeiro subway. The final structure consists of an outside diaphragm wall and an inside secondary wall cast against the outside wall. The design is carried out treating the system as a built-up wall with moments and axial forces distributed according to Eqs. (7-27) and (7-28).

Design parameters. For reinforced concrete, the strength parameters are $f'_c = 240$ kg/cm², $f_c = 80$ kg/cm², or 120 kg/cm² (temporary load).

Bond stress $u_{all} = 18$ kg/cm²   or 27 kg/cm² (temporary load)

Shear stress $u_{all} = 9$ kg/cm²   or 13.5² kg/cm (temporary load)

The allowable stress in the reinforcement steel is $f_s = 1600$ kg/cm², or 2400 kg/cm² (for temporary load). These stresses conform to the structural requirements of Japanese codes. The weight of reinforced concrete is 2.4 t/m³ (150 lb/ft³).

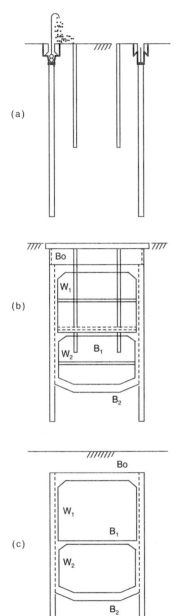

(a)

(b)

(c)

Figure 7-47 Construction sequence, subway structure of Design Example 7-7.

The soil parameters are summarized as follows:

$$\text{Unit weight of soil } \gamma = 1.8 \text{ t/m}^3$$

$$\text{Submerged weight } \gamma' = 1.0 \text{ t/m}^3$$

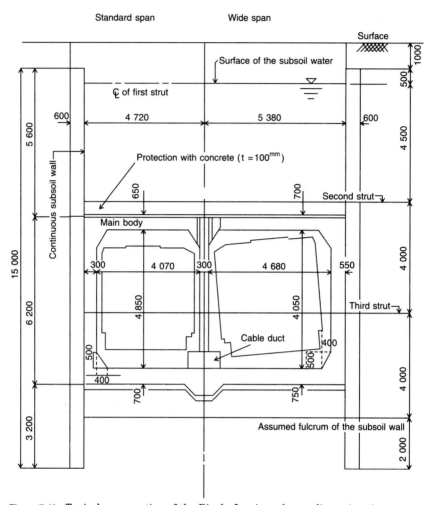

Figure 7-48 Typical cross section of the Rio de Janeiro subway; dimensions in mm.

At rest earth pressure coefficient $K_0 = 0.5$ (based on $\phi = 30°$). Active earth pressure coefficient $K_a = 0.3$. Other vertical loads result from live load surcharge applied at ground level (summarized in Table 7-9).

Moments and shears, diaphragm walls only.   These are calculated for two construction stages, shown in Fig. 7-49a and b. A modified equivalent beam is used for the first construction stage with the excavation completed (Fig. 7-49a). A fixed end is assumed at distance H_0 below excavation level, and this is taken as the point of zero load. The dimension H_0 is estimated empirically as follows:

$$\text{Hard compacted soil } H_0 = 0.5 \text{ m}$$

$$\text{Ordinary soil } H_0 = 1.0 \text{ to } 2.0 \text{ m}$$

$$\text{Soft, loose soil } H_0 = 3.0 \text{ to } 4.0 \text{ m}$$

TABLE 7-9 Effect of Live Load Surcharge at Surface, Design Example 7-8

Depth from surface, meters	Effect of live load, t/m^2
1.5–2.0	2.2
2.0–2.5	1.6
2.5–3.0	1.4
3.0–3.5	1.2
3.5–4.0	1.1
4.0–5.0	1.0
5.0–6.0	0.9
6.0–7.0	0.8
7.0	0.7

For this example, $H_0 = 1$ m. Lateral earth stresses are computed from the equation $q = \gamma'Kh + \gamma_w h$. For the first construction stage, the pressures shown in the diagram of Fig. 7-49a are computed for $K_a = 0.3$, as follows: $q_1 = 0.81$ t/m^2, $q_2 = 2.16$ t/m^2, $q_3 = 11.86$ t/m^2, $q_4 = 15.76$ t/m^2. Likewise, the pressures for the second construction stage are $(K_a = 0.3)$ $q_1' = 0.81$ t/m^2, $q_2' = 2.16$ t/m^2, $q_3' = 15.04$ t/m^2, with the wall assumed to be fixed or pinned at the base slab.

The equivalent continuous beams are shown in Fig. 7-50a and b for the first and second construction stage, respectively. For the second construction stage, two analyses are carried out for case 1 and 2, bottom of wall fixed and pinned, respectively.

Bending-moment and shear diagrams for the foregoing loading conditions and equivalent beams are shown in Fig. 7-51. For the second construction stage, two diagrams are shown, for fixed end and pinned end, respectively.

In this analysis the wall is treated as one-way slab spanning vertically and reinforced in the vertical direction. Moments and shears are computed from first-order analysis and small-deflection theory. From Fig. 7-51 it follows that the second construction stage controls. An approximate preliminary design moment is obtained by taking the mean value of the moments computed for case 1 and 2.

Moment at second strut. $M_1 = -(15.00 + 26.63)/2 = -20.82$ t-m (negative).

Positive moment. $M_2 = +(17.50 + 34.44)/2 = 25.97$ t-m, occurring with the third strut removed (second construction stage).

Moment at bottom slab. $M_3 = -(39.47 + 0)/2 = -19.73$ t-m (negative) obtained assuming support condition between full and zero fixity.

Likewise, the shears are averaged from case 1 and 2 of the second construction stage as follows:

$$\text{Shear at first strut } V_1 = (0.50 + 3.08)/2 = 1.79 \text{ t}$$

$$\text{Shear at second strut } V_2 = (17.02 + 24.90)/2 = 20.96 \text{ t}$$

$$\text{Shear at both struts } V_3 = (38.46 + 30.54)/2 = 34.50 \text{ t}$$

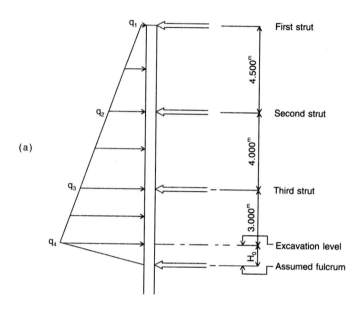

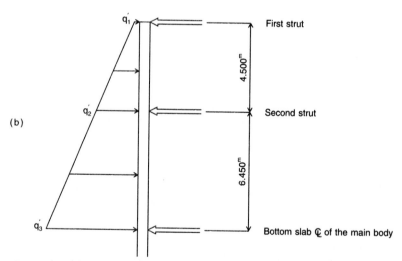

Figure 7-49 Lateral pressure diagram for diaphragm wall: (*a*) First construction stage with all three temporary struts in place and full excavation. (*b*) Second construction stage with the bottom slab in place and third strut level removed.

The requirements of steel reinforcement are based on a wall length of 1 m. For allowable stress design the area of steel per meter of wall length is

$$A_s = \frac{M}{f_{\text{all}} jd} \tag{7-30}$$

The area of steel A_s required at each location is summarized in Tables 7-10 and 7-11 for the first and second construction stage, respectively.

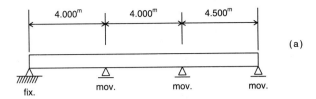

(a)

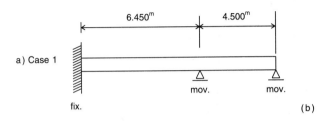

a) Case 1

(b)

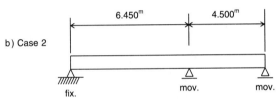

b) Case 2

Figure 7-50 Continuous-beam models: (a) First construction stage. (b) Second construction stage. Wall of Fig. 7-49.

Moments and shears, main structure.   Referring to the loading diagram shown in Fig. 7-52, we calculate the following loads:

- Dead load on the upper slab

$$q_1 = (1.5)(1.8) + (5.0)(1.0 + 1.0) + (0.65)(2.40)$$
$$+ (0.1)(0.23) + 0.9 = 15.18 \text{ t/m}^2$$

- Earth pressure on sidewall (based on $K_0 = 0.5$)

$$q_2 = (1.5)(1.8)(0.5) + (5.42)(1.0)(0.5) + (1.0)(5.42) = 9.49 \text{ t/m}^2$$

$$q_3 = (1.5)(1.8)(0.5) + (10.95)(1.0) = 17.78 \text{ t/m}^2$$

- Dead load on sidewalls and center column

$$p_1 = (2.4)(5.42)(0.60 + 0.50) + (2.4)(0.4)(0.5)(\tfrac{1}{2}) = 13.04 \text{ t/m}$$

$$= (4.05)(2.40)(0.3) + (0.4)(0.4)(2.4)(2) + (0.5)(0.4)(2.4) = 4.05 \text{ t/m}$$

Reaction on the bottom slab:

$$q_4 = (15.18) + (2 \times 13.04 + 4.05)/9.54 = 18.33 \text{ t/m}^2$$

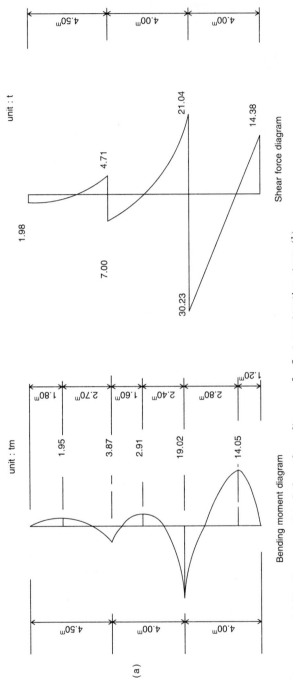

Bending moment diagram

Shear force diagram

Figure 7-51 (*a*) Bending-moment and shear-force diagrams for first construction stage. (*b*) Bending-moment diagrams for case 1 and case 2 of second construction stage. (*c*) Shear-force diagram for case 1 and case 2 of second construction stage.

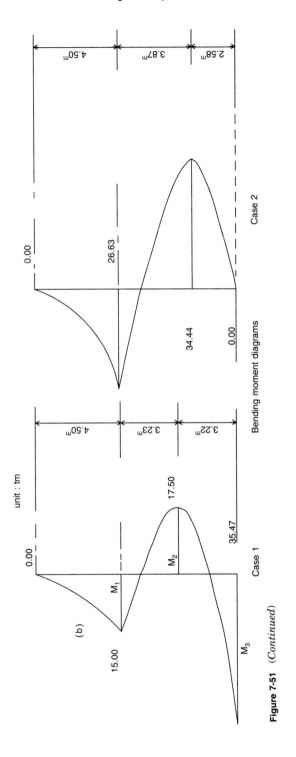

Figure 7-51 (*Continued*)

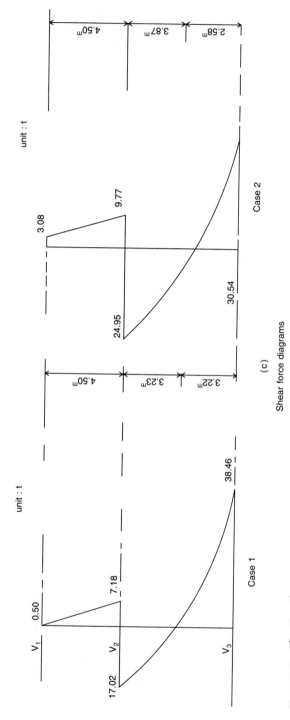

Figure 7-51 *(Continued)*

TABLE 7-10 Required A_s for First Construction Stage, Design Example 7-8

M, kg-cm	f_{all}, kg/cm^2	d, cm	A_s, cm^2	Arrangement of A_s, cm^2
195,000	2400	50	1.85	D13 × 4 = 5.07
	(1600 × 1.5)			
387,000	2400	50	3.68	—
	(1600 × 1.5)			
291,000	2400	50	2.77	—
	(1600 × 1.5)			
1,902,000	2400	50	18.10	—
	(1600 × 1.5)			
1,447,000	2400	50	13.78	—
	(1600 × 1.5)			

Bending-moment and shear diagrams are shown in Fig. 7-53a and b for the standard section and the wide-span section, respectively, and for the loads of Fig. 7-52.

The moments and shears distributed to the outside (diaphragm) wall and the inside wall are computed from Eqs. (7-27) and (7-28), where M_0 and N_0 are the total moment and shear, respectively, shown in the diagrams of Fig. 7-53, and other notation corresponds to the symbols of Eqs. (7-25) and (7-26).

Standard-span section. First we calculate the section properties

$$I_1 = \frac{1 \times 0.6^3}{12} \qquad I_2 = \frac{1 \times 0.5^3}{12}$$

$$k_1 = \frac{I_1}{I_1 + I_2} = \frac{0.6^3}{0.6^3 + 0.5^3} = 0.633$$

$$k_2 = \frac{I_2}{I_1 + I_2} = \frac{0.5^3}{0.6^3 + 0.5^3} = 0.367$$

$$A_1 = 0.6 \times 1.0 = 0.6 \qquad A_2 = 0.5 \times 1.0 = 0.5$$

$$k_1' = \frac{A_1}{A_1 + A_2} = \frac{0.6}{0.6 + 0.5} = 0.545 \qquad k_2' = \frac{A_2}{A_1 + A_2} = \frac{0.5}{0.6 + 0.5} = 0.455$$

TABLE 7-11 Required A_s for Second Construction Stage, Design Example 7-8

M, kg-cm	f_{all}, kg/cm^2	d, cm^2	A_s, cm^2	Arrangement of A_s, cm^2
2,082,000	2400	50	19.83	—
	(1600 × 1.5)			
2,597,000	2400	50	24.73	D22 × 8 = 30.97
	(1600 × 1.5)			
1,973,000	2400	50	18.79	D22 × 8 = 30.97
	(1600 × 1.5)			

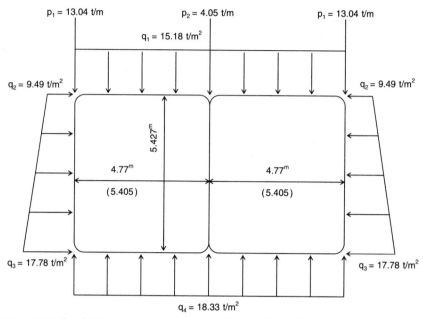

Figure 7-52 Load diagram for main structure, Design Example 7-8.

Moments and shears for the diaphragm wall and the secondary wall are computed at three locations: (1) negative moment at the junction of wall and upper slab; (2) positive moment near midheight of wall; and (3) negative moment at the junction of wall and bottom slab. These moments and shears are tabulated in Table 7-12.

Wide-span section. Likewise, the section properties are

$$I_1 = \frac{1 \times 0.6^3}{12} \qquad I_2 = \frac{1 \times 0.55^3}{12}$$

$$k_1 = \frac{I_1}{I_1 + I_2} = \frac{0.55^3}{0.6^3 + 0.55^3} = 0.565$$

$$k_2 = \frac{I_2}{I_1 + I_2} = \frac{0.55^3}{0.6^3 + 0.55^3} = 0.435$$

$$A_1 = 0.6 \qquad A_2 = 0.55$$

$$k_1' = \frac{A_1}{A_1 + A_2} = \frac{0.6}{0.6 + 0.55} = 0.522$$

$$k_2' = \frac{A_2}{A_1 + A_2} = \frac{0.55}{0.6 + 0.55} = 0.478$$

Moments and shears are likewise calculated from the same locations for the diaphragm and the secondary wall, and are tabulated in Table 7-13.

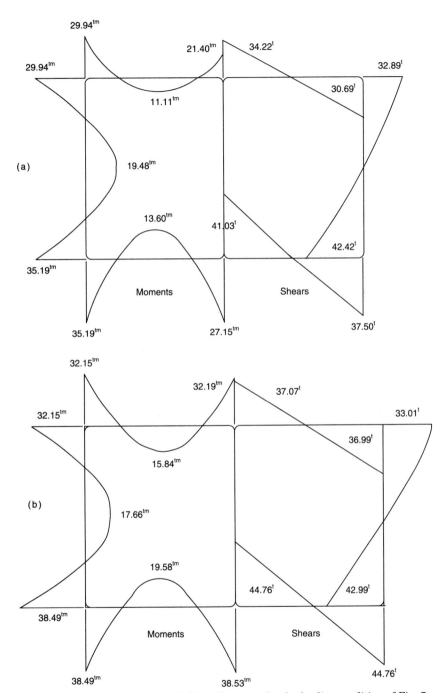

Figure 7-53 Bending-moment and shear diagrams for the loading condition of Fig. 7-52: (*a*) Standard-span section. (*b*) Wide-span section.

TABLE 7-12 Moments and Shears for Diaphragm and Secondary Wall, Standard Span Section, Design Example 7-8

M_0, t-m	N_0, t	k_1, k_2	k_1', k_2'	M_1, t-m	M_2, t-m	N_1, t	N_2, t
29.94	42.42	0.633	0.545	18.95	10.99	23.12	19.30
		0.367	0.455				
19.48	42.42	0.633	0.545	12.33	7.15	23.12	19.30
		0.367	0.455				
35.19	42.42	0.633	0.545	22.28	12.91	23.12	19.30
		0.367	0.455				

Stresses in steel and concrete, diaphragm wall.   Stresses in the steel and the concrete are computed for the second construction stage and for the final construction stage with the entire structure in place.

Second construction stage.   Stresses in the steel and the concrete are tabulated in Table 7-14 for the selected area of steel A_s. The moment M in the first column is the average moment M_1 and M_2 calculated from the diagrams of Fig. 7-51b. Note that the allowable stresses are 50 percent higher because the loads are temporary. Both f_c and f_s are below the allowable.

The maximum shear is 34.50 t, calculated as v_3 (average value of shears shown in Fig. 7-51c). The maximum shear stress is

$$v = 34{,}500/(100)(60) = 5.75 \text{ kg/cm}^2 < 13.5 \text{ kg/cm}^2$$

Final construction stage.   Stresses in the steel and the concrete are tabulated in Table 7-15 for the standard-span section and for the wide-span section. The moments shown are the M_1 values taken from Tables 7-12 and 7-13. Both the concrete stresses and the steel stresses are below the allowable (recall all $f_c = 80 \text{ kg/cm}^2$, $f_s = 1600 \text{ kg/cm}^2$).

Commentary

The choice between single, built-up, and composite walls usually is a straightforward problem based on construction feasibility and economy, and subject to the following comments:

1. Single walls are economical where the structural capacity (also wall thickness) in the long-term condition does not exceed the opti-

TABLE 7-13 Moments and Shears for Diaphragm and Secondary Wall, Wide Span Section, Design Example 7-8

M_0, t-m	N_0, t	k_1, k_2	k_1', k_2'	M_1, t-m	M_2, t-m	N_1, t	N_2, t
32.15	42.99	0.565	0.522	18.16	13.99	22.44	20.55
		0.435	0.478				
17.66	42.99			9.98	7.68	22.44	20.55
38.49	42.99			21.75	16.74	22.44	20.55

TABLE 7-14   Stresses in Steel and Concrete; Diaphragm Wall, Second Construction Stage

M, t-m	A_s, cm^2	$p = A_s/A_g$	f_c, kg/cm^2	f_s, kg/cm^2
20.82	8-D19 = 22.92	0.0045	60	2047
25.97	8-D22 = 30.97	0.0062	68	1901

mum wall thickness for the temporary (construction) stage. The design must also consider the connection details, changes in residual stresses, and stresses induced by a tendency for differential settlement.

2. For the built-up wall only moments at the joints (caused by long-term stresses) are redistributed to the two components, diaphragm wall and secondary wall. The design should check, however, any tendency to undergo differential settlement. At the worst case the diaphragm wall may end up supporting the entire structure.

3. A composite wall has the highest structural capacity, but this is an advantage where long-term stresses far exceed construction stresses. Any reduction in total wall thickness must be balanced against the cost of shear connections.

4. The design for the long-term condition is based on simple assumptions and load diagrams (for example, the load diagram shown in Fig. 7-52). With load factor analysis several load diagrams must be prepared for each type of load, and the resulting effects computed and factored separately. Often the construction stage may be a more complex problem and may even govern the design. Since this is a temporary condition, increased allowable stresses are acceptable in the design.

5. Wall embedment below excavation level at a given stage may be omitted if there is sufficient bracing above this level, if the wall is checked as a cantilever below the lowest bracing, and if base failure is not expected. For example, referring to Fig. 7-49a the wall could be terminated just below excavation level ($H_0 \approx 0$) if its structural capacity is enough to resist cantilever effects.

TABLE 7-15   Stresses in Steel and Concrete; Diaphragm Wall, Final Construction Stage

	M, t-m	A_s, cm^2	$p = A_s/A_g$	f_c, kg/cm^2	f_s, kg/cm^2
Standard span section	18.95	8-D19 = 22.92	0.0045	57	1420
	12.33	8-D22 = 30.97	0.0062	34	575
	22.28	8-D22 = 30.97	0.0062	59	1230
Wide span section	18.16	22.92	0.0045	54	1300
	9.98	30.97	0.0062	27	380
	21.75	30.97	0.0062	58	1190

6. Live loads acting on the bottom slab may be ignored only if they can be assumed to be resisted directly by bearing below the slab.

7-7 Walls Used as Underpinning

Design considerations

As a general method underpinning involves the addition of structural units to the foundation to give extra support at or below grade. In the technical context it is the insertion of a new foundation of support below an existing one for the transfer of load to a lower level. In a broader sense underpinning may also refer to the lateral protection of a foundation, the strengthening of ground, or both. The decision to underpin, protect laterally, or introduce ground strengthening depends on various interrelated factors such as cost, technical expediency, and associated risk of each alternative. In this section, we consider the lateral protection of a foundation provided by a diaphragm wall.

The need for underpinning.   Consider the structure shown in Fig. 7-54. For the existing footing shown in Fig. 7-54a the need for underpinning and/or protection is obvious; in Fig. 7-54b, although the excavation level is above the existing footing, the removal of the overburden can weaken the supporting ground and thus decrease the load-carrying capacity of the foundation. Instead of providing a conventional underpinning element, a diaphragm wall can be constructed to protect the open excavation and the existing structure.

This solution is feasible provided that large ground movement is prevented and the protection is supplemented by ground strengthen-

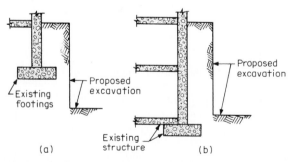

Figure 7-54   Excavation adjacent to existing structures: (a) Base of excavation below existing footing. (b) Base of excavation above existing footing.

ing where necessary. The treatment may be temporary or permanent and includes freezing or grouting. An underpinning scheme based on the foregoing principle is shown in Fig. 5-24 and is discussed in Sec. 5-12.

Assessment of existing structures. The intent of underpinning is to control settlement associated with new construction. Since the settlement that a building or structure can tolerate is not predictable within the scope and means of engineering analysis, correlation with documented history and performance records under similar conditions is essential. Useful conclusions can be drawn by studying buildings with known settlement records, and this reference can provide the basis for an adequate underpinning scheme.

Estimating actual loads acting on foundation elements is difficult but essential. If the building records and plan examination do not produce these data, a structural analysis is mandatory.

Effects of construction. In a physical sense a building or structure can be successfully protected yet suffer some damage associated with construction effects. These effects may be caused by (1) overloading a soil by spread footing if the soil strength is reduced because of the construction; (2) introducing unexpected eccentric loading with torsional components; (3) not considering fully the sensitivity of the building; (4) inducing lateral displacement causing cracking, particularly if the building shifts differentially; and (5) failing to make allowance for these effects in the design.

Criteria of tolerable conditions. The diaphragm walls are designed and constructed to prevent damage, but indiscriminate elimination of damages is not considered practical or economically expedient. An equally viable approach is to limit the extent of damage provided structural collapse and loss of utility is not involved.

Acceptable tolerance should be defined by the amount of external settlement and lateral movement that can occur and still render the building or structure usable and safe under the provisions of applicable building codes. In the usual case time will permit steps to stop ground movement, with provisions for restoration of damage.

Design approach to underpinning. The usual approach to the design of diaphragm walls for lateral protection and as ground support involves three basic steps: (1) predict probable wall movement and settlement because of the new excavation, and apply these data to estimate tolerable settlement and deformation of adjoining buildings and structures; (2) estimate potential changes in soil strength underneath existing footings, and study the feasibility of soil strengthening to maintain the same load-carrying capacity; and (3) estimate the effect of existing foundations on the lateral pressures acting on the diaphragm wall. Wall and ground movement are discussed in other sections, and hence this discussion covers steps 2 and 3.

The soil strength beneath a footing can be assessed by reference to bearing capacity theories, but at best only an estimate is obtained. The bearing capacity of the soil may have to be determined either immediately beneath the foundation or at some other critical depth, taking into account the initial geometry of the failure surface and changes caused by the new construction. Since 1940, about 15 theoretical solutions have been proposed, including the Terzaghi, Meyerhof, Hansen, and Vesic methods (Bowles, 1988). The Terzaghi method was proposed from a slightly modified bearing capacity theory developed by Prandtl in 1920, who used the theory of plasticity to analyze the punching of a rigid base into a softer (soil) material.

Using the Terzaghi approach, the problem is as presented in Fig. 7-55. The existing footing is under the action of load P, tending to push the wedge into the ground underneath, with resulting displacement of zones II and III. This tendency is resisted by shear stresses developed along the slip planes ab and ac and by the weight of the soil mass in these zones.

The adjacent continuous excavation intercepts the right zone III and deprives this zone of soil weight; the removal of earth can also cause long-term changes in shear strength. The result may be some tilting of the foundation by clockwise rotation because the right side is weaker than the left.

If a weak zone exists at depth z from the base of the foundation, there may be loss of bearing capacity if the walls intercept the ge-

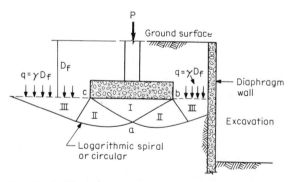

Figure 7-55 The bearing-capacity solution according to the Terzaghi method, modified to include the effect of excavation.

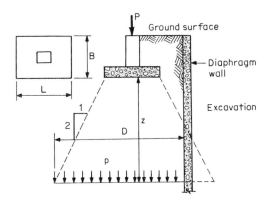

Figure 7-56 Load distribution and increase in the average soil pressure at depth z because of adjacent excavation.

ometry of pressure distribution as shown in Fig. 7-56. For simplicity the vertical pressure is distributed according to a 1:2 slope. The excavation intercepts the pressure zone as shown, and the result is more pressure unevenly distributed. In both cases shown in Figs. 7-55 and 7-56 increased soil stress will result in more strain. In most cases settlement criteria will control the allowable bearing capacity. Interestingly, analysis based on bearing capacity theories gives results that at best are crude estimates.

Lateral effects of heavy loads. Heavy loads are permanent surcharges at ground surface, and loads within a soil mass. Examples are foundation mats or heavy individual footings. A theoretical method is based on elastic theory. Simple solutions can be obtained by referring to the diagrams of Figs. 4-101 and 4-102 that apply readily to the most common cases of lateral underpinning.

Factors affecting choice. Diaphragm walls used as underpinning justify the idea of a low-cost solution if they are incorporated in the final structure. This cost is also influenced by (1) the required wall embedment below excavation level; (2) the nature of ground to be excavated; (3) overall stability during trenching, concreting, and general excavation; and (4) method of lateral bracing. Secant pile walls in prebored holes in bentonite slurry may be better choices in difficult ground conditions, and can provide a higher factor of safety during the construction of the wall.

Observed performance

The literature contains a well-documented record of diaphragm walls used as underpinning in a variety of conditions and soil types. This record includes the effect of construction operations, soil strength, wall stiffness, bracing stiffness and prestressing, and interaction with final structure.

An example reported by Ware et al. (1980) includes four buildings field-instrumented in Washington, D.C. The excavation was 65 ft long and was braced by a composite steel-and-concrete diaphragm wall. The wall consists of 33-in beams spaced at 7-ft intervals and concrete panels, with strut bracing at four levels and 10 to 15-ft embedment below excavation level.

At the site the ground consists of fill in the upper layers, underlain by stiff to medium-stiff clay ($c = 1.2$ kips/ft^2), and compact brown fine-to-medium sand ($\phi = 32°$ to $34°$, $\gamma = 130$ lb/ft^3). The depth of these layers varies from 25 to 30 ft. Below these strata is a layer of hard red-brown and gray plastic clay ($c = 2$ to 5 kips/ft^2) interbedded with layers of sand, cobbles, and some boulders ($\phi = 32°$ to $38°$). This clay extends 10 to 15 ft below the base of excavation.

Initially, the excavation was carried out in front of an 8-story building with exterior walls applying a load of 53 kips/ft. Inward lateral movement reached 0.8 in, or slightly higher than the specified maximum ¾ in. As a result this building underwent settlement that reached ½ in maximum. The remaining three buildings were subjected to heave that, although measurable, was small and inconsequential.

A recent example reported by Winter et al. (1991) involves a diaphragm wall built adjacent to a historic church in Washington, D.C., as lateral protection against movement during excavation for a deep basement. The wall also serves as the structural wall in the finished structure. A typical section of the closest wall-building proximity is shown in Fig. 7-57; at this location the wall is less than 10 ft from the building line and is braced by two rows of ground anchors in the upper section and by sufficient embedment below excavation level. The soil profile indicates 10 ft of fill, underlain by sand and clay to about 50 to 70 ft. Some of the clay layers are relatively soft. The new structure is therefore designed to have caisson foundations drilled into very compact clayey sand, a stratum selected also to support the loads carried by the diaphragm wall.

For temporary excavation support conditions, the diaphragm wall was designed for a trapezoidal pressure diagram with $p = 0.24\gamma H$. This includes a 20 percent increase over normally expected earth pressures as allowance for the lateral effect of the existing foundation. The diaphragm wall is 2 ft thick and was formed using steel stop ends. The ground anchors were prestressed to 120 percent of their design load and locked in at 90 percent.

Lateral wall movement for the wall of Fig. 7-57 is shown in Fig. 7-58 for two inclinometer locations. The displacement curves corre-

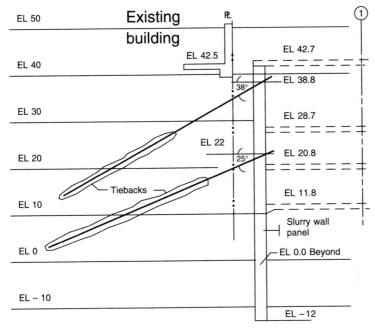

Figure 7-57 Typical design section, wall adjacent to historic church, Washington, D.C. (*From Winter et al., 1991.*)

spond to the initial, intermediate, and final excavation stage. The deflection pattern indicates a typical bowing out of the wall with maximum movement near the lower third of the excavation height. Maximum displacement is less than 10 mm (0.4 in).

7-8   Structural Combinations

Prefounded columns

The use of underpinning implies that an underground structure cannot be built until some form of excavation has been completed to reach the intended foundation level. By analogy, underpinning may not be necessary if an underground structure or the below-ground portion of a building can be built either before or simultaneously with the excavation.

Using a deep basement or a deep excavation level to support loads from superstructure has technical merits since the load intensity on the ground below that level is reduced by the weight of ground excavated, and this provides the basis for the design of compensated foun-

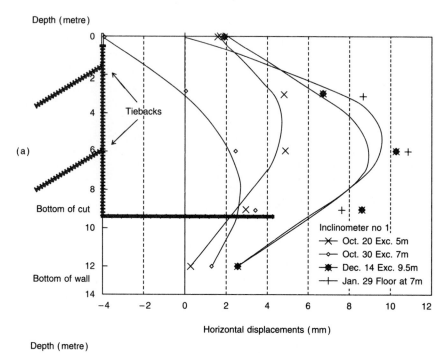

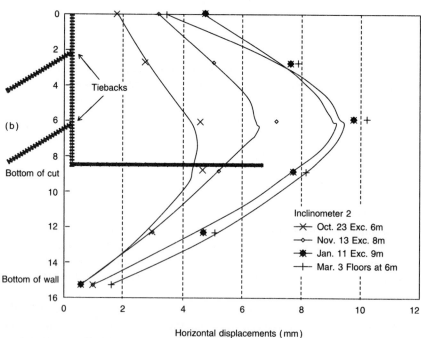

Figure 7-58 Lateral wall movement at two inclinometer locations, wall of Fig. 7-57: (*a*) Inclinometer 1. (*b*) Inclinometer 2. (*From Winter et al., 1991.*)

dations. Theoretically, therefore, the deeper the basement the cheaper the foundation, but in reality the deeper the excavation the more expensive the ground support and the higher the cost of excavation. Thus building a deep basement for the purpose of supporting superstructure loads is rare and unorthodox, but a deep basement accommodates better load transfer, particularly for relatively large loads and where a foundation mat is used.

Other considerations result from architectural and structural trends that tend to dictate heavier column loads because of larger panels used to provide unobstructed floor space. In other instances, the main superstructure is formed as a central core and covers only a small part of the usable underground space. These arrangements affect the load distribution through the basement substructure and, by analogy, the load-transfer scheme. In many instances conventional column-and-beam construction provides for loads from superstructure to be transferred to load-bearing diaphragm walls in the basement, but a high-rise tower supported on a central core cannot derive these benefits unless the basement is locally deepened at the core (see also Chap. 9).

Alternate construction methods. Conventional designs are based on two construction methods. In the first case, the foundation (usually extended to rock or hardpan) is inserted from the level of general excavation, after making allowance for the underground portion of the building. In the second instance, deep foundation elements (circular, prismatic, etc.) are inserted from ground level but are terminated at the level of the basement raft. If the ground includes clayey soils and a natural water table, unloading at any excavation stage can cause upward swelling of the ground below the excavation level, subjecting the deep foundations to appreciable tension, applied as negative friction. It is well known that concrete subpiers subjected to this action can fail unless they are heavily reinforced.

Prefounded column concept. The prefounded column method is shown conceptually in Fig. 7-59. Beginning at ground level, and in a single operation, it is possible to construct the foundation element and the basement portion of a column as shown in Fig. 7-59a and b. In this example, a casing is sunk to just below the basement level as the hole is bored, and the excavation is continued below this level under bentonite slurry. When boring is completed, the steel column (below-ground portion) is lowered into the casing, accurately positioned, and firmly held in place. Concrete is tremied into the hole and up to the intended basement level, with the column maintaining sufficient embedment for load transfer. When this operation is completed, the

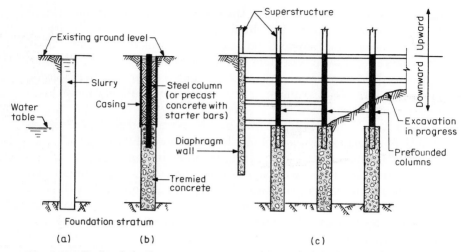

Figure 7-59 Prefounded columns and use in downward construction: (*a*) Drilling hole under slurry. (*b*) Lowering and positioning column and concreting the foundation element. (*c*) Simultaneous construction of superstructure and substructure by upward and downward process.

casing is withdrawn and the hole above the concrete is backfilled with granular material. The preexcavation stage is completed with the perimeter diaphragm wall, constructed simultaneously with the foundation elements.

The construction is carried out as shown in Fig. 7-59c. With the diaphragm wall, the interior foundation, and the basement columns in place, the excavation is carried down in stages, one floor at a time. Beams and slabs are directly supported on the basement columns and are used to brace the walls laterally. The procedure is essentially stage underpinning for all adjoining buildings and structures, and can be completed simultaneously with the erection of the superstructure. The resulting advantages are (1) elimination of temporary lateral bracing for the ground support; (2) overall time savings; and (3) early release of the lower part of the building for immediate use.

Unlike the steel-concrete column-foundation combination shown in Fig. 7-59, the foundation element can have a prismatic or rectangular configuration, built in slurry, and concreted to ground level. Beams and slabs from the basement structure are directly connected to these members as excavation progresses. A notable example of prefounded rectangular shafts is the Manhattan Building in Brussels. This building has 31 stories above ground and contains seven basement levels for parking and services (see also Sec. 5-18).

Connection details.   For steel columns supported on concrete shafts the transfer of vertical load must be made by sufficient embedment supplemented by shear devices attached to the steel flanges, since column base plates are not practical. U-shaped bars are welded to the flanges of the column in a horizontal position. Although the load transfer begins with shear resistance in the contact area of steel and concrete, the ultimate capacity of the member depends on bearing of concrete on the U bars and on the tip of the column, and therefore it can be taken as the crushing strength of concrete on the same area. The load transfer can also be made with shear studs, as in Fig. 5-32.

Another concern in the design of the base connection is the degree of fixity that may be present because of the column embedment into the concrete considering the difference in the flexural stiffness between the two materials.

For strength design, the bearing stress f_b of steel on concrete should not exceed $0.85\phi f'_c$, where $\phi = 0.70$ (both AASHTO and ACI provide the same strength criteria). For allowable stress design, AASHTO gives a working stress $f_b = 0.30f'_c$. In some instances these stresses may be increased by a multiplier $\sqrt{A_2/A_1}$ with 2 as maximum, where A_1 = actual bearing area and A_2 is defined according to the appropriate geometry of a specific pyramid and cone. These results are based on tests of unreinforced-concrete blocks supported on a stiff support and loaded through a stiff plate.

Example Consider a column supporting a dead load of 220 kips and a live load of 180 kips. The column is founded on a 36-in-diameter bored pile. Design a base connection detail to transfer the load. The column is a W × 12 × 161, with $A = 47.4$ in². The ultimate strength of the steel section is determined by slenderness considerations and is not part of this problem.

We choose concrete strength $f'_c = 3500$ lb/in². For maximum bearing we use $f_b = 0.85\phi f'_c$, and for a conservative design we do not apply the strength multiplier. Therefore, $f_b = (0.85)(0.7)(3500) = 2080$ lb/in², say 2 kips/in².

The loads are factored according to the AISC LRFD criteria so that

$$P_u = 1.2D + 1.6L = (1.2)(220) + (1.6)(180) = 552 \text{ kips}$$

The tip of the column provides a bearing area of 47.4 in² and resists 47.4 × 2 = 95 kips. Therefore, the load to be transferred by U bars is 552 − 95 = 457 kips, requiring 457/2 = 229 in² of bearing area. We select No. 8 bars bent to a U shape so that the short leg is 6 in and the U side is 12 in, total area = 23 in². Number of bars required is 229/23 = 9.9, say 10 bars, 5 each side. The bars are arranged with the U plane placed horizontal and are welded to the flanges of the column. Using a spacing at 9 in, the required wall embedment is close to 4 ft.

A somewhat different solution is obtained if the loads are factored according to ACI criteria. If allowable stress design is used, for a total service load 220 + 180 = 400 kips and an allowable bearing stress $f_b = 0.30 \times 3500 = 1.05$ kips/in², the required bearing area is 400/1.05 = 380 in².

In lieu of the U bars, the transfer of load can be made by studs, plates, angles, etc. For example, two steel angles 4 × 6 with the larger leg set horizontal, and a length of 20 in each will provide a bearing area of 20 × 12 = 240 in², sufficient for the foregoing problem. Likewise, a square plate 19 in $\times$ 19 in welded at the tip of the column with a 10-in-diameter hole for the tremie pipe will provide a net bearing area of $19^2 - 3.14 \times 5^2 = 282$ in^2, giving a structural capacity of $282 \times 2 = 564$ kips > 552 kips. Any of these solutions should be consistent with the concrete placement and the requirements of tremied concrete. Extra care will be necessary to ensure that the fresh mix flows unrestricted and fills the underside of the plate for full contact and without trapping bentonite.

For this example the structural capacity of the foundation element is, ignoring any reinforcement,

$$P_u = \phi P_n = 0.75 \times 0.85 \times 3.50 \times 3.14 \times 18^2 = 2115 \text{ kips}$$

The factored loads are, however, computed using ACI criteria, or

$$P_u = (1.4)(220) + (1.7)(180) = 614 \text{ kips (ignoring buckling)}$$

If the foundation element is extended to the ground level, the column-to-foundation connection is made with a conventional base plate. The AISC-LRFD criteria do not give a specific design procedure for base plates. Design formulations are suggested by DeWolf (1978) and Murray (1983). Extending the foundation shaft to the ground level may be necessary where the column carries heavy loads ($P_u > 1500$ kips) since in this case a practical load transfer must be based on base plates under sufficient control of concrete strength. The factoring of loads according to AISC criteria for plate design and according to ACI criteria for shaft design is consistent with current practice.

Comments on diaphragm wall design.   The analysis and design of the wall is greatly simplified because the bracing is provided by the permanent floors or beams; i.e., bracing levels or points of support remain unchanged. Although moment diagrams and shears will shift during the stage excavation and insertion of bracing floors, the design will generally be governed by the final stage with all floors in place and lateral pressures and load corresponding to full use of the structure.

Strip panels

Strip panels, discussed in Sec. 1-8 and shown in Fig. 1-32, are structural companions of prefounded columns. They may be combined in a downward construction process where both interact structurally with the floor system rather than functioning as isolated elements. The design in this case must be consistent with the stage construction and the transfer of loads.

A strip-panel wall is shown in Fig. 7-60 as part of the general structural system of prefounded columns, beams, and girders. The construction is processed in the following sequence.

1. Construct strip panels marked l using square end details. Note that the dimension s is selected with regard to soil conditions but is also governed by the strength of the pillars or poles.

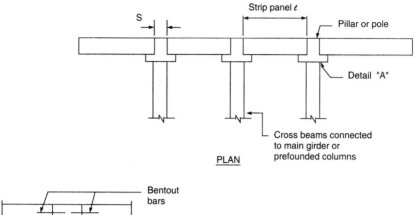

DETAIL "A"

Figure 7-60 Strip panels combined with prefounded columns in downward construction.

2. Simultaneous with the perimeter strip-panel wall construct the interior prefounded columns.

3. Construct 2 to 3 ft of pillars (the uppermost part), and pour the framing (girders and cross beams) for the uppermost (ground) floor. Note that bentout bars are used to connect the strip panels to the pillars. Note also that the pillars have an inverted T shape since they support the strip panels horizontally.

4. Excavate to below the first basement level, construct this portion of the pillars, and pour the framing (girders and cross beams) for this level. Likewise, the strip panels are connected to the pillars using bentout bars.

5. Continue the excavation and construction in stages by repeating the procedure outlined in step 4.

The floor slabs can be cast against the ground or, after the excavation is completed, in conventional forms. The lateral loads from the strip panels are resisted by the pillars and then transferred to the cross beams acting as struts. Vertical loads from the floors and cross beams are resisted by the pillars and transferred to the strip panels through the structural connection.

Diaphragm walls with mat foundations

A mat foundation may be used where the base soil (in this case the basement level) has a low bearing capacity and/or column loads are so large that more than 50 percent of the area will be covered by conventional footings. The choice also means that deep load-bearing elements may not be equally feasible and economical. In the most common use the mat foundation serves to support and spread the column loads and provides the floor slab. Where the groundwater is higher than the basement level, the mat provides a water barrier.

A continuous mat is subjected to positive and negative moments and hence requires reinforcing steel at the top and the bottom. A mat foundation may also be subjected to large settlement unless there is a stress compensation from excavated soil so that it is possible to control the net increase in pressure (see also Sec. 9-7). In most cases the foundation must be designed to limit settlement to tolerable amounts. This settlement may be (1) caused by consolidation, including secondary effects; (2) immediate or elastic; and (3) a combination of consolidation and immediate. Means to control the settlement may include a lower soil contact pressure; flotation effects because of displaced volume of soil; and bridging effects associated with mat and structure rigidity.

Figure 7-61a shows a deep basement enclosed by diaphragm walls and with a mat foundation. Until the interior columns are constructed and begin to transfer vertical loads, the mat foundation must resist possible heave and uplift pressure, and since it interacts with the diaphragm wall it will transfer these effects as upward forces. The walls,

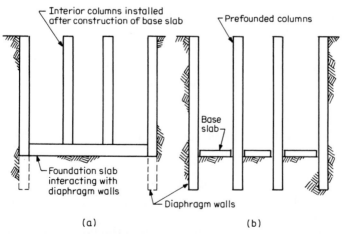

Figure 7-61 Alternate designs for a deep basement: (a) Continuous ground-bearing slab supporting interior columns. (b) Prefounded columns and separate base slabs.

in turn, will induce lateral loads on the mat on account of earth stresses. These conditions may require a thick and heavily reinforced mat that would also help to stabilize any tendencies of the mat and the walls for uneven settlement.

If for the same problem prefounded columns were feasible (without making allowance for relief of overburden in estimating the bearing capacity of the soil since the columns would lie within a large excavation area), the solution would be as shown in Fig. 7-61b. The use of an intermittent mat separated from the columns reduces the relative heave movement considerably, so that heave pressures can be taken up by thin slab sections. However, this solution cannot deal directly with water underseepage, and hence it will be necessary to install filter beds or increase the wall embedment in order to reduce the amount of water infiltration.

References

AASHTO, 1992: Standard Specifications for Highway Bridges.

Abeles, Bardhan-Roy, and Turner, 1976: *Prestressed Concrete Designer's Handbook,* 2d ed., A Viewpoint Publ. by C & CA, Slough (England).

ACI-ASCE Committee 326, 1962: "Shear and Diagonal Tension Slabs," *ACI J. Proc.,* vol. 59, no. 3, March, pp. 353–396.

Alexander, S. D. B., and S. H. Simmonds, "Ultimate Strength of Column-Slab Connections," *ACI Struct. J. Proc.,* vol. 84, no. 3, May–June 1987, pp. 255–261.

Barker, R. M., et al., 1991: *Manuals for the Design of Bridge Foundations,* NCHRP Rep. 343, TRB, National Research Council Washington, D.C., December.

Bowles, J. E., 1988: *Foundation Analysis and Design,* McGraw-Hill, New York.

Braun, W. M., 1972: Post-tensioned Diaphragm Walls in Italy, *Ground Eng.,* March.

Brown, D. A., L. C. Reese, and M. W. O'Neill, 1987: "Cyclic Lateral Loading of a Large Scale Pile Group," *ASCE, JGED,* vol. 113, no. 11, November, pp. 1326–1343.

Brown, D. A., C. Morrison, and L. C. Reese, 1988: "Lateral Load Behavior of Pile Group in Sand," *ASCE, JGED,* vol. 114, no. 11, November, pp. 1261–1276.

DeWolf, J. T., 1978: "Axially Loaded Column Base Plates," *J. Struct. Div., ASCE,* vol. 104, ST5, May, pp. 781–794.

DiStasio, J., and M. P. Van Buren, 1960: "Transfer of Bending Moment between Flat Plate Floor and Column," *ACI J. Proc.,* vol. 57, no. 3, September, pp. 299–314.

Evans, L. T., Jr., and J. M. Duncan, 1982: "Simplified Analysis of Laterally Loaded Piles," *UC Berkeley Rept.* UCB/GT/82-04, July, 245 pp.

Focht, J. A., and K. J. Koch, 1973: "Rational Analysis of the Lateral Performance of Offshore Pile Groups," *Proc. 5th Offshore Techn. Conf.,* Houston, Tex., vol. 2, Paper OTC 1896, pp. 701–708.

Fuchsberger, M., and H. J. Gysi, 1978: "Post-tensioned Diaphragm Wall at Irlams O' Th' Height-Manchester," Tech. Paper 8th Int. Congr. of F.I.P., London, May.

Gysi, H. J., et al., 1976: "Vorgespannte Schlitzwaende," *Proc. 6th Eur. Conf. Soil Mech. Found. Eng.,* vol. 1.1, p. 141, Vienna.

Gysi, H. J., et al., 1977: "Behavior of a Prestressed Diaphragm Wall," *Proc. 9th Int. Conf. Soil Mech. Found. Eng.,* vol. 2, 3/17, p. 83, Tokyo.

Gysi, H. J., A. Linder, and R. Leoni, 1975: "Prestressed Diaphragm Walls," *Proc. Eur. Conf. Soil Mech. Found. Eng.,* Vienna.

Gysi, H. J., A Linder, and R. Leoni, 1975: "Prestressed Diaphragm Walls," *Proc. 1975 Eur. Conf. Soil Mech. Found. Eng.,* Vienna.

Lin, T. Y., and N. H. Burns, 1981: *Design of Prestressed Concrete Structures,* Wiley, New York.

Martin, L. D., S. A. Gill, and N. L. Scott, 1977: "Prefabricated Structural Members for Cut-and-Cover Tunnels," FHWA Report RD-76-113, March.

Matlock, H., and L. C. Reese, 1961: "Foundation Analysis of Offshore Pile Supported Structures," *Proc. 5th Int. Conf. Soil Mech. Found. Eng.,* vol. 2, pp. 91–97.

Miyoshi, Y., et al., 1976: "Steel and Unreinforced Concrete Panels Built in Slurry Trenches," *Constr. Techniques Mag.,* vol. 7.

Moe, J., 1961: "Shearing Strength of Reinforced Concrete Slabs and Footings under Concentrated Loads," *Development Dept. Bull.* D47, Portland Cement Assoc., Skokie, Ill., April.

Murray, T. M., 1983: "Design of Lightly Loaded Steel Column Base Plates," *Eng. J., AISC,* vol. 20, no. 4 (4th Quarter), pp. 143–152.

PCI, 1972: *Design Handbook Precast and Prestressed Concrete,* Prestressed Concrete Institute, Chicago.

PCI, 1977: *Post-tensioning Manual,* Prestressed Concrete Institute, Chicago.

Sartoris, G., 1975: "Baugrubensicherung mit vorgespannten Schlitzwaeden," *Mitteilungen der Schweiz. Ges. f. Boden- & Felsmech.,* no. 92.

Terzaghi, K., 1955: "Evaluation of Coefficients of Subgrade Reaction," *Geotechnique,* vol. 5, no. 4, December.

Ware, K. R., R. N. Evans, and J. G. Beck, 1980: "Use of Slurry Walls in Lieu of Underpinning," *Proc. Slurry Walls for Underground Transp. Facilities,* FHWA, Cambridge, Mass.

Winter, E., T. S. Nordmark, and G. Tallard, 1991: "Slurry Wall Performance Adjacent to Historic Church," Symp. Slurry Walls, ASTM, Atlantic City, June.

Xanthakos, P. P., 1974: "Underground Construction in Fluid Trenches," Colleges of Engineering, University of Illinois, Chicago.

8

Underground Transportation Systems

8-1 General Construction Requirements

Physical constraints

Rapid transit systems, underground motorways, and traffic underpasses are typical examples of underground transportation facilities where diaphragm walls have been used as permanent structures. These systems are usually constructed in congested metropolitan areas where a main problem is competition for space where space hardly exists. The scarcity of vacant sites often implies unusually high land values and excludes the opportunity of expanding the public right-of-way. In these conditions construction is further complicated because of the presence of streets, buildings, and utilities above and below grade.

Underground utilities in particular can bring long delays and increase the cost accordingly. Utilities are usually found within 10 to 15 ft (3 to 5 m) below ground surface and often occupy 30 to 40 percent of the street width. They typically require some form of rearrangement such as temporary support, diversion, relocation, or complete reconstruction. Utility preparatory work often extends for many months. Because of these requirements the usual practice is to focus on construction techniques and solutions that will have minimal disturbance to utilities and deal only with the problem of their temporary support or minor diversion.

Environmental considerations

Minimal vibrational disturbance. Trenching operations for the construction of diaphragm walls have little vibratory effect on the adjoining ground except when percussion or blasting operations must be carried out close to existing buildings and facilities.

Minimal noise disturbance.   The noise level associated with diaphragm wall construction can be demonstrated by reference to specific projects.

Slurry wall construction operations for the Charles Center Subway Station in Baltimore were restricted to nighttime, and noise level criteria in nearby hotels limited the maximum noise level to 70 dB after 10 P.M. Throughout the construction phase the noise level was maintained within this limit. Noise was also of major concern for the Red Line Extension (MBTA) in Cambridge, Mass., and became a major factor instrumental in the decision-making process that eventually led to the selection of diaphragm walls as ground support and final structure.

Minimal traffic disruption.   Initial trench excavation and concrete operations require a nominal use of street space for the usual slurry wall projects. In these conditions a normal traffic pattern can be maintained through the construction corridor, and usually requires the closing of one and possibly two traffic lanes. With the diaphragm walls in place, the general excavation can be carried out under several construction options to minimize the disruption of street functions and activities (see also subsequent sections).

The foregoing favorable considerations must be balanced against certain construction requirements such as (1) sufficient space for slurry mixing facilities and slurry disposal; (2) adequate facilities for assembling the reinforcement cages; and (3) protection of facades of existing buildings from damage that may incur from crane and grab bucket operation. The waterproofing of basement walls must also be considered when working close to existing buildings with basement levels. Although bentonite is a seal itself, some mixed fluid may penetrate existing basements through wall cracks until rheological blocking stops further penetration.

Economic factors.   The use of diaphragm walls as part of the permanent structure, and to a lesser extent as temporary ground support, can result in economic benefits in terms of cost and construction time. A rigid and fairly watertight wall provides better control of ground movement and settlement associated with deep excavations, and reduces the need for dewatering outside the construction site and underpinning of existing foundations. Typical cost savings related to these factors can be found in case histories, and examples are the Federal Center Subway Station of the Washington, D.C., metro and Charles Center Station of the Baltimore metro. In both cases underpinning was eliminated (Dennis et al., 1981).

Further advantages and cost savings can be realized when the diaphragm wall becomes part of the permanent structure. Significant time savings result in this case from an accelerated construction rate.

General guidelines

In many instances local site conditions will preclude the use of a single method and instead require a combination of various types of ground support supplemented by other forms of ground engineering. Thus specific procedures are difficult to establish without knowing the details and characteristics of the project, except for certain general comments summarized as follows:

1. For long projects utility rearrangement will necessitate (Jobling, 1975) simultaneous preconstruction of shorter sections at intersections. The use of continuous diaphragm walls at these locations will require frequent dismantling, moving, and resetting of plant facilities, rigs, and equipment, and this constitutes a major operation with a fixed cost. In these conditions, it is better to use fairly simple and mobile rigs such as bored pile machines with maximum construction efficiency.

2. At an intersection, an existing extensive utility system can bring construction to a sudden halt. In order to resume activity it will be necessary to locate obstructions and carry out considerable preexcavation to divert them. This problem is avoided if utilities are left in place and supported, while a mobile ground support is chosen as intermittent bored piles or strip panels supplemented by grouting.

3. For long structures or where time is of essence secant pile walls will not offer the most optimum schedule. For an average excavation depth of 12 m (40 ft) a single rig can produce five to six piles daily, equivalent to about 5 m (16 ft) of wall. Thus, unless several rigs are available, the construction period may be too long.

4. Difficult ground and hydrologic conditions can be handled with diaphragm walls where other techniques may not be as effective. With an extensive network of underground utilities the best choice often is to consider the rationale of convergence (see also Sec. 2-1) and plan a flexible construction of ground supports and controls. The possibility of changes in the field should be included in the planning stage.

5. In stiff, firm clayey soil bored piles can be used as sidewalls for a transit tunnel; bracing in this case can be sufficient with top and bottom lateral support only and for a nominal pile diameter. In soft clay the same piles will require intermediate bracing which is not practical for the permanent condition, so that the only choice is to increase the pile size.

6. Street congestion and traffic maintenance can force the contractor to operate on one side only, avoid the use of rigid-arm excavators, and concentrate within a narrow enclosure to locate plant facilities and assemble reinforcing cages. All these restrictions have a marked effect on productivity.

7. A single-story, fairly deep subway station is not necessarily built more economically with diaphragm walls. The rationale is that the cost of excavation and ground support represents a major portion of the total project cost. A multilevel section justifies the cost of excavation and utilizes the ground support to a full extent, resulting in an economical construction. There are no fixed limits regarding the cost range of the application, and hence all pertinent factors should be considered.

8. Exposed permanent diaphragm walls are visually acceptable and functional in subway construction unless they are within station limits where some face treatment must be provided.

9. Diaphragm walls can be successfully combined with bored piles, sheet piles, soldier piles and lagging, and ground strengthening to remedy the problems of underground construction for transportation systems. Most types of this work will require, however, specialist contractors with the necessary expertise and equipment, and this availability must be ensured in the planning stage.

10. Where construction methods are combined and intermixed, mutual effects should be considered. An example is construction of diaphragm walls combined with sheet piling driven in the same vicinity to form a box for a subway entrance. Vibrations associated with sheet pile driving caused parts of the slurry trench near the surface within the water-bearing formations to cave in, so that severe blisters appeared on the exposed walls.

11. For construction along streets, problems related to trench stability, slurry loss, spillage of slurry mud, disposal of used bentonite, maintenance of pedestrian traffic, commercial accessibility, etc., should be neither underestimated nor exaggerated.

8-2   Basic Procedures for Subway Tunnels

Construction under the roof for single tunnels

The main advantage of construction under the roof is the reduced disruption of street activities. If the work is to be carried out with temporary decking, a typical construction sequence and phasing is as shown in Fig. 8-1, and is self-explanatory. In this example the upper part of excavation (usually 10 to 12 ft, or about 3 m) is braced by

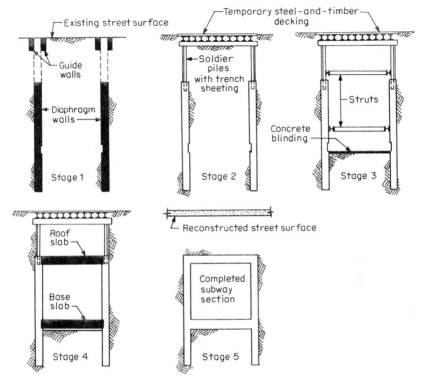

Figure 8-1   Construction under the roof for a single tunnel; temporary decking supported on soldier piles.

soldier piles with lagging, embedded on top of the wall. This arrangement allows the ground immediately below the surface to remain unobstructed for future utility usage (often requested by local codes), and is consistent with the fact that the diaphragm walls in this part of the ground are not needed in the final function.

If there are no future utility requirements, the construction shown in Fig. 8-2 may be considered. Provisions are made only for existing utilities, and usually include suitable gaps and omissions in the walls as shown. These considerations must be addressed in the design stage since they influence panel sequence and configuration as well as lateral bracing.

If the construction is to be carried out without temporary decking, it can follow the sequence shown in Fig. 8-3. The walls can be extended to guide wall level, but more frequently they are terminated just above the roof slab and temporary bracing is used above this level. Note that stage 2 includes excavation to the underside of the top slab and casting of this slab, stage 3 involves excavation to the underside of the bottom

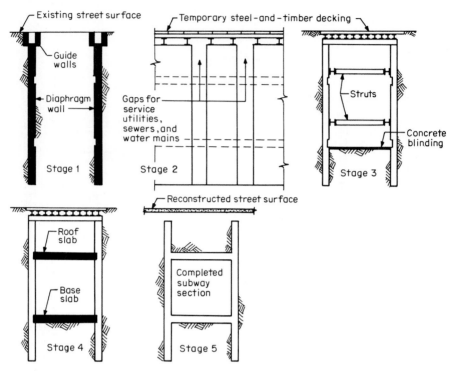

Figure 8-2 Construction under the roof for a single tunnel; temporary decking supported on diaphragm walls.

slab, and stage 4 completes the construction with the casting of the base slab. Intermediate bracing (not shown) may be needed during these stages, depending on soil conditions, wall stiffness, structure dimensions, and permissible movements.

Temporary decking. The walls can also be built from a lower level in conjunction with a modified cut-and-cover construction that involves a temporary decking carried on soldier piles with lagging installed outside the main excavation as an independent support system. Excavation is carried down under the temporary decking to a suitable level that allows sufficient headroom for the operation, and this level is used as a working platform. The advantage is that the street is not used as a construction site for the walls.

A temporary decking is also indicated under specific site and project conditions, and is built as shown in Fig. 8-1. Examples are: (1) existing utilities that must be supported and protected rather than diverted or relocated during construction, and this cannot be done without a temporary decking; (2) a construction sequence requiring a separate box

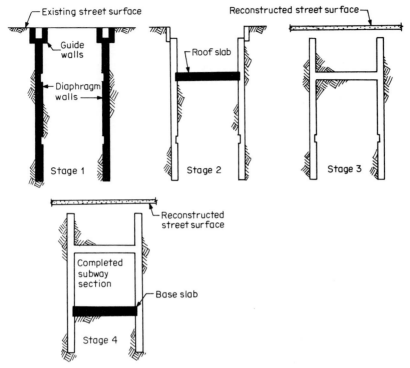

Figure 8-3 Construction under the roof without temporary decking; single subway tunnel.

inside the diaphragm walls with the structure built from the bottom up; (3) excavations braced with dissimilar wall systems (see also subsequent sections; (4) where the walls in stage 3 of Fig. 8-3 cannot carry the structural loads until stage 4, with the base slab in place, is completed (Note: In this case the preferred sequence would be to start filling the excavated area as soon as the concrete for the top slab has gained the required strength and reconstruct the street surface while the excavation is carried down under the roof to the level of the base slab; all structural loads including the weight of fill and live load surcharges must be carried by the diaphragm wall); (5) stages 2 and 3 in Fig. 8-3 cannot be coordinated with the time period during which street disruption is permitted in the construction schedule; and (6) where the subway is so deep that the excavation period will be too long for the permitted disruption.

Construction under the roof for multiple tunnels

Multiple tunnels (not to be associated with stations) involve more than one trackway on split alignment or on two different levels. The con-

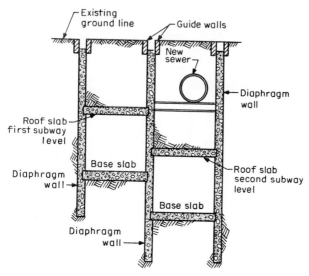

Figure 8-4 Construction of a subway tunnel with split alignment.

struction is basically similar to single tunnels except that it may require a center wall. A typical example is shown in Fig. 8-4. In this case the exterior walls were built first, while for the center wall it was required to close one side of the street to traffic. The upper (left) tunnel was constructed first in order to give some relief to the bracing of the lower (right) tunnel section. When the difference between the two subway levels is nominal, the structure can be designed with a roof slab common to both sections.

The construction shown in Fig. 8-5 involves a multiple tunnel and is carried out under a temporary decking. The construction requirements are: (1) support and protect the existing sewer; (2) accommodate an irregular split subway alignment with one exterior wall located almost directly below the sewer; (3) keep the area below the street free and usable for future utility installations; and (4) deal with fairly uniform ground conditions, and a relatively low groundwater table.

From these considerations the following construction phasing is evolved: (1) construct the left diaphragm wall from street level and install soldier piles with lagging in the upper part as shown; (2) install soldier piles as ground support for the right side of the excavation, and place temporary decking; (3) excavate under temporary deck to second construction platform (note that this process includes also the installation of lagging for the right soldier pile wall and the intermediate bracing struts); (4) construct the right diaphragm wall from the second construction platform using low-head equipment and pro-

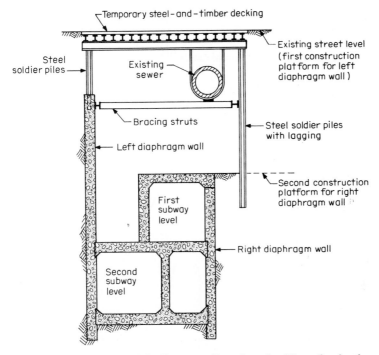

Figure 8-5 Combination of diaphragm walls and steel soldier piles for the construction of a subway.

vide dewatering as needed; (5) excavate for the section from the second construction platform level to the final excavation level (note that this phase must include intermediate temporary bracing for the diaphragm walls and the right soldier piles); (6) build the subway section from the bottom up as shown; and (7) backfill, dismantle the temporary decking, and restore the street.

Construction from a lower level

The example of Fig. 8-5 shows a case where it is necessary to continue construction from a lower level. In other instances it may be prudent to carry out the entire new construction from a lower level. Thus, if a subway is proposed beneath an existing building and does not involve conventional tunneling, the only available solution is to plan the new construction using the lowest basement level as a working platform.

An example is shown in Fig. 8-6 for a subway structure passing under a six-level underground parking garage. The construction level is the base of the parking center, about 15 m (49 ft) from existing

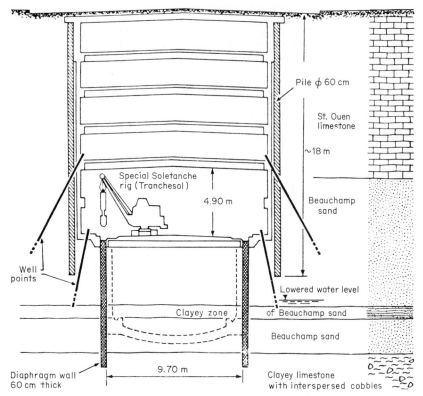

Figure 8-6 Construction of a subway section in Paris from an existing six-level underground parking garage.

street level. Construction in these conditions is difficult, and some of the problems are associated with the following conditions:

1. Trench stability, and particularly the requirement to balance the lateral earth stresses and pore pressures by the slurry thrust and without lowering the groundwater table. For the example shown in Fig. 8-6 well points were used continuously to lower the water table to the level shown.

2. Equipment mobility under limited clearance and low headroom restricting the choice to crawler-type machines and specially made rigs that can work in confined space. For the excavation shown in Fig. 8-6 it was necessary to (a) remove part of one floor to increase headroom to about 5 m; (b) use a lightweight machine with a hydraulic bucket attached to a short boom; (c) assemble end tubes and reinforcing cages in short sections and splice them as needed.

3. Lack of working space with an immediate effect on the handling of excavated materials, accessibility to the construction area from outside, and the delivery of fresh concrete to the working level.

4. Noise and ventilation problems because of the closed and restricted working area.

In spite of these difficulties this form of construction is the only viable technique for an underground facility beneath an existing building and hence can have unexpected applications. Favorable factors are the independence of the operation from surface activities and better scheduling because of stable weather conditions.

Construction at crossings

From the construction standpoint a major problem at street crossings is the maze of existing underground utilities. As already mentioned in the general guidelines, it is better to avoid diversion or relocation of these lines, and instead concentrate on a construction sequence using the hit-and-miss method shown in Fig. 8-7. The type and location

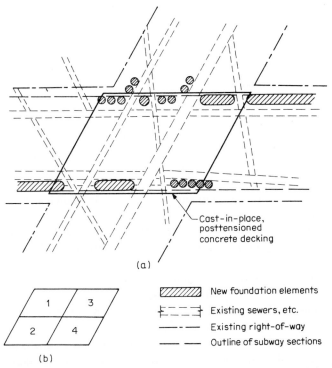

Figure 8-7 Construction at crossings and street intersections: (a) Arrangement of wall panels, bored piles, and the like by a hit-and-miss method. (b) Construction of concrete decking at street level in four quarters to avoid complete closing of intersection to traffic.

of new structural elements is decided after an exact and complete survey at the site.

The intermittent wall consists of individual linear panels, bored piles, and probably ground strengthening, installed from street level and arranged to miss any underground obstacles. Once a basic support system is in place, a general concrete mat is cast at ground level in a proper sequence (see Fig. 8-7b) to permit part of the streets to remain open. The slab may be prestressed (posttensioned) after all four quarters are in place or it may be combined with intermediate temporary supports.

This basic layout brings full restoration to street activities at the intersection and allows the excavation to proceed under an umbrella type of cover. In unstable conditions or in ground with high water table the gaps between supporting elements must be filled as the excavation is taken down or the work may be combined with supplementary ground strengthening. When enough clearance is obtained below the utilities, the construction can be completed from a lower level.

Miscellaneous details

Wall-roof joints. A usual connection between roof slab and sidewalls is made with the use of shear keys combined with shear reinforcement. Details are discussed in Sec. 6-13. Such a connection transfers only shear and is equivalent to a hinge.

More often it is desired to provide a rigid connection between the roof slab and the wall in order to reduce the bending moment at midspan and allow better structural response to sidesway action. A moment connection can be designed as discussed in Sec. 6-13. Alternatively, a different moment connection can be detailed as shown in Fig. 8-8, and is feasible when the wall can be terminated just below the roof slab, or consists of lean concrete above this level, which can be removed as needed. A concrete blinding is first placed to make the base for the roof slab. The top of the wall is cleaned and roughened to assist the transfer of shear. The moment bars are bent as shown and spliced or connected to the roof slab bars with couplers, and the roof concrete is cast to the outside line of the wall. A concrete fillet can be added to improve frame action.

Examples where this connection has been used are shown in Figs. 8-1 and 8-5. In both instances the diaphragm walls are extended only to the perimeter of the final section.

The concept of the rigid and hinged joint has received considerable attention because of the obvious significance. Rigid connections should

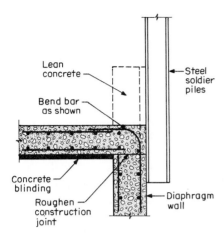

Lean
concrete

Steel
soldier
piles

Bend bar
as shown

Concrete
blinding

Roughen
construction
joint

Diaphragm
wall

Figure 8-8 Roof slab and wall
connection for a subway section.

be preferred because of the resulting frame action, but hinged connections are easier to execute. In actual practice hinges are often assumed at the base slab-wall joint, whereas rigid connection is specified between the roof slab and the wall.

A variation of the joint concept may be developed in connection with temporary and permanent action. A temporary hinge may be designed and detailed to provide the advantages of both permanent hinges and rigid joints simply by designing the detail for flexibility during early-stage loading and for rigidity during long-term loading. This advantage is clearly relevant to multistage loading conditions that a permanent structure must withstand when it is also used as temporary support.

For example, the joints between the concrete slabs and the diaphragm walls can be left as no-moment-transmitting hinges when the dead load and uplift hydrostatic pressures are applied to the structure during the corresponding construction stages, so that these loads do not induce additional moments to the diaphragm walls. After the corresponding short-term load effects have taken place, and before the entire structure is exposed to the long-term (at rest) conditions, the joints can be made rigid by cement grouting of the areas around the moment-connection bars. The additional stiffness supplied by the rigidified connection enhances frame action and keeps sidesway to a minimum under unbalanced lateral earth loads. This procedure is intended to allow some moment to "leak out" in the hinged state but in a controlled manner. The extent and timing of rigidifying the joint should be within the control of design.

Waterproofing. Despite the wide variation in local standards for waterproofing, the associated details usually are worked out as a compromise between complete watertightness and economy. In some instances leakage through tunnel sections is attributed to poor construction methods and execution rather than to poor details. Among the critical areas, special attention should focus on the junction between roof slab and sidewalls and on shrinkage effects, so that it is necessary to correlate construction joints with tunnel length sections and then detail the joints to avoid the formation of shrinkage cracks.

There are two waterproofing trends. One emphasizes treatment of the roof of the section externally with bituminous waterproofing materials and overlap of the joint between tunnel walls and roof. Since a small amount of seepage is unavoidable, drainage channels should be provided alongside the walls leading to sump pits, where the seepage is collected. Leaking joints can also be corrected from outside.

By contrast, the second method shows complete reliance on waterproof concrete and joints. Since few tunnels exist that do not leak, regardless of method, the former trend is suggested as more economical and corresponds to the realities of any underground construction.

Excavation and ventilation.   A usual complaint about the under-the-roof method is that the excavation is delayed and costs more owing to lack of space to move and maneuver the equipment. For example, a single-track tunnel may have a distance face-to-face of walls 12 to 14 ft (or 4 m) and a headroom from the underside of the roof to excavation level of 18 ft (5.5 m). For conventional equipment the vertical clearance is enough to complete the mucking out of the section, but there is room for only one access ramp and hardly any room for turnarounds.

Slow excavation progress can also give rise to ventilation problems from the exhaust fumes of excavators and engines. For a single-track tunnel this problem becomes serious when the length exceeds about 500 ft (150 m), and for longer subpavement sections it is therefore necessary to modify the roof casting method in order to provide improved natural ventilation. A practical solution is the use of a shuttering system placed some 3 ft (1 m) below the underside of the roof slab to provide an airspace. The necessary formwork supports only the wet concrete during placing and compaction. The reuse of the shuttering components can become part of the tunnel roof construction routine.

Occasionally contractors prefer to install a belt-conveyor system at the pit head, which is extended in short lengths and reaches a maximum of about 350 m (almost 1100 ft). This is intended to remove the muck on the lower belt, while excavation at the face is done with an excavator equipped with a side-tipping bucket. Again, some trouble will be experienced with fumes from the excavator.

Transfer of loads

For the example shown in Fig. 8-1, the weight of the temporary decking plus all loads applied at street level are transferred to the diaphragm walls, and must be resisted by the wall embedment below excavation level at stage 3 (side shear or base bearing). Side shear above base level along the outside wall face should not be considered because possible loosening of the soil as the excavation is carried down may deprive the interface of shear strength. These loads may be increased, reduced, or redistributed after stage 4, with the walls still resisting all vertical loads until the base slab is in place. With the bottom slab in place, additional vertical loads, such as subway loads, may be assumed to be resisted along the underside of this slab by direct base bearing.

For the example shown in Fig. 8-3, the walls must carry the weight of the roof slab as excavation begins in stage 3. If the backfill is placed before the base slab is in place (which is the procedure shown), the walls must resist all vertical loads by wall embedment below final excavation level as in the example of Fig. 8-1. If sufficient bearing capacity is not available, or if an unusually deep embedment is required for the load transfer, backfilling may be delayed until the base slab is in place.

The left diaphragm wall shown in Fig. 8-5 initially carries the dead load from the temporary decking and all live loads applied at street level. As the excavation is carried down, additional loads are imposed by the weight of the final structure, in this case the roof of the second subway level. All these loads must be resisted by base bearing or by side shear below excavation level. With the base slab in place, subway loads plus the weight of the fill above the finished structure can be assumed to be resisted by direct bearing at the base of the bottom slab. The steel soldier piles on the right side of the excavation must carry the corresponding reaction from the temporary decking and moving street loads. In all the foregoing examples, the distribution of load must consider the actual construction sequence and also have a displacement compatibility basis.

8-3   Subway Stations

Modern subway stations in central business districts or in high-density residential areas have provisions for efficient vertical travel and interline transfer and communications and also house auxiliary facilities, relay rooms, control offices, amenities, and equipment. Thus they commonly comprise at least two floors and often three or four.

A relatively simple station, shown in Fig. 8-9, demonstrates a construction procedure with diaphragm walls and prefounded columns implemented in a downward process. The simplicity is that the same ground support systems and foundation elements are used throughout. The operation is completed in five main stages. Stage 1 requires partial street disruption to install the bored piles and the prefounded columns, and in stages 2 and 3 one side of the street is closed to traffic. Street restoration is attained in stage 4, which involves the simultaneous excavation under roof to construct the mezzanine floor. Stage 5 consists of excavating to the underside of the track level and constructing the base slab and the main platform.

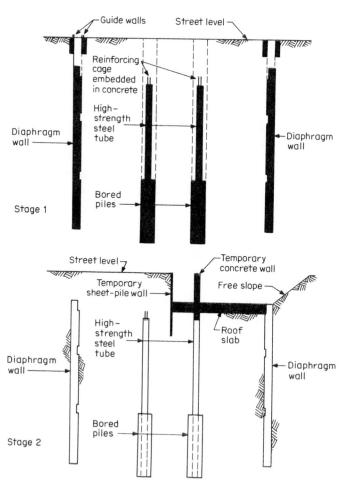

Figure 8-9 Station construction by diaphragm wall method; downward process.

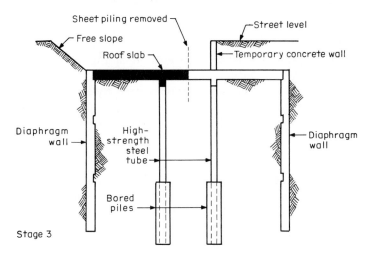

Stage 3

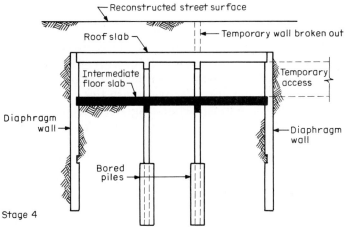

Stage 4

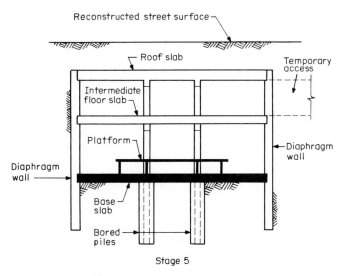

Stage 5

Figure 8-9 *(Continued)*

Construction with temporary decking. The station of Fig. 8-9 can be built with diaphragm walls and temporary decking, as shown in Fig. 8-10. For simplicity the construction is represented by three stages. In this case the entire excavation is carried down to the track level using temporary bracing, and the final subway structure is built from the bottom up.

Construction of multilevel sections. Multilevel stations usually contain, besides the subway facility, commercial establishments and joint development. Whereas it is unorthodox to place a subway line deep below ground surface solely for the purpose of releasing space above for commercial functions, where the subway alignment must be placed at great depth, the utilization of the entire space may be economically justified.

With four or more levels, the design should consider doing the construction from two different levels, so that the structure can be built by proceeding upward and downward simultaneously. The initial requirement is to advance the excavation to a level that provides adequate headroom while dealing also effectively with the groundwater.

Figure 8-11 shows the main construction stages of a deep multilevel station. The upper part of the excavation is braced with soldier piles and lagging to the second construction level, in this case level B-2. Diaphragm walls and prefounded columns are built from this platform, and thereafter the construction proceeds upward and downward simultaneously.

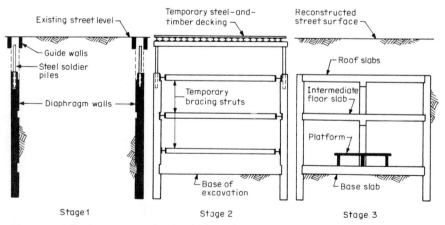

Figure 8-10 Station construction by diaphragm wall method and temporary decking; upward process.

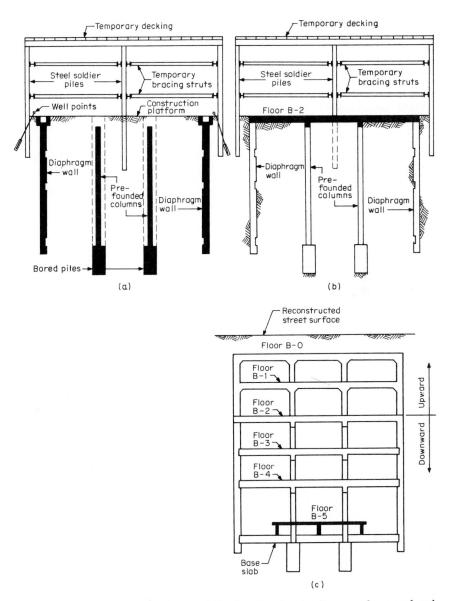

Figure 8-11 Construction of a deep multilevel section by simultaneous downward and upward process: (*a*) Installation of soldier piles, excavation to intermediate construction platform, and construction of diaphragm walls. (*b*) Installation of intermediate floor level. (*c*) Upward and downward construction.

Transfer of loads.   For the structure shown in Fig. 8-9, the transfer of loads begins with the roof slab in place and continues as the excavation is carried down. Each element receives a proportionate load from the structure, the fill, construction loads, and final subway loads. Note that the base slab interacts with the bored piles; hence the division of live loads must have a displacement compatibility basis, since these loads may be resisted by the deep elements and by direct bearing beneath the base slab according to the actual displacements.

For the structure shown in Fig. 8-10, the diaphragm walls must resist service loads from the temporary decking and street traffic. These loads continue until the final excavation level is reached, and at this stage they must be transferred to the ground by base bearing at the tip of the walls and side shear along the wall embedment; they increase as the permanent floors are constructed and transfer an appropriate reaction at the end supports. Subway loads may be assumed to be resisted by direct bearing at the base slab.

Considerable load relief is possible for the configuration of Fig. 8-11, since in this case the temporary loads from the street decking are resisted outside the diaphragm walls. The walls and prefounded columns begin to receive a proportionate shear of loads when floor B-2 is in place and these loads increase as the construction is completed. Maximum loads are applied, therefore, with the entire structure and fill in place.

8-4   Examples of Subway Construction

Northumberland Park Depot, London

Figure 8-12 shows two typical sections for the new depot at Northumberland Park, London, serving the trains for the Victoria Line. The entire line is underground but the depot is a surface facility. An approach tunnel between the depot and the driven tunnels was constructed in cut-and-cover using diaphragm walls as shown in parts a and b of Fig. 8-12 (Jobling, 1980).

Part of the tunnel near the surface is covered with a lightweight roof for snow loads only, but in the deeper sections of the cut-and-

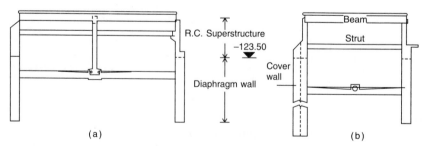

Figure 8-12 Typical sections, Northumberland Park Depot, London. (*From Jobling, 1980.*)

cover structure the diaphragm walls support a roof of prestressed concrete beams to carry vehicular loads.

This is an early example of diaphragm walls as part of the permanent structure, and typifies the early problems of this work. Some caving in the upper part of the trench, partly due to the unguided grab tool tending to twist and hit the face of the trench, caused considerable blips on the finished wall. The ground in the area has high water table, and there were several serious leaks at the joints in two locations. These were treated by drilling holes through the wall and injecting grout in the defective areas. As an alternative, drainage channels were placed at the bottom of the walls to divert infiltrating water into sumps for pumping out. Jobling (1980) notes that the cost of grout treatment to produce a wall fairly watertight was much higher compared with the cost of drainage with sump pumps.

Heathrow Central Station, London

A more recent London Transport project is the new underground station at Heathrow Central, shown in Fig. 8-13. The diaphragm walls

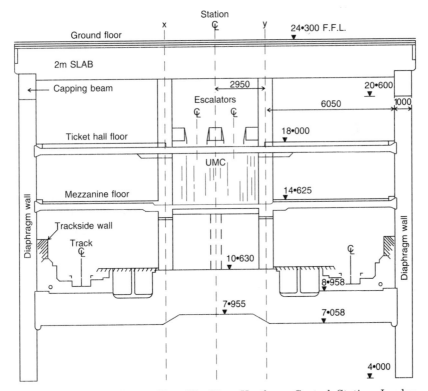

Figure 8-13 Typical section, Piccadilly Line, Heathrow Central Station, London. (*From Jobling, 1980.*)

are the permanent exterior walls of the structure, and carry a proportionate load from the intermediate floors and the roof. The two intermediate floors are connected to the exterior walls by shear keys, and shear reinforcement bent out and spliced with the reinforcing bars of the slabs.

Jobling (1980) reports that the main problem during construction was the cutting of the tunnel eyes in the diaphragm wall after completion of the box, an operation proved to be slow and time-consuming. Manual breakers, machine breakers, and thermic lances were combined but the process still required six times the scheduled period. After this experience, the London Transport made provisions for special procedures where tunnel eyes must be cut within a diaphragm wall.

As in the preceding example, the top 30 ft of ground at the site consists of water-bearing gravel with a normal water table only 6 ft below ground surface. Hence the design concept emphasized a wall that would not be 100 percent watertight, and incorporated drainage channels between the main walls and the interior brick facing.

Secant piles. The London Transport has used this method widely for the construction of subway stations, especially in confined space and with erratic underground obstacles. Examples are the King Cross Station and the structures at Silvertown and Woolwich Arsenal, being adjacent stations on the River Thames line. Both sites are characterized by unfavorable ground conditions.

At Woolwich Arsenal the station site is extremely confined and surrounded with property that was very expensive to buy and demolish for the project. In addition very poor ground conditions posed serious problems for any tunnel work. To remedy this situation, a diaphragm wall was built around the upper chamber as a closed box, the limits of which were dictated by the surface features. From this box probes were driven to freeze the ground using artificial freezing techniques that enabled the rest of the shaft and the lower concourse to be driven safely and without substantial settlement of the overlying facilities and buildings. The remaining part of the station was constructed using secant pile walls because of the older and unknown building foundations and underground services, and also because of the very confined and congested character of the site.

Subway station for BART

The steel and concrete panels mentioned in Sec. 1-7 have been found advantageous in poor soil conditions, for construction close to buildings, and where the interior framing of the finished underground

structure consists of structural steel. If it is not practicable or economical to lower the water table for a deep excavation close to buildings,
the associated lateral loads (earth pressure, pore pressure, and surcharges) can be balanced by an effective ground support system that
must also limit ground movement. With relatively deep excavations
(say 80 ft or more), and for construction inside a watertight wall without lowering the outside water table, the combined lateral loads will
result in unusually heavy bracing loads to the extent that temporary
bracing is impracticable and costly. In principle, therefore, the advantage of the downward construction method is the opportunity to use
the permanent floor levels to brace the walls and thus confine additional temporary bracing to certain locations only.

These principles have been applied to the structure shown in Fig.
8-14, taken from the construction of the Civic Center Station, BART,
San Francisco (Thon and Harlan, 1971). The finished station is shown
in Fig. 8-14a. The staging required first the construction of the two
exterior steel-and-concrete diaphragm walls to a level below the mezzanine floor. The general excavation was carried down to the mezzanine level, and this was used as a construction platform for the two
interior steel-and-concrete diaphragm walls. The structure was completed in an inverted process using two interior temporary bracings
and the permanent floors as shown in Fig. 8-14b. The diaphragm walls
carry a proportionate load from the structure and subways.

The permanent structural steel framing is connected to the steel
beams of the walls, and the vertical construction accuracy was at-

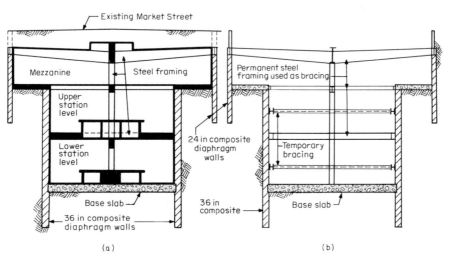

Figure 8-14 Civic Center Station, Market Street, BART San Francisco: (a) Finished section. (b) Bracing system during excavation.

tained by setting and positioning the vertical beams in predrilled holes, filled with weak grout. Before the main operation, the contractor undertook preparations for relocating the utilities in the vicinity of the walls. A trench 12 ft deep was excavated and used as storage for the slurry.

Edmonton subway, Alberta

Figure 8-15 shows a typical cross section for the Churchill Station (Jasper Street) of the Edmonton subway. The soil profile is typical for this area and consists of an upper sediment (silty material with fissures and sand beds, fairly stiff) underlain by local till containing some cobbles and boulders to a depth of 50 ft; a formation of dense

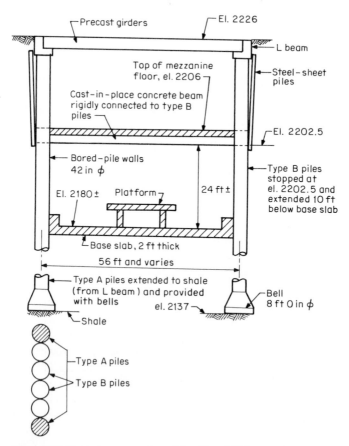

Figure 8-15 Typical cross section of the Churchill Station for the Edmonton subway.

moist sand to approximately 90 ft below ground line; and clay shale below that level, with average bearing capacity 20 kips/ft^2.

The structure comprises two floors, requiring excavation to about 50 ft below existing grade. The upper floor is space left open between the street and the main station facility for underground pedestrian use. Bored piles (tangent pile walls) are used as ground support, both temporary and permanent. The construction phasing consisted of the following stages:

1. Install bored piles. Type A piles are extended from ground level to the shale layer and are provided with bells. Type B piles have a 10-ft embedment below excavation level and their tops are terminated at mezzanine floor level. A wall omission is thus created between type A piles above that level.

2. Install steel sheet piles in the wall omission to retain earth temporarily above mezzanine floor.

3. Construct L beams on top of A piles and excavate down to the mezzanine level.

4. Place precast prestressed U beams on the L beam of the roof, and cast beams and slabs of the mezzanine floor. The beams flare out and are overlapped with type B piles to form a rigid connection with the pile walls.

5. Excavate to base-slab level and construct rail floor and platforms.

6. Complete exterior wall between A piles above mezzanine floor and remove steel sheet piles.

Type A piles carry all the loads (weight of structure, and loads from street and mezzanine floor) and are therefore the main load-carrying elements of the structure. The base slab carries the loads from moving trains and also resists hydrostatic uplift if the water table rises outside the excavation. This slab merely touches the pile wall, and its movement is only restrained by friction or adhesion along the interface with the A piles. An isometric view of the station with all structural elements and platforms is shown in Fig. 8-16.

An alternate construction scheme utilizing diaphragm walls could be carried out in essentially the same sequence shown for the downward process of Fig. 8-9. The section would be supplemented with one row of prefounded columns or strip panels along the center platform, and this might eliminate the extension of load-bearing elements to shale depth. The use of sheet piles in the wall omission would be unnecessary, and the base slab would be structurally connected to the wall. Note, however, that the caisson scheme articulated the transfer

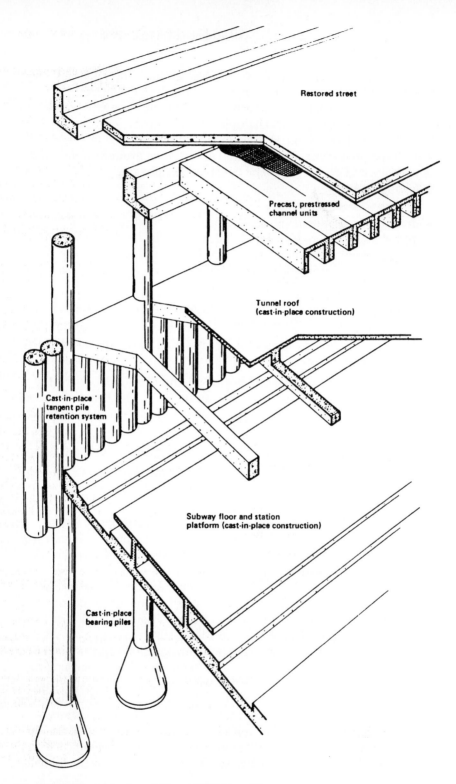

Figure 8-16 Isometric view of Churchill Station, Edmonton, Alberta.

of loads, and attains the transfer at a level where the soil bearing capacity is a maximum, i.e., the shale level.

Subway for Akasaka Block, Tokyo

This is a three-story underground structure located in the central business and commercial district of Akasaka, Tokyo. The execution typifies the optimum combination of techniques and structural systems to maximize construction efficiency and reduce total cost taking into account relevant site conditions. The sequence involves four main stages, shown in Fig. 8-17.

1. First stage.
   a. Drive exterior sheet pile walls and construct interior prefounded columns. These are temporary elements only.
   b. Place temporary decking.
   c. Excavate under roof to level 1 and install first row of anchors and lateral strutting beams.
   d. Excavate to level 2 and install second row of anchors. (Note that the strutting beams are intended merely to brace the prefounded columns and reduce the slenderness ratio.)
2. Second stage.
   a. Build guide walls at second construction level (excavation level 2).
   b. Construct diaphragm walls from this level.
   c. Place concrete slab (roof of the station) using ground as formwork.
3. Third stage.
   a. Excavate to level 3, and install third row of anchors and second level of bracing beams.
   b. Excavate to level 4 and install third level of bracing beams. These brace the walls and the prefounded columns.
   c. Excavate to level 5, which is the final excavation level.
4. Fourth stage.
   a. Place base concrete slab using ground as formwork.
   b. Construct walls and columns for lower floor.
   c. Place concrete slab for intermediate level.
   d. Construct walls and columns for intermediate level.
   e. Place concrete slab for the upper level and complete the wall and column construction.
   f. Cut off prefounded columns and interior bracing inside the permanent structure, and distress ground anchors. At this stage all loads above the top slab are carried by this slab and are transferred to the permanent structure.

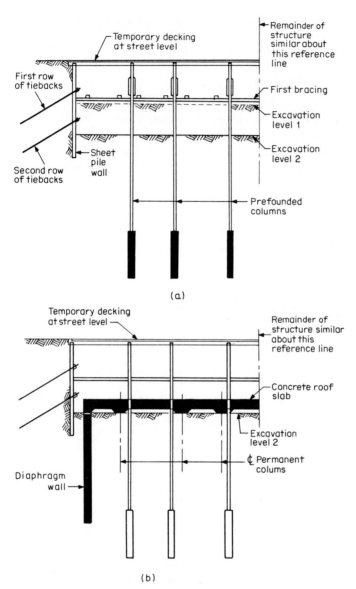

Figure 8-17 Construction of a subway station in Akasaka, Tokyo. The installation was completed in four stages: (*a*) Stage 1, exterior sheet pile walls, prefounded columns, temporary decking, excavation to levels 1 and 2, and installation of bracing. (*b*) Stage 2, diaphragm wall and concrete roof slab. (*c*) Stage 3, excavation of levels 3 to 5 and installation of bracing. (*d*) Stage 4, final structure and cutting off and removal of temporary bracing.

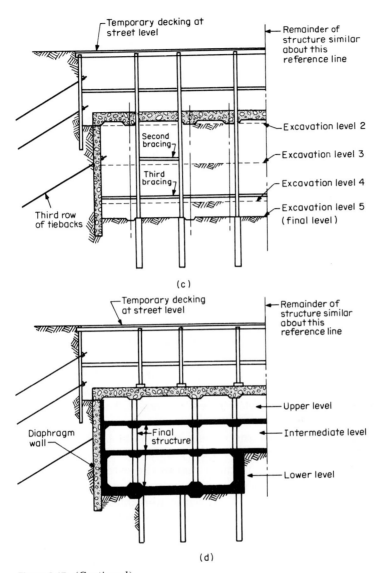

Figure 8-17 *(Continued)*

There are several points of interest: The secondary walls are connected to the diaphragm walls to provide composite action; the bottom slab acts as a mat foundation so that all loads are resisted at this level, except for some residual loads still carried by the diaphragm walls; the roof slab is thicker than usual since it must support and transfer all loads acting above; the steel framing (prefounded columns and struts) above the roof slab remains structurally active and becomes part of the permanent framing for the structure to be built above the main subway station and below street level. It appears from these comments that because of the considerable number of staging levels, it was necessary to investigate the structural capacity of the members for all corresponding loading conditions and load transfers.

Kire Station, Osaka, Japan

This project has a total length of 464 m (1520 ft) and consists of a station section and a three-track section. The diaphragm walls are part of the permanent structure and were designed and built as composite walls in the crossover section and as single walls in the other sections (see also Sec. 7-6 and Fig. 7-42). The ground at the site consists of an upper layer of alluvium 6 m deep, underlain by clay and sand interbedded with diluvium. The normal water level is 2 m below ground surface.

Working space was provided by excavating to a shallow depth between two lines of intermediate steel piles. Construction equipment was then placed under the street to reduce noise and to restrict the area occupied by machinery.

The diaphragm wall thickness and depth are 80 cm and 20.5 m, respectively, at the station section, and 70 cm and 16.8 m, respectively, in the three-track section. Wall panels are 5.5 m long and have the common interlocking pipe joints. Strength tests of concrete cores of the in situ wall gave strength values between 291 and 343 kg/cm^2 (4150 and 4900 lb/in^2).

A typical cross section for the crossover segment of the project is shown in Fig. 8-18a, completed from the bottom up. The inner wall is 70 cm thick and is compositely connected to the exterior diaphragm wall. Connection bars were bent in styrofoam placed along the inner side of the reinforcement cage. Heat bents were used to restore the bars and establish composite action with the secondary wall.

For the station section, waterproofing of the roof slab was provided with sheets bent at the end to cover the interior and top of the wall. For the floor slab, the use of expansive concrete proved effective. In order to improve the watertightness of the connection between the diaphragm walls and the slab, the expansion of the concrete and the resulting compressive stress (although small) caused the encroachment of the slab concrete into the finished wall and resulted in a tight connection. Fukui (1980) reports that neither water leakage nor cracks in the concrete have occurred. However, where single walls have been used, water often leaks through construction joints. This problem is first allowed to occur, and then the leaking area is cut and filled with waterproofing material or grout if the leakage is extensive.

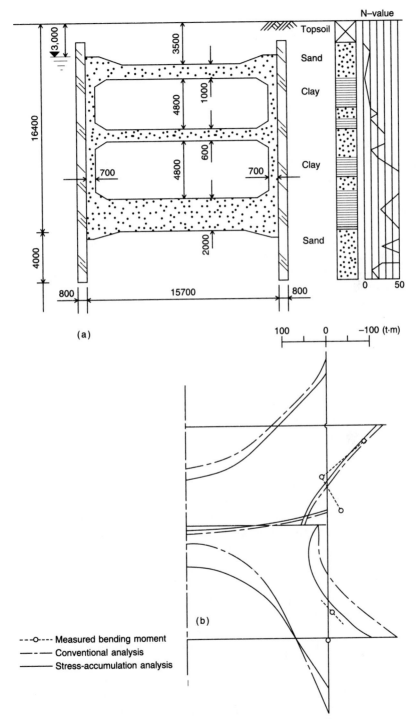

Figure 8-18 Kire Station, Osaka, Japan: (a) Typical section at the crossover segment. (b) Bending-moment diagrams. (*From Fukui, 1980.*)

Bending-moment diagrams for the composite structure of the cross-over segment are shown in Fig. 8-18*b*, and compare measured and computed values.

8-5   Underground Roadways and Traffic Underpasses

The variation and combination of methods and structural systems often introduced in subways (particularly in train stations) is seldom if ever necessary for traffic underpasses unless a covered motorway must be constructed under a street to handle more traffic, or where extensive work is contemplated (for example, the proposed Central Artery Transfer in Boston).

Motorways have the advantage of regular configuration and section geometry, and usually they are depressed at congested intersections or at grade separations with minimum clearance. The selection of ground support is governed essentially by the same factors that affect cut-and-cover excavations for subway construction. Policies and standards regarding planning and design are established by local authorities and are not considered in this text.

Construction with cast-in-place walls

The four-lane roadway with safety walks is adopted in most regions of the United States and is also popular abroad. It may require from 50 to 60 ft (15 to 18 m) face-to-face of walls. For the usual requirements of vertical clearance (14 ft 6 in) the depth of excavation from street level is of the order of 19 to 20 ft (about 6 m) which is within the range of vertical cantilever walls, with or without counterforts, as shown in Fig. 8-19.

In the covered (bridge) portion the superstructure deck can brace the walls laterally at the top, and usually it is constructed before excavation so that all earth moving is done under cover while the street is open to traffic. In general, provisions for temperature changes should be made when the span exceeds 40 ft (AASHTO specifications). This may include thermal movement and freedom of the system for end rotation under load. When the superstructure is not allowed to move freely to accommodate changes in temperature, the design should provide for the accommodation of thermal stresses for both the superstructure and the walls. At the bottom the walls may be laterally braced by sufficient embedment or by the base slab if the latter has sufficient rigidity; in this case temporary bracing must be provided near the bottom until the base slab is in place.

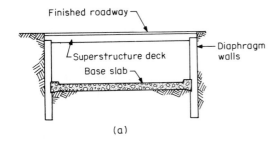

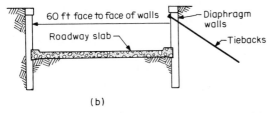

Figure 8-19 Diaphragm walls for traffic underpass: (*a*) Covered section. (*b*) Uncovered section for approach roadway.

In the open segment the walls must be checked for the probable movement, regardless of embedment and soil stiffness, below excavation. This movement will be partly stopped and controlled if some bracing is provided near the top, usually with ground anchors, and if the base slab is placed as soon as the excavation reaches the final depth.

Since the walls are exposed to public view, face treatment is necessary. The choice includes precast panels, brick facing, or a separate concrete wall. Complete joint waterproofing at panel connections is often debated, the alternative being drainage channels taking seeping water to a sump.

Construction with a center wall. If the roadway width exceeds the optimum length of single spans, a center wall can be considered. If minimum traffic disruption and street closings are required, this wall (continuous or intermittent) is built from ground level. The center wall will receive more loads (dead and live) than the outside walls; hence it may have to be deeper for adequate bearing capacity; this wall, however, will be subjected to less lateral thrust. Strip panels capped with a continuous beam will satisfy these requirements.

Construction with prefabricated panels

The advantages of precasting mentioned in Sec. 1-5 are, by contrast to the complexity of subways, more applicable to traffic underpasses.

Usually the size of the job will offset the fixed cost of precasting; the uniformity of section geometry results in standard panel sections and configurations; sufficient space is available at the site as casting yard; and the smooth wall finish is acceptable as final face treatment.

Figure 8-20 shows a typical cross section for a depressed motorway. The exterior walls have continuous precast panels, and the center support consists of strip sections. When all supports were in place, the top slab was cast and posttensioned; earth moving was carried out under cover. The roadway bed was formed by a cast-in-place slab.

Because the center wall supports heavier loads it has a deeper foundation, provided by extending the trench to a suitable stratum and filling with lean concrete. With a considerable portion of the trench filled with cast-in-place plain concrete, the prefabricated panels are extended only below the finished road bed, and their size is reduced. Thus the strip sections for the center wall have average dimensions of 9 by 1.80 by 0.40 m (30 by 6 by 1.35 ft) and were easy to lift, handle, position, and suspend until the concrete had set.

The panels for the outside walls were set in cast-in-place concrete filling the lower part of the trench, with a displacement grout left along the panel height as shown in Fig. 8-20. These panels are set deeper to provide greater wall embedment for lateral stability. Typical panel depth is 12 m.

Construction details.   The excavation for the example of Fig. 8-20 was carried out with a kelly rig equipped with a grab 0.60 m wide (about 24 in), allowing sufficient grout to envelop the precast panels for watertightness. Solid guide walls served also to hold the precast panels. Guide wall details and method of suspension are shown in Fig. 8-21.

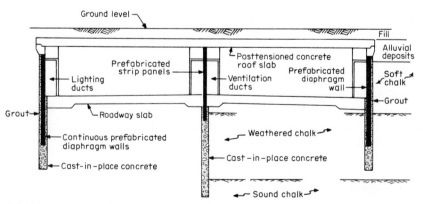

Figure 8-20 Cross section of a covered motorway built with prefabricated diaphragm walls. (*From Leonard, 1974.*)

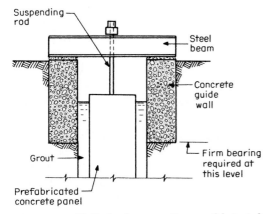

Figure 8-21 Method of suspending prefabricated panels.

The trench was filled with a single grout consisting of water, bentonite, cement, and a retarding agent to regulate setting time. Leonard (1974) has provided data on strength-time characteristics, shown in Fig. 8-22. The diagram confirms that the grout remained essentially liquid for the first few days and offered no impediment to the excavation, concrete placement, and installation of precast sections. With time, the graphs (although conceptual) show that the grout gained strength and blended with the precast panels.

Plain concrete was tremied to about 1 m (3 ft) above the base of the panels, and while it was still workable and fresh, the precast sections were inserted and seated with their tips fully submerged in the concrete mix.

Figure 8-23 shows details of the panel joint. When the wall was exposed, part of the joint on the exposed face was scraped and cleaned

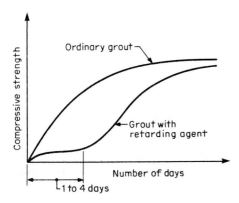

Figure 8-22 Grout characteristics for installing prefabricated panels.

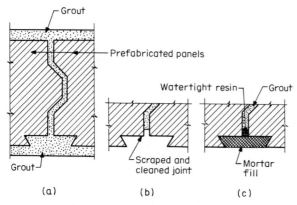

Figure 8-23 Construction joint details for prefabricated panels: (*a*) Joint before treatment. (*b*) Joint scraped and cleaned. (*c*) Joint waterproofed with resin and filled with mortar.

to a depth of 2 cm (0.8 in). Its watertightness was improved by the application of a special resin compound, and then filling the omission with cement mortar as shown in Fig. 8-23c. Leonard (1974) makes a distinction between initial (short-term) and permanent (long-term) watertightness. Initially the grout in the joint and along the back of the wall must enable the excavation to be carried out under nominal dry conditions. Later the grout is likely to shrink because of drying out, and in addition small differential panel movement may cause cracks to develop across the joints. With time, damp patches are likely to be noticed unless the joints are properly seated. Treatment is easier and more effective if the joint is wide enough to accept and hold a watertight resin; a wide joint is also easier to clean.

Commentary

It appears from these examples that for construction in urban areas the use of structural elements that can reduce design effort and minimize delays and public inconvenience should be favored. In addition, the posttensioned diaphragm walls discussed in Sec. 1-4 should be part of the systems-study process because of the technical merits and economic advantages that may result in certain conditions. A problem still facing engineers today is the high cost of prefabricated elements (superstructure and substructure) in areas where they are not readily available or where the project size does not justify mass production. However, even at a higher cost this form of construction can be found acceptable considering the reduction in traffic disruption.

The construction of traffic underpasses and grade separations in congested urban sites has two major drawbacks: (1) the associated high costs and (2) the often extended disruption of surface activities. Suggested options include the use of prefabricated members and the design of the permanent structure to act also as ground support during excavation. Interestingly, as the highway program is extended to include maintenance, rehabilitation, and replacement policies, these choices will become more viable options.

Motorways in cut-and-cover tunnels, example

The proposed Central Artery—North to Causeway in Boston, Mass., includes 2300 lin ft of mainline cut-and-cover tunnel with 8 to 10 lanes of traffic, 800 lin ft of ramp tunnels of cut-and-cover construction, 1800 lin ft of depressed and open roadways, and extensive underpinning, surface bracing, and support systems for the existing Central Artery viaduct. This is part of the CA/T Project that will replace the existing elevated section of I-93 with an underground expressway and will also extend I-90 (Mass Pike) directly to Logan Airport.

The general subsurface profile shows an upper fill extending to 10 to 20 ft below ground surface, and consisting primarily of sand and gravel with some zones of clayey or silty materials, and cobbles, brick, concrete, and other items. The fill is underlain by a silty clay stratum, usually stiff to hard near the top and becoming medium stiff to soft with depth. The silty clay stratum has a thickness up to 90 ft, which occurs toward the southern end of the contract limits. Glacial till exists below the clay stratum and consists of a mixture of sand, gravel, silt, and clay; it is found immediately above the bedrock at practically all locations. The top of this stratum usually occurs at a depth of 60 to 110 ft from the ground level. Bedrock is found typically at depths of 70 to 110 ft and is variably weathered and fractured. Groundwater is usually encountered within the top fill 5 to 15 ft below the ground surface.

A main feature of the tunnel construction is the excavation support system. The proposed scheme consists of steel-and-concrete panels, discussed in Sec. 1-7. These are also referred to as SPTC walls (soldier pile–tremie concrete). The steel beams will be spaced from 4 to 6 ft. The slurry walls are shown to penetrate 10 ft into the glacial till or 10 ft below the bottom of the base slab if the latter is below the top of the till. The depth of excavation in the cut-and-cover tunnels varies from 38 to 82 ft, and the width ranges from 58 to 182 ft.

A typical section of the cut-and-cover tunnel is shown in Fig. 8-24. The roof slab system has steel girders with concrete composite con-

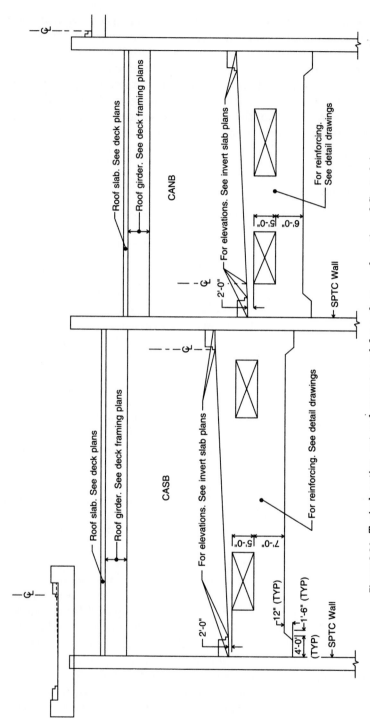

Figure 8-24 Typical section, cut-and-cover tunnel for underground portion of Central Artery, Boston.

struction. The girders are spaced to match the layout of the soldier piles in the walls and may be rolled sections or built-up members. Preliminary design indicates a pinned connection but does not exclude fixed connections at some locations. The base slab shown in Fig. 8-24 is cast-in-place reinforced concrete. A preliminary design of this slab considers the connection of base slab and walls as fixed. The final design should consider the advantages of an appropriate model such as the Vierandeel truss in analyzing the structural action of the base slab in conjunction with the vent openings.

8-6 Design Concepts, Subway Sections

Section geometry

Dennis et al. (1981) have studied existing and planned subway structures and concluded that a minor variation in the geometric configuration can make a marked difference in the structural action. The effects of varying geometry on moments at the joints of section slabs and walls were investigated for various configurations.

Arched roof. As structural units, arches are members shaped and supported in such a manner that intermediate transverse loads are transmitted to the supports (in this case walls) primarily by axial compressive thrusts rather than by bending. In addition, they must be sustained by supports capable of developing lateral as well as normal reaction components. For a given loading the arch shape must be chosen so as to avoid the introduction of bending moments. Under the definition, an arched tunnel roof connected to strong diaphragm walls can respond as a true arch.

Under live loads, a certain moment will be induced, especially near the ends of the arch. If, however, the geometry accommodates the axial thrust line, the reinforcing steel requirements are reduced significantly and simplify the moment connection with the walls.

In practice arches require extensive formwork and offer limited compatibility with the method of construction (downward or from the bottom up). Arched structures are thus expensive to construct with either cast-in-place or precast units. This cost increases where the arch curvature is large and the reinforcement must be bent to fit the surface contour, resulting in additional work.

Folded plate roof. A compromise between a flat and an arched roof is the folded plate, shown in Fig. 8-25. Conceptually, a folded plate can have as many folds as structurally desired, but for simplicity, the two-

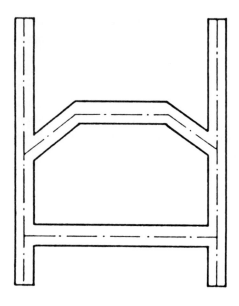

Figure 8-25 Folded plate roof section.

fold configuration is considered as optimal. In terms of structural response it approaches the ideal arch but is much simpler to construct. Through a successful selection of frame dimensions the bending moment applied at the joints can be kept within desired limits. The folded plate also exerts an axial thrust against the wall at the joint, and this reduces the connection requirements including the bars that must be extended into the wall.

Intermediate supports.   Another alternative is to provide intermediate supports, as shown in Fig. 8-26. Within a station or a double-track section, these supports reduce the moments considerably by reducing the horizontal spans to one-half. Columns or panels spaced intermittently along the centerline of the station are nearly as effective as a continuous center wall.

Frame stiffness by counterforts

One of the problems in the section frame analysis is the requirement to provide high flexural rigidity (EI/L) to resist asymmetrical loading conditions, especially if hinges are assumed at the wall-slab joints. This rigidity can be provided by the use of counterforts as shown in Fig. 8-27. The counterfort spacing and depth can be varied and coordinated with optimum T-beam action. The walls are processed in T panels with dimensions selected to satisfy the design rather than conformity with equipment characteristics. The resulting T-beam action is utilized at

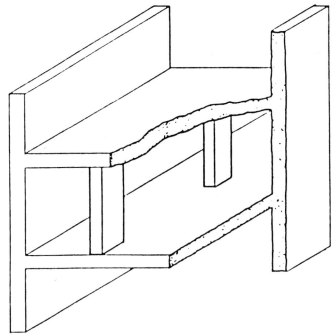

Figure 8-26 Perspective view of a box section with intermediate column supports.

the joints of the top and bottom slab with the walls where the moments are negative and consistent with the profile of the T beam. Since moment reversal will occur in certain segments of the walls, the T beam should ideally be constructed with the stem on alternating sides, which is impractical. Generally, however, the moments near the wall-slab joints govern the design so that the counterforts will be needed on the exterior side.

Moment releasing and rigid joints

These joints, discussed briefly in Sec. 8-2, allow the connection between slabs and walls to respond to the actual loading conditions that exist at a given construction stage, and hence they are advantageous in multistage loading application. Conversion from a simple to a rigid joint will ensure that the flexural capacity of the slabs can be developed by redistributing the positive moments at midspan to the ends of the member as negative moments. In this respect rigidity does not mean full fixity, where the joint is restrained against rotation, but rather frame action through the ability of the joint to transfer moments from one member to the other. Likewise, where the flexural stiffness of the slab is much greater than that of the wall, such as the

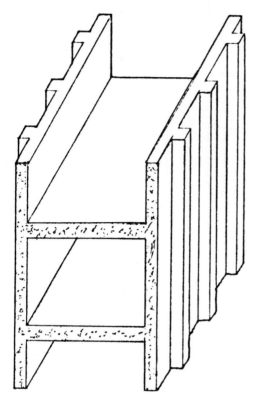

Figure 8-27 Isometric projection of slurry walls with counterforts.

bottom slab of the section of Fig. 8-24, making a rigid wall-slab joint will benefit the wall by reducing midheight moments. If the wall design does not require this relief and the base slab is still subjected to large midspan moments, a hinge connection can be provided and counterforts incorporated on the underside of the slab to create a T-beam action. These options must be studied in conjunction with the final (permanent) stage of load application.

Alternate joint. This detail is a variation of the steel beam and concrete wall and can sometimes be more practical where diaphragm walls are part of the permanent structure. The wall is reinforced at the joint location by rolled structural steel shapes. Through the use of good-quality welding the rolled shapes are easily connected to the bars of the slabs for moment transfer.

The application of this detail is shown in Fig. 8-28 for a diaphragm wall that is part of the permanent structure with interior framing of

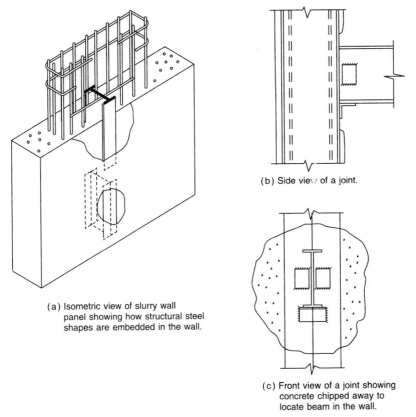

(b) Side view of a joint.

(a) Isometric view of slurry wall panel showing how structural steel shapes are embedded in the wall.

(c) Front view of a joint showing concrete chipped away to locate beam in the wall.

Figure 8-28 Alternate method to steel beam and concrete type of slurry wall.

structural steel shapes. Short segments of structural steel sections are embedded in the diaphragm wall at levels where connections are desired. These sections are rigidly clamped into the reinforcing steel cage so that concrete can be tremied around it, as shown in Fig. 8-28a. When the wall is exposed enough concrete is chipped off to locate the beam in the wall, and the connection with the beam or girder of the interior floors is made by welding angles as shown in Fig. 8-28b and c. This detail is suitable for the transfer of shear and can be expanded to include the transfer of moment if a steel angle is added to the top of the far beam.

The same principle can also be used to make a temporary hinge, following the sequence shown in Fig. 8-29. In Fig. 8-29a a temporary hinge is created by welding the slab steel to the wall steel beam only at position A (bottom flange). Angles on both sides of the slab beams

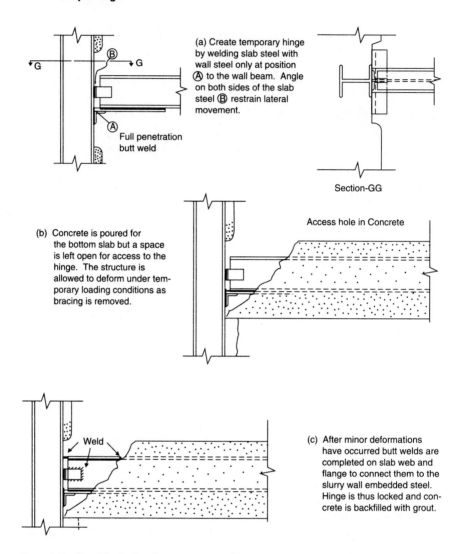

Figure 8-29 Possible design for a temporary hinge.

are welded to the exposed flange of the wall beam at position B and restrain lateral movement. An access hole is left in the concrete slab around the joint so that further welding can be done after the structure is loaded while the rest of the slab is poured, as shown in Fig. 8-29*b*, and the structure is allowed to deform under temporary loading conditions as bracing is removed. After these deformations have occurred, butt welds are completed as shown in Fig. 8-29*c* on slab web and flange to finish the connection with the slurry wall steel beam. The hinge is thus locked and the concrete omission is filled with cement grout.

8-7 Parametric Studies, Subway Stations

Dennis et al. (1981) have investigated various design concepts for underground subways and motorways. These studies were carried out by selecting frame size, shape, and dimensions, and then determining the moments at critical sections. The results were analyzed for comparison of the various schemes in the context of structural action and cost, and then were used in actual case histories.

Study No. 1: Varying roof geometry and thickness

The frame outline and loading conditions are shown in Fig. 8-30a and b, respectively. The objective is to study the effects of top slab geometry and thickness on moments at the wall-slab intersections (points A and B). The wall and base slab thickness is kept constant at 4 ft (1.22 m). The results, obtained by finite-element techniques, are summarized in Table 8-1. Only maximum moments at wall-slab joints are shown. For the asymmetrical loading condition full at rest pressure was applied to the left side of the structure, but only one-half the at rest pressure was applied to the right side.

For the loading conditions shown the folded plate geometry results in considerable moment reduction at the critical wall-slab interface, and this is comparatively greater at the top slab-wall joint. Increased thickness of the roof helps to further reduce moments. Interestingly, the total moments of Table 8-1 show the compound effect of the various loads without differentiation between dead load, live load, earth pressure, and pore pressure; hence these results can be used only for allowable stress design.

Study No. 2: Arched roof vs. folded plate roof

The frame outline and loading conditions are shown in Fig. 8-31a and b, respectively. Since the objective is to study asymmetrical loading, half of the at rest pressure is applied to the right side of the section. Note that the soil-structure interaction assumed along the base of the bottom slab is a diagram derived from a parabolic bearing pressure distribution with more load near the walls and less load at the center.

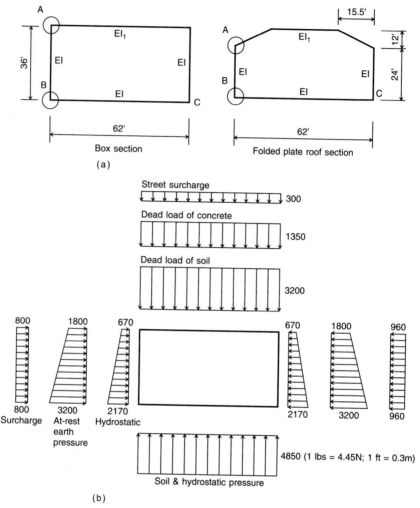

Figure 8-30 Parametric Study No. 1: (a) Frame configurations studied. (b) Loading conditions. (*From Dennis et al., 1981.*)

The load application differs from the previous study in that load factors are used according to ACI Code (applicable in 1981). Thus the governing equation is

$$M_u = 1.4DC + 1.4EW + 1.7LL + 1.7EA \qquad (8\text{-}1)$$

where all symbols correspond to the notation of Eq. (4-40).

The results are summarized in Table 8-2 for two critical joint locations marked A and B on the frame outline. In terms of moments and resulting stresses, the arched roof does not have any advantages over

TABLE 8-1   Results of Parametric Study No. 1: Varying Roof Geometry and Thickness

	Simple box section		Folded plate roof section	
	Moment at A, ft-kip	Moment at B, ft-kip	Moment at A, ft-kip	Moment at B, ft-kip
Symmetric loading, full (at rest) earth pressure on both sides of structure:				
6-ft-thick roof $I = 5.333$ ft^4 $I_1 = 18$ ft^4	-847	-654	-499	-612
7-ft-thick roof $I = 5.333$ ft^4 $I_1 = 28.583$ ft^4	-721	-671	-424	-629
3-ft-thick roof $I = 5.333$ ft^4 $I_1 = 42.667$ ft^4	-626	-685	-351	-643
	Moment at B, ft-kip	Moment at C, ft-kip	Moment at B, ft-kip	Moment at C, ft-kip
Asymmetric loading,* full (at rest) earth pressure one side, one-half (at rest) earth pressure other side:				
6-ft-thick roof $I = 5.333$ ft^4 $I_1 = 18$ ft^4	-835	-921	-750	-667

Note: Only maximum moments at wall-slab intersections shown (1 ft-lb = 1.36 N-m). Results obtained by using finite-element analysis method.

*For this analysis one-half (at rest) earth pressure was applied to the right side of the structure, replacing the full (at rest) earth pressure shown above on both structures for the asymmetrical loading condition.

the folded plate, and in fact the moments are somewhat less for the folded plate configuration. In addition, the arch shape is more difficult to construct; hence it is more expensive.

The reinforcement requirements for the ultimate (factored) moments of Table 8-2 will be checked at point B of the folded plate for the wall section. For a wall thickness of 48 in, $d = 44$ in (approximately). For $A_s = 9$ in^2, we compute

$$a = \frac{9 \times 60}{0.85 \times 35.5 \times 12} = \frac{540}{35.7} = 15.1 \text{ in}$$

(This is based on $f'_c = 3500$ lb/in^2 and $f_y = 60,000$ lb/in^2.) The nominal moment is therefore (ignoring axial thrust)

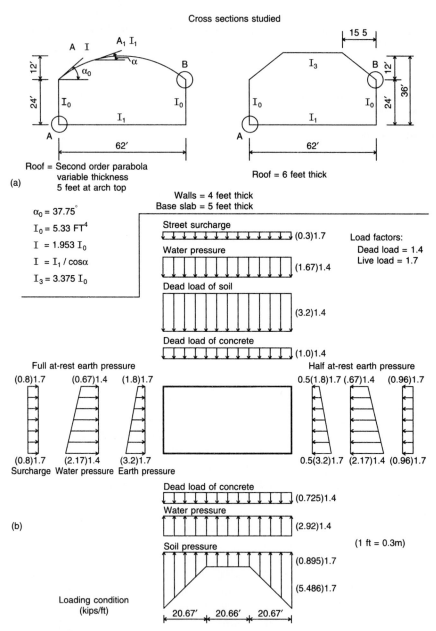

Figure 8-31 Cases studied and loading condition for Parametric Study No. 2, analysis based on load factor method. (*From Dennis et al., 1981.*)

TABLE 8-2   Results of Parametric Study No. 2: Arched Roof vs. Folded
Plate Roof

	Arched roof section		Folded plate roof section	
	A	B	A	B
Moment, ft-kip	−1471.34	−1652.22	−1468.7	−1386.89
Shear, kip:				
Wall	114.59	108.67	126.8	91.95
Slab	−277.06	−172.52	−256.08	−187.92
Axial force, kip:				
Wall	−255.22	−285.30	−262.07	−279.07
Slab	—	−240.89	—	−242.52

1 ft-lb = 1.36 N-m.

$$M_n = 9 \times 60 \, \frac{44 - 7.5}{12} = 1642 \text{ ft-kips}$$

or

$$\phi M_n = 0.90 \times 1642 = 1478 \text{ ft-kips} > 1469 \quad \text{OK}$$

Also note that $p = 9/(44 \times 12) = 0.017 < 0.75p_b$.

Although for the given wall thickness this reinforcement will provide the required structural capacity while the concrete is stressed well below the 0.003 strain limit, in practice this design will result in a large number of bars per foot of length of wall, probably arranged in three or four layers. In this case a practical wall-slab connection is the detail shown in Fig. 8-8. For a 4-ft-thick wall, the required bend bar diameter plus the splice extension length for the coupling device gives a total dimension that fits well within the limits of the wall. The bars can be prebent and installed with the reinforcing cage, to be removed after the top portion of the wall is exposed.

Effect of axial thrust on reinforcement requirements. This effect was studied in the same investigation for a cross section with a folded roof slab but for two base slab configurations: a straight shape, and a slab with a variable thickness and a shape that approaches a folded plate. The results show the following: (1) the moment at the slab-wall joint can be reduced by changing the geometry of the base slab, but this increases also the axial load in the latter; (2) increasing the wall thickness increases the joint moments; and (3) axial thrust of a permanent nature in the wall or in the slab creates a compression effect and hence compensates for some of the flexural tensile stresses, provided the ultimate concrete strength at 0.003 strain is not reached before the tensile steel attains its yield condition.

Study No. 3: Effect of counterforts

Cross sections with counterforts in the diaphragm walls and on the underside of the roof slab were analyzed for the standard loading conditions and unsymmetrical lateral loads. The results show that for unsymmetrical loads the counterforts reduce the deflection of structure associated with sidesway. A section with rigid joints at all slab-wall connections but without counterforts was compared with a structure of the same geometry but with hinges in the wall-base slab joints and counterforts. The sidesway caused by the same unsymmetrical loads was less in the section with counterforts.

Study No. 4: Effect of center posts

A set of four different tunnel configurations is shown in Fig. 8-32a and b, and cover sections without and with a center post, respectively. Typical dimensions of a section are shown in Fig. 8-33, and represent a station from the Washington, D.C., metro. The internal dimensions of the box are: width = 62 ft (18.9 m), height = 36 ft (10.97 m). The study assumes full vertical load, long-term lateral load on one side of the structure, and short-term lateral load on the other side. The top slab is considered unrestrained against horizontal translation, and horizontal springs are provided to account for elastic soil support.

The groundwater table is as shown in Fig. 8-33. A street surcharge of 300 lb/ft^2 is applied as vertical load. The surcharge from buildings

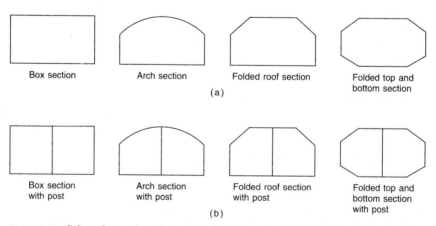

Figure 8-32 Selected tunnel configurations for cost analysis: (a) Sections without center post. (b) Sections with center post. (*From Dennis et al., 1981.*)

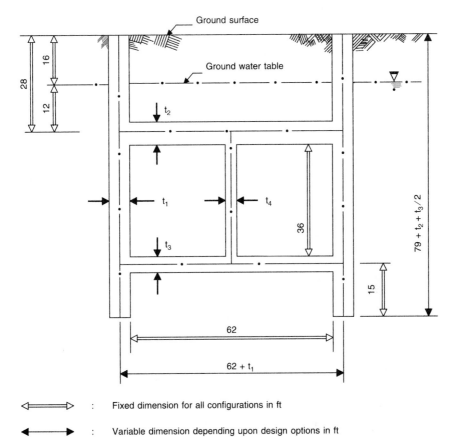

Figure 8-33 Dimensions of a typical tunnel section.

is 960 lb/ft^2 on one side and 800 lb/ft^2 on the other. For analysis purposes, the subgrade modulus is assumed as 200 kips/ft^3, and the pressure coefficients are $K_a = 0.40$ and $K_0 = 0.58$. Allowable stress design is used.

The results of the study are summarized in Table 8-3. For the same configuration, the section with the center post provides the most desirable moment, shear, and axial load distribution; hence the center post results in the most favorable tunnel dimensions and member thickness. The center post has a section 1.5 by 3.0 ft (0.46 by 0.91 m) and is spaced at 20-ft (6.1-m) intervals.

The dimensions and spacing of the center posts were determined from architectural and structural considerations. Slender supports at greater spacing are architecturally desirable since they result in a more attractive interior. Larger and closely spaced posts are, however, structurally more effective. The effect of post spacing and size on the

TABLE 8-3 Summary of Parametric Study of Tunnel Dimensions, Section of Fig. 8-32

Case	Type	Configuration	SI units, meters							U.S. customary units, ft						
			t_1	t_2	t_3	t_4	t_5	t_6	c	t_1	t_2	t_3	t_4	t_5	t_6	c
1	U		1.52	2.13	2.44	2.13	2.44			5	7	8	7	8		
	V		1.52	1.83	2.13					5	6	7				
2	U		1.52	1.52	2.13	1.83	2.13			5	5	7	6	7		
	V		1.52	1.22	1.83					5	4	6				
3	U		1.52	1.83	2.13	1.83	2.13			5	6	7	6	7		
	V		1.52	1.52	1.83					5	5	6				
4	U		1.52	1.52	1.83	1.83	2.13			5	5	6	6	7		
	V		1.22	1.52	1.52					4	5	5				

5		UP	1.22	1.52	1.83	0.46 × 0.91	6.1	4	5	6	1.5 × 3.0	20
6		UP	1.22	1.22	1.83	0.46 × 0.91	6.1	4	4	6	1.5 × 3.0	20
7		UP	1.22	1.22	1.83	0.46 × 0.91	6.1	4	4	6	1.5 × 3.0	20
8		UP	1.22	1.22	1.52	0.46 × 0.91	6.1	4	4	5	1.5 × 3.0	20

c: center-to-center distance between the posts
U: uniform thickness without post
V: variable thickness without post
UP: uniform thickness with post

global structural capacity was studied using finite-element analyses, with both three-dimensional plate element and plane frame options. The results are presented in tabulated form in Tables 8-4 and 8-5.

The 1.5- by 3-ft post spaced at 20-ft intervals was selected after analyzing the structural response of the section for 20-, 25-, and 50-ft post spacing. As can be seen in Fig. 8-34, increasing the post spacing results in increased joint moments at critical section locations, and these values eventually approach the moments corresponding to the same section without posts. The axial compression in the post is likewise increased to values that cannot be sustained with posts of normal dimensions and foundation conditions. The 20-ft spacing is therefore a compromise between structural performance and architectural criteria.

8-8 Design Considerations

The foregoing sections show the influence of several key factors on the selection of structural systems and the methods of design; these factors are: (1) construction staging and traffic management; (2) presence of underground obstacles and groundwater; and (3) functional characteristics and size of the proposed underground facility.

Traffic conditions

The decision to maintain, interrupt, or partially disrupt traffic usually lies with the supervising authority. The criteria are likely to be different for a facility built underground along the alignment of an existing street or road, and for a facility that crosses existing streets.

The maintenance of safe, efficient vehicular and pedestrian traffic flows during construction is a sensitive issue that must be resolved between the interfacing construction contracts and local authorities. Provisions for traffic maintenance usually are expressed in a traffic plan to implement the requirements for construction mitigation and staging. This plan gives consideration to the work and schedule of all contractors and includes an interface with public agencies expected to influence traffic flow as well as utilities both in and adjacent to the construction corridor.

In general the traffic plan will include a detailed construction staging and level of traffic disruption to ensure vehicular and pedestrian flow in the construction area. In addition, the staging of the removal of existing facilities, including utilities, should be part of this plan. The traffic plan should also detail the direct relationship between the traffic flow and the contemplated construction staging with the methods of construction considered in the design.

The influence of traffic plan on the method of construction is demonstrated in the following examples. Figure 8-35 shows the construc-

TABLE 8-4 The Effect of Post on the Bending Moment at the Joints

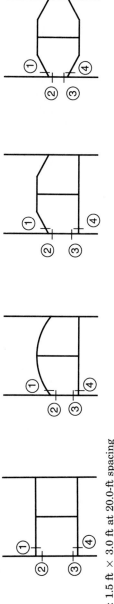

Posts: 1.5 ft × 3.0 ft at 20.0-ft spacing
Loading: unsymmetrical

No.	Box section			Arch section			Folded roof section			Folded top and bottom section		
	A	B	C	A	B	C	A	B	C	A	B	C
①	−1241.2	−599.3	55	−730.7	−220.1	70	−452.6	−63.8	86	−498.6	−96.2	81
②	−828.5	−535.3	35	−652.2	−222.6	66	−439.1	−105.9	76	−480.4	−152.4	68
③	−1061.4	−766.0	28	−873.4	−668.8	23	−935.9	−700.5	25	−739.9	−472.3	36
④	−1317.7	−870.0	34	−1244.0	−900.6	25	−1321.3	−897.5	32	−1047.2	−556.9	47

A: bending moment in kip-ft/ft for sections without post
B: bending moment in kip-ft/ft for sections with post
C: percentage of reduction in bending moment
(1 ft = 0.3 m)

TABLE 8-5 The Effect of the Center Post Spacing on the Section (Rectangular Configuration)

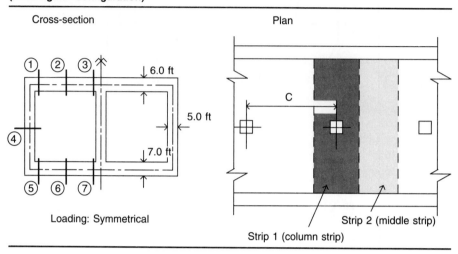

Cross-section   Plan

Loading: Symmetrical

Strip 2 (middle strip)
Strip 1 (column strip)

Section	No post	Posts at 15 ft		Posts at 30 ft		Posts at 45 ft	
		Strip 1	Strip 2	Strip 1	Strip 2	Strip 1	Strip 2
①	−1130.8	−494.8	−494.8	−544.1	−544.1	−579.8	−603.0
②	730.0	237.8	272.0	292.0	299.9	−299.0	335.0
③	1349.8	−397.0	78.0	−316.1	107.0	107.0	294.1
④	297.0	629.0	617.8	598.9	598.9	598.9	569.0
⑤	−725.9	−756.9	−756.9	−774.9	−774.9	−773.8	−719.0
⑥	291.4	469.0	377.9	535.1	375.0	375.0	379.0
⑦	1571.9	−55.1	136.0	15.3	288.9	288.9	437.0

Moment redistribution due to use of center posts		Effect
At section ①	Moments are reduced ~ 50%	Good
At sections ③ and ⑦	Moments are reduced ~ 80%	Good
At section ④	Moments are increased ~ 50%	OK

Conclusion: The use of center posts has favorable effects.

tion phasing for the Brussels metro. Because of the requirement for traffic maintenance throughout the construction period, the ground support is a secant pile wall. In stage I the left lane of the street is used as a construction strip for the installation of the pile wall. In stage II the construction operations occupy the right lane, and consist in the installation of the right pile wall. In stage III the center lane is closed to traffic to complete the center portion of the tunnel roof. Note that during phases I, II, and III two lanes of the street remain open to traffic. Thereafter street activities return to normal while the

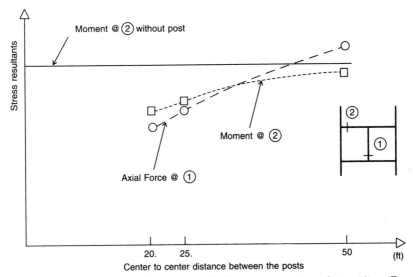

Figure 8-34 Effect of post spacing on critical moments, rectangular section. (*From Dennis et al., 1981.*)

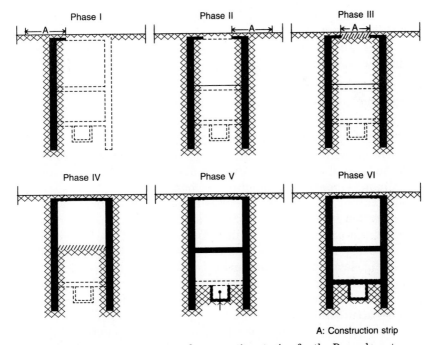

A: Construction strip

Figure 8-35 Traffic maintenance and construction staging for the Brussels metro.

excavation is carried out under the roof. In this case the requirement for traffic maintenance dictated the wall system and a concrete slab as the roof of the tunnel.

The station on Jasper Street, Edmonton (Figs. 8-15 and 8-16) is 700 ft long and 61 ft wide. The contractor moved onto the site on Apr. 21, 1975, and work started the following week. Automobile and bus traffic was allowed to use the street for the first month, and then traffic was limited to buses only for the next two weeks. All vehicular traffic was shut down on June 8, 1975. With the street partially open the contractor installed type A and B piles.

With the street closed, the contractor poured the L (grade) beam and drove the continuous sheet pile wall (see also Sec. 8-4). With this part of the work completed on one portion of the project, the bulk excavation was started and taken down 18 ft to the mezzanine level. The precast prestressed inverted U channels were then placed on the L beam with the legs of the U down on continuous neoprene. The precast members were grouted without provisions for expansion and contraction. The top of the U beams was treated with a waterproofing membrane followed by insulating sheets. A lightweight concrete filler was placed on top to form the roadway crown, and a 9-in concrete pavement completed the resurfacing. The street was reopened to all traffic on Sept. 2, 1975. By contrast with the Brussels subway example where complete street closure was not permitted, full utilization of street space allowed the use of precast panels for the roof slab, and dictated the construction staging.

Underground structures and utilities

Utilities that must remain during construction and foundations that must be underpinned are probably the two most critical elements to be interfaced with the structural design. Utilities may result in the use of the hit-and-miss method discussed in other sections, and dictate special requirements for temporary support.

Underpinning may be carried out as an independent process, as lateral protection (see also Sec. 7-7), or as part of the main structural system of the underground facility. An example of the latter is the Central Artery in Boston. In this case traffic will be maintained on the existing elevated structure during construction of the underground artery. In order to construct the underground facility, which is below the existing elevated roadway, it is necessary to underpin the existing bridge structure and transfer the loads to the SPTC walls.

An underpinning scheme may be planned in conjunction with the proposed construction and with the intent, if feasible, to incorporate the underpinning system in the lateral support of the permanent structure. In most cases the decision to underpin has a technical merit, and less often it may reflect a subjective judgment based on risk assessment that quantifies site and ground conditions, construction practices, public attitudes, and effects of jurisdictional authority.

Needle beams.   These are installed horizontally to transfer the load of a wall, pier, or column to either or both sides of the foundation. Needles are steel wide-flange beams or plate girders, usually used in pairs with bolts and pipe spreaders in between to increase resistance to lateral buckling and torsion. The needles may be prestressed with jacks to help eliminate settlement that may occur when the load is intercepted. The needles may transfer the load to grade beams resting on the new foundation, or directly to the diaphragm walls. Where only limited settlement can be tolerated, the shoring scheme may include several concrete pads and jacks at the support points for the load transfer, and to control and adjust structural movement.

At best the underpinning scheme will bear on the diaphragm walls or other foundation elements of the new structure. The design must therefore ensure that the loads from the underpinning process are distributed longitudinally between panels to minimize the effect on soil bearing.

Ground conditions and water table

These are parameters affecting the choice of structural systems as well as design and construction methods. They may also dictate the decision to use diaphragm wall technology on a global basis or in conjunction with ground control techniques.

The rationale of convergence between support and control choices is discussed in Sec. 2-1. Adverse soil conditions and groundwater are not necessarily an impediment to the design and construction of diaphragm walls. On the contrary, this technology emerges as a viable option when these conditions exist at the site to an extent that limits other methodologies. However, they can influence the wall system and its design and construction. Typical examples are included throughout this text and demonstrate this interaction.

Function and size of proposed facility

Structures with regular configuration and section will in most instances simplify design and construction. Examples are subway lines with two tracks side by side or two tracks on two different levels; station configurations such as those shown in Fig. 8-32; and traffic underpasses with the basic cross section of Fig. 8-19. In these instances the structural systems are limited to the ground support that is also to become the permanent wall of the tunnel, and to a suitable slab type of cast-in-place concrete or precast members.

More complex configurations are shown in Figs. 8-10, 8-14, and 8-17. Their design reflects the multiple function and combines the multiple-stage construction with the structural supports of the final structure.

It appears from the foregoing comments that the planning and design of underground transportation systems goes far beyond the range of structural issues, and must resolve nontechnical considerations before any structural work can be done.

8-9   Design Fundamentals

Loads and loading groups

In Sec. 4-13 loads have been classified as permanent and as transient; the designation and grouping is consistent with the proposed LRFD specifications for bridges (Modjeski and Masters, 1992). According to AASHTO (1992), structures should be designed to carry the following loads and forces:

Dead load

Live load plus impact

Wind loads

Other loads, when they exist, as follows: longitudinal forces, centrifugal force, thermal forces, earth pressure, pore water pressure, buoyancy, shrinkage stresses, rib shortening, erection stresses, ice and current pressure, and earthquake effects.

Dead load.   This consists of the weight of the structure (actual) plus the weight of the earth above the structure. Some designers make an allowance in the weight of the earth above a culvert (usually 70 to 80 percent of the actual weight) to account for the effect of arching. For those structures that have the diaphragm walls extending at or near the ground, it is doubtful that any arching beyond the walls is possible, except for some shear friction at the wall-soil interface mobilized if the earth mass above the structure moves vertically with respect to the walls. Any reduction in the weight of earth will reduce the moments and shears in the top slab. Thus total weight is suggested for shear and moment on horizontal members and for vertical load-bearing members, haunches, brackets, or other connections between horizontal and vertical members.

Live load plus impact.   Live load may originate on the street or roads above the structure (for example, grade separations and tunnels under streets) or within the structure. Load models are specified by AASHTO, and include the standard H trucks or the standard lane loading. The proposed LRFD specifications include a design tandem load consisting of a pair of 25-kip axles spaced 4 ft apart. These specifications combine the design tandem or one design truck with the design lane load. For negative moment and reaction of interior supports, the extreme force effect should be determined for the loading combination consisting of 90 percent of the effect of two design trucks spaced a minimum of 50 ft between the lead axle of one truck and the rear axle of the other, and 14 ft between the two axles of the HS truck, combined with 90 percent of the effect of the design lane load.

AASHTO includes provisions for the distribution of wheel load through earth fills, when the depth of fill is 2 ft or more.

Impact allowance is not included for abutments, retaining walls, or structures with 3 ft or more of fill.

For underground subways and rail systems, the Owner should specify the transit load characteristics and the expected interaction between transit and highway traffic. These data should include loads, load distribution, load frequency, dynamic allowance, and dimensional requirements.

Longitudinal forces (braking).   Provisions should be made for the effect of a longitudinal force of 5 percent as stipulated by AASHTO.

Wind loads.   These may be considered where applicable, although the load combination that includes wind is unlikely to control the design.

Thermal forces.   These are associated with movement resulting from variations in temperature. They are important with grade separations where the roadway is exposed to temperature changes. Since the superstructure is not free to move if it braces the walls at the top, any expansion or contraction will cause the walls to move by the same amount. This movement will change the lateral earth stresses from partially passive to partially active state and vice versa.

Earthquake effects.   Where earthquakes may be anticipated, the structural response to seismic action should be analyzed according to AASHTO Guide Specifications for Seismic Design (1983).

Lateral loads.   Lateral earth stresses, effects of surcharge loads, and pore water pressures are discussed in detail in Chap. 4.

Structural combinations

In general the choice of wall types (including section configurations, structural framing, connections, horizontal members, and details) follows the analysis of pertinent factors discussed in the foregoing sections. Quite often, wall systems are merely chosen as regional preference or are based on previous experience. In many cases adherence to familiar types appears to strengthen confidence in structural performance but tends to inhibit technical justification.

The wall types reviewed in Chap. 1 can be combined with cast-in-place concrete slabs and beams, prefabricated members, steel decking, sheet piles, soldier piles with lagging, and ground strengthening. Review of current trends and practice suggests that two concepts are emerging in shallow cut-and-cover tunnels and vehicular underpasses. These are prefabricated elements for tunnel roofs, and integral structures.

Prefabricated elements. A wide range of shapes and configurations is available primarily for bridge superstructures, and some may be applicable in cut-and-cover tunnels. A complete summary is given by VHTRC-NCHRP Report 222 (1980) and 243 (1981). To help condense the synthesis, the grouping should focus on the four elements and systems with the highest structural potential. These are: (1) precast concrete slab spans; (2) precast box beams; (3) prestressed I beams; and (4) precast deck panels.

Precast concrete slab spans are shown in Fig. 8-36. They may be fabricated in various lengths and widths to accommodate the range of spans. Solid slab sections, shown in Fig. 8-36a are suitable for spans up to 30 ft. For longer spans, pretensioned or posttensioned voided slabs are found structurally more efficient.

Precast box beams, shown in Fig. 8-36c, can be used side by side (adjacent configuration). Their range covers 50 to 100 ft, and except for the longer spans the boxes are easy to transfer and erect. A wearing surface or concrete overlay is usually provided.

Prestressed I beams are popular in conventional bridges in connection with a cast-in-place concrete deck. For traffic underpasses utilizing diaphragm walls as end supports, prestressed I beams should be considered only when thermal movement and the associated end support conditions can be accommodated.

Precast deck panels represent a recent innovation, particularly when they are used in connection with steel beams as shown in Fig. 8-37. This combination is efficient with steel-and-concrete (SPTC) walls. Shear transfer between transverse panels is usually achieved by means of grouted keys. Composite action between deck panels and steel beams is developed by shear connectors (preattached to the top flange) after the voids left in the panels are filled with epoxy mortar. Deck panels eliminate most on-site formwork and concreting typically required for a steel beam superstructure or roof deck, and this favors their use where street closure restrictions are applied.

Integral structures. Integral structures (without bearings or expansion joints) are the only options where the top deck must support the walls

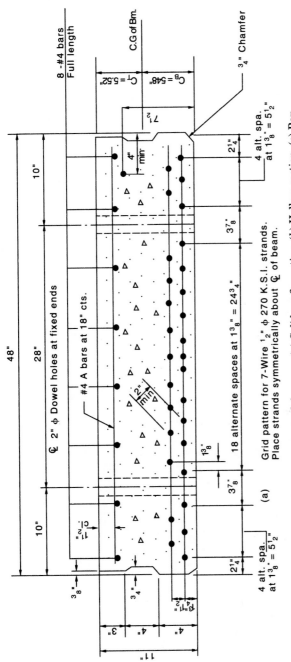

Figure 8-36 Precast concrete slab spans: (*a*) Solid configuration. (*b*) Hollow section. (*c*) Box beam section.

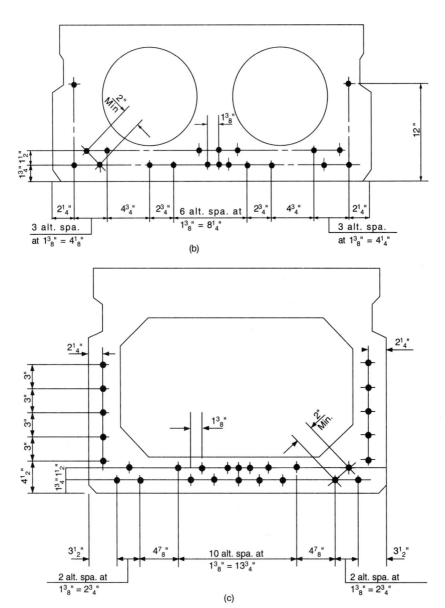

Figure 8-36 (*Continued*)

laterally. With longer spans and end restraint, the assumption is often made that the resulting continuity will induce secondary stresses in the superstructure, caused by thermal expansion and contraction, moisture gradients, and posttensioning effects. This assumption is valid if it can be demonstrated that the wall and the earth behind it will oppose cyclic movement on the top system. Thus the problem must

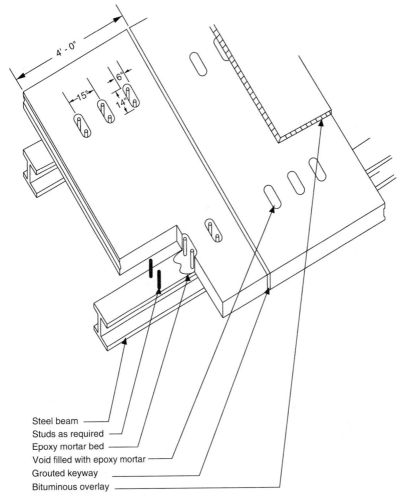

Steel beam
Studs as required
Epoxy mortar bed
Void filled with epoxy mortar
Grouted keyway
Bituminous overlay

Figure 8-37 Precast concrete deck panels on steel I beams.

be analyzed for soil-structure interaction, particularly in two cases, where the top deck or slab is fully exposed to temperature changes, and where the wall is in very stiff or dense soil. At best, it may be necessary to accept secondary stresses as part of the design in order to achieve a simple and less expensive structure.

Although current practice shows a trend toward integral construction, caution is necessary where certain components of the structure are likely to be subjected to high thermal stresses that cannot be readily quantified. For example, a relatively thin diaphragm wall supporting loose or soft soil represents a soil-structure system that can accommodate longitudinal thermal cycling of the deck. If the wall has counterforts or if it is placed against dense or stiff soil, the associated load effects may be considerably higher in both the deck and the soil. Since these stresses cannot be eliminated, they must be considered in the design.

The detail of wall-deck connections in integral construction is shown in Fig. 8-38 and is relatively simple. A capping beam usually is cast on top of the wall to distribute the vertical loads and make the panels act as one unit. A roughened construction joint is provided between the capping beam and the deck and is detailed with shear reinforcement as shown. Placing the bars near the outer face gives the deck some freedom to rotate as it deflects near midspan under load.

The connection between capping beam and deck slab may be considered as the shear-friction type and analyzed accordingly. It must be designed to resist the lateral reaction at the top of the wall induced by passive resistance as the wall moves with the thermal expansion of the deck. The problem is similar to the preload of struts by jacking, except that the jacking force is generated by thermal expansion. The earth stress pattern and distribution behind the wall should be inferred from the actual wall movement and may be related to apparent pressure diagrams. The temperature force is relieved somewhat as the deck contracts and the wall reverts to the original profile. The shear capacity at the top of the wall is increased if the connection is detailed as shown in Fig. 8-38b.

Design methodology

With the broad range of configurations in which the walls become part of the permanent structure, the design must consider the complete loading and unloading history of the system. This includes the temporary phase of the construction operations with stage excavation and bracing, integration of the walls with the permanent structure, removal of temporary bracing, backfilling, and long-term loading.

Some designers carry out the analysis with incremental load application. Each stage or increment of stress is determined by a change in the supports or by a change in the applied loads. The stress distribution and magnitude are estimated for each stage and superimposed to the previous stage, so that the final result is the summation of all loading stages. Conceptually, this approach is similar to the method of equivalent support discussed in Sec. 4-8. With changes in loads and support conditions, incremental superposition of stresses is typical in structural analysis.

Support of vertical loads. Loads and load groups may include underpinning loads, ground level traffic decking, weight of structure, overlying soil, seismic forces, and downdrag forces. These loads must be transferred to the soil by base bearing and side shear in the embedded wall portion below excavation level.

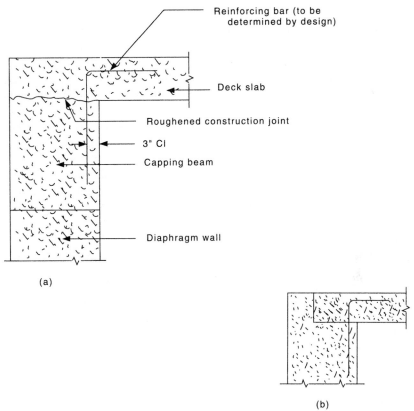

Reinforcing bar (to be
determined by design)

Deck slab

Roughened construction joint

3" Cl

Capping beam

Diaphragm wall

(a)

(b)

Figure 8-38 Detail of integral construction; diaphragm wall and cast-in-place concrete slab.

Downdrag forces may be present if there is a downward differential settlement of the soil with reference to the wall-soil interface, sufficient to mobilize shear resistance. This will occur, for example, if the wall bears on fairly unyielding strata such as glacial till or rock.

The placement of the bottom slab creates a mat foundation provided the subgrade soil is not disturbed. With the slab connected to the walls, additional loads, or loads removed and reapplied, will be resisted jointly by the walls and by direct bearing along the underside of the base slab. This division should have a displacement compatibility and usually requires refined methods of analysis. If the walls rest on rock and the base slab is cast on compressive soil, the walls will carry all the loads, and the slab should be designed as a beam supported at its ends.

Uplift may be a formidable force, especially where the groundwater level is not altered, and can thus control the design. This force must be considered as stipulated by AASHTO.

Lateral earth loads. Since the walls serve as both temporary and permanent support, lateral loads must be considered for both stages. The usual approach is to analyze these conditions separately and design the walls to satisfy both cases. The stage construction analysis is still feasible and expedient with a single design if the contractor is made responsible for the design of temporary support in the excavation stage.

For the final condition the walls are designed for the at rest pressure using effective stress analysis. Apparent pressure diagrams may be used, however, for the excavation stage, especially if a preload is applied to the bracing to control movement. Brace loads are computed from these diagrams considering a tributary area. Since apparent pressure envelopes are intended to provide an upper-bound condition, they are assumed to yield conservative results. For structural design of the wall in the construction stage certain simplified assumptions are introduced together with increased allowable stresses. For example, bending moments are usually computed using approximate formulas, such as $wl^2/10$ for continuous spans. This procedure gives a crude approximation of loads and load effects, and should be refined if these results control the design.

Interestingly, apparent pressure envelopes have certain inherent limitations, namely, (1) the method does not explicitly consider the unbalanced (net) pressure on the wall below excavation level; (2) it does not explain the continuity between the loads existing at the end of excavation and the long-term loads; (3) it ignores moments below excavation level and their effect on moments above excavation level; and (4) it does not explicitly consider the effect of system stiffness (EI/l) on moments and brace reactions. However, modified apparent pressure envelopes are appropriate in conjunction with actual soil conditions, soil stiffness, and wall stiffness.

Beam on elastic foundation. The analysis can model stage construction if a computer program is available that can store loads and displacements computerized at each stage for use as the initial conditions in analyzing the next stage. The process is sequential, beginning with the initial unexcavated condition and applying a series of loads combined with elastic supports. Passive resistance is modeled as a network of spring supports activated as the wall displaces the soil inward, and cannot exceed the radius obtained for classical theories. In a simple form, the analysis requires the use of bilinear elastic-plastic models to represent the passive pressure.

8-10 Design Example 1, Stage Construction

For simplicity, a Rankine earth pressure distribution is assumed, without water or surcharge loads. The same principles should apply for stratified soil, soil with water, and surcharge loads but with more complex load diagrams.

Stage 1. This stage includes excavation to first level for the installation of the first brace. The wall acts as a cantilever, as shown in Fig. 8-39a, and resists the active pressures by developing passive resistance below excavation level. The assumed hinge support is also the point of maximum cantilever moment (full fixity with zero rotation). Since the wall is already built to its predetermined depth, the portion below the assumed hinge location is ignored in the analysis. A net pressure diagram is constructed as in Fig. 4-62. The depth below excavation level is obtained from the equilibrium of horizontal forces.

The braces are assumed to be elastically loaded struts connected to the wall with a hinge but fixed at the other end.

The wall deflection that occurs at each bracing level prior to the installation of the brace is taken into account by applying an initial support displacement δ to the fixed end of the compression strut. The value of δ is equal to the actual wall deflection computed at the same level just prior to the insertion of the brace. The initial support displacement at each brace is not changed in the subsequent stages.

If a preload must be applied, either a concentrated force equal to the preload is applied to the wall or the initial support displacement is reduced by the elastic compression of the member under the same load.

Stage 2. This stage is shown in Fig. 8-39b. For the wall portion above excavation level, a hinge is assumed at the point of zero lateral load, as shown in Fig. 4-63. Thus the upper wall portion is simply supported at the zero-pressure point and at the upper brace level 1. A second calculation may be needed to check the moment in the lower portion of the wall as discussed in Sec. 4-8.

Stage 3. For stage 3, shown in Fig. 8-39c, and with the two brace levels in place, the wall may be assumed to rotate about brace 2, and a hinge is placed at this location. The moments are summed up about this level, including the internal moment in the wall of this brace level taken from the analysis of stage 2. This summation gives the required embedment below excavation level. An important assumption is that appropriate conditions exist below excavation level for passive resistance to develop as shown in the pressure diagram of Fig. 8-39c.

Other stages, not shown in Fig. 8-39, include (1) the construction of the bottom slab of the permanent structure, and assuming that the diaphragm wall is a single wall, the degree of fixity of the wall-slab junction should be included in the remaining analysis; (2) removal of bracing level 2; (3) construction of the top slab; and (4) removal of bracing level 1, and backfill.

The feasibility and usefulness of this analysis must be judged in terms of the actual preload system, compatibility with lateral earth

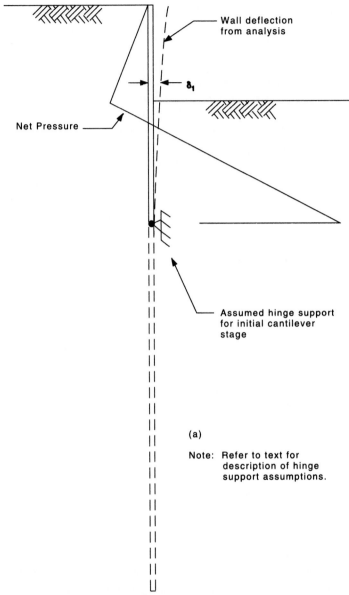

Net Pressure

Wall deflection from analysis

δ_1

Assumed hinge support for initial cantilever stage

(a)

Note: Refer to text for description of hinge support assumptions.

Figure 8-39 Stage construction analysis: (*a*) Cantilever stage 1. (*b*) Stage 2, bracing at upper level and excavation to second level. (*c*) Stage 3, two bracing levels and excavation to final level.

pressure diagrams, soil stratification, soil stiffness, and wall-brace stiffness. Moments and shears are computed at critical points for each stage. Assumptions that influence these parameters include the location of hinges, location and degree of fixity in the embedded wall, beam

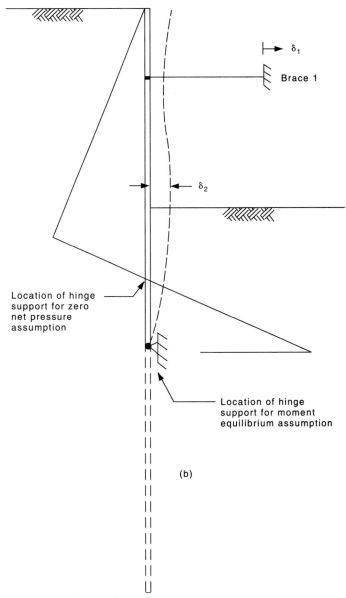

δ_1

Brace 1

δ_2

Location of hinge
support for zero
net pressure
assumption

Location of hinge
support for moment
equilibrium assumption

(b)

Figure 8-39 *(Continued)*

continuity, and actual support deflections that may realistically be considered only with large-deflection theories and second-order analysis.

8-11 Design Example 2, Subway Station

The construction of the Charles Center Station in Baltimore, Md., encountered typical urban conditions: close proximity to existing tall

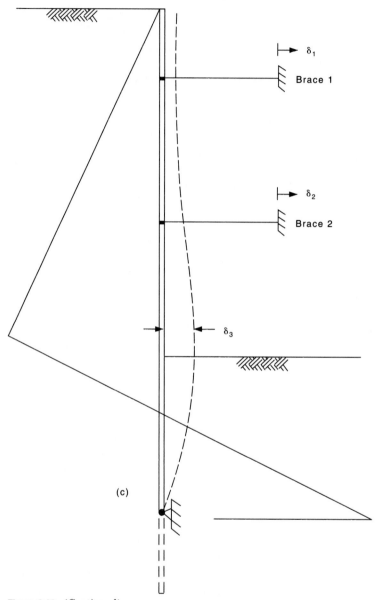

Figure 8-39 *(Continued)*

buildings requiring extensive underpinning; vehicular traffic maintenance through the construction corridor; control of groundwater; and
accessibility to commercial establishments.

The soil conditions are quite general for the downtown Baltimore
area. They include granular deposits of dense to very dense sand of
the Patuxent formation that frequently contains levels of silt and clay.

This formation is primarily composed of light-colored sands typically merging into gravels with pebbles of considerable size. The bottom of the excavation for the station structure is in decomposed rock.

A further constraint was the limited space between the face of existing buildings and the exterior of the subway structure, in some instances only 3 ft.

Design considerations. Design alternatives were confined to a composite construction system with a slurry wall and rigid frame structure. Two concepts were investigated: (1) the diaphragm wall would carry the lateral loads directly to the floor levels, while the internal structure would resist unbalanced lateral loads and moments from the roof and slabs (in this case the slurry wall would not be in direct contact with the rigid frame); (2) the slurry wall would share all long-term loads (the wall would be in direct contact with the rigid frame and structurally connected to it).

The selected scheme is shown in Fig. 8-40 (Piccagli and Desai, 1980) and consists of an SPTC system. Primary soldier piles were installed at 8- and 6-ft centers, depending on location and extent of footing width exposed to the panel. These were augered under slurry to prevent any soil relaxation. With the primary piles in place, the slurry wall panels were excavated, intermediate soldier piles were inserted, and the panels were concreted. This process is similar to the construction method shown in Fig. 1-26. The primary soldier piles are extended 10 ft below the bottom of the structure and are 5 ft deeper than the secondary beams.

Detailed designs were prepared for existing footings that had to be cut (as much as 25 percent) for major high-rise buildings. In these instances the soil underneath was stabilized with grout injection. Figure 8-41 shows the estimated and pattern of footing settlement expected to result from such a cut. The diagrams show also the redistribution of soil pressure resulting from the eccentric load application.

Construction constraints. These exemplified all factors typical in urban excavation, namely, site limitations and availability of working space, presence of underground and overhead utilities, environmental controls (noise level, disposal of used slurry, etc.), groundwater control, temporary bracing, exposure of existing footings, limitations in panel sequence and concreting operations, and close monitoring of structure movement.

Because of the requirement for traffic maintenance, the contractor was forced to operate only at night. At 7:00 P.M. the street was closed to traffic, temporary sidewalks and barriers were removed, guide walls exposed, and equipment moved in for construction operations. By 6:00 A.M. the following morning the site was completely restored, equipment removed, and pedestrian and automobile traffic reinstated.

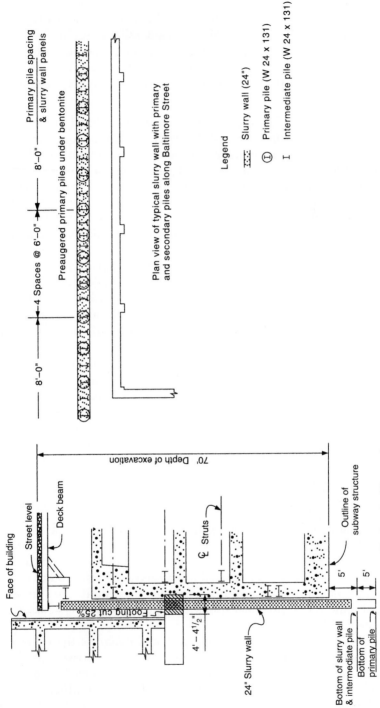

Figure 8-40 Plan and section, diaphragm walls for Charles Center Station, Baltimore, Md. (*From Piccagli and Desai, 1980.*)

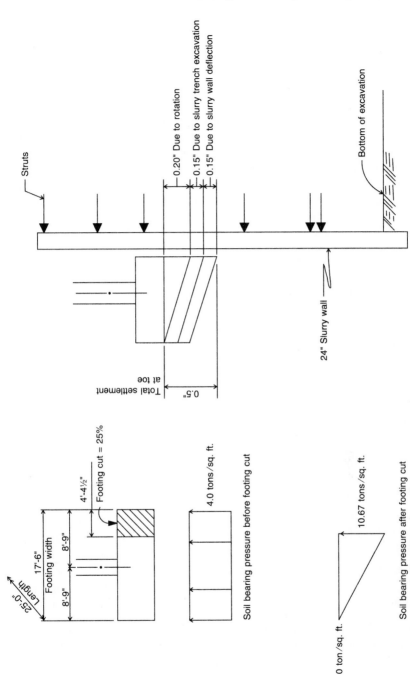

Figure 8-41 Estimated footing settlement and redistributed soil pressure resulting from footing cut. *(From Piccagli and Desai, 1980.)*

8-12   Design Example 3, Traffic Underpass

Loads and forces. A traffic underpass carrying a four-lane roadway with safety walls has an opening 60 ft face-to-face of support. The design specifies construction with cast-in-place diaphragm walls 30 in thick, and a superstructure consisting of precast box beams, such as those shown in Fig. 8-36c, with a 4-in concrete overlay. The system will function as an integral structure, i.e., without bearings or expansion joints, and hence it must be designed for stresses associated with thermal expansion and contraction.

From superstructure analysis we select 27 in × 36 in beams with the grid pattern shown in Fig. 8-36c, structurally adequate for HS 20 loading and 50 lb/ft² concrete overlay. Each beam has a cross-sectional area of 523 in² and a weight per lin ft of 565 lb. A 16-ft vertical clearance is required for special vehicles. The resulting cross section with final dimensions is shown in Fig. 8-42.

The wall is assumed to have a pinned connection with the superstructure. The base may be detailed as pinned, partially fixed, or fully fixed. The wall at the bottom is laterally supported by the roadway slab, so that the base is assumed pinned, giving a vertical beam freely supported at both ends. The superstructure accommodates a roadway 30 ft wide with 3-ft walks on either side, giving a total bridge width of 36 ft, or 12 precast sections. Design criteria must comply with AASHTO specifications.

Step 1.   Establish effective span length (height) for diaphragm walls. Since the walls are not built integrally with the supporting slabs, the span length (height) is the clear span plus the depth (width) of the wall but need not exceed the distance between centers of supports. Either criterion gives approximately a span length of 18.5 ft.

Step 2.   Establish all loads from superstructure, as per AASHTO.

- Dead load. Weight of beams plus overlay (per foot width of deck) is $(565/3) + 50 = 240$ lb, D.L. reaction $= 240 \times 31 = 7440$ lb $= 7.44$ kips.

- Live load. For standard truck loading the end reaction (per lane) is 61 kips, or L.L. reaction $= 61 \times 2/36 = 3.4$ kips, per foot of length of wall.

This load is assumed to be distributed uniformly along the entire length of the wall. An allowance for impact is based on the standard impact formula and is computed as $I = 26.9$ percent; impact will be applied to the walls as a compressive force but not in the design for lateral earth pressure.

- Surcharge load. Alternatively live load may be considered on the approach roadway as surcharge and thus generate a corresponding

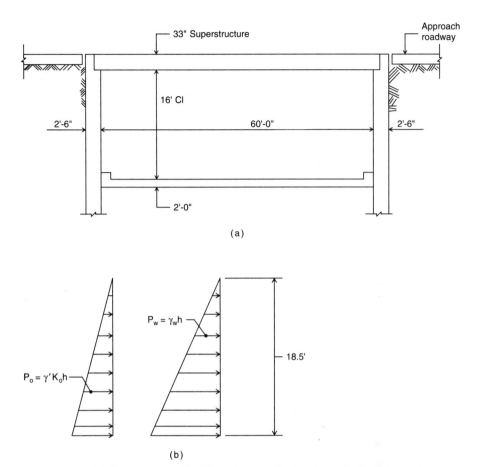

Figure 8-42 (*a*) Cross section of traffic underpass, Design Example 3. (*b*) Lateral pressures (earth and water).

lateral effect. Unlike the complex elastic solutions discussed in Sec. 4-11, a uniform surcharge loading can be assumed by considering a tributary area of two HS trucks with dimensions 28 ft × 24 ft (axle length × roadway width at the approach) or $144/672 = 0.21$ kip/ft^2. The design will also consider a uniform surcharge load from the weight of the approach slab, or 0.15 kip/ft^2. These surcharges are converted to a lateral pressure by multiplying by the coefficient of earth pressure.

- Longitudinal forces. For one lane, the longitudinal force is $(0.05)(0.64 \times 61 + 18) = 2.9$ kips.

- Wind load. May be disregarded since it is unlikely to control.

- Thermal forces. Assume cold climate with a temperature range of 80°.

Total expansion $= 61 \times 12 \times 80 \times 6 \times 10^{-6} = 0.35$ in, to be assumed equally distributed to both ends of the superstructure (point of zero movement is taken at the midpoint of the span).

- Earthquake forces. Assume that the structure is in an area of moderate seismic activity so that group VII in load factor design is unlikely to control.

Step 3. Calculate lateral earth loads. The soil consists of a thick layer of medium dense sand with $\phi = 37°$, $K_0 = 1 - \sin \phi' = 0.40$, and $K_a = 0.25$. The sand layer extends approximately to a depth of 30 ft below ground surface and is underlain by a thick layer of stiff clay with $S_u = 3.0$ kip/ft^2. The water table fluctuates within narrow limits, with high water elevation 2 ft below ground surface (near the underside of the approach slab), and low water level 5 ft below this elevation. The walls are designed, therefore, for full hydrostatic pressure and soil pressure for the K_0 condition. Because the sand extends to considerable depth below the bottom of excavation, the structure must be designed to resist uplift. For design purposes the pressure diagrams corresponding to the effective (design) wall height of 18.5 ft are shown in Fig. 8-42b. For $\gamma = 122$ lb/ft^3, $\gamma' = 60$ lb/ft^3. Accordingly, the pressure at the base is

$$p_0 = (60)(0.40)(18.5) = 440 \text{ lb/ft}$$

$$p_W = (62.5)(18.5) = 1160 \text{ lb/ft}$$

Design of walls. For load factor design, the following groups are considered.

$$\text{Group I} = \gamma[DC + 1.67(LL + I) + \beta_E(EA) + \beta_w(EW)]$$

where $\gamma = 1.3$; $DC = $ dead load from structure; $LL + I = $ live load plus impact from vehicles moving on superstructure; $\beta_E = 1.3$ (from Table 4-11); $EA = $ earth pressure for K_0 state; $\beta_w = 1.0$; and $EW = $ water pressure.

$$\text{Group I alternate} = \gamma[DC + \beta_{ES}(ES) + \beta_E(EA) + \beta_w(EW)]$$

where ES is lateral load due to surcharge from approach slab for both dead and live load and $\beta_{ES} = 1.50$ (Table 4-11). Group I gives less moment and more axial load, whereas Group I alternate produces more moment and less axial load.

$$\text{Group IV} = \gamma[DC + 1.00(LL + I) + \beta_E(EA) + \beta_w(EW) + \beta_T(T)]$$

$$\text{Group IV alternate} = \gamma[DC + \beta_{ES}(ES) + \beta_E(EA)$$
$$+ \beta_w(EW) + \beta_T(T)]$$

where $\gamma = 1.3$; $\beta_{ES} = 1.0$ (the same as the load coefficient for live load in Group IV); $\beta_E = 1.3$; $\beta_w = 1.0$; and β_T and T are the load coefficient and the force due to temperature, respectively.

The value of T is the earth pressure (additional) mobilized as the wall moves toward the soil to accommodate the thermal expansion of the deck. Recall that the thermal expansion is 0.35 in. For a more conservative design we assume that one end of the bridge is fixed against movement so that the other end will accommodate the total expansion of 0.35 in. For a wall height of 18.5 ft the ratio Δ/H is $0.35/(18.5 \times 12) = 0.0016$. The coefficient K (denoting partial passive resistance) is obtained graphically from Fig. 4-55 for $\phi' = 37°$ and $\Delta/H = 0.0016$ as $K = 1.4$. The earth pressure representing T is the difference between $K = 1.4$ and $K_0 = 0.4$. Since T is not a resistance but an active force, we apply a load coefficient $\beta_T = \beta_E = 1.3$ so that in Group IV and alternate the sum $(EA + T)$ is consolidated into one calculation for earth pressure using $K = 1.4$. Note also that ES in Group IV alternate will be computed from a uniform surcharge $0.21 + 0.15 = 0.36$ kip/ft² by multiplying by $K = 1.4$.

Analysis for Group IV alternate. The analysis is reduced to the following: (1) an axial load $P = (7.44 + 0.38\, h)$ kips where h = height from wall top and p is the load per linear foot of wall; (2) a uniform pressure $P_s = 0.36 \times 1.4 \times 0.50$ kip/ft along the entire wall height; (3) an earth pressure $P_e = (60)(1.4)(h)$; and (4) hydrostatic pressure $p_w = (62.5)(h)$. The corresponding lateral pressure diagrams are shown in Fig. 8-43.

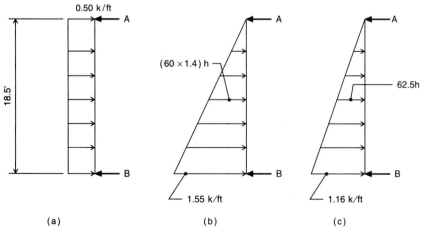

Figure 8-43 Pressure diagrams, analysis for group IV alternate. (a) Surcharge. (b) Earth pressure. (c) Water pressure.

From Fig. 8-43a we calculate

$$R_A = R_B = 4.62 \text{ kips}$$

From Fig. 8-43b we calculate

$$R_A = 14.34 \times \tfrac{1}{3} = 4.78 \text{ kips} \qquad R_B = 9.56 \text{ kips}$$

From Fig. 8-43c we calculate

$$R_A = 10.73 \times \tfrac{1}{3} = 3.57 \text{ kips} \qquad R_B = 7.16 \text{ kips}$$

The maximum moments are computed as follows:

$$M_{ES} = (0.125)(0.50)(18.5)^2 = 21.4 \text{ ft-kips}$$

$$M_{EA} = (0.1283)(14.34)(18.5) = 34.0 \text{ ft-kips}$$

$$M_w = (0.1283)(10.73)(18.5) = 25.5 \text{ ft-kips}$$

and

$$M_u = 1.3(21.4 + 1.3 \times 34.0 + 25.5) = 118 \text{ ft-kips}$$

For a wall 30 in thick, $d = 26$ in. Also $f_y = 40{,}000$ lb/in^2 and $f'_c = 3500$ lb/in^2. We select $A_s = 1.60$ in^2, provided by No. 9 at 7½ in. From Eq. (6-8) we compute

$$a = A_s f_y / 0.85 f'_c b = (1.60 \times 40{,}000)/(0.85 \times 3500 \times 12) = 1.8 \text{ in}$$

The nominal moment capacity is now computed from Eq. (6-12) as

$$M_n = A_s f_y \left(d - \frac{a}{2} \right) = (1.60)(40)(2.08) = 133 \text{ ft-kips}$$

or

$$\phi M_n = 0.9 \times 133 = 120 \text{ ft-kips} > 118 \text{ ft-kips} \qquad \text{OK.}$$

The reinforcement ratio is $1.60/(12 \times 26) = 0.005$ OK.

In the foregoing analysis the strength is controlled by tension since the nominal axial load P_n is less than the balanced load strength.

Uplift. Assuming the water table at the underside of the approach pavement gives an extreme design water level and is a condition producing the most severe force effect.

With allowable stress design the usual practice is to provide a safety factor of 1.5 to 2.0 in resisting uplift (see also Table 4-10). If uplift is resisted solely by dead weight (dead load from structure, overlying soil, etc.), the load factor design method simply reverts to ADS because loads and resistances are explicitly grouped and have a nominal variability (dead load, water pressure). If dead load is not the only means for resisting uplift, the problem may be analyzed using load factor methodology where the standard calibration process yields a safety index that compares favorably with the intent of ADS. The following analysis will demonstrate this approach.

Step 1. Compute the dead load from Fig. 8-42 where member sizes and dimensions are selected to provide the required structural capacity. All loads are per foot of length of structure.

- D.L. weight of superstructure $= 7.44 \times 2 = 14.9$ kips
- D.L. diaphragm walls. Assume the walls to extend 3 ft below underside of base slab, or total height $= 24$ ft.

$$\text{Weight} = 2 \times 24 \times 0.37 = 17.8 \text{ kips}$$

- D.L. bottom slab =
  $0.30 \times 60 \qquad = \underline{18.0} \text{ kips}$
  Total D.L. $\qquad = 50.7 \text{ kips}$

Next we compute the uplift caused by a water head $= 20$ ft.

Water pressure $= 20 \times 62.5 = 1.25$ kips/ft², or total uplift $= 65 \times 1.25 = 81$ kips. For a load reduction factor of 0.67 (corresponding to a safety factor of 1.5 in ADS) the structure resists $50.7 \times 0.67 = 34$ kips of uplift. The balance $81 - 34 = 47$ kips will be resisted by a deep foundation, such as drilled shafts, designed to resist pullout and with structural capacity to resist tensile stresses. (This analysis does not consider swell potential in expansive soils.)

Step 2. Since we choose underreamed shafts, the uplift resistance will be estimated neglecting the side resistance above the bell, and assuming that the bell behaves as an anchor. Referring to Fig. 8-44, the factored uplift capacity of the belled shaft is

$$Q_R = \phi Q_n = \phi Q_{s(\text{bell})} \qquad (8\text{-}1)$$

where

$$Q_{s(\text{bell})} = q_{s(\text{bell})} A_u \qquad (8\text{-}2)$$

where $q_{s(\text{bell})} = N_u s_u)$, $A_u = \pi(D_p^2 - D^2)/4$, N_u = uplift resistance factor; D_p = diameter of bell; D = diameter of shaft; D_b = depth of embedment in the founding layer; s_u = undrained shear strength averaged

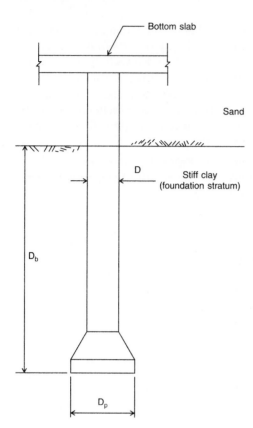

Figure 8-44 Uplift of under-reamed drilled shaft.

over a distance 2 bell diameters above the base; and ϕ = resistance factor.

We select D = 3 ft, D_p = 6 ft, and D_b/D_p = 2.5, or D_b = 15 ft, so that N_u = 8. Recall that s_u = 3.0 kips/ft^2. The factor ϕ is taken as 0.55. In general resistance factors for uplift may be less than those for axial compression, the reason being that drilled shafts in tension unload the soil, which reduces the overburden stresses and hence the uplift resistance.

From the foregoing data we compute

$$A_u = 3.14(6^2 - 3^2)/4 = 21.2 \text{ ft}^2$$

$$q_{s(\text{bell})} = 8 \times 3.0 = 24$$

$$Q_{s(\text{bell})} = 21.2 \times 24 = 509 \text{ kips}$$

and

$$Q_R = 0.55 \times 509 = 280 \text{ kips/shaft}$$

The bottom slab is 36 ft long (in the direction of the underpass) and hence the total uplift (remaining) is $47 \times 36 = 1692$ kips. The required number of shafts is therefore $1692/280 = 6$ shafts. These should be arranged so that each shaft receives the same uplift reaction, and also possible reduction in resistance from group effects is avoided.

For the permanent condition, uplift may also be eliminated if the walls are extended into the clay layer, but this solution is not always possible, especially if the direction and source of groundwater flow are not known and where the structure should not block underground water flow (see also subsequent sections).

8-13   Design Example 4, Soil-Cement Walls

Storage facility. The soil-cement structural walls reviewed in Sec. 1-12 (shown in Fig. 1-47) have been used in subway projects in Japan. Suzuki et al. (1987) give an example of soil-cement wall design for a storage facility, consisting of an underground two-level structure constructed in water-bearing sand and gravel. A cross section of the structure is shown in Fig. 8-45.

The subsurface consists of an upper 8-m-thick soft-to-firm silty clay layer underlain by interbedded loose to very dense sand and gravel with N values varying from 20 to 50 blows per 30 cm. At the site perched groundwater is encountered in the upper silty clay about 6 m from the surface during the rainy season. The free groundwater table is about 9 m below ground surface.

The depth of excavation for the storage facility is 15 m (49 ft) and is thus extended about 7 m (23 ft) into the water-bearing sand and gravel. Relevant design requirements included the following: (1) no dewatering allowed at any construction stage; (2) ground subsidence to be kept to a minimum; (3) short construction period; and (4) minimum noise and vibrations.

The soil-cement wall was used as temporary ground support and is extended to 40 m below ground surface to penetrate into an impermeable clay layer and cut off the groundwater from the sides and the bottom of the excavation. At least half of the drilling depth was in very dense sand and gravel, and hence the predrilling was performed as shown in Fig. 8-45b. The soil-cement wall was reinforced with steel H piles in every column for stability and strength. The required penetration depth for lateral stability below excavation level was 4 m. This gave a required pile length of 19 m, leaving the lower 21 m of the soil-cement wall unreinforced to perform only as a cutoff wall.

Excavation and stage construction. For this example, the excavation is 300 m (985 ft) long, 60 m (197 ft) wide, and 15 m (49 ft) deep. Two

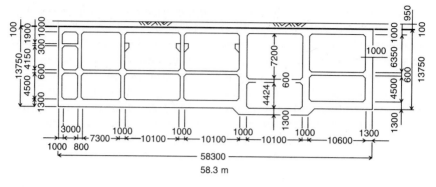

(a)

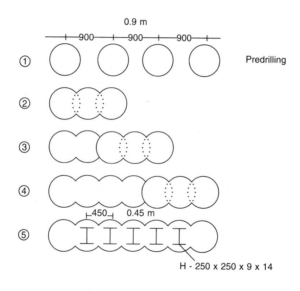

(b)

Figure 8-45 (*a*) Cross section of subway vehicle storage facility. (*b*) Construction procedure of soil-cement wall. (*From Suzuki et al., 1987.*)

schemes were considered: (1) full area excavation in one operation; and (2) stage excavation where the perimeter area is excavated first to allow for the outer bays of the structure to be built, and is followed by the center section. Full excavation would require a long internal bracing with high cost and possible elastic deformations leading to excessive lateral ground movement. Ground anchors were precluded because of unavailable ground for the fixed anchor zone.

Stage construction with partial excavation was therefore selected as the least expensive and technically best method, as shown in Fig. 8-46. In this process the two perimeter zones of the project are excavated first. The interior edge of each excavation strip is protected by conventional soldier piles with lagging. As the excavation is carried down, struts are installed as shown to brace the two dissimilar ground supports, namely, the soldier pile wall along the inside and the soil-cement wall along the outside face. The outer bays of the concrete structure are constructed from the bottom up as shown, and serve as ground support as the center strip is excavated and the soldier pile walls are removed.

This construction procedure was effective in controlling ground movement and adverse effects on surroundings.

Cut-and-cover tunnel. A section 1.4 km long of the Ikoma tunnel in Osaka (Japan) is built in cut-and-cover (Iima et al., 1983). The subsurface conditions are mixed with interbedded sand and gravel layers. Quoted N values range from 20 to 50. An underground stream at the site maintains the groundwater table about 2.5 m from ground surface. A typical section of the subway structure is shown in Fig. 8-47. The excavation is about 15 m deep.

The design requirements included similar restrictions on groundwater lowering, ground subsidence, and short construction time as in the example of Fig. 8-45. Among the available temporary supports, the designers selected a soil-cement wall braced with four levels of struts. A preconstruction mixing ratio test provided optimum constituent percentages, and data on expected permeability. As in the pre-

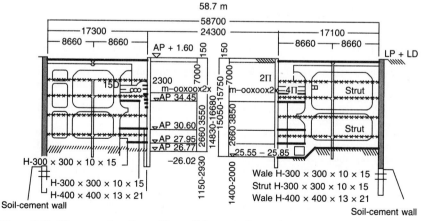

Figure 8-46 Stage construction with partial excavation and support.

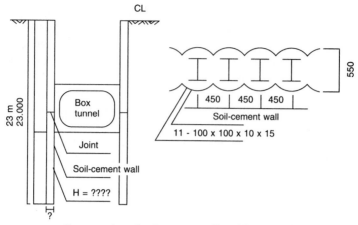

Figure 8-47 Cross section of soil-cement wall and box tunnel.

vious example, the soil-cement wall served as temporary ground support and provided a cutoff system during excavation.

References

AASHTO, 1992: Standard Specifications for Highway Bridges, and Interim, 1990, 1991.

AASHTO, 1983: Guide Specifications for Seismic Design of Highway Bridges, and Interim, 1985, 1987–1988.

Barr, M., 1977: The Rupel tunnel, personal communication.

Dennis, B., M. Chi, and M. Basci, 1981: "Slurry Walls as a Part of Underground Transportation Structures," FHWA Rept. RD-80/047, November.

Fukui, S., 1980: "Diaphragm Wall Experiences in Japan," Proc. Slurry Walls for Underground Transp. Systems, FHWA Rept. TS-80-221.

Iima, H., K. Ujihara, and M. Uenaka, 1983: "S. M. W. Underground Continuous Earth Retaining Wall Method, Ikoma Tunnel West Section, East Osaka Line Project," Found. Eng., July.

Japan Material Society, 1987: Guidelines on Design and Construction of the Soil-Cement Mixing Wall (S.M.W.).

Jobling, D. G., 1980: "Slurry Wall Construction for Transportation Systems in Britain," Proc., Slurry Walls for Underground Transp. Systems, FHWA Rept. TS-80-221.

Jobling, D. J., 1975: "Diaphragm Walls and Secant Piles in Subway Construction," U.S. Dept. Transp., Urban Mass Transp. Adm. Proc. Semin. Underground Constr. Probl., Techniques Solutions, Chicago.

Leonard, M., 1974: "Precast Diaphragm Walls Used for the A13 Motorway," Paris, Proc. Diaphragm Walls Anchorages, Inst. Civ. Eng., London.

Modjeski and Masters, 1992: Development of Comprehensive Bridge Specifications and Commentary, LRFD Approach, Third Draft, NCHRP, TRB, Washington, D.C.

Piccagli, U., and D. B. Desai, 1980: "Charles Center Station, Baltimore, Slurry Wall Design and Installation," FHWA Report TS-80-221, Slurry Walls for Underground Transp. Systems.

Suzuki, S., M. Hirano, and H. Nozaki, 1987: "Large Scale Excavation in Water-Bearing Sand and Gravel Strata, Takamatsu Garage, Municipal Subway No. 12," Tunnel and Underground, October.

Thon, J. G., and R. C. Harlan, 1971: Slurry Walls for BART Civic Center Subway Station, ASCE J. Soil Mech. Found. Div., September.

9

Buildings and Deep Basements

9-1 Assessment of Deep Basements

Economic considerations

In general deep basements are underground enclosures 6 m deep or more (20 ft), but the definition is associated with the particular conditions and uses of underground space. Given the client's general requirements and criteria, factors to be considered in the decision to build a deep basement are: (1) the influence of subsoil and groundwater conditions on the choice of construction method; (2) the effect of plan area and shape of the basement; and (3) the effect of completion time on the proposed use.

Relationship of cost and expected use. To the owner of land the expediency of excavating deep will depend on the relationship between the estimated expenditure and expected revenue from the use of the space. The expenditure is represented by the total construction cost, and the anticipated revenue by rental from tenants. Obviously, the finished form of a deep basement, hence the method of construction, depend on the intended use.

From the owner's point of view no advance technological solution to the construction problems can be acceptable if it is to prolong the construction time and increase the overall cost. It appears that the four main criteria that impact on the economy of the design and construction are: (1) the ability of the permanent (final) wall to supplant the temporary sheeting; (2) the ability to brace the ground support at each floor level temporarily and permanently; (3) the ability to take advantage of the ground as a formwork by casting the floor slabs directly on it; and (4) the ability to do the earth moving within the excavation area rapidly and continuously.

Normally the choice of method at a given site should result from the decision regarding the need for the basement and after confirming the feasibility of construction. The assumption that high land values provide the incentive to build deep may be erroneous. Disincentives are the suspected high costs of underground construction, particularly those associated with unforeseen ground conditions or obstructions; code standards of natural lighting for habitable areas that would limit their location to one level below street; and restrictions on space use (for example, planning that excludes cars from city centers would eliminate the use of underground space for parking garages).

Cost control. A prime difficulty in assessing the merits of different methods and structural systems is related to the large fluctuations that are likely to occur in three main cost components, namely, contractor's estimate of cost, margin to allow for profit and loss, and cost of variations and claims.

Typically, with diaphragm walls the contract price for this item may constitute more than 30 percent of the total basement price, with large variations caused by commercial pressure on margins rather than by different criteria in cost estimates. In these circumstances, specialized foundation techniques initially chosen because they are technically efficient and economically attractive may finally result in a very wide spread of prices at bid stage that is difficult to rectify. The lowest bid may be unacceptable because of the opportunity of high contractual claims, whereas higher bids may constitute a financial risk. Frequently, these considerations are not analyzed in a total feasibility study to compare the merits of different forms of basement construction.

Use of deep basement as supports

As the excavation for a basement becomes deeper, the net intensity of load on the ground below is reduced according to the weight of ground excavated. For a given exterior imposed load the net stress per unit area is decreased with depth, and eventually there will be no increase in the resultant; i.e., the system returns to the initial overburden condition.

Building a deep basement solely for the purpose of supporting superstructure loads is often rare and unorthodox. Conversely, a deep basement allows the transfer of load at a level where more strength usually is available in the soil and also allows reduction of the net bearing pressure by the displacement of overburden.

The use of diaphragm walls, contiguous pile walls, and secant pile walls allows a threefold purpose to be achieved from the periphery wall: temporary ground support, permanent wall in the final structure, and transfer of vertical load from the superstructure (or the removal of loads in the case of uplift). Improved versions of this concept are the structural forms discussed in Sec. 1-8, namely, strip panels, and walls on stilts, subpiers, etc. Whereas the load-carrying capacity of diaphragm walls is discussed in Chap. 5, it is interesting to mention examples from the use of the walls as load-bearing elements. Loads of the order of 150 t/m have been transferred to dense fine sand from an 80-cm-thick wall in Croydon, South London. Diaphragm walls 30 in thick (75 cm) have been used in Chicago as load-bearing elements to carry a vertical load 25,000 lb/ft (linear) or a bearing pressure of 10,000 lb/ft^2 (Xanthakos, 1979). At working loads much of this transfer may occur as side resistance at the wall-soil interface.

9-2 Superstructure-Substructure Interaction

Tall buildings in urban sites usually encounter special foundation problems. Because of height and stiffness, column loads tend to be very heavy. This trend is amplified by current architectural and functional criteria that dictate heavier column loads because of larger panels used to provide greater unobstructured floor space. Most tall buildings have multiple deep basements, usually extended to the lot lines even though the superstructure may be set back and used only above part of usable underground space. The structural form of the superstructure predetermines the distribution of loads through the basement substructure. In some instances conventional column-beam construction allows the loads from the periphery of the superstructure to be transferred to load-bearing walls in the basement, but a high-rise block supported on a central core cannot derive these benefits unless the basement is locally deepened at the core.

Where rock or strong, stable soils such as compact glacial tills are encountered at a reasonable depth (as in Chicago and New York), foundations may be carried down to these stable formations. This may be done by utilizing deep basements, caissons, or piles to carry column loads to competent materials. Such foundations provide good flexibility and freedom in architectural layout and structural systems, since large variations in column spacing and loading can be accommodated with acceptable differential settlement.

Where strong, stable foundation materials are not readily available, loadings of foundation elements must be limited to prevent shear failure of the soil and excessive differential settlement. The overall added load from the structure must also be controlled to limit overall settlement. A usual practice is to excavate and remove a weight of soil equal to a major portion of the gross weight of the structure (as already mentioned), a process commonly termed a compensated foundation. The allowable amount of the net added load will depend on the physical soil characteristics and its previous stress history. With adverse conditions a weight of soil equal to the weight of the building may have to be removed, whereas in some cases preloading may be advantageous to reduce compensatory excavation.

Whereas this requirement suggests a superstructure-substructure interaction exemplified by a deep basement (contrary to the comments made in the foregoing section), the practicality and cost of compensated foundations are significantly affected by structural arrangements already mentioned, i.e., column loads and spacing, and variations in structural loads over the plan area of the building. Furthermore, the soil supporting these foundations will rebound during excavation and then recompress under the weight of the structure. Since an elastic deflection in the soil mass is a function of the imposed load, a flexible uniform load acting on soil will cause nonuniform settlements which will be greatest at the center and least at the corners. Additional soil settlement may be time-dependent. If the resulting deflections from a given application of loads are incompatible with the structural deflections used in the analysis, the stresses in the structure will be redistributed, resulting in new contact pressures at the soil-structure interface until the deflections become compatible. Thus contact pressures at the base of foundations of tall structures are likely to be nonuniform and persist with time.

It appears from these brief comments that a diaphragm wall supporting the excavation for a deep basement may be selected to accommodate the following three main design solutions: (1) a deep basement built in conjunction with a compensated foundation; (2) a deep basement constructed in conjunction with a deep foundation; and (3) a deep basement constructed solely for the utilization of subsurface use.

Basic concepts of compensated foundations. These are used in deep subsoil deposits of medium to very highly compressible materials, usually of lacustrine or marine deposits, in which the shear strength (and therefore the load-carrying capacity) of the soil is very low. The soil should be considered as a two-phase material, namely, a skeleton structure reacting like a solid with well-defined stress-strain-time properties of elastoplastic viscosity and shear strength, and the water behaving like a liquid. Compensated foundations constructed without considering the mechanical action of the skeleton structure of the soil have shown large settlement even though the total weight of the soil mass was excavated and replaced by the building weight. Therefore, when a stress relief in the soil skeleton is induced because of excavation and thereafter the stress is reapplied as building weight, the reactions involved will be those of a solid governing the behavior of the foundation.

A simple expression of a compensated foundation for a rigid impervious structure constructed deep into a soil mass may be obtained by considering the basic form of the soil skeleton with water. The foundation is placed at depth d where an effective overburden stress σ'_{vd} and a hydraulic pressure u_d exist. The total available stress for compensation of the load from the building is

$$p_d = \sigma'_{vd} + u_d \qquad (9\text{-}1)$$

The first term in Eq. (9-1) defines the stress in the soil skeleton structure, and the second term the effect of a liquid. The implicit conclusion is that the foundation is dependent on the first term that describes the mechanical soil properties. Judgment in selecting these parameters must be based on the type of sediment, whether a normally consolidated or preconsolidated formation.

If in an imaginary situation the overburden effective stress and hydraulic pressure could be replaced without making an excavation, theoretically there would be no vertical displacement to consider in a totally compensated foundation. This ideal case is impossible to achieve. Methods are available, however, to minimize and control the effects of vertical expansion as the excavation is carried down because of stress relief, and consequently to reduce subsequent settlement related to hysteresis effects (Zeevaert, 1972).

A satisfactory prediction of the behavior of a compensated foundation may be obtained if the design addresses explicitly the subject of heave, subsequent settlement, and lateral contraction of the excavation.

Deep foundations. Discussed in Chap. 5, these include drilled or bored round, prismatic, and linear elements. The classification is amplified according to whether a casing is used and method of installation, and whether the excavation is carried out under slurry. The category of deep foundations includes also driven piles, precast piles, and variations therefrom (Prakash and Sharma, 1990). Selection aspects relating to buildings are: (1) the higher concentration of loading over the plan area of the building; (2) the trend toward the use of much higher individual pile (or shaft) loads up to the level of a single pile or caisson used per column; (3) differential settlement and tilting; and (4) higher wind overturning moments and shear loading.

The significance of the presence of a basement, and hence of a perimeter wall, is in its effects on access to install the foundation. A strutted excavation will tend to restrict the choice of foundation type on economic grounds to those not requiring tall and heavy equipment. Alternatively the foundation elements may be installed from existing ground level (see also the prefounded column method discussed in other sections). These combinations combined with an economic utilization of basement space will dictate the number of basement levels and the method of construction.

9-3 Comparative Evaluation of Ground Support Methods

Soldier pile walls

The use of soldier piles at spacings 6 to 10 ft together with timber, concrete, or steel lagging has been stimulated by the availability of efficient drilling plant and the development of ground anchors. The piles receive and carry the full lateral loads. The system is limited to subsoil with little or no groundwater and to soils that may be economically augered and excavated without support for sufficient depth to allow the placement of horizontal lagging. The latter may be omitted in hard clays, soft shales, or where cohesion and natural cementation binds the soil and the piles are inserted at relatively close spacing.

Loss of ground. The installation procedure can contribute markedly to ground loss. Typical example is the soil response behind the lagging and the flexural deflection of the boards with increased pile spacing. Movement caused by overcut must be controlled by packing of soil behind the lagging.

Loss of ground also is likely in soft clays and loose soils of low plasticity below the water table. The fast exposure of these soils by excavating below installed lagging gives rise to the opportunity for deformation. In the same context, stress relief associated with arching can be uncertain and is unlikely in very soft soils or in soils prone to plastic creep. Conversely, where soils are difficult to drain, dewatering in advance of the excavation is indicated. Dry cohesionless soil can cause problems, particularly in hot and arid areas, and the remedy is to moisten the face by spraying while placing the boards.

Permanence of system. Soldier piles with lagging provide only a temporary support. The verticality of its installation can be critical if it is used as a back shutter to the permanent wall to be built inside it. Drilling tolerances may require an additional thickness of sacrificial cover to the reinforcement of the permanent wall. If the soldier pile wall is not used as back shutter, partial recovery of materials may be possible. If recovery is intended, sufficient working space must be allowed for the removal. This represents a net loss of usable space and may be the cause of lateral movement if this space is not properly backfilled.

Structural response.   Structurally the support is flexible, particularly below excavation level, and offers little resistance to ground movement in this region. Since the system requires dewatering, settlement can occur as a result of lowering the water table.

Economy.   The method is particularly economical in stiff clays and in cohesive soils overlain by limited thickness of cohesionless strata where the groundwater is low. On a regional basis, it is common practice to fasten a mesh to the soldier piles and use gunite where the subsoil can stand for a height of at least 3 ft. In terms of initial price using timber lagging, the cost may be 80 percent or less of the cost of sheet piling. However, the system may not be as economically attractive if total cost is considered.

Steel sheet pile walls

The use of steel sheet piling may be limited in city centers for environmental reasons. Although methods of silent driving are available and may diminish this objection, undue vibration during driving will still limit this application. Economical driving can be achieved in loose to medium dense sands and gravels and in cohesive soils. If the ground is hard or contains boulders, driving sheet piles is difficult and often impracticable. Depth limitations are imposed by site conditions and available headroom, and in congested urban sites there is a danger of cutting utilities.

In economic terms the viability of the method as ground support for deep basements is enhanced if the sheeting can be extracted for reuse. Extraction may not be possible in a large basement covering a large proportion of the site area because of lack of access for a suitable crane. An expendable lining will be necessary, however, between the permanent wall and the piles to allow for easy extraction, and some waste of fresh concrete into the pile pans must be allowed for.

Interlocked sheet piling is effective in cutting off concentrated water flow through pervious formations within or below the excavation and in protecting against a blow condition or other form of ground loss. The seal obtained at the base of the excavation ensures groundwater control for the construction period, but it does not imply that groundwater lowering will be prevented.

Contiguous bored piles and secant interlocking piles

The availability of efficient augers allows the economical construction of piles along the periphery of the basement as temporary and permanent ground support. Stiff homogeneous clays without groundwater are ideally suitable for such construction, and in these conditions the contiguous bored pile wall probably forms the cheapest wall type. A gap, probably 5 cm (2 in) wide, is likely to appear between adjacent piles and should be sealed by gunite.

Secant interlocking piles may be considered if suitable equipment is locally available and can provide a structurally interlocked pile wall. Since the piles are cased for their entire length during construction, the method should be chosen in ground conditions that preclude other methods. These include running sands, boulder clay, and varying rock strata where the excavation is made by hammer grab. If well executed, the system provides a watertight wall even in poor soil conditions. The secant pile wall may be cantilevered or braced by rakers, struts, or ground anchors.

Diaphragm walls

Deep-basement construction on private property is unlikely to encounter underground obstacles and utilities to the extent they occur along streets. In the past more than 80 percent of all diaphragm walls built as boundary support were permanent, and the trend shows a continuous increase. The walls become more attractive in the structural context if they are designed to carry vertical loads since this normally requires a moderate extension of the normal embedment below excavation level. If differential lateral movement is predicted and may cause the walls to leak, provisions should be made to correct the problem using the methods discussed in other sections.

The construction restrictions that control the work along streets and public right-of-way are seldom considered. There is usually sufficient space for plant layout and facilities, and the contractor has the flexibility to select the most advantageous panel sequence and schedule, whereas vehicular movements in and out of the site are better controlled.

9-4 Plan Area, Shape, and Completion Time

Plan area and shape. The decision to utilize the entire or only a portion of the buildable area as basement reflects all the foregoing considerations and factors. Given the area of the basement, the plan shape can affect the construction method and cost. For the same area a square basement gives the minimum wall perimeter, and a long rectangular shape the maximum. Basements of circular or elliptical shape have a certain fascination and are most functional for certain uses, i.e., underground parking or storage tanks. Like squares, these shapes provide high utilization area with minimum perimeter.

Where there is prime need for full utilization of space, the result is limited working space between basement wall construction and adjacent boundaries or buildings. A summary of the requirements of various ground supports and clearance necessary to construct them is given in Table 9-1. If the fullest utilization of space is planned, reducing the wall thickness to the structural minimum is necessary, and in this respect the high efficiency of diaphragm walls in bending is an advantage over bored piles.

The design should consider a possible compromise between the cost of a battered excavation and the cost of a vertically supported excavation. The effectiveness of using sloped sheeting has been demonstrated in several job sites (Schnabel, 1971), the contention being that in specific cases where the sheeting had a slope of 10° from the vertical the measured brace loads were consistently less than two-thirds of the computed brace loads for vertical sheeting in the same soil (see also other sections).

Completion time. Puller (1974) gives the following recommendations in order to minimize completion time: (1) basement walls should be

TABLE 9-1 Minimum Distance between Soil Support System and Site Boundary

Support system	Installation plant	Distance* in	Distance* cm
Underpinning	Conventional bulk excavation plant, e.g., hydraulic excavator with hydraulic grab	0	0
Steel sheet piling	Crane and piling hammer	20	50
Contiguous bored piles	Rotary piling equipment 60 cm pile	24	60
	Tripod piling equipment 50 cm pile	6	15
Secant piles 88 cm thick	Benoto rig	42	106
Diaphragm walls	Rope grab, kelly-mounted grab, or Tone reverse-circulation drill	6	15
Soldier piles and horizontal lagging	Rotary piling equipment 60-cm-diameter bore	24	60

From Puller, 1974.
*Minimum distance between outer face of support system and site boundary. Distances quoted are those at ground level; considerations must be given to verticality tolerances of support system.

built in one operation for both temporary and permanent support, and both designs should proceed simultaneously; (2) ideally the two supports should be consolidated into the same system; (3) where technical feasibility exists, construction methods that allow simultaneous work upward and downward should be adopted; and (4) where basements are constructed in open excavations the working space for wall and floor construction should be uninterrupted as far as possible (for example, using ground anchors).

The construction time and financial penalties of basement construction impeded by natural or man-made obstructions have long been recognized. Adjacent structures with shallow foundations, multilevel basements, unusual plan shapes, and existing utilities increase construction time and cost. Other factors that constitute less serious constraints but are likely to prolong construction are restrictions on noise levels, headroom limitations, unavailability of working space, and difficult access to the site.

9-5 Protection in Water-Bearing Ground

Protection of the base of an excavation is provided in anticipation of groundwater effects and uplift pressures.

Temporary condition. Temporary protection of an excavation from groundwater usually means keeping the bottom dry. At best the site may be underlain by a naturally impermeable layer at a reasonable distance from the intended excavation base, and clearly the solution is to carry the diaphragm wall down and let it penetrate the impervious bed, although this may mean that the wall is deeper than necessary for structural stability. Below the minimum required structural embedment it will be sufficient to fill the trench with a watertight but less rigid material, i.e., plastic concrete, and omit reinforcement in this section of the wall. This operation is carried out in two steps: (1) fill the bottom part with plastic concrete and allow it to set, and (2) tremie the structural concrete.

If it is feasible and nonobjectionable to lower the groundwater table, the excavation is protected merely by dealing with any water and seepage emerging from the bottom. Water control by lowering the natural level may also be indicated if there is an impervious bed some distance below excavation level but is too thin to resist full uplift; in this case the water level is lowered to reduce uplift to a safe value.

Where a naturally impervious formation does not exist close to the bottom and the ground is too pervious to allow pumping from sump pits, the perimeter diaphragm wall can be combined with grouting to form a relatively impermeable bed enclosure below the base. The location of the bed is established so that the uplift component at the base of the ground zone does not exceed the weight of soil above it. The thickness of the grouted zone should be enough to prevent blowout failure. An artificially made watertight layer is, however, relatively impervious so that any residual quantity of water should be handled by normal pumping.

An example of base protection is shown in Fig. 9-1, and is based on the foregoing principles. The construction is adjacent to the Seine River in Paris and involves a basement 15 m (50 ft) deep with its base on permeable limestone under a water head almost 14 m (46 ft) responding to the river level. The walls are laterally braced with two rows of prestressed ground anchors and by penetration into the limestone bed. Protection is provided by a vertical grout screen and a horizontal grout layer as shown.

Permanent condition. Permanent protection requires a fairly watertight perimeter wall and base slab as well as a structural capacity to resist uplift. The construction of a deep basement often gives rise to permanent uplift, and in some instances this situation relates to a groundwater level that may not be the maximum flood level stipulated by building codes. A usual solution is to install a thick raft or mat to increase the dead load that resists uplift, but this can be expensive and requires additional earth moving in unused space.

Another feasible structural solution, often less expensive, is to use a thinner mat and maintain stability by the use of vertical anchors with a fixed zone in a stiff formation. An alternative is to use drilled shafts, straight or belled, as shown in Design Example 4-3. For relatively small uplift pressures simple anchoring in suitable formations by sealed bars is sufficient without prestressing if the displacement

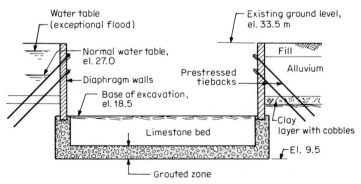

Figure 9-1 Protection of excavation from groundwater. Construction adjacent to the Seine River, Paris. (*From Fenoux, 1971.*)

necessary to mobilize tension in the bars is small and within the elastic range. Where interior deep foundation elements are provided, uplift is incorporated in their design.

If the direction and source of seepage flow are known, it may be possible to reduce uplift merely by extending the diaphragm wall sufficiently into the substratum below the base, but in many instances this will only reduce the amount of flow toward the ground beneath the raft. A more positive control against a short-term condition, such as seasonal or temporary rise in the water table, can be provided with a perimeter enclosure wall and a relatively impervious base, either natural or by grouting. An example of how uplift is handled in this case is shown in Fig. 9-2. Within the excavated area pumping is carried out during construction and extended to a level below the base; this level constitutes a permanent groundwater lowering within the excavation area. A drainage layer is provided below the raft or floor slab. Water infiltrating underneath is conveyed to a deep screen wall from where it is pumped out. Relief holes in the floor will permit excess flow to enter the area in case of multiple breakdown or power failure, and flood it temporarily without structural damage.

Wall embedment below excavation level. Normally wall embedment is determined by the structural stability below excavating level. Quite often, however, wall embedment may be related to the soil character-

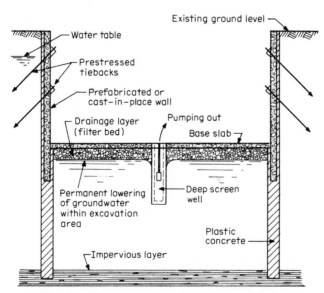

Figure 9-2 Protection of excavation from groundwater by lowering the water table permanently within the excavation area.

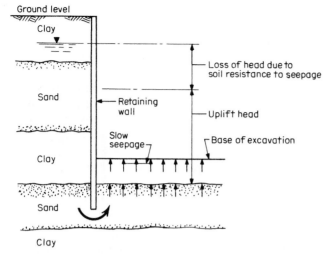

Figure 9-3 Seepage flow and uplift beneath an excavation. The uplift in this case can be considerable since the wall does not penetrate into the impervious formation.

istics and mainly its permeability. In pervious ground the penetration depth of the wall can materially change the rate of seepage and effective uplift at the base, but at best this is a complex problem. If an excavation is underlain by impervious layers but pervious soil exists a little below and the wall is terminated as shown in Fig. 9-3, it will not cut off the water completely from the permeable layer. Seepage pressure from water in the sand can lead to rapid softening or actual uplift of the overlying layers.

9-6 Bracing

The bracing systems discussed in Sec. 4-3 are used singly or combined in deep basement excavations. Bracing schemes and possibilities are summarized briefly in this section. Bracing details are shown in Fig. 9-4.

Cantilever walls. These are self-supported by embedment below excavation level, but this arrangement is feasible with shallow excavations and firm soil, and where ground movement can be tolerated. Unbraced walls should be used with caution, and in spite of the quick installation and simplicity of construction.

Ground anchors. Anchored walls have become very common in deep basements for the reasons mentioned in previous sections (see also Sec. 1-3). The installation is particularly effective when the anchors

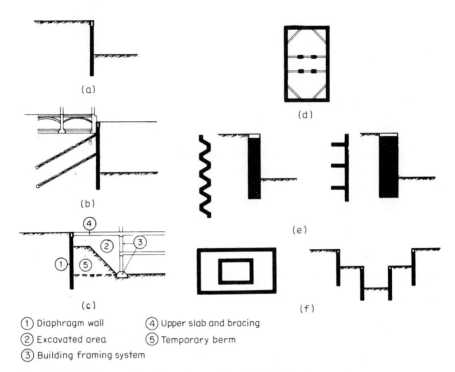

(a)

(b)

(c)

(d)

(e)

(f)

① Diaphragm wall   ④ Upper slab and bracing
② Excavated area   ⑤ Temporary berm
③ Building framing system

Figure 9-4 Bracing combinations of excavation for building basements.

are fixed in rock. Since performance that is poor or unsatisfactory can result from a choice based merely on a cost comparison, the design of ground anchors should consider the following aspects (Xanthakos, 1991): (1) the applicability of a rational design method with a predictive capacity; (2) suitability and consequences of the installation; (3) safety factor against structural failure; (4) local experience and reliability of performance prediction; and (5) quality assessment and the possibility of providing corrosion protection.

Temporary berms. Bracing with temporary berms is discussed in Sec. 4-3. Examples of building basement excavations braced with berms are shown in Figs. 4-14 and 9-4c, and in both instances berm bracing is eventually replaced by the permanent structure of the basement. In the temporary stage berms are combined with ground anchors in the upper part of the wall and rakers in the lower. Berms can be subjected to long-term effects and creep or move excessively if the installation of the permanent bracing is delayed.

Long flying struts. These are suitable for narrow excavations. Besides impeding construction, the monitoring of jacks is more difficult than with other methods. The corner bracing shown in Fig. 9-4d is economical, but it often results in undesirable redistribution of earth stresses in order for the strut end from one side to equalize the reaction from the other side.

Walls with counterforts or keys. These are shown in Fig. 9-4e, and as mentioned in other sections they have a much greater flexural strength; because of this, they need less bracing. However, they should not be expected to stop or reduce ground movement. Although they are often used in waterfront installations, they are not recommended in building basements because of the large space that the counterforts require unless there are restrictions on the interior bracing.

Center core bracing. Where the depth of a basement is varied to accommodate a center core, extending the outer perimeter walls below the lowest excavation level is not necessary. Instead, the construction can be carried out as shown in Fig. 9-4f. In this case, two analyses are necessary: (1) build the interior walls first from ground level, continue with the construction of the exterior walls, excavate for the central core, and brace the interior walls (a sequence that could reduce composite movement); or (2) build the exterior walls first, excavate to top of interior wall level, and install interior walls from this level.

Commentary. Bracing is also possible with the permanent floor system in the downward construction discussed in other sections.

Walls with reentrant corners in plan result in more complicated bracing with struts, rakers, or ground anchors than is possible with regular plan shapes. Adjacent walls at a reentrant corner must be braced in a manner that will prevent ground anchors from clashing with each other or having a common potential failure wedge. At a reentrant corner it is sometimes better to have the walls tied horizontally and diagonally within the exterior part of the corner across the ground, so that they become self-supported.

9-7 Diaphragm Walls with Compensated Foundations

Theoretical concepts

Viscoplastic flow. As stated, the most important aspect to consider in a compensated foundation is the method of excavation. Consider an excavation made to the full depth d of the intended compensated foundation, confined between two adjacent existing buildings. A properly braced diaphragm wall in this case will serve as ground support and as lateral underpinning for the existing buildings. At the base of the excavation, the existing total vertical effective stress outside the wall will be equal to the effective overburden stress at the same depth plus the load imposed from the adjacent buildings, or

$$p_d = \sigma'_{vd} + q \tag{9-2}$$

where P_d = existing total effective stress σ'_{vd} = effective overburden stress, and q = surcharge load from adjacent buildings.

The depth of the excavation is limited by the desired behavior of the subsoil under shear stresses. Hence this depth is determined by the shear strength of the soil below the excavation level (foundation grade). The bearing capacity of the soil is calculated for the load $(\sigma'_{vd} + q)$, and the compensated foundation will be limited to the depth that can be excavated without inducing damage to the adjacent buildings or to the soil.

Heave and settlement. During excavation to construct the foundation and because of stress relief heave occurs as elastic response of the soil. The literature contains a fair amount of material on the heave problem; hence this discussion is confined to the subject of compensated foundations.

If an excavation is made deep into soft soil deposits and the work is not carried out promptly, heave will be accompanied by swelling due to adsorption of water molecules into the clay structure. This has the effect of increasing the compressibility of the soil and hence reduces the shear strength. In some instances the compressibility is so badly damaged that the initial design must be abandoned.

Heave taking place cannot be readily noticed because this is continuously cut by the excavation process. Therefore, to detect any heave in deep excavations it is necessary to establish reference points in the soil. When the building load is applied, the heave will be recompressed and settlement will occur. This settlement will be larger than the heave for the same reapplied effective pressure, and if swelling of the clay has taken place because of adsorption of water it will be even greater. Instances have been reported where the subsequent settlement was two to three times the initial heave. If proper procedures are followed during excavation, and the highly compressible soil is kept under its original compressing state, the subsequent settlement may not exceed 20 percent of the heave. If the diaphragm walls extend fairly below the base of the excavation, heave will be resisted by shear at the wall-soil interface.

Stresses from earthquakes and wind. With static loads, a totally compensated foundation satisfies the bearing capacity theories as long as the resultant load coincides with the center of gravity of the loaded area so that there will be no static tilting of the structure.

During earthquake events or heavy wind applications, the associated horizontal forces induce overturning moments and a base shear that tends to rotate the building and push it toward the edge. The increment of stress on the static subgrade reaction distribution may be considered to have a linear variation, and should be investigated for two reasons: (1) it should be considerably less than the pressure causing local shear failure; otherwise the building will tilt considerably; and (2) the increment of stress over the static subgrade reactions should be investigated to obtain elastic response of the soil during the dynamic event so that the building will maintain its vertical position after the motion. Zeevaert (1972) reports cases in earthquake zones where buildings tilted considerably and had to be underpinned and rectified to their initial position.

Construction procedures to avoid undesirable effects

Figure 9-5 shows an excavation that must be carried down to depth $d = d_1 + d_2$ for a compensated foundation. If the excavation is done continuously to the full depth, base heave is likely to occur. Thus the stability requirements can be satisfied if the work is performed in steps. In the first step the excavation is carried down to about one-half of the total depth. With the diaphragm walls in place and because the subsoil is maintained in a precompressed state, heave is reduced considerably. The second step involves a process of substitution, and for this purpose it is expedient to select foundation elements that can be easily constructed in braced trenches. These are shored and braced

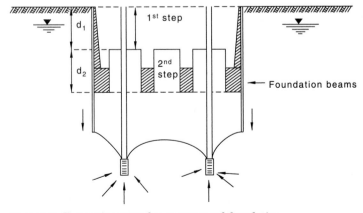

Figure 9-5 Excavation steps for compensated foundation.

carefully so that the same level of passive resistance is maintained and transmitted against the perimeter diaphragm walls to control overall inward movement. During the second step, the secondary trenches are excavated one at a time, with the foundation element immediately cast, replacing the weight of excavated material by an equivalent weight. When all the foundation elements are in place in this sequential construction, the erection of the building begins. The foundation slab is finished in a similar manner by excavating the earth panels one at a time.

Structural combinations

Suitable structural combinations are those that are compatible with the method of excavation. From the point of view of differential settlement, the bridging effects associated with mat and structure rigidity are beneficial to the system. Thus proper combinations are derivatives of diaphragm walls with mat foundations discussed in Sec. 7-8, and suitable versions are shown in Fig. 9-6.

The foundation system shown in Fig. 9-6a is a beam grid. The reaction slab and basement slab are monolithically connected to the beams and the diaphragm walls to give a unit of high rigidity. The hollow spaces can be used as sumps for seepage water. This cellular box-type foundation has been found suitable for large spans and column bays in heavy buildings.

The hollow flat-slab type shown in Fig. 9-6b is semirigid. It is formed by leaking tubes in the concrete slab to save concrete but without reducing flexural capacity, and to reduce reinforcement requirements. The excavation must be made to full depth, and compensation provided by partially excavated areas.

The third scheme shown in Fig. 9-6c is a conventional mat foundation consisting of a flat slab, usually treated as semiflexible and suitable for short spans and relatively lighter loads in conjunction with one basement. The excavation can be made to full depth in sequentially excavated areas.

These types should be analyzed for allowable total and differential settlement loads, and as a function of spans and depth in conjunction with the intended excavation procedure.

9-8 Requirements During Construction

The primary requirement of the lateral support is to control movement during excavation. In addition to the discussion presented in the foregoing sections and Chap. 4, the following remarks can be made:

- The largest movements and therefore the most serious problems will arise in excavations in soft and medium soft clay. With higher soil stiffness, movement caused by excavation decreases rapidly.

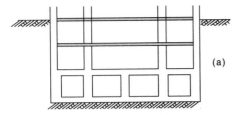

Rigid cellular - box type structure

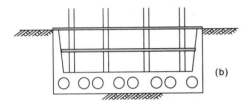

Hollow flat - slab type structure

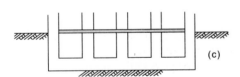

Flat - slab type structure

Figure 9-6 Suitable structural combinations for compensated foundation: (*a*) Rigid cellular box-type structure. (*b*) Hollow flat-slab-type structure. (*c*) Flat-slab-type structure.

- In cohesionless sand and cohesive granular material (which have a relatively high shear strength), movement can be expected to be small provided there is sufficient horizontal bracing. In this case it is important to maintain control of seepage pressure and monitor changes in pore pressure due to groundwater flow.

- If an excavation is carried out in soft soils, initial movement will be followed by further secondary permanent deformation as a result of creep and horizontal consolidation below excavation level. The magnitude of this movement depends on the time that the excavation is left open.

- Movement is caused by inward soil displacement toward the excavation above the excavation level, and by an inward movement of the soil below the excavation level as a result of upward movement of the bottom of the cut.

The stiffness of diaphragm walls is utilized to control these movements. However, it is unlikely that the bottom of the ground support for a deep basement can be braced below excavation level before general excavation, as is the case with narrow cuts braced with cross walls, since the supports are too far apart. Therefore, the sequence in which the ground support is built and braced will affect these deformations. Although it is unrealistic to expect that ground movement can be stopped completely, it can be significantly reduced by a careful construction sequence and bracing.

If the completed structure of the basement has a form whereby permanent members can be used to brace the walls, the introduction and sequence of this bracing should be part of the design. Such permanent members are often provided with a jacking system at the boundary-wall face to compensate for effects due to construction tolerance, or because of structural shortening in elastic compression, shrinkage, creep, and temperature changes.

The uncertainties of site control and the substantial extra costs incurred if the initial methods and sequence must be changed after construction begins suggest the importance of choosing a construction sequence and excavation procedures that are simple and practicable to follow.

Structural compatibility. Almost all deep basements built in the past have utilized some, many, or all of the temporary work members as part of the permanent structure. This dual role and function implies a wide variety of loading combinations and support conditions that the walls must withstand, and this in turn results in changes in the type and magnitude of stresses and deformations induced in the system. On a global basis, these changes are approached with different safety factors and strength criteria as the design is shifted from one phase to another. Conversely, some undesirable effects can occur in many ways, i.e., by overstressing in the temporary stage if the unsupported sections are much greater than they are in the permanent condition and if the assumed lateral pressures are much smaller than the actual; by excessive cantilever lengths allowed either at the top or at the bottom until the completed structure rectifies this situation; and by poor performance because of construction limitations and shortcomings or by failure of the soil-structure interaction such as excessive kicking of the wall inward during excavation to final level and before the base slab is in place.

The design and construction of a wall to withstand the broad range of stresses and deformations caused by the temporary and permanent condition becomes more difficult because the scope of the structural requirements is limited and because these requirements often conflict from one stage to another. In almost every excavation, but especially with walls relatively deep and soft plastic soil, stresses caused by soil pressures, temperature effects, and poor bracing can cause some form of damage. This is true if the walls are allowed to be overstressed and if this overstressing is assumed to be temporary only. Examples are (1) diaphragm walls that developed cracks because they were built to resist shear but were not provided with shear reinforcement; (2) rotation of bearings supporting struts because of poor connection with the wall or rotation of a waling beam due to the reaction of inclined strut; (3) temperature changes in a long strut causing stress changes greater than estimated; and (4) accidental movement or displacement of parts of the temporary bracing, i.e., column supporting a strut, because of construction operations or unforeseen conditions.

9-9 Soil-Structure Interaction

Three- or four-level basements for buildings in urban sites are not unusual, and where space is at a premium the basement may be even deeper. Likewise column loads in modern tall buildings have been increasing as designers use larger bays to provide uninterrupted floor space, and it is not unusual to have single column loads of the order of 6000 to 8000 kips.

These design requirements articulate the function and structural service of diaphragm walls and load-bearing elements built by the slurry trench method. In addition, the following remarks characterize the design and performance of the structure:

■ Unlike walls in subway construction, usually terminated below ground level, diaphragm walls for building basements typically are built to finish grade along the perimeter and to intended grade along interior central cores. The most common configurations are single walls often combined with stilts, piles, and subpiers. Composite or integral walls, often used in subway construction, are unlikely except for special cases such as the structure shown in Fig. 9-6a, where the diaphragm wall is thickened locally in the lower part to increase the stiffness of the box.

■ In building basement walls the temporary loads are quite nominal and include mainly surcharges from construction operations and moving vehicles. However, permanent loads may be quite heavy and include dead load from weight of the structure and service live loads. This is contrary to subway construction, where the walls may have to resist heavy temporary loads but light permanent loads. Besides vertical loads, other governing loads result from wind and earthquake effects.

- A temporary bracing used more frequently than any other bracing system is with ground anchors. These are destressed or removed when the permanent bracing provided by the floors is in place.

Soil-structure interaction for static effects

Basic principles. When a foundation rests on soft soil or if a wall is acted upon by lateral earth stresses, the analysis of the interaction is complicated by the nonlinear and time-dependent soil behavior. The application of load to the foundation of a partially floated system is represented approximately in Fig. 9-7. For the mat the settlements begin at time A, but for the completed structure the settlements start at time B. The nonstructural parts of the building feel settlements only after time C. Because of the time dependence of both loading and deformation the design must be clear as to which part of the behavior is under consideration. Regardless of how the time-dependent deformations of the soil are analyzed, or whether they should be considered at all, the analysis must model the ultimate deformability in some way. Thus the various methods for analyzing soil-structure interaction are articulated by the model used to represent the structure and the soil.

Theory of the modulus of subgrade reaction. The beam on elastic foundation mentioned briefly in Sec. 8-9 has its basis in this theory. The

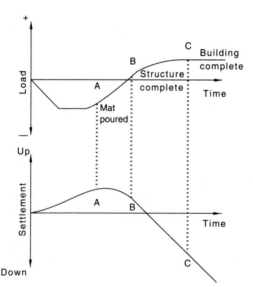

Figure 9-7 Typical construction history. (*From Christian, 1972.*)

representation of the soil as a type of elastic spring under load is attributed to Winkler (1867), who proposed that the vertical normal stress σ_v and the vertical movement δ_v at a point are linearly related by

$$\sigma_v = k_s \delta_v \qquad (9\text{-}3)$$

where the parameter k_s is the modulus of subgrade reaction (vertical). A similar relationship is proposed for a horizontal stress and movement, related by the modulus of horizontal subgrade reaction.

An extensive theoretical analysis has been developed from the foregoing concept. Hetenyi (1946) has derived most of the useful solutions that have been based on analytical methods. Allen and Severn (1960, 1961, 1963) have introduced numerical techniques to handle slabs on the elastic Winkler foundation. Several computer programs are available today to enable solutions of most practical problems.

Equation (9-3) can be rewritten as follows:

$$P = K\delta_v \qquad (9\text{-}4)$$

where P = load transmitted to a system of springs and K = linear spring constant, measured in force per length. In this manner it is possible and expedient to modify structural computer programs or analytical schemes simply by including a spring for each reaction. Useful versions are provided by Sved and Kwok (1963), Lee and Harrison (1970), Heil (1969), Lytton and Meyer (1971), and others. In spite of the overwhelming availability of solutions, two questions remain: (1) the derivation of the values of k_s or K; and (2) how well the theory represents actual soil behavior.

Procedures for obtaining the modulus of subgrade reaction. A comprehensive summary of the state of the art of the modulus of subgrade reaction, both horizontal and vertical, is given by Terzaghi (1955). The main comment is that the modulus is not a fundamental property but depends on many factors, including the size of the loaded area and the length of time it is loaded. Terzaghi proposed that the values of k_s for a loaded area of dimensions b by bl (ft) can be found from the modulus k_{s1}, for 1 ft by 1 ft plate. For sands the relation is

$$k_s = k_{s1} \left(\frac{1 + b}{2b} \right)^2 \qquad (9\text{-}5)$$

and for heavily precompressed clay it is

$$k_s = k_{s1} \frac{1}{b} \left(\frac{l + 0.5}{1.5l} \right) \qquad (9\text{-}6)$$

These relations are applicable to surface or near-surface conditions, so that their value for deep foundations or deep wall embedment is questionable. Terzaghi also gives an extensive discussion of the modulus of horizontal subgrade reaction and how to obtain it.

The conventional Winkler model assumes that each point moves independently so that a load over region A in Fig. 9-8a causes settlement only under A and nowhere else. In reality, the surface will deform as shown in Fig. 9-8b so that the Winkler theory is fundamentally unrealistic. Thus refinements have been proposed by De Beer (1957) assuming a semi-infinite elastic half-space (see Fig. 9-8b) with Young's modulus E constant or varying linearly with depth. Modifications have also been proposed by Vesic (1961), Cheung and Nag (1968), Vlasov and Leont'ev (1966), Klein and Duraev (1971), and Harr et al. (1969).

These modifications represent a more rational approach than the simple Winkler theory, although there are no obvious reasons why the soil model of a semi-infinite half-space of constant modulus is any more reasonable than the set of independent springs. On the other hand, these representations are more difficult to use. In Fig. 9-8b the load at A causes movement at B and at all other points. Hence the stiffnesses of all reaction points are interconnected. This complicates the analysis and inhibits computer use of available structural programs.

Other work (Gibson et al., 1967, 1972; Carrier and Christian, 1971) suggests that when the elastic modulus of a layer of soil or of a half-space increases with depth, for a large range of parameters the settlements behave similarly to the Winkler model; i.e., they are uniform for a uniform load. Thus it appears that the Winkler approach is in some respects valid but can be improved, although such improvement gives rise to complexities that may not be warranted given the uncertainties of soil properties.

Commentary.   Several investigators prefer to use the $E_s - \mu$ analysis when the soil is modeled as an elastic continuum. Others suggest the concept of the modulus of subgrade reaction because of the present

Figure 9-8   Soil behavior under load: (a) Winkler foundation. (b) Semi-infinite elastic half-space.

inability to obtain fairly representative estimates of E_s. A general form for either the horizontal or vertical k_s is

$$k_s = A_s + B_s Z^n \qquad (9\text{-}7)$$

where A_s = constant for either horizontal or vertical members; B_s = coefficient related to depth; Z = depth of interest below ground; and n = exponent to give the best fit, if load tests or other data are not available.

Either A_s or B_s in Eq. (9-7) may be zero. For a horizontal k_s, A_s is zero at the ground surface but $A_s > 0$ at any small depth. For footings and mats (plates) $A_s > 0$ and $B_s \approx 0$.

With finite-element analyses k_s is used in the passive region for the walls embedded below excavation level. Estimates of k_s can be made by approximating Eq. (9-7) as follows:

$$k_s = C(SF)q_a \qquad (9\text{-}8)$$

where C = 12 for units in ft-lb, q_a = bearing capacity at several depths within the range of wall embedment, and SF = safety factor.

Alternatively the design may consider the following bearing capacity equation:

$$k_s = \frac{q_u H}{\Delta H} C(cN_c + \bar{q}N_q + 0.5\gamma BN_\gamma) \qquad (9\text{-}9)$$

where ΔH = displacement of $\frac{1}{12}$ ft, giving C = 12. Isolating the terms in the second part of Eq. (8-7) gives

$$A_s = C(cN_c + 0.5\gamma BN_\gamma)$$
$$B_s Z^n = C(\gamma N_q Z^1) \qquad (9\text{-}10)$$

Values of N_c, N_q, and N_γ are given in Table 9-2, and c is the soil cohesion. An upper limit on k_s is based on the ultimate bearing pressure at the depth under consideration. Analysis based on the foregoing estimate for k_s will give reasonable values for bending and node soil pressure but may result in unrealistic predictions on wall deflections.

Nonlinear springs will provide a behavioral model closer to reality, particularly for the pressure-displacement function, but this refinement is not always warranted considering the uncertainties of spring stiffness. With stage excavation the limiting values of passive pressure for the soil springs change as the excavation continues, and must be revised.

The initial at rest pressure on the passive side (inside of excavation) can be assumed as an initial load on the soil springs or as pressure on the inside face of the wall. If it is modeled as pressure (partial

TABLE 9-2   Bearing-Capacity Factors for the Terzaghi
Equations

ϕ, deg	N_c	N_q	N_γ	$K_{P\gamma}$
0	5.7*	1.0	0.0	10.8
5	7.3	1.6	0.5	12.2
10	9.6	2.7	1.2	14.7
15	12.9	4.4	2.5	18.6
20	17.7	7.4	5.0	25.0
25	25.1	12.7	9.7	35.0
30	37.2	22.5	19.7	52.0
34	52.6	36.5	36.0	
35	57.8	41.4	42.4	82.0
40	95.7	81.3	100.4	141.0
45	172.3	173.3	297.5	298.0
48	258.3	287.9	780.1	
50	347.5	415.1	1153.2	800.0

Values of N_γ for ϕ of 34 and 48 are original Terzaghi values and used to back-compute $K_{P\gamma}$.
  * = $1.5\pi + 1$

passive), the initial pressure on the passive side should be subtracted from the ultimate passive resistance when making estimates of the passive limits of the soil springs. The soil springs have a constant stiffness until the load reaches the ultimate passive pressure (computed from classical theory), and beyond this point the springs behave plastically and continue to deform at constant load.

The lateral unloading on the inside (passive side) of the wall is represented by reducing the lateral soil pressure (initial load) in the springs for each succeeding stage. The lateral unloading due to excavation in cohesive soils under undrained conditions differs from the lateral unloading in granular soils under drained conditions, and this difference reflects total and effective soil weight.

Values of k_s computed from Eqs. (9-10) may be checked by referring to Table 9-3. Since in both cases these values are approximate, if the computed values are two or three times larger than the table indicates the computations must be checked for possible gross errors. In any case judgment is essential since the k_s values computed by any method are representative guidelines only, and noting also that the pressure at the wall-soil interface may reach ultimate passive pressure and thus exceeds the applicable range for typical subgrade modulus values.

Examples of lateral ground supports where the passive resistance in the embedded portion is modeled as a beam on elastic foundations, based on the theory of the modulus of subgrade reaction, are given by Bowles (1988).

TABLE 9-3   Range of Values of Modulus of Subgrade Reaction k_s

Soil	k_s, kips/ft^2	k_s, kN/m^3
Loose sand	30–100	4,800–16,000
Medium dense sand	60–500	9,600–80,000
Dense sand	400–800	64,000–128,000
Clayey medium dense sand	200–500	32,000–80,000
Silty medium dense sand	150–300	24,000–48,000
Clayey soil:		
$q_u \leqq 200$ kPa (4 kips/ft^2)	75–150	12,000–24,000
$200q_u \leqq 400$ kPa	150–300	24,000–48,000
$q_u > 800$ kPa	>300	>48,000

Use values as guide and for comparison when using approximate equations.

Dynamic effects

The dynamic interaction of a basement structure and soil is caused by several phenomena such as blasts, wind effects, and seismic events. Earthquakes include all the problems associated with other categories, and hence considerations of seismic loads cover the entire range of dynamic effects.

Amplification and interaction.   Most antiseismic codes include provisions for including the effect of soil conditions in the design. This effect consists of two separate contributions: amplification and interaction. Amplification refers to the effect of the various soil layers on the earthquake signal before it reaches the building. Referring to Fig. 9-9, an earthquake signal must propagate from the rock at point B through the soil to the building at C. The resulting pattern of motion at C will be affected by the soil properties and could be quite different from the motion at point A, and irrespective of the presence of the building.

Interaction articulates the effect of the building being present at point C on the motions. The building and soil together are a more

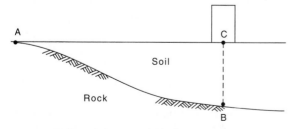

Figure 9-9   Geometry of amplification problem, earthquake effects.

complex system than the building alone on a rigid foundation or the soil alone without the structure. The combined soil-structure system has therefore a different behavior.

A main conclusion from research on these topics is that, with the exception of massive structures like nuclear power plants, the effects of soil amplification are far more important than those associated with interaction (Ohsaki, 1969; Seed et al., 1969, 1971). Analysis of the effects of the 1967 Caracas earthquake (Whitman, 1969; Seed et al., 1970) shows that the greatest damage occurred where the fundamental period of the structures coincided with the fundamental period of the soil beneath the building. Therefore, the first question to be addressed by the design is whether the structure has a vibratory frequency that corresponds to one of the characteristic frequencies of the foundation strata. Removing the building from this condition of resonance will decrease the major effect of the foundation on the structural response.

The conceptual separation of earthquake effects can be further articulated. Thus soil amplification refers to the manner in which the stiffness and thickness of soil strata affect the motion at ground surface. Soil-structure interaction relates to the manner in which the deformability of the soil beneath a building affects the response of the structure to ground motion.

Interaction analyses are usually carried out by the use of the lumped springs and finite-element techniques. The lumped springs method involves the replacement of soil and foundation by several springs and masses, whose properties are selected to represent the soil in the appropriate frequency range. Finite-element analyses involve a division of the soil into discrete elements and then solving for the dynamic behavior of the resulting multiple-degree-of-freedom systems.

When a foundation is not at the surface, or when the soil is not very deep, the conventional models must be modified, usually at considerable theoretical expense. The effect of the depth of the foundation soil on its interaction with the structure has been investigated by Hashiba and Whitman (1968). The work deals primarily with horizontal swaying motion, but the results identify the factors that must be considered in evaluating spring constants. One of the conclusions is that only shorter buildings are affected by soil-structure interaction with shallow soil depths.

Certain structures, such as those supported on pile foundations, do not have a clearly defined boundary between soil and structure. However, analyses show that for normal pile types the relative movement between piles and soil is very small. This means that the effect of the piles on horizontal swaying is negligible because the piles move with the soil, and in most instances the piles have no apparent effect on the soil-structure interaction. With buildings supported by relatively rigid foundations, such as concrete piers and caissons, the soil-structure interaction problem should be considered in evaluating earthquake response. Practical experience also shows that buildings with rigid basements behave better during earthquakes than buildings without them.

From the foregoing remarks it follows that the main objectives in the analytical study of earthquake response are (1) evaluation of rigidity, strength, and hysteresis characteristics of structures and structural components against lateral forces, and (2) the natural periods and damping characteristics of buildings.

Design criteria. Lessons learned from catastrophic earthquakes (Skopje, 1963; Anchorage, 1964; Acapulco, 1962; Niigata, 1964; and Caracas, 1967) provided the following data:

- Failure to understand and quantify the influence of the supporting soil on structural response can result in structural damage.

- Shear walls can be adequate in resisting seismic forces if properly designed and built.

- Arbitrary omission of some rigid elements in distributing the forces can cause high localized stresses in critical structural members.

- In numerous instances the global rigidity will attract a greater amount of the lateral forces. If the more rigid elements are brittle, failure may result as these elements impose excessive forces on the structural frame.

- The building must resist all the effects resulting from structural response. Thus axial shear and flexural forces, including those from torsion, must be provided for in the design.

- The efficiency of providing structure continuity was clearly demonstrated.

- Connection details should receive close attention, not only to provide adequate strength but also to ensure ductile behavior.

- Overturning forces can occur that are in excess of those anticipated in the past.

- If there is a single zone of weakness in the resisting systems, or if there is a sudden localized change of stiffness, there is a zone of danger.

- Adequate interconnections of shear walls and diaphragms are necessary.

- In some instances the design philosophy has been to accept some form of structural damage if the possibility of structural collapse is minimal. In this case geologic and foundation considerations are important parameters.

- The design of buildings that exhibit dynamic irregularities should recognize the potential for increased dynamic response over the level that a dynamically regular building will undergo.

Current design approach. Seismic analysis of buildings generally is performed either by the method of equivalent static loading or by dynamic methods based on applied earthquake motions judged to be appropriate for the site and soil conditions. The equivalent static seismic forces to be distributed over the height of the building are determined (1) by a base shear coefficient considering the response of the structure during an earthquake or (2) by applying a lateral seismic coefficient at each floor level.

The provisions included in most seismic codes address (1) the distribution of lateral shear; (2) evaluation of overturning moments and horizontal torsional moments; (3) drift limitations; (4) separation of buildings and setbacks; and (5) structural requirements such as ductility, possible reversal of axial forces, shears, and moments, specified yield strength of reinforcement, etc. In particular, the overall ductility property of a structure provides an important contribution to its earthquake resistance. The capability of a building to deflect large distances and to absorb a large amount of energy in the inelastic range is essential to avoid catastrophic failure. Moment-resisting frames of ductile materials such as structural steel and ductile reinforced concrete have performed satisfactorily. However, reinforced-concrete buildings in which failures are due to shear cannot absorb much energy in the inelastic range under repeated cyclic loadings and can suffer damage due to brittle failure.

Ductility. This is defined by reference to Fig. 9-10; the structure has the ability to undergo increasing deformation while still sustaining load. A useful treatment of the subject is provided by the references at the end of this chapter, and deals with bending and shear deformations of heterogeneous members consisting of concrete and ductile reinforcing steel.

The ductility factor is defined as the ratio of the maximum permissible inelastic deflection or displacement to the initial yield deflection, b/a. A recommended minimum ductility factor for reinforced-concrete buildings is from 4 to 6. However, the use of a constant displacement ductility factor is questioned by several investigators (Bertero, 1972), the contention being that this alone is not an adequate criterion.

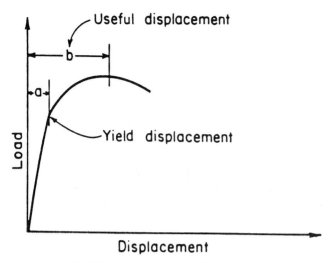

Figure 9-10 Ductility defined in terms of load-displacement curve.

These investigators make several points, namely: (1) when a building is expected to be strained well into the inelastic range, it should be designed using inelastic models (based on the limit state rather than on a fictitious state of static-type codes); (2) an acceptable ductility ratio should depend on the total number of reversals to which the building may be subjected during a long extreme earthquake or on the cumulative damage from successive earthquakes; and (3) in tall buildings it does not appear expedient to use constant ductility throughout the entire height (the structural members of the lower stories are subjected to higher axial and shear forces and have shear span ratios smaller than those of members in upper stories, and hence it is logical to expect that the ductility in the inelastic region of members located in lower levels will be smaller). For seismic design details of reinforced concrete buildings see Paulay and Priestley (1992).

The use of diaphragm walls to resist dynamic effects

Lateral forces and overturning.   The ACI considers three types of lateral loads: wind loading, earthquake loading, and blast loading. The usual approach to lateral load analysis involves an assessment of the character and magnitude of loads, followed by a prediction of the structural response. A distinction should be made between externally applied forces and inertia forces resulting from the response of the building to ground motion. The latter are of a dynamic character so that the supporting medium not only transmits the motion to the foundation but must also absorb the feedback from the structure.

Diaphragm walls combined with stiff monolithic rafts or mats are effective in the control of differential settlement. This action is particularly useful during liquefaction of fine sands or sudden consolidation of loose soils under the effect of jarring motions. Lateral loads, whether externally applied or internally created by inertial resistance to ground motions, must be safely transferred to the ground, and this can be done by the development of passive earth resistance. For reasons of serviceability of the superstructure, mobilization of passive resistance over large areas (such as wall-soil interface) is more advisable than individual resistance against smaller independent units such as foundation piers or piles. The construction procedure of diaphragm walls ensures that tight contact between the soil and the substructure is established and maintained. The resisting action is enhanced where lateral ties from the framing and basement floors are integrated with the walls.

Resistance to overturning usually is estimated under a complete absence of live load and with a low estimate of dead load. The presence of diaphragm walls on opposite sides of the building will modify the reference lines for establishing the overturning moment. Passive resistance will develop along opposite sides and form a couple balancing overturning. Other factors that may be introduced are the weight of structure, soil shear and friction, and the fact that laminar tilting is not possible since the entire system must be extracted like a tooth before it fails by overturning.

Amplification and interaction. Where rock exists at relatively shallow depth, diaphragm walls have been extended to bear on solid material, thus eliminating the role of subsoil in amplifying ground motion. Relevant factors to be considered are the following:

1. Buildings with a fundamental period in the same range as characterized by the ground motion are subjected to greater seismic response than those with fundamental periods markedly different from the exciting ground motion. Recommended ratios between characteristic periods of ground and structure are from 1.5 to 4.0.

2. The period and amplitude of a wave motion traveling from rock through overlying soil generally increases with increasing density and thickness of the soil material. However, every seismic ground motion is created as a complex action resulting from a combination of direct and reflected waves.

3. The foundation, including the basement walls, represents an important link in the transmission of a shock from the ground to the superstructure and back. Depending on the type of foundation and the

character of the ground, the transmission may vary from a hinged to an almost fully restrained condition.

Ductility.   As mentioned in previous sections, the ductility of a flexural member decreases as the steel ratio p approaches the steel ratio p_b necessary for balanced conditions. Ductility is thus assured by placing an upper limit on p. The minimum value of p is provided to prevent a sudden brittle flexural failure in a lightly reinforced wall where the bending resistance of the concrete acting alone may be greater than that of the reinforced wall after tension cracks occur. Diaphragm walls have been demonstrated to satisfy these ductility requirements.

These minimum provisions allow for shifts in inflection points that are not predicted by combinations of design loads, including seismic forces.

The energy absorption capacity of a wall is related to its ductility in that it is equal to the work done in straining or deforming the structure to the limit of useful deflection, and hence is numerically equal to the area under the load-deformation curve. For walls in bending, it is equal to the area under the moment-rotation curve up to the limit of useful rotation.

Shear walls.   Shear walls are often used in buildings when large lateral loads must be resisted, such as seismic loads or very high wind loads. They are placed at locations where they are the least detrimental to the use and aesthetics of the building. When they are located on the outer perimeter they provide maximum flexibility for the use of floor space, although they can also eliminate windows.

For design purposes shear walls act as cantilever beams fixed at the base to transfer the load to the foundation. The forces that must be considered are (1) varying shear that is maximum at the base; (2) varying flexure that is maximum at the base and produces compression on one end and tension on the opposite end; and (3) gravity loads producing compression on the wall.

These forces are the deflected profile of the shear wall are shown in Fig. 9-11. In addition the foundation must be designed to resist the shear and moments at the base of the wall. This applies to the base details, bar anchorage into the foundation, and bar splicing in the wall at the base. When a shear wall is supported on a diaphragm wall whose length is many times the length of the shear wall, shears, moments, and axial loads are merely absorbed by the massive stiffness of the diaphragm wall. The associated stresses generally dissipate or may be resisted at the end by soil-wall interaction. An essential requirement is to design and provide a structural joint between wall panels to transfer shear and axial load and resist laminar tilting.

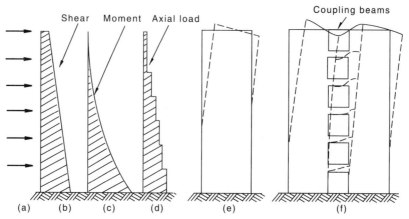

Figure 9-11 (*a*) Lateral loads. (*b*) Shear diagram. (*c*) Moment diagram. (*d*) Axial loads. (*e*) Isolated wall. (*f*) Coupled wall.

The interaction of the shear and diaphragm wall along the horizontal construction joint is controlled by the possible failure mode of the former, particularly with large height-to-length ratios. Figure 9-12 shows a wall with insufficient vertical reinforcement. As the wall responds to the loads by deforming, the tensile steel elongates, and a separation or crack forms. In Fig. 9-12*b* the wall fails in shear after several flexural cracks have formed. The critical crack is a flexural crack that inclines downward at about 45°. At failure, some of the horizontal reinforcement across the critical crack may fracture and lead to more cracking with crashing of the compression zone at the roof of the critical crack. Figure 9-12*c* shows a common failure mode that involves considerable yielding of the flexural steel and eventually leads to crushing of the concrete at the base. Crushing can be prevented if the compression boundary area can be locally enlarged.

The term shear wall is sometimes taken to imply that shear is the governing mode of failure. As can be seen from the example of Fig. 9-12, the design is usually governed by the flexural capacity of the wall. Shear walls are normally stiffer than frames, and hence attract higher-inertia response forces. In addition, for a given amount of drift, the apparent distress in a wall might be much higher than in a frame. Most codes, therefore, require higher design forces on walls than are specified for frames. Invariably, the intent is to provide a ductile shear wall system when the wall is subjected to flexure and a significantly large axial load.

Design for Flexure. As shown in Fig. 9-11 the shear wall must be designed to resist the moment at the base, and this involves interaction with the diaphragm wall. If the axial compressive load is ignored

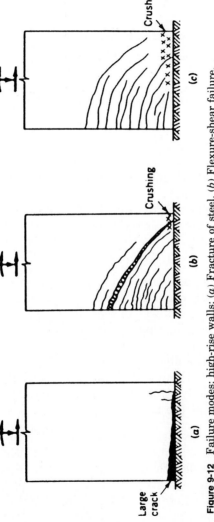

Figure 9-12 Failure modes: high-rise walls: (*a*) Fracture of steel. (*b*) Flexure-shear failure. (*c*) Failure by concrete crushing.

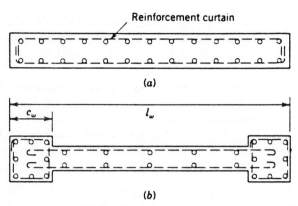

Figure 9-13 (*a*) Wall without boundary members. (*b*) Wall with boundary elements.

(which gives a conservative design), the wall is designed as a beam. The analysis is further simplified if the distributed steel is ignored along the wall length, and only the end reinforcement is included as resisting the moment.

If boundary elements are used, a close approximation of the vertical steel required at the boundary element is

$$A_s = M_u/f_y(l_w - c_w) \qquad (9\text{-}11)$$

where l_w and c_w are as shown in Fig. 9-13. The same area of steel must be provided in both boundary elements since the lateral force can act in either direction. For a wall of constant thickness the same approach can be used by considering a reinforcement zone at the ends with length c_w.

In some cases the distributed reinforcement will provide sufficient moment capacity without additional reinforcement at the ends. In this case a flexural analysis of the section is necessary to determine the moment capacity at the base.

Code requirements for seismic design. For design purposes, the ACI Code defines a flexural member as one in which the factored compression axial force is less than $A_g f_c'/10$. In order to ensure ductility the maximum steel ratio p is limited to 0.025. Hoops (closed ties) are required in regions where flexural yielding is anticipated, since hoops confine concrete and provide lateral support for longitudinal reinforcement.

For structural (shear) walls the code also specifies a minimum horizontal and vertical reinforcement ratio $p = 0.0025$ of the gross area in each direction. The spacing of reinforcement should not exceed 18 in in each direction. At least two curtains of reinforcement should be used in walls if the factored shear exceeds $2\sqrt{f_c'}A_{cv}$ where A_{cv} = cross-sectional area of the web of the wall in the direction of shear.

The nominal shear strength V_n of a shear wall is taken as

$$V_n = A_{cv}(2\sqrt{f_c'} + p_n f_y) \tag{9-12}$$

but less than $10\,A_{cv}\sqrt{f_c'}$. Where a number of walls resist shear in a given direction, the nominal shear strength of all the walls should not exceed $8\sqrt{f_c'}A_{\text{total}}$ where A_{total} is the cross-sectional area of all the walls in that direction.

Boundary elements of walls are needed if compressive stress at the edges exceeds $0.2f_c'$. Transverse reinforcement must be provided in the boundary element.

9-10   Loads and Load Groups

Loads and load combinations were discussed in Sec. 4-13 in conjunction with the ϕ factors for either AASHTO or ACI load factor (limit state) design. This section reviews briefly loadings and actions that are characteristic to buildings.

Direct and indirect actions. A direct action results from concentrated or distributed forces due to the weight of the structure and its contents, or pressures from wind, water, or earth. An indirect action or imposed deformation is associated with movement or deflection causing stresses in the structure. Examples are uneven support settlements, shrinkage, and long-term creep.

Load classification. Loads may be classified according to their variability with respect to time and location. Permanent loads remain nearly constant, and examples are self-weight and soil pressure against the walls. (This may also vary.) Variable loads change from time to time, and examples are occupancy loads and wind.

Loads may also be described as static, or as dynamic if they cause appreciable acceleration or vibration of the structure and its members.

Three levels of live load and wind load are important. With ultimate limit states the load should represent the maximum load during the lifetime of the structure. In checking the serviceability limit states, it may be expedient to use a frequent live load, usually a fraction of the mean maximum lifetime load (50 to 60 percent). For estimating sustained load deflections, it may be desirable to consider a sustained live load, usually 20 to 30 percent of the specified live load. In most codes these concepts are quantified by introducing load factors, generally applied to the service loads specified for ASD.

In the United States there are three basic building codes: the Uniform Building Code, the Standard Building Code, and the Basic Building Code (see also bibliography at the end of this chapter). These are essentially similar but differ considerably in the area of wind loading.

Wind loads. The wind loads discussed here are as specified in ANSI A58 (1982). These procedures include the normal analytical calculation based on tabulated coefficients, a detailed calculation for tall slender buildings or flexible buildings based on the natural frequency and size, and recommendations for a dynamic analysis possibly supported by a wind tunnel investigation.

In the analytical procedure the basic equation for computing the wind pressure on a building is

$$p = qG_hC_p \tag{9-13}$$

where p = design pressure, equivalent static pressure or suction (lb/ft^2) assumed to act perpendicular to the surface under consideration.

Velocity pressure q. This is the pressure exerted by the wind on a flat plate suspended in the wind stream, calculated as

$$q_z = 0.00256 \ K_z(IV)^2 \tag{9-14}$$

where V = basic wind speed (mph) at a height of 33 ft (10 m) above the ground in open terrain; I = importance factor (0.95 to 1.11); and K_z = velocity pressure exposure coefficient increasing with height above the surface.

Gust response factor G_h. This reflects the dynamic properties of the wind in relation to the structure. Tables and equations are given in the standard.

External pressure coefficient C_p. When wind blows past a building, it exerts a positive pressure on the windward side and a negative pressure (suction) on the leeward side. Suction also exists on the sidewalls and roof. The coefficient C_p used in Eq. (9-14) is the sum of the pressure coefficient for the windward and leeward sides.

Earthquake loads. Studies of hypothetical elastic and elastic-plastic buildings subjected to a number of different earthquake records suggest that the maximum lateral deflections of the elastic and elastic-plastic structures are roughly the same. Referring to Fig. 9-14, the load-deflection diagrams are compared for an elastic structure and an elastic-plastic structure subjected to the same lateral deflection Δ_u. The ratio of the maximum deflection Δ_u to the deflection Δ_y at yielding is the ductility factor discussed in Sec. 9-9 (see also Fig. 9-10). From

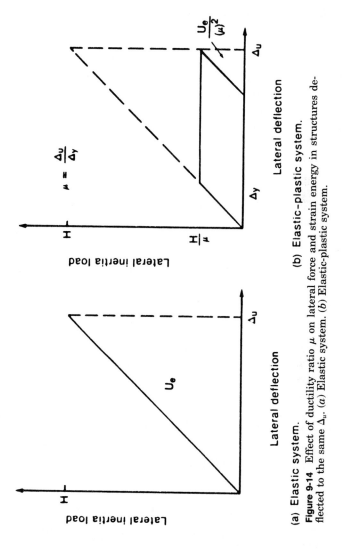

(a) Elastic system.   (b) Elastic–plastic system.

Figure 9-14 Effect of ductility ratio μ on lateral force and strain energy in structures deflected to the same Δ_u. (a) Elastic system. (b) Elastic–plastic system.

Fig. 9-14 it can be seen that for a ductility ratio 4, the lateral load acting on the elastic-plastic structure would be $1/\mu = \frac{1}{4}$ of that on the elastic structure, and the energy recovered in each cycle would be $\frac{1}{16}$ as great. This suggests that if the structure is ductile, it can be designed for lower seismic forces.

The design of buildings for earthquake loads can be carried out to several levels of complexity, the more complex procedures being for structures expected to be strained well beyond the elastic range, large buildings, buildings with unsymmetrical or unusual floor plans, or buildings with major changes in stiffness in the height of the structure. The most complex procedure is a time-dependent response analysis where the displacement-force response history is determined analytically for a representative earthquake. Less complex is a spectral model analysis where the major vibration modes are determined analytically and used to compute the seismic shears (Paulay and Priestley, 1992).

If an equivalent static analysis is made with a design base shear V, the latter can be calculated from

$$V = ZIKCSW$$

$$(9\text{-}15)$$

where V = total lateral force at the base
Z = seismic zone coefficient (0.125 to 1), depending on severity of earthquake
I = occupancy importance factor (1.0 to 1.5)
K = numerical coefficient ranging from 0.67 for very ductile structures to 2.5 for very earthquake-susceptible structures
C = spectral constant that relates the shear to the fundamental period of the building
S = soil factor ranging from 1.0 to 1.5 depending on the stiffness of the soil profile
W = total dead load plus a fraction of the live load

For design purposes the lateral load may be distributed according to the pattern shown in Fig. 9-15a, with a lateral force F_i at each floor plus a force F_t at the top. This produces the distribution of shears shown in Fig. 9-15b, approximating the earthquake shear distribution. Specific details and calculation procedures are given by the ACI Code.

Load groups. The required strength V refers to factored load effects according to Eq. (4-40). For buildings that are not subjected to signif-

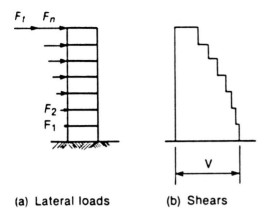

(a) Lateral loads **(b) Shears**

Figure 9-15 Distribution of equivalent lateral shears: (*a*) Lateral loads. (*b*) Shears.

icant wind and earthquake forces, or for members that are not affected by wind and earthquakes, the required strength is computed from

$$V = 1.4D + 1.7L \tag{9-16}$$

where D and L are dead and live load, respectively.

If wind loads affect the design, three load combinations must be considered, with the largest value of V selected.

1. Where the load effects due to wind and those due to dead and live load:

$$V = 0.75 (1.4D + 1.7L + 1.7W) \tag{9-17}$$

or

$$V = 0.75 (1.4D + 1.7W) \tag{9-18}$$

2. Where the effects of dead loads stabilize the structure against wind effects:

$$V = 0.9D + 1.3W \tag{9-19}$$

where W is the wind load. For any combination of D, L, and W, the required strength should not be less than the value given by Eq. (9-16).

Similar load combinations are given by ACI for earthquake loads, lateral earth pressure, fluid pressure; impact, differential settlement, creep, shrinkage, and temperature change.

9-11 Design Example 1, Economic Analysis of Deep Basement

This example assumes a theoretical project and considers the three basic stages: design, subcontract, and site work. The building is a city office tower with n stories, each floor measuring 20,000 ft², with a central utility and elevator core. Construction is a steel frame, composite deck, concrete fill with a metal curtain wall.

In establishing the basic design parameters, the first question relates to the number of basement levels. As mentioned in previous sections, a complete analysis of this topic requires input of all disciplines, and includes costs vs. income, construction time, potential damage to surroundings, and so on. A study of foundation schemes, construction methods, and various designers leads to the following conclusions, applicable to this particular project:

   Three-basement scheme.   Suggested ground support is interlocking steel sheet piles, wale beams, and diagonal bracing. The permanent wall is cast-in-place reinforced concrete.

   Four-basement scheme.   Suggested ground support is a diaphragm wall 3 ft thick bearing on hardpan and braced internally with cross-lot and diagonal bracing. This is also the finished basement wall with some patching.

   Five-basement scheme.   Again the suggested ground support is a 3-ft-thick diaphragm wall, but braced with ground anchors fixed in rock. This is also the finished basement wall with some patching.

   The analysis should only be used as a three-scheme comparative study. The associated costs are computed only for those phases that would be essential and normal to the foundation wall and/or sheeting system, bracing, excavation, dewatering, and ramping. Building items such as structure, interior work, caissons, elevators, grade beams, pits, sumps, and services are assumed to be essentially common to all schemes and are not included. Unit prices are based on the construction price level of the early 1970s. A cost summary is shown in Table 9-4. Escalation figures are based solely on construction costs and do not reflect carrying charges, taxes, etc.

   Based on planned uses, additional construction time, and expected income from rentals, the owner chose the four-basement scheme. This conclusion, however, should not be applied on a general basis, and is valid for this example only.

9-12 Design Example 2, Resistance to Earthquake and Wind

The lateral forces due to wind action or earthquake are to be resisted by two 40-ft-high solid concrete shear walls. Wall A is 15 ft long and wall B is 30 ft long. The wall thickness is 12 in. Determine the distribution of lateral forces to the two walls referring to Fig. 9-16, and assuming the following:

1. Relative rigidities of walls are proportional to the shear deformation of the walls.

TABLE 9-4 Summary and Cost Data, Design Example 9-1

Item	Three basement	Four basement	Five basement
Sheeting	360,000		
Diagonal bracing	280,000	550,000	
Slurry wall		810,000	1,470,000
Tiebacks			750,000
Foundation wall	210,000		
Ramps, pumping	150,000	250,000	325,000
Excavation	350,000	700,000	850,000
Miscellaneous		35,000	45,000
Subtotal	1,350,000	2,345,000	3,440,000
Foundation timing	7.5 months	8.75 months	11 months
Escalation at 7% of total project cost beyond 7.25 months	0	750,000	1,875,000
Subtotal	1,350,000	3,095,000	5,315,000
Omit "standard" foundation	1,350,000	1,350,000	1,350,000
Premium add for deeper basement	0	1,745,000	3,965,000

Note: Escalation figures are based solely on construction costs and do not reflect carrying charges, land taxes, etc.

2. Relative rigidities of walls are proportional to shear deformations plus foundation deformations assuming that the soil deforms ⅛ in under 6000 lb/ft² and footings are 2 ft wide by the wall length.

3. The same as in 1, but the walls are supported directly on foundation diaphragm walls with infinite rigidity.

Step 1. Relative rigidities proportional to shear deformation. These deformations can be computed assuming an elastic cantilever element.

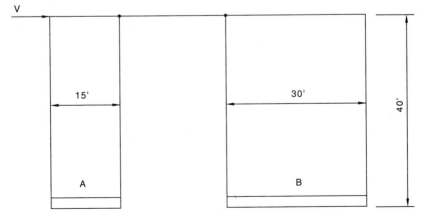

Figure 9-16 Design Example 9-2, shear walls.

Then

$$\Delta = \frac{1.2Vh}{AG} \tag{9-20}$$

where V = applied lateral load, h = wall height, A = wall area, and G = shear modulus. For an equal load applied to each wall, the wall deflection is inversely proportional to the wall length, since the height, wall thickness, and shear modulus are constant for both walls. Wall rigidity is the inverse of the deflection under equal load, and hence rigidity is proportional to length. Accordingly,

$$\text{Rigidity of wall A} = 15$$

$$\text{Rigidity of wall B} = 30$$

$$\text{Total} \qquad = 45$$

or

$$\text{Percentage transferred to wall A} = 15/45 = 33.3$$

$$\text{Percentage transferred to wall B} = 30/45 = 66.7$$

Step 2.   As in step 1 plus a foundation deformation. Assume V = 20 kips to each wall.

For wall A, the bearing pressure due to V = 20 kips is

$$p = \frac{20(40)}{2 \times (15)^2/6} = 10.7 \text{ kips/ft}^2$$

Therefore, the foundation deformation is Δ = (10.7/6) (0.125) = 0.2225 in.

Wall A horizontal deflection due to foundation deformation

$$= 0.2225\left(\frac{40}{10}\right)\left(\frac{1}{12}\right) = 0.075 \text{ ft}$$

Likewise, bearing pressure due to V = 20 kips for wall B is

$$p = \frac{20(40)}{2(30)^2/6} = 2.67 \text{ kips/ft}^2$$

Therefore, the foundation deformation is Δ = (2.67/6) (0.125) = 0.057 in, and

Wall B horizontal deflection due to foundation deformation

$$= 0.057\left(\frac{40}{10}\right)\left(\frac{1}{12}\right) = 0.019 \text{ ft}$$

Rigidity of wall A $= 1/0.075 = 13.3$

Rigidity of wall B $= 1/0.019 = 52.6$

Total $= 65.9$

Percentage of load to wall A $= 13.3/65.9 = 20$

Percentage of load to wall B $= 52.6/65.9 = 80$

Note that the foundation consideration is a significant factor in determining resisting capacity, and reduces the percentage of load in wall A from 33.3 to 20 percent.

Step 3. If the walls are supported on a diaphragm wall of infinite rigidity, the foundation deformation for walls A and B may be assumed zero, and hence the load transfer depends only on the shear deformation.

9-13 The Downward Construction Methods in Buildings

In this process, mentioned in other sections in conjunction with prefounded columns, the objective is to build part or all of the underground portion of a building from the top down rather than from the bottom up; hence it also provides progressive underpinning. The method is particularly compatible with deep excavations because it eliminates strutting, anchoring, or bracing berms.

The initial phase is to construct the perimeter diaphragm wall, providing also connection details with floor slabs, beams, etc. Next the prefounded interior columns are installed from ground level. With the exterior ground support and foundation elements in place, the top slab is cast and supports the walls laterally at the top. Excavation is carried out beneath this slab to the first basement level, the second slab is placed, and the process is repeated for the remaining basement levels.

An obvious disadvantage is the difficulty of earth moving compared with the freedom and speed of conventional excavation. Under these conditions, excavation and earth moving are slower and more expensive, and the added cost will depend on the type and size of equipment that can be used, the traveled distance to access openings, and the type of soil to be excavated. The main difficulties relate to restrictions on equipment type and size. Under a street, the method saves the cost of temporary decking and permits early restoration of street activities. Under a building it allows concurrent upward and downward construction from ground level.

The technical requirements are essentially the same as in conventional construction. The location of slabs, beams and columns depends

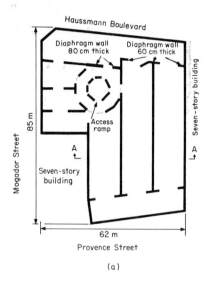

(a)

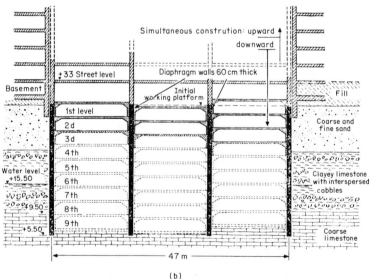

(b)

Figure 9-17 Example of downward construction showing a multilevel structure for underground parking in Paris: (*a*) Plan. (*b*) Section *A-A*. (*From Fenoux, 1971.*)

largely on superstructure loads and the final function of the basement; hence it is seldom affected by the excavation procedure. For large basements, prefounded columns are mandatory and accommodate the superstructure framing. Since the excavation is done sequentially, so that for every level excavated there is a corresponding bracing tier, the process provides progressive underpinning.

An example of downward construction is the multilevel underground parking structure shown in Fig. 9-17. This site is confined by streets on all four sides, and the groundwater level is close to the base of the sixth basement. Diaphragm walls, continuous and strip panels, provide the exterior support, interior walls and partitions, and supports for the access ramps. The construction procedure resulted in substantial time savings, and the upper parking levels were released for service before the lower levels were excavated.

Figure 9-18 shows a cross section of a basement construction in London (Hodgson, 1974), comprising a two-block development from an existing basement level shown in dashed line. A third basement is partially provided as shown, and extends about 7 m (23 ft) from the second basement, or some 14 m (46 ft) from the street level. Because of the close proximity of nearby buildings, the exterior diaphragm walls were braced by a concrete waling slab at the second basement level according to the downward process. The interior diaphragm wall and the concrete subpiers were built in slots or boreholes using the second level as working platform. The subpiers have a cutoff level at the underside of the third basement raft. The steel columns were tem-

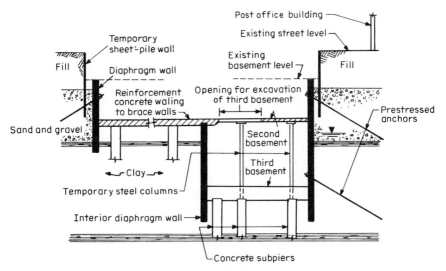

Figure 9-18 Basement construction on Victoria Street, London. (*From Hodgson, 1974.*)

porary only, necessary to carry heavy construction loads; they were not preset in the holes, but the steel casing was left in place and enabled workers to descend to the base to position, grout, and anchor the columns. Excavation of the third basement was carried out through a large opening left in the waling slab.

In more restricted sites, the usual practice is to construct only the structural frame of the underground portion to brace the walls, thereby providing several openings for vertical access and earth-moving operations. Alternatively, steel lattice columns are built to rest on small temporary bases, and support waling slabs as excavation continues downward, leaving a central core open for earth moving. When the final excavation level is reached, the column loads are transmitted to a raft and the center core is built from the bottom up.

Useful data from applications in the United States are given by Becker (1990).

References

Allen, D. N. de G., and R. T. Severn, 1960: "The Stresses in Foundation Rafts I," *Proc. Inst. Civ. Eng.,* vol. 15, pp. 35–48, discussion vol. 17, pp. 339–350.

Allen, D. N. de G., and R. T. Severn, 1961: "The Stresses in Foundation Rafts II," *Proc. Inst. Civ. Eng.,* vol. 20, pp. 293–304.

Allen, D. N. de G., 1963: "The Stresses in Foundation Rafts III," *Proc. Inst. Civ. Eng.,* vol. 25, pp. 257–266.

Barda, F., J. M. Hanson, and W. G. Corley, 1977: "Shear Strength of Low-Rise Walls with Boundary Elements," ACI SP-53, Detroit, p. 149.

Becker, J. M., 1990: "Up/Down Construction—Decision Making and Performance," Design and Performance of Earth Retaining Structures, Proc. ASCE Specialty Conf., Ithaca, N.Y., June, pp. 170–189.

Benjamin, J. R., and H. A. Williams, 1957: "The Behavior of One-Story Reinforced Concrete Shear Walls," *ASCE J. Struct. Div.,* ST-3, vol. 83, May, p. 1.

Bertero, V. V., 1972: "Ductility and Seismic Response," Proc., Planning and Design of Tall Buildings, Lehigh University, August, vol. Ib, pp. 303–309.

Bowles, J. E., 1988: *Foundation Analysis and Design,* McGraw-Hill, New York.

Blume, J. A., N. M. Newmark, and L. H. Corning, 1961: *Design of Multistory Reinforced Concrete Buildings for Earthquake Motions,* Portland Cement Assoc., Skokie, Ill., 318 pp.

Cardenas, A. E., and D. D. Magura, 1973: "Strength of High-Rise Shear Walls—Rectangular Cross Section," Response of Multistory Concrete Structures to Lateral Forces, ACI SP-36, Detroit, p. 119.

Carrier, D. W., and J. T. Christian, 1971: "Rigid Circular Plate Resting on a Non-Homogeneous Elastic Half-Space," submitted to *Geotechnique.*

Cheung, Y. K., and D. K. Nag, 1968: "Beams and Plates on Elastic Foundations—Linear and Non-Linear Behavior," *Geotechnique,* vol. 18, no. 2, June, pp. 250–260.

Cheung, Y. K., and O. C. Zienkiewicz, 1965: Plates and Tanks on Elastic Foundations—An Application of the Finite Element Method, *Int. J. Solids Struct.,* Vol. 1, pp. 451–461.

Christian, J. T., 1972: "Soil-Structure Interaction," Proc., Planning and Design of Tall Buildings, Lehigh University, August, vol. Ia, pp. 967–983.

Clough, G. W. and T. D. O'Rourke, 1990: "Construction Induced Movements of In situ Walls." Design and Performance of Earth Retaining Structures, *Proc. ASCE Specialty Conf.,* Ithaca, N.Y., p. 439–470.

Clough, G. W., Smith, E. M., and B. P. Sweeney, 1989: "Movement Control of Excavation Support Systems by Iterative Design." *Foundation Engineering: Current Principles and Practices,* vol. 2, ASCE, N.Y., pp. 869–882.

Cunningham, J., and J. I. Fernandez, 1972: "Performance of Two Slurry Wall Systems in Chicago," Proc. ASCE Conf. Performance Earth Earth-Supported Structure, Purdue University.

De Beer, E., 1957: "The Influence of the Width of a Foundation Raft on the Longitudinal Distribution of the Soil Reactions," *Proc. 4th Int. Conf. Soil Mech. Found. Eng.,* London, vol. 1, pp. 269–274.

Fenoux, Y., 1971: "Deep Excavations in Built-up Areas," Soletanche Enterprises, Paris.

Gibson, R. E., 1967: "Some Results Concerning Displacements and Stresses in a Non-Homogeneous Elastic Half-Space," *Geotechnique,* vol. 17, pp. 58–67.

Gibson, R. E., P. T. Brown, and K. R. F. Andrews, 1972: Some Results Concerning Displacements in a Non-Homogeneous Elastic Layer, to be published in *Zeit. ang. Math. Ph.*

Harr, Milton E., J. L. Davidson, Du-Min Ho, L. E. Pombo, S. V. Romaswamy, and J. C. Rosner, 1969: "Euler Beams on Two Parameter Foundation Models," *ASCE J. Soil Mech. Found. Div.,* vol. 95 (SM3), May, pp. 933–948.

Hashiba, Tomonori, and R. V. Whitman, 1968: "Soil-Structure Interaction During Earthquakes," *Soils Found.,* vol. 8, no. 2, June, pp. 1–12.

Heil, H., 1969: "Studies on the Structural Rigidity of Reinforced Concrete Building Frames on Clay," *Proc. 7th Int. Conf. Soil Mech. Found. Eng.,* Mexico, vol. II, pp. 115–121.

Hetenyi, M., 1946: *Beams on Elastic Foundation,* University of Michigan Press, Ann Arbor.

Hodgson, T., 1974: "Design and Construction of a Diaphragm Wall on Victoria Street," London, *Proc. Diaphragm Walls Anchorages, Inst. Civ. Eng.,* London.

Klein, G. K., and A. E. Duraev, 1971: The Effects of the Increase of Modulus of Deformation of Soil with Increasing Depth for Calculation of Beams on a Continuous Foundation (in Russian), Gidrotekhniskoie Stroitelstro, June, pp. 19–21.

Lee, I. K., and H. B. Harrison, 1970: "Structure and Foundation Interaction Theory," *ASCE J. Struct. Div.,* vol. 96 (ST2), February, pp. 177–197.

Lytton, R. L., and K. T. Meyer, 1971: "Stiffened Mats on Expansive Clay," *ASCE J. Soil Mech. Found. Div.,* vol. 97 (SM7), July, pp. 999–1019.

Ohsaki, Y., 1969: Effects of Local Soil Conditions upon Earthquake Damage, Soil Dynamics, *Proc. Spec. Sess. 2, 7th Int. Conf. Soil Mech. Found. Eng.,* Mexico, pp. 3–32.

Paulay, T., 1977: "Ductility of Reinforced Concrete Shear Walls for Seismic Areas," ACI SP 53, Detroit, p. 727.

Paulay, T., and M. J. N. Priestley, 1992: "Seismic Design of Reinforced Concrete and Masonry Buildings," Wiley, New York.

Prakash, S., and H. D. Sharma, 1990: *Pile Foundations in Engineering Practice,* Wiley, New York.

Puller, M. J., 1974: "Economics of Basement Construction," *Proc. Diaphragm Walls Anchorages, Inst. Civ. Eng.,* London.

Schnabel, H., 1971: "Sloped Sheeting," *Civ. Eng.,* vol. 41, no. 2, pp. 48–50.

Seed, H. B., 1969: "The Influence of Local Soil Conditions on Earthquake Damage, Soil Dynamics," *Proc. Sess. 2, 7th Int. Conf. Soil Mech. Found. Eng.,* Mexico, pp. 33–66.

Seed, H. B., and I. M. Idriss, 1969: "Influence of Soil Conditions on Ground Motions During Earthquakes," *ASCE J. Soil Mech. Found. Div.,* vol. 95 (SM1), January, pp. 99–137.

Seed, H. B., I. M. Idriss, and H. Dezfulian, 1970: Relationships between Soil Conditions and Building Damage in the Caracas Earthquake of July 29, 1967, University of California, Berkeley, Earthquake Eng. Res. Center Report EERC70-2, to Presidential Commission, February.

Structural Engineers Association of California, 1967: "Recommended Lateral Force Requirements and Commentary," San Francisco.

Sved, G., and H. L. Kwok, 1963: "The Effect of Non-Linear Foundation Settlement on the Distribution of Bending Moments in a Building Frame," *Proc. 4th Aust.-N.Z. Conf. Soil Mech. Found. Eng.*, Adelaide, pp. 18–22.

Terzaghi, K., 1955: "Evaluation of Coefficients of Subgrade Reaction," *Geotechnique,* vol. 5, pp. 297–326.

Vesic, A., 1961: "Beams on Elastic Subgrade and the Winkler's Hypothesis," *Proc. 5th Int. Conf. Soil Mech. Found. Eng.*, Paris, vol. I, pp. 845–850.

Vlasov, V. Z., and U. N. Leont'ev, 1966: *Beams, Plates, and Shells on Elastic Foundations,* Translated under Israel Program for Scientific Translations, Jerusalem, Orig. Pub. in Russian in Moscow.

Whitman, R. B., 1969: Effect of Soil Conditions upon Damage to Structures—Caracas Earthquake of July 29, 1967 (in English and Spanish), report to Presidential Comm., November 1969.

Winkler, E., 1867: *The Laws of Elasticity and Strength* (in German), H. Dominicus, Prague, pp. 182–184.

Xanthakos, P. P., 1979: *Slurry Walls,* McGraw-Hill, New York.

Xanthakos, P. P., 1991: *Ground Anchors and Anchored Structures,* Wiley, New York.

Zeevaert, L., 1972: "Design of Compensated Foundations," *Proc. Planning and Design of Tall Buildings,* Lehigh University, August, vol. Ia, pp. 853–880.

10

Other Uses and Applications

10-1 Utility Tunnels

General considerations

Utility tunnels are structures containing more than one public utility system. They have been used abroad, but in the United States response has been slow, and often uncertain.

The concept is particularly adaptable with cut-and-cover transportation tunnels. The resulting benefits are less disruption time of surface activities combined with economic advantages for the entities operating the services. Utility tunnels should be considered where new utility services are contemplated either concurrently or at some future time. However, the concept is not always applicable, and may even be objectionable with a restricted right-of-way or, conversely, with a wide right-of-way that allows the complete relocation of utilities.

The incentives for utility tunnels abroad have varied. In Japan and Germany, where utility tunnels have been built more frequently, three main factors have contributed to the choice: (1) both countries suffered extensive damage during World War II that required complete reconstruction of utilities; (2) rapid urban growth has occurred and rapidly increased the demand for modern utility services; and (3) both countries have supported the policy of reducing the incidence of street cuts because of new installations.

The feasibility of the installations usually is determined from a combined analysis of technical, economic, and operational considerations. A concurrent need for a new transit line and utility is a positive aspect, but the potential of gas explosion or utility interference can lead to the idea's being rejected. Considerable work has been done here and abroad to identify the merits as well as the objectionable aspects of the concept, but no conclusions can be drawn yet. With the exception of sewers, almost every utility type may be included in the same tunnel, usually in the upper chamber. The gravity-flow sewer system is excluded mainly because of grade requirements, normally incompatible with the subway profile, although successful examples are reported in urban areas.

Utility safety.   Functional and safety-system failure has been the main concern in utility tunnels. Problems can also arise if the structure is not structurally sound. In particular, differential settlement may be the cause of problems, even if it does not cause structural damage, since it can affect utility function and increase maintenance cost. A second problem, less frequent but more serious, is explosion at street level.

Insufficient space in the tunnel will result in operational deficiencies, difficulties in making repairs, problems in transporting equipment, and utility damage. A further problem can arise from vibrations and impact caused by rail or vehicular traffic moving along the roof of the tunnel. Unless the supporting frame has a damping effect, impact can eventually loosen pipe joints and service connections, with accompanying utility damage. Some concern has also been expressed about the watertightness of a utility tunnel. If the seepage is excessive, it will require frequent pumping and may create unfavorable humidity conditions.

Examples of utility tunnels

Bourse Station, Brussels.   This station was built in cut-and-cover using diaphragm walls and prefounded columns. A main phase was to transfer two existing elliptical sewers, shown in Fig. 10-1a, to a lower level in order to utilize the space for the mezzanine floor of the station.

Three main stages of the construction are shown in Fig. 10-1. Stage I, shown in Fig. 10-1a, involves the construction of the diaphragm walls and the installation of the exterior prefounded columns. The permanent slab at street level is placed along the outer lanes, and is supported by the walls and the columns while a small section is cantilevered as shown. In stage 2, shown in Fig. 10-1b, the center prefounded columns are installed, followed by the completion of the center section of the street decking. The excavation is then carried under roof, and while this is done the existing sewers are underpinned. Stage 3 is shown in Fig. 10-1c. During this stage, the subway structure is completed, and this includes all the floors and various compartments

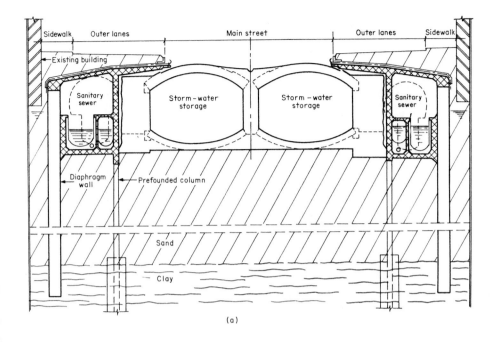

(a)

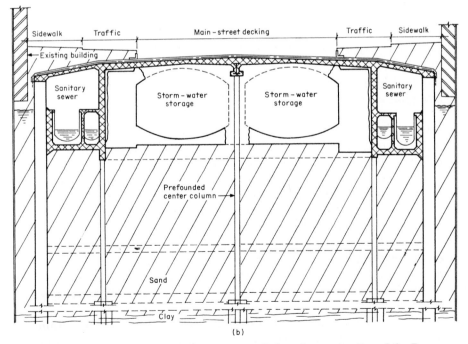

(b)

Figure 10-1 The concept of utility tunnel as applied to the construction of the Bourse Station in Brussels: (a), (b), and (c) Construction phases. (*Franki.*)

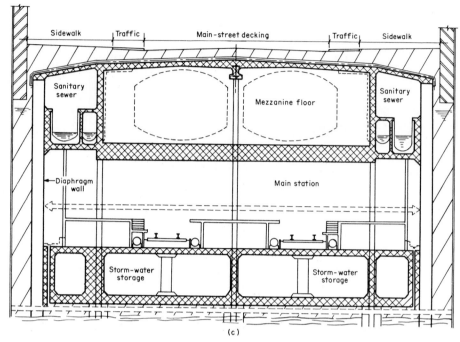

Figure 10-1 (*Continued*)

below track level for the relocated sewers. The new storage space consists of four separate sections. Note that because of grade requirements the sanitary sewers are rearranged but maintained at the initial level.

Utility tunnel in Osaka. This is a relatively deep and narrow tunnel built in cut-and-cover along the center of a street in the commercial center of the city. A typical section of the structure is shown in Fig. 10-2*a*. The upper chamber houses cables for communication services, electrical distribution systems, gas lines, and water mains. The lower chamber accommodates a circular sewer placed as an independent unit so that its profile satisfies the hydraulic requirements.

The construction was mainly in water-bearing ground, consisting essentially of fine loose silt. The ground surface in the immediate vicinity shows a normal consolidation settlement of 10 to 20 mm/year (0.4 to 0.8 in), and the contractor was required to ensure protection of existing buildings during construction and provide liability for possible damage. Diaphragm walls were used as ground support and tunnel walls, except at intersections where bored piles were more advantageous and flexible. The walls have an embedment about 5 m (16.5 ft)

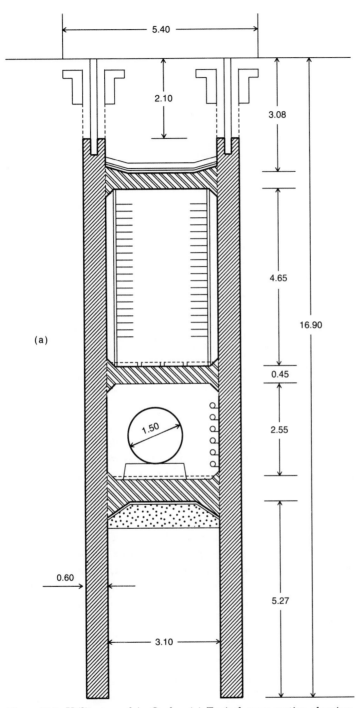

Figure 10-2 Utility tunnel in Osaka: (a) Typical cross section showing utility arrangement. (b) Detail of construction joints (dimensions in meters).

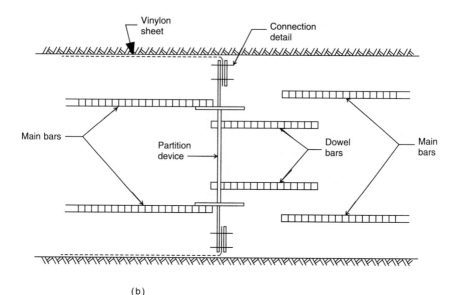

(b)

Figure 10-2 (*Continued*)

below excavation level, and during excavation they were braced at four levels. Maximum observed movement was 1.7 cm (0.67 in).

Because of the sensitivity of the utilities to differential settlement, structural continuity was essential across construction joints between panels, and is provided by the use of a partition plate that allows bars from adjoining panels to be spliced. This detail was executed as shown in Fig. 10-2*b*.

During excavation for the right diaphragm wall trench stability was checked using the conventional analysis presented in Chap. 3. However, trench excavation for the left wall was close to the right diaphragm wall, already in place. Because of the close proximity, this wall interfered with the sliding wedge, changing both the active and resisting forces along the face of the trench so that the analysis of stability had to be modified accordingly. Likewise, wall stability below excavation level was not based on passive resistance since the two wedges from either side intercept. The soil mass between the two walls was treated as compressible material squeezed between two rigid boundaries.

10-2   Underground Parking

Besides providing parking areas in the underground portion of buildings, commercial or residential underground parking garages are also built as independent facilities. The main problem in this case is the availability of suitable property at reasonable initial cost or rent that can be recovered from the intended use.

Provisions for underground parking are made in the planning stage. The chief objective of the space allocation subsystem is to minimize the costs of interaction between activities and to maximize the efficiency with which the floor space is used. This implies making available as much space as possible for rentable activities considering also the initial cost. Thus the planning process must iterate through the design subsystems, feeding back information of each iteration to the allocation model. Convergence of this process is determined when the efficiency of the floor space becomes constant.

In general, a specific model is developed to accomplish optimum allocations of user activities to zones within a building. The objective is to establish the total benefits less costs of establishing and maintaining the activities of the spaces, and those of the interactions between these activities. The list includes user activities together with the necessary services such as mechanical facilities and parking. The cost-benefit model may be developed in linear terms in the objective function, or it may be more complex. In any case, this topic is beyond the scope of this book. Instead, the parking concept will be presented in three different examples to demonstrate the structural possibilities in the uses of underground space.

Underground parking for buildings

Figure 10-3 shows a typical section through a building with three parking levels placed underground. Besides height limitations and restrained foundation access, a variety of structural permutations were necessary, including core structures, rigid frames, and pinned-end frames.

As is common with all basement car parks, minimum headroom is necessary to reduce excavation depths, a point of special importance in this case since sandstone rock existed relatively near the surface. The best floor system is therefore a flat slab rather than an arrangement of beams and slabs.

The choice of column type is mutually dependent on the slab design. Reinforced columns are considered but rejected because of overall size compared with structural steel columns. A problem in this case is the connection of flat-plate reinforced-concrete slabs to steel columns. Since steel columns are also suitable for the superstructure concept, the designers initiated a research project to investigate concrete slab-steel column interaction. This program involved finite-element analyses and full-scale tests.

For a column spacing of 22.5 ft and a flat slab thickness of 9 in, the span-to-depth ratio is 30, meaning that shear stresses around a col-

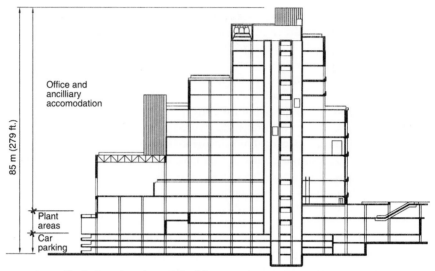

Figure 10-3 Typical section through building.

umn are excessive. The design has incorporated, therefore, steel stubs of I section bolted to the columns and cast with the slab. A tapered drop panel is thus provided around the columns to carry and distribute the shear.

For this example, a continuous ventilation gap between the perimeter wall and the parking levels was required. This gap can also be used as access for pumping water and foam directly from ground level. Because the diaphragm walls are braced only at the top and bottom, they are posttensioned.

Circular underground parking garage

The Bloomsbury Square underground parking garage in London provides off-street parking in a congested central area. The garage is a drum-shaped structure entirely below ground level, having a 160-ft outside diameter diaphragm wall about 65 ft deep that provides seven parking levels. The facility houses a pair of interleaved spiral access and parking ramps 52 ft wide, surrounding a central service core that contains a system of lifts, stairways, and other facilities. A typical cross section of the garage is shown in Fig. 10-4.

Interestingly, the diaphragm wall technique was just introduced in Britain when the garage project was conceived. With the technique available, the concept of superimposed double helical ramps with interlocking cross-overs was evolved, developed, and first applied to this structure.

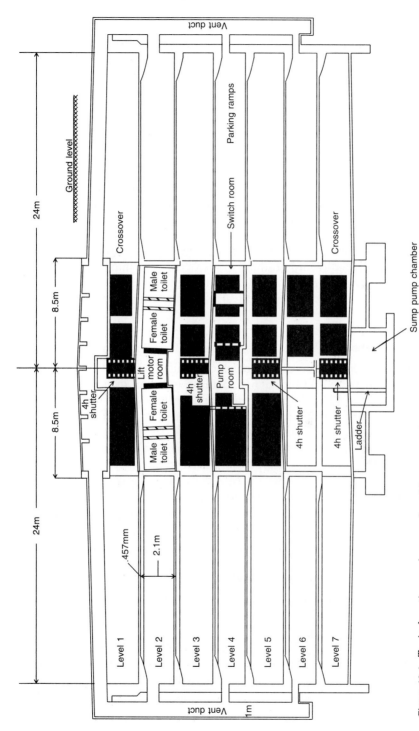

Figure 10-4 Typical section, underground parking garage, London.

Problems associated with existing conditions included the requirement of maintaining the groundwater level during construction to
avoid damage to the landscape. Severe restrictions on working space
and plant facilities were imposed by the small construction site.

The design of the permanent structure stipulated a 24-in-thick diaphragm wall built along a circular alignment, and braced with the
floor slabs at the parking levels. The initial design was reconsidered
and the structure was redesigned using a 32-in-thick wall. The extra
wall thickness ensured wall stability during excavation without the
need for temporary bracing with ground anchors. This decision, based
on a predicted performance of the wall as a circular ring, accelerated
construction by improving the pace of work. The overall advantages
related to the totally unobstructed interior of the structure during
excavation.

During excavation the wall was monitored for lateral movement.
The accumulated record gradually revealed a deformation pattern that
gave no indication of any local distortion in the circular shape of the
wall, and hence the ability of the structure to carry hoop stresses was
sustained.

Elliptical enclosures

For independent structures circular configurations or elliptical shapes
satisfy structural and functional requirements. An example of the latter type is the 11-story underground garage shown in Fig. 10-5. This
facility is built inside an elliptical enclosure supported by diaphragm
walls. The elongated shape of the structure accommodates a symmetrical arrangement of two rows of parking, one on each side of the
central access core. The curved configuration of the structural support
consolidates external lateral stresses in primary compression. This
plan offers good solutions where parking must be provided in small
sites that exclude access ramps. It requires, however, elaborate vertical lifts that can also move horizontally to move cars in and out of
the garage.

10-3   Industrial and Service Installations

A large number of industrial facilities, waterworks, sewage works, and
service installations have structures built below grade. Examples are
intakes for thermoelectric power stations near the sea, lakes, and rivers; hydroelectric power stations; pumping stations; sewage treatment
plants; water-cooling facilities; underground vaults to house industrial
machinery; tanks and reservoirs; and deep shafts. Structural analysis
of these structures according to the intended purpose and use may
lead to overlapping. In principle the enclosure for a pumping station

Figure 10-5 Interior of a box-shaped underground elliptical parking garage in Milan, showing the access core for the elevators and the parking levels. (*ICOS.*)

or a power station may be controlled by the same structural requirements. Likewise a circular reservoir, a circular gas tank, and a circular tar tank may have a similar design. Hence these structures are identified here according to use, and are treated in subsequent sections according to shape, construction details, and loads.

Interlocking enclosures

If a facility must be wholly placed underground and has a plan layout that can fit within an enclosure wall, a viable solution is a circular structure. If machinery and functions must be spread irregularly, a good solution can be provided with interlocking enclosures. These consist of two intersecting circular structures that divide the plan into two or more sections without sacrificing the advantages of circular walls or making the structure larger than need be.

Figure 10-6 shows the perimeter enclosure wall for the Beckton surface water pumping station (England), consisting of two separate cir-

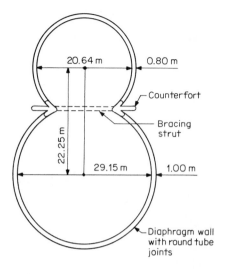

Figure 10-6 Interlocking circular enclosures for the Beckton (England) surface-water pumping station.

cular structures interlocking as shown. At their intersecting points the structures have common panels with counterforts, whereas permanent struts extend inside across the common chord to resist the compression forces.

Tanks and reservoirs

Figure 10-7 shows new versions of tank construction for storage of industrial liquids, as gasholder tanks, tar tanks, and the like. In Fig.

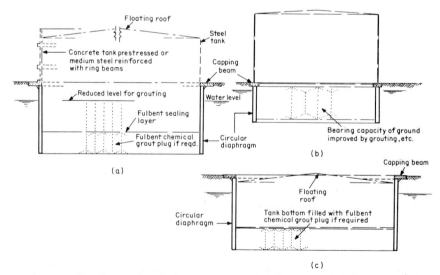

Figure 10-7 New forms of tank construction: (*a*) Diaphragm tank below ground supporting concrete or steel upper structure. (*b*) Circular diaphragm supporting steel tank in soft ground. (*c*) Diaphragm tank below ground.

10-7a the facility consists of a diaphragm wall below ground, extending above ground as a separate steel or concrete structure. In Fig. 10-7b the circular diaphragm wall is the foundation of a steel tank. This solution may be necessary in soft ground, and is compared with the cost of excavation and a mat foundation. The tank shown in Fig. 10-7c is completely below ground.

It appears from the foregoing that the selection of a suitable structural system for underground storage of liquids and gases is sensitive to environmental regulations. Whereas many substances are not injurious to concrete, some are distinctly harmful, i.e., all acids and many salts. In these cases the concrete must be protected, either by special linings and acid-resisting cements or by coating with asphalt, paraffin wax, lead linings, mixtures of pitch and tar, and the like.

Where storage tanks are permanent installations at fixed locations, circular concrete tanks below ground should be considered over steel tanks above ground for the storage of crude oil and its products. Cement should not be expected to harm the oil, and a concrete floor at the bottom is useful in protecting the tank from rust caused by water separating from the oil.

With relatively large or deep tanks, even when very dense concrete has been used and utmost care exercised during construction, losses have occurred when volatile liquids, i.e., petroleum, percolate through the finished structure, particularly in ground with low water table. The resulting pollution warrants every precaution and measure to prevent this problem. Suggested solutions include a double wall separated by a void space from the exterior wall, and a false bottom. The cavities in the wall and the floor are filled with water, and its hydrostatic pressure prevents the liquid from leaking.

Deep shafts

The advantages of polygonal enclosures are best utilized in the construction of deep and medium- to small-diameter shafts for mining, ventilation, access, and hydraulic purposes. Usually these shafts are built in two- or three-sided panels. In order to avoid lack of structural contact that may cause some movement, the construction joints are grouted from within as the wall is exposed. Grouting is also mandatory in water-bearing ground. Where the load action is uncertain, structural continuity at the joints is recommended (see also Sec. 1-9).

When the perimeter diaphragm wall of the shaft is built and before starting excavation of the core, it is advantageous to install drainage wells to reduce hydrostatic pressure and the tendency for bottom heave, and also to allow core excavation in the dry. Some difficulties will arise if it is not possible to lower the water table inside the shaft and the excavation must continue below that level. In some instances the bottom slab may have to be placed underwater, and in order to

Figure 10-8 Panoramic view of an access shaft for the Mersey River underpass in Liverpool. (*ICOS.*)

make the connection with the walls divers may have to be used. Some special attention must be given to the stability of the main earth core while excavating a multisided panel, particularly if another panel is still open and the rig operates inside the core.

A polygonal shaft is shown in Fig. 10-8. This shaft is 63 ft deep (19 m) and has a diameter of 27 ft (8.2 m). It provided ventilation and exhaust for the second underpass beneath the Mersey River in Liverpool. The wall sides are merely keyed into underlying rock and terminated at this level. The main excavation was carried down using conventional equipment but was continued by blasting when it reached rock.

10-4 Design Considerations, Deep Shafts

Lateral earth stresses and load factors

In general it is assumed that lateral earth pressures develop under conditions of no lateral deformation. Hence the coefficient K_0 is an essential parameter in the design of deep shafts. Because of the usually considerable depth to which these structures are constructed, reliable estimates of K_0 values are warranted.

In addition to the empirical expression proposed by Jaky [formulated by Eq. (4-14)], and the modified form suggested by Brooker and Ireland (1965), Rowe has proposed the so-called $c_e = 0$ hypothesis for the equilibrium state of normally consolidated clays subjected to a sustained shear stress smaller than that necessary to cause failure. Under these conditions a clay mass would creep, and its ultimate lateral pressure on a restraining boundary would be related only to the true frictional strength component. Within the context of this hypothesis, Rowe derived the expression

$$K_0 = \tan^2 \left(45 - \frac{\phi_{em}}{2} \right) \tag{10-1}$$

where ϕ_{em} = angle of shear strength mobilized at rest, which can be taken approximately equal to the Hvorsley (1960) angle of true friction ϕ_e for most normally consolidated clays. A correlation between ϕ_{em} and ϕ' would be most useful in practical applications because the measurement of ϕ_e required tedious work. Based on a number of triaxial tests, Abdelhamid and Krizek (1976) derived the expression

$$\phi_e = 1.15(\phi' - 9) \tag{10-2}$$

which reflects results that can be reasonably fitted by a straight line. In this expression ϕ_e and ϕ' are given in degrees. For normally consolidated soils the use of an effective friction angle to determine K_0 indirectly appears to be practical, and Jaky's formula shows good agreement with direct measurements.

For overconsolidated soils the K_0 values may be estimated as suggested by Mayne and Kulhawy (1982). By reviewing data from over 170 different soils, these investigators established that K_0 behavior during virgin compression, rebound, and reload can be represented approximately by a simple empirical relationship. Statistical analysis provided the expression

$$K_{ou} = K_0(\text{OCR})^{\sin \phi'} \tag{10-3}$$

where K_{ou} = coefficient at rest for overconsolidated soil; K_0 = coefficient at rest for normally consolidated soil ($K_0 = 1 - \sin \phi'$); and OCR = overconsolidated ratio or maximum previous vertical pressure divided by current effective vertical pressure. Typical values of K_0 corresponding to various values of OCR are given in Table 4-14.

Likewise, the passive earth pressure coefficient K_p for overconsolidated soils may be assumed to be the upper limit of K_{ou}. This defines a limiting value of OCR above which at rest conditions do not apply and passive pressure is mobilized. For simplicity, it is assumed that $K_p = (1 + \sin \phi')/(1 - \sin \phi')$. When $K_{ou} = K_p$, it follows from Eq. (10-3) that the limiting value of OCR for at rest condition is

$$\text{OCR}_{\text{limit}} = \left[\frac{1 + \sin \phi'}{(1 - \sin \phi)^2} \right]^{1/\sin \phi'} \tag{10-4}$$

An obvious conclusion from the foregoing is that a reliable estimate of K_0 is a prime design criterion of deep shafts because (1) the depth is usually considerable and exceeds 100 ft; and (2) the lateral earth pressure combined with water pressure is the governing loading condition. For these reasons it is suggested to use the upper range of values for load coefficients related to earth pressure, shown in Table 4-11, if strength design is used.

Structural aspects

Configurations. The evolvement of the polygonal configuration is shown in Fig. 1-35. The usual design and construction practice is to provide a continuous structure joint with through reinforcement every two to three chord panels, or use I beams as construction joint at the corners of panels. The two versions are shown in Fig. 10-9 (see also Sec. 1-9). Although the geometry, construction procedure, and loading conditions in the two versions are essentially similar, the structural response is much different.

The shaft section shown in Fig. 10-9a is a closed ring that resists external lateral stresses primarily in compression. However, since the pressures act normally on the chord sides, flexural effects are also produced and must be resisted internally by tension reinforcement. Bending can also be generated by unsymmetrical loading causing elastic deformations from the initial shape. The design of the shaft requires an estimation of loads and load effects, and selection of a suitable section with appropriate reinforcement to provide the required structural capacity. Shafts continuously reinforced are recommended for large diameters, small deflection angles between adjoining chords, and where unsymmetrical loading is expected.

The shaft section shown in Fig. 10-9b is initially treated as a curved shell or folded plate constructed in chord segments. The panels are structurally discontinuous at the I-beam junction where they can only transfer axial compressive thrust. In the final loading condition each segment acts independently, and the joints are assumed to be maintained tight under the effect of outside pressures. Sufficient thickness must be provided to resist hoop stresses as in a circular ring, but the

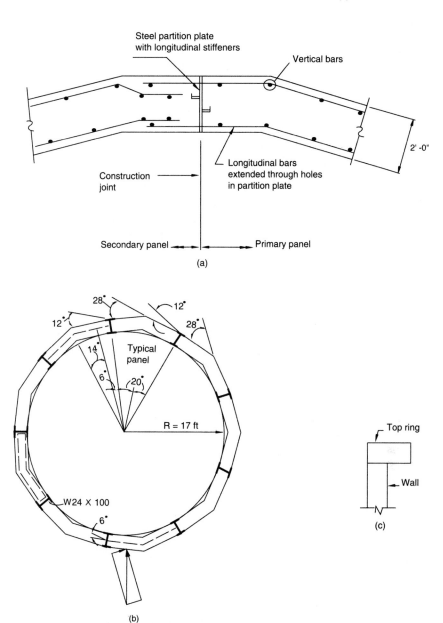

Steel partition plate
with longitudinal stiffeners

Vertical bars

2' -0"

Construction
joint

Longitudinal bars
extended through holes
in partition plate

Secondary panel

Primary panel

(a)

28°

12°

12°

28°

14°

Typical
panel

6°

20°

R = 17 ft

W24 × 100

6°

Top ring

Wall

(c)

(b)

Figure 10-9 Details and construction joint for polygonal shafts: (*a*) Joint at midpanel (chord) with continuous reinforcement. (*b*) Joint at corner with steel I beams. (*c*) Capping beam functioning as top ring.

usual practice is to provide horizontal reinforcement assuming each panel to act as a simple beam simply supported at the I-beam joints. These bending moments are therefore controlled by the panel length and the location of I-beam sections, and may be further reduced if different deflection angles are provided in the panels, as shown in Fig. 10-9b.

The overall stability against the effects of unsymmetrical loading is better maintained if the shaft is structurally continuous, as in Fig. 10-9a. However, for either scheme the structural performance is greatly improved if the walls penetrate into rock or dense material at the bottom, and if a stiff ring is provided at the top as a capping beam, as shown in Fig. 10-9c. With top and bottom support each panel behaves as an ideal folded plate and can resist flexural effects in both the vertical and the lateral direction. The ring beam at the top can be designed to resist slippage of the joints, and panel distortion from geometric imperfections and uneven pressures. A reinforced slab at the base can provide permanent protection against bottom heave and hydrostatic uplift, and also serves as additional bottom lateral bracing.

The combined function of shafts articulates two design requirements, so that the structure must resist loads during the construction phase and service conditions. Loads during the construction phase include earth and water pressures, distributed surcharges from live loads acting alongside the shaft, and commonly heavy weights suspended at the top and associated with construction operations. Service conditions include the same loads, and a frequently heavier localized surcharge.

Structural action.   The configurations shown in Fig. 10-9b may be considered a typical folded plate. The principal structural elements are: (1) a slab spanning transversely between folds; (2) slanting plates spanning vertically from top to bottom support; and (3) an edge member consisting of the steel I beam.

Figure 10-10 shows profiles of the two common types of configurations used in deep shafts, the two-element and the three-element

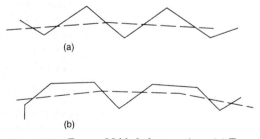

(a)

(b)

Figure 10-10   Types of folded plate sections: (a) Two-element. (b) Three-element.

plate. Assuming that the shaft has a top stiff beam and embedment in hard or dense material, each two-sided or three-sided panel can be designed as a beam spanning longitudinally and as slab spanning transversely. A factor to be considered is the relative movement of the joint. If all plates have the same depth and configuration, and have the same lateral load, then there will be no relative deflection. However, with geometric imperfections and unsymmetrical loading, the end plates may be affected by the relative deflection of valleys and ridges with respect to the joint beam. This may be so great that both longitudinal stresses and transverse moments will be affected.

Referring to Fig. 10-11, the two-sided polygon is supported at the ends in such a manner that it can exert lateral thrust as well as vertical forces against the supports. By definition this is a two-hinged arch, since the member is not restrained against rotation at the ends. However, the arch shape is not necessarily of the structural form necessary to avoid the introduction of bending moments.

Given the span l and the rise h, the correct chord line for the ideal arch shape will depend on the loads alone. For the given arch shape of Fig. 10-11 (two chords between support points), this means that there is only one set of loads along the shaft height to which the arch responds by compressive action. Hence flexural stresses are induced all along the height of the panel in the transverse direction, except at some specific q value causing the ideal truss action.

As an approximate but conservative method of analysis, shears, horizontal thrusts, and bending moments may be computed from rigid frame formulas. Assuming a uniform load q over the entire frame as shown in Fig. 10-11, load effects are computed from the following:

$$M_B = \frac{-ql^2}{32} \qquad M_{\max} = \frac{ql^2}{512}$$

$$V_A = V_c = \frac{ql}{2} \qquad H_A = H_c = \frac{5ql^2}{32h} \tag{10-5}$$

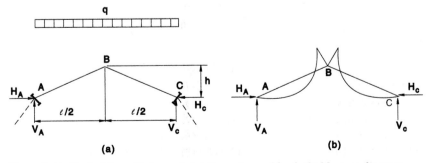

Figure 10-11 Typical two-sided panel: (a) Geometry and load. (b) Moment diagram.

The assumptions that justify the use of the foregoing formulas are: (1) the panel acts independently from the rest of the shaft; (2) there is no displacement of the supports; (3) the influence of axial and shear force is neglected; and (4) the ratio h/l is large enough to warrant frame action. The supporting beam is subjected to the action of the V_A and H_A components along the axis of principal bending and should be designed for these loads.

The positive moment from Eq. (10-5) is smaller than in the simple beam formulas, nonetheless justified since the compressive action of the shaft is ignored. For the structurally continuous shaft shown in Fig. 10-9a, the usual practice is to fit a circular ring of thickness t within the area confined by the chord perimeters until the resulting ideal circular shaft can resist compressive hoop stress computed from $p = rq$ where r is the radius of the ring and q maximum soil pressure. In this process the outside chord perimeter is moved until the required t is provided. In this manner a satisfactory shaft thickness is obtained. However, a minimum transverse reinforcement should again be provided to resist positive flexural stresses. This reinforcement may be computed from Eq. (10-5) using l = length of two adjoining chords.

Both configurations of Fig. 10-9 have considerable structural capacity in the vertical plane because of folded plate action, and this characteristic should be used to the full advantage by providing a nominal vertical reinforcement, distributed preferably in the corner regions and along the tension side of the shaft.

The use of refined methods of analysis is not warranted because of the uncertainties associated with the effect of boundary conditions, geometric imperfection, differential deflections, and unsymmetrical loading.

10-5 Design Considerations, Circular Enclosures

General principles and criteria

The analysis and design of circular walls built underground is usually based on the assumption that the finished structure, when acted upon by exterior lateral pressures, will behave essentially as a compression ring. The compression force on a horizontal strip 1 ft deep is

$$P = r\sigma_h \tag{10-6}$$

where r = mean radius and σ_h = uniform lateral earth stress (or effective stress plus water pressure) at the depth under consideration. A trial wall thickness is thus selected and checked for its adequacy to resist the design compressive stress (for either ASD or strength design). For relatively small ratios of wall thickness to wall diameter, wall depth, or panel length, the enclosure is more likely to perform like a thin shell, so that it must be investigated for buckling behavior and buckling loads. Since the external forces usually consist of lateral as well as of considerable vertical loads, a thin wall must be analyzed for vertical compressive buckling causing plastic deformations, for torsional buckling causing twisting and buckles of a spiral shape, and for flexural buckling in both the horizontal and the vertical directions. A discussion of these topics is outside the scope of this book, and the reader is referred to the many available texts and papers on the subject.

Since the minimum practical wall thickness is seldom less than 18 in (45 cm), it follows that buckling might be a problem primarily with large-diameter enclosures. For the purpose of analysis, circular walls are conveniently grouped as follows:

- Small diameter, up to 35 ft (10 m), usually classified as polygons
- Medium diameter, 35 to 130 ft (10 to 40 m)
- Large diameter, over 130 ft (40 m)

The analysis must further consider the actual construction details, especially the type and compressibility (take-up) of the joints.

For well-constructed enclosures and in uniform loading conditions the approximate procedure usually is adequate and leads to a conservative design. Nonetheless, large-diameter walls are often overstressed or become prone to local buckling because of (1) misalignment or deviation from the true circular configuration; (2) base restraint and fixity by rigid connection to a base slab or by embedment in dense material below excavation level; and (3) nonuniform or unsymmetrical loading on the exterior face.

Model tests

Useful data regarding these effects have been obtained from representative model tests. Rigden and Rowe (1974) have investigated the stability of circular diaphragm walls, designed as thin shells in unreinforced concrete, by building 1:80 scale models and carrying out a series of centrifuge tests. The plan of the original structure, shown in Fig. 10-12a, consists of an underground car park in Amsterdam. The intermediate floors provide six parking levels and are supported on columns and a central core built independently of the exterior wall. This wall is therefore unbraced and free-standing. The inside diameter is 52.5 m (172 ft), but the diaphragm wall is only 80 cm (32 in) thick,

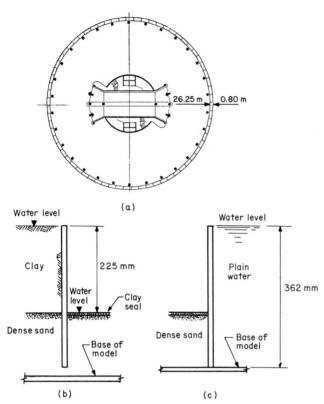

Figure 10-12 Underground car park in Amsterdam, built with a diaphragm wall circular enclosure: (*a*) Sectional plan of the actual structure. (*b*) and (*c*) Sections through model walls used to check the effect of base restraint.

giving a wall thickness to wall diameter ratio of 0.015. The excavation depth from ground level is 18 m (59 ft) and the wall is embedded about 1 m (36 ft) below excavation level in gray medium-fine sand.

Five models were tested to investigate the influence of noncircular construction, base fixity, and nonuniform loading. The results from these tests are summarized in the following sections.

Effect of base restraint. In one of the two models used to study this effect, the significant stress was the one caused by vertical bending; it was noticed at or just above excavation level, and is the direct result of fixed-end moment. This stress exceeded the tensile strength of concrete (6 N/mm²), and consequently horizontal cracks appeared at this level. The model, shown in Fig. 10-12*b*, retained an undisturbed sample of organic silty clay above its base and dense sand (corresponding to $\phi' = 40°$) in the embedded portion. During the test an excess pore pressure occurred at the center of the clay layer because a differential pressure was applied on the wall and thus increased total stress in the same zone. Without this excess head the model would have remained undamaged and free of cracks at an overload factor of 1.35.

The second model, shown in Fig. 10-12c, was tested under full water head on the exterior face, and only dense sand on the inside face below excavation level. The centrifuge was accelerated to 135g before the test was terminated. The highest vertical bending stress occurred at maximum acceleration level at about 25 mm below the base of the excavation. Collapse occurred at an overload factor of 1.67.

Effect of noncircular construction. The model for this test was similar to the one shown in Fig. 10-12b except that the clay was remolded and consolidated under a pressure of 140 kN/m². The strength parameters remained at $c = 0$, $\phi' = 31°$, and saturated density $\gamma = 1.8$ t/m³ so that the long-term pressures would be similar to those for the model of Fig. 10-12b.

The noncircular condition was simulated by increasing and decreasing two perpendicular diameters by 5 mm each, so that the new shape resembled a relatively flattened circle.

During the test the model was sustaining an external lateral load from effective earth stress and static groundwater pressure corresponding to the construction sequence of the actual structure. The centrifuge was accelerated to 80 and 102g and then stopped to examine the wall. No cracks or signs of distress were noticed. The vertical bending stress measured at 80g was again near excavation level and had values between 4 and 5 N/mm². At an overload factor of 1.3 for 102g, the maximum vertical bending tensile stress just exceeded 5 N/mm², again below the tensile strength.

Following the first cycle the test was repeated to 147g without flooding the interior of the model, and during this acceleration some swelling of the clay occurred, confirmed by the excess pore pressure recorded. The model was undamaged at 147g (corresponding to an overload factor of 1.84), with the maximum bending stress near excavation level at 5.9 N/mm², or just below the tensile strength.

Effect of nonuniform loading. The model for this test was similar to the previous. Unsymmetrical loading was introduced with the addition of two surface loads diagrammatically opposite and each acting over one-eighth of the model perimeter. When an acceleration of 80g was reached, a load of 2 t/m² was applied on two adjoining quarters, followed by a load of 4 t/m². The model was finally accelerated to 135g.

The maximum vertical bending stress at 80g before any surface load was applied ranged from 3.8 to 4.5 N/mm² at a depth of 210 mm (just above excavation level). The first surface load of 2 t/m² had little effect on the stress measured at or below excavation level, but caused a marked increase in stress in the zone 130 to 170 mm from the top. At 80g and with the two surface loads of 2 t/m² acting, the maximum stress at 210 mm was increased to 4.75 N/mm². For a nominal tensile strength of 6.0 N/mm², there was therefore a moderate decrease in the factor of safety from 1.33 to 1.26. At 80g with 4 t/m² on the surface, the maximum recorded stress was from 5.1 to 5.5 N/mm². When the model was accelerated above 80g, with both surfaces loaded, certain strain gages failed when recording a stress between 5 and 6 N/mm² at an acceleration between 85 and 110g. This is equivalent to local surface pressures of 4.25 to 5.5 t/m² and an overload of g of 1.08 to 1.38. The model was extensively cracked although structurally sound.

Conclusions.   Although these results quantify load conditions for the prototype, namely, a cylindrical unreinforced wall 0.8 m thick with a free height of 18 m, and penetrating 11 m into dense sand, some general conclusions can be drawn. If the wall is restrained at excavation level, either by connection to a rigid slab or by embedment, vertical bending stresses will develop there and must be provided for in the design. These stresses may be reduced or even eliminated by reducing the depth of penetration and hence the degree of fixity. However, embedment is recommended in most cases because it stabilizes the wall at the base and helps resist uneven distortions. If vertical bending near the excavation level is not desired, any portion of the wall below the base necessary to cut off seepage should be formed with plastic materials.

Deviations from the true circular alignment do not appear to have a critical effect on vertical bending but may give rise to horizontal bending. The effect of nonuniform, unsymmetrical loading and local surcharge at ground surface is related to the manner in which surcharge loads are distributed laterally, and may cause considerable vertical bending in the midwall sections that must be provided for by the design.

Relationship to polygonal enclosures, and design guidelines

Circular structures actually approach polygons since they are constructed along a series of chords. Those of relatively small diameter appear as true polygons in plan. The division between the two types for analysis and construction is usually arbitrary. A convenient criterion is the deflection angle of two chords meeting at a corner. If this angle is less than 15°, the structure approaches a circle. If it is greater than 15°, the structure may be looked upon as a polygon.

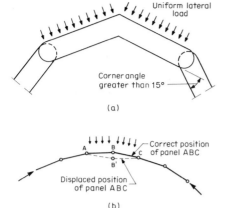

(a)

(b)

Figure 10-13 Examples of plan configurations that can influence the distribution of load and the performance of the wall: (a) Partial plan of polygonal wall. (b) Stability of a circular wall with relatively large diameter.

Figure 10-13 shows two walls that in terms of nomenclature are classified as polygons since they are built along a series of chords. By inspection, the wall shown in Fig. 10-13a is indeed a polygon in terms of analysis, and may be designed according to the principles discussed in Sec. 10-4.

The wall shown in Fig. 10-13b is by inspection an enclosure of relatively large diameter. In this case the in situ structural response may be influenced to a great extent by the manner in which the individual panels are fitted against each other and stay clamped together. Although this is not a theoretical problem, it indicates the possibility of serious distortion beyond the control of design. An example is a panel that becomes loose at one joint and moves out of position. This can happen as shown in Fig. 10-13b. The wall in this case is designed and built as a true circle very closely, and hence expected to act like a closed ring. Now consider panel ABC isolated from the structure that remains stationary and fixed. The lateral loads acting on panel ABC tend to push it inward, and if the take-up of the joints is broken the panel may become loose and start moving away to a new position $AB'C$. At this stage the structure is unstable and on the verge of complete collapse.

This problem can be avoided if (1) the panels are structurally continuous so that they can transfer transverse shear at the joints; (2) the panels can resist bending moment in the transverse direction; and (3) the structure is stable against progressive failure.

A rational design can be carried out if joint B is assumed to be misaligned and built at position B'. The dimension BB' is the permitted construction tolerance, and is usually established considering the feasible quality controls and construction capability; it usually ranges from 3 to 6 in. Let $BB' = \Delta y$ = permitted tolerance. Then panel $AB'C$

is acted upon by a compressive force P given by Eq. (10-6) and a bending moment $P\Delta y$. If P represents the factored load effects, then the reinforcement in the transverse direction is designed to provide a moment resistance so that the structural capacity of the section is sufficient under combined axial compression P and bending $P\Delta y$. Interestingly, the thickness of the wall should be large enough so that the dangerous concrete strain is not reached first; i.e., ensure ductility in the member.

Example

A circular diaphragm wall 57 m (187 ft) in diameter and 21 m (69 ft) deep has been constructed as the upper part of a vertical access shaft, for the opening of the Eurotunnel on the French side of the English channel. A typical section of the structure is shown in Fig. 10-14 (Evers and Hovart, 1991). As shown in Fig. 10-14, the tunnel consists of two 7.6-m inside diameter main tubes for the railway traffic and one 4.8-m diameter central service tube. The three tunnels are spaced at 15-m centers.

The design requirements specified a wall completely protected from groundwater effects during the complete duration of the tunnel work, in order to minimize the structural requirements and make the construction easier. During the initial stage of boring it would also be necessary to dewater to a depth of 30 m (100 ft). The solution was to consider a general impervious barrier around the shaft (the cutoff wall shown in Fig. 10-14) such that the total discharge would not exceed

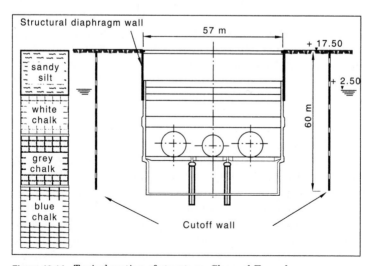

Figure 10-14 Typical section of structure, Channel Tunnel.

10 liters/s (36 m³/h). The enclosing wall is a cement-bentonite cutoff of semielliptical form with a perimeter of 482 m, 60 m deep and penetrating 3 m into blue chalk. The choice was made after a comparative study of several solutions involving grouting.

Structural diaphragm wall. The wall is 100 cm thick (40 in) and has about 50 kg/m³ of reinforcing. The circular wall is designed for two phases.

During the construction phase the wall is under the effect of lateral earth pressure and distributed surcharges; it functions as a self-supported slender arch, mainly under compressive stresses.

During service the wall is subjected to the same loads but with a heavier localized surcharge. Under the latter effects the wall must function as a vertical beam supported at the top by a stiff capping beam and at the bottom by the facing of the lower shaft.

Vertical deviation was specified less than 0.5 percent, or 10 cm (4 in), with joints structurally capable of transmitting forces without inhibiting the arching response.

The trenching operations were carried out using the Hydrofraise system discussed in Sec. 2-12, under conventional bentonite slurry, and concreting by the tremie method. Primary panels are 5.5 m long and 2.2 m apart. The construction joint between primary and secondary panels was obtained by cutting 0.1 m from the ends of the primary panels.

10-6 Selection Criteria of Waterfront Installations

Section 1-10 presented three basic types of diaphragm walls used in waterfront installations, namely, buttressed or T walls (shown in Fig. 1-36), arch-type quay walls (shown in Figs. 1-37 through 1-40), and diaphragm wall cells (either open or closed), shown in Figs. 1-41 and 1-42.

These types of facilities represent the renewed interest in waterfront development resulting from land uses, limitations in the urban core, and the need to provide modernized facilities for industrial use and other elements of urban renewal. The expansion of waterfront needs to include both marine and nonmarine uses is derived from the fact that efficient access and size of usable areas needed for modern functions are not always available in the central harbor system. Thus waterfront installations are typically needed to accommodate urban projects, industrial or major utility sites, marine terminals, and other transportation-oriented facilities and loading areas. Unlike past functions, marine terminals for storage and handling of containers or break-bulk cargo require stable structures to support delicate loads and utilities.

General guidelines.   It appears from the foregoing brief comments that the functional requirements and type of waterfront development have a marked influence on the structural system. A modern marine terminal and site preparation for urban construction or industrial use are two main examples. Details of the intended site utilization can have a major effect on type of construction and project cost. For example, for a marine terminal operation, the type and location of loading facilities must be determined and considered in the design. These factors will control the loads applied to the structure that must also withstand the impact from ships, barges, and other vessels.

Waterfront structures built to retain fill or nonmarine urban land use will not carry perimeter loads as heavy as those for a marine terminal facility. In this type of construction, the perimeter structure must support loads from retained earth, current and wave forces, floating ice, and superimposed surcharge loads from immediately behind and upon the structure.

The perimeter retaining system contributes markedly to the total cost of creating new land. The choice of perimeter structure depends mainly on planned use and anticipated life. For example, a marine terminal facility is usually developed for an economic life of 25 to 30 years and requires maximum economy in planning perimeter structures. For urban land development, longer life is commonly expected. Development of marginal land through landfill is closely associated with the selection of a waterfront wall system.

Traditional types of perimeter structures.   The traditional bulkhead walls built in harbors and along waterfront developments include the following main types.

Gravity retaining walls.   This construction has in the past provided a satisfactory bulkhead structure, and examples can be mentioned that are 100 years in age or more and are still in service. However, these walls were built in water depths considerably less than that required on many modern projects. They have a high first cost, least maintenance, and potentially longest life.

Circular sheet pile walls.   These consist of interlocking steel sheet pile cells, joined by steel sheet pile arcs, and are filled with sand, stone, concrete, or other deformation-resistant materials. Cells have provided a satisfactory and economical solution, having a medium initial cost but subject to damage from vessel impact and deterioration from corrosion.

Precast floating boxes. These are constructed of high-quality concrete, and carry a long life and relatively low maintenance. They are usually more expensive than other alternatives because the precast floating box must be built in a graving dock or basin, floated to the site, and sunk in place on a specially prepared stone bed. The local availability of such a basin is a prime factor affecting choice and cost.

Retention dikes or embankments. These involve a low first cost and facilitate future modifications and expansion, but the structure encroaches on upland area and is subject to erosion. A shear key is typically required as added resistance to lateral loads.

Anchored sheet pile bulkhead. These are common in most parts of the world. However, they may experience rapid corrosion in the presence of stray currents. Because soils at the exterior mudline are usually soft and fine-grained, the ordinary commercial sheeting cannot always sustain positive moments resulting from draft greater than about 35 ft below mean water.

Deterioration and maintenance. Corrosion of steel members in waterfront structures is maximized in tidal and splash zones and most severe near mean low water level. Corrosion losses on steel surfaces may be insignificant below the mudline if the steel is surrounded by clay, silt, and fine sand but can be severe if the steel is in contact with coarse rubble, fill, ashes, boulders, or large stones where oxygen can penetrate.

Concrete surfaces are subject to deterioration by abrasive action of moving water containing suspended materials, wedging of debris or ice, or repeated freezing and thawing of water absorbed in the pores of concrete. This action can eventually lead to corrosion of steel bars through reaction with absorbed salt water. For exposed concrete in marine structures, good mix of dense concrete, proper placing, and curing are essential.

This brief review is useful in the selection of marginal retaining structures for long-term developments for nonmarine use and commercial marine terminals. First cost, low maintenance, long life, and the presence of favorable subsoil conditions may be examined jointly and lead to a choice. This choice is enhanced with the potential use of buttressed walls, cells, and arched structures with diaphragm walls discussed in these sections.

10-7   Loads for Waterfront Structures

Loads to be considered in the design of waterfront structures are lateral earth and water pressures, current and wave forces, floating ice, superimposed surcharge loads, and impact from ships, barges, and other vessels. Seismic forces must be included in earthquake zones.

Force from floating ice.   Ice forces may be selected with reference to local conditions and expected modes of ice action as follows: (1) dynamic pressure due to moving sheets or floes of ice being carried by stream flow, wind, or currents; (2) static pressure due to thermal movements of ice sheets; (3) pressure resulting from hanging dams or jams of ice; and (4) static uplift or vertical load resulting from adhering ice in waters of fluctuating level.

Much of the material currently used to quantify floating ice effects is taken from the work of Montgomery et al. (1984) that provided background for the clauses on ice loads for the Canadian Standards Association. A useful reference is also Neill (1981). The two basic conditions that produce ice forces on waterfront structures are dynamic and static.

Dynamic forces occur when a moving ice floe strikes the structure. The imposed force depends on the size of the floe, the strength and thickness of the ice, and the geometry and individual resistance of the structure or parts therefrom. Static forces may be caused by the thermal expansion of ice in contact with the structure or by irregular growth of the ice field. The resulting ice pressure should receive special consideration while there is reason to believe that these effects are manifested.

Dynamic ice force.   The horizontal force F resulting from the pressure of moving ice may be calculated from the following:

$$F = C_n ptw \tag{10-7}$$

where C_n = coefficient related to inclination of the ice nose; p = effective ice crushing strength (lb/in^2); t = thickness of ice in contact with the structure; and w = width of structure or member at the level of ice action. Values of coefficient C_n may be taken from Table 10-1.

The effective ice strength p normally may be taken in the range of 100 to 400 lb/in^2 on the assumption that crushing or splitting of the ice takes place on contact with the structure. The value used should

TABLE 10-1   Values of Coefficient C_n

Inclination of nose to vertical, deg	C_n
0–15	1.00
15–30	0.75
30–45	0.50

also be based on the assessment of the probable ice condition at the time of movement, on previous local experience, and the expected structural performance. Further guidelines are given by Montgomery et al. (1984).

Static ice loads. Ice pressures should be investigated where the ice sheets are subject to significant thermal movement relative to the structure, or where the growth of ice on one side only can produce substantial unbalanced forces.

Vessel collision. Marine installations typically are designed for vessel impact. The vessel model, speed, and capacity to be used in design is normally specified by the user-owner of the facility. The user-owner should also specify or approve the degree of damage which the structure and its protective systems will be allowed to sustain.

The intent of vessel collision provisions is to minimize the risk of catastrophic failure. The collision impact forces represent a probabilistically based case of collision with a vessel assumed to be moving in some forward direction at some specific speed. The requirements for collision design usually are developed in conjunction with a risk acceptance alternative. The analysis considers the following factors: (1) the probability of aberrancy, defined as the causation probability or measure of the risk that the vessel is in trouble; (2) geometric probability, defined as a condition that the vessel will hit the facility given the fact that it is out of control; and (3) the probability of structural collapse, expressed as the ratio of the ultimate structural resistance to the vessel impact force.

The vessel collision impact may be taken as

$$P_s = \frac{220(\text{DWT})^{1/2}V}{27} \tag{10-8}$$

where P_s = equivalent static vessel impact force (kips); DWT = dead weight tonnage of vessel (metric tons = 2205 lb); and V = vessel impact velocity (ft/s).

For waterfront structures the determination of the impact load from a vessel collision is complex and, besides the vessel characteristics, depends on the geometry of the collision and the geometry and strength characteristics of the structure.

For design purposes, the impact force may be applied as an equivalent static force at the water level. Two cases need to be evaluated: (1) overall stability with impact activity as concentrated force at the waterline; and (2) the ability of any portion or member of the wall to withstand the collision force.

Wave action. Wave pressure against waterfront structures consists of hydrostatic pressure, which varies as the wave rises and falls along the wall, and dynamic pressure exerted by the moving water volume.

A simple method for calculating wave pressure is shown in Fig. 10-15. The parameter H is the wave height, and h_{dc} indicates the rise in the height of the center of oscillation above still-water level. The parameter p_2 is the change in pressure from the hydrostatic pressure

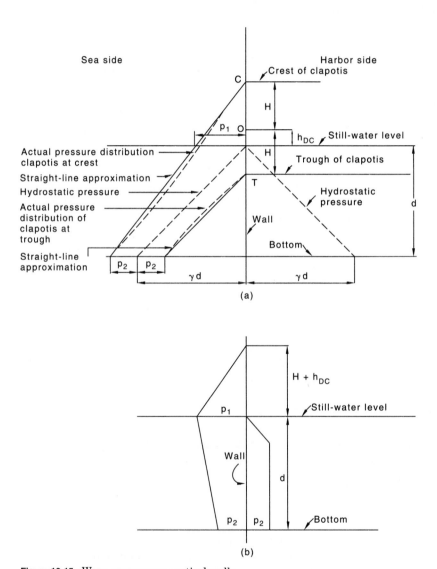

Figure 10-15 Wave pressure on vertical walls.

γd. For the wave at crest position, the wave pressure at still-water level is

$$p_1 = (\gamma d + P_2) \frac{H + h_{dc}}{H + h_{dc} + d} \qquad (10\text{-}9)$$

where

$$h_{dc} = \frac{\pi H^2}{L} \coth \frac{2\pi d}{L} \quad \text{and} \quad p_2 = \frac{\gamma H}{\cosh(2\pi d/L)}$$

where L = wavelength.

Wave action against waterfront walls would tend to have a beneficial effect on wall stability. In some instances, however, wind can produce waves that have the most influence on the design.

10-8 Design Considerations of Buttressed (T) Walls

The series of contiguous T sections like that shown in Fig. 1-36 will usually be analyzed as a stiffened cantilever and not necessarily as a gravity wall. Although a great advantage is the resulting rigidity and increased flexural capacity, the wall derives its stability by sufficient embedment below dredge line. The structural strength of the wall is maximized if the T sections are oriented as shown in Fig. 1-36. Most of the flange and probably a portion of the stem are in compression, and the reinforcement is more effective if placed at the end of the stem according to the principles of T beams.

Since the walls are designed vertically, the construction joints between T panels consists of the simple round tube. With well-executed joints there is sufficient shear resistance to accommodate any tendency of adjoining panels to move differentially. The assumption of adhesion or friction at the soil interface of the stems normally would mean that the weight of the soil column between the stems could be taken into consideration when computing the moments in the wall. A compromise in this case is to include the column weight of back soil above the dredge line in computing the balancing moments.

Stiffened cantilevers of T section are usually considered where lateral top bracing, i.e., anchorages, are not feasible. Optimum flange-stem geometry is obtained from a consideration of bending moments as they relate to the unbraced cantilever length. However, the maximum fill height that can be supported will depend also on permissible wall movement. The presence of stems, and the assumption of shear at the stem-soil interface, is beneficial in reducing movement but should not be expected to stop movement completely. Unbraced walls of this type will normally be used in nonmarine applications such as reservoir enclosures and lakefront developments.

The loading conditions are mostly critical during the construction stage, with the full height of earth acting against the wall, and the reservoir fully excavated but dry. Construction surcharges should also be included.

Embedment depth. The formulation of the problem involves essentially a vertical cantilever restrained below dredge line by passive resistance. It is essential that the dredge line be stable as the sole wall resistance is developed in this zone. A common assumption is a simple loading condition whereby the wall on the backfill side is subjected to active pressure to the dredge line. Under this influence the wall tends to rotate, developing passive pressure in front of the system and active pressure behind it. Referring to Fig. 10-16, at the pivot point b the soil behind the wall shifts from active to passive pressure, with active pressure in front of the wall for the remaining distance to the bottom of the wall.

The design requires the solution of a fourth-degree equation for the embedment depth. In order to illustrate the procedure, a solution will be obtained for a wall in cohesionless soil, as shown in Fig. 10-17 (Bowles, 1988). The analysis is based on unmodified values of K_p and K_p'.

An expression for z is given by

$$z = \frac{\bar{p}_p Y - 2R_a}{\bar{p}_p + \bar{p}_p''} \qquad (10\text{-}10)$$

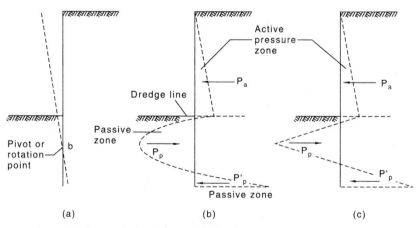

Figure 10-16 (a) Assumed elastic line of the support. (b) Probable and as obtained in finite-element solution qualitative soil pressure distribution. (c) Simplified pressure diagram for computational purposes (granular soil and no water as shown).

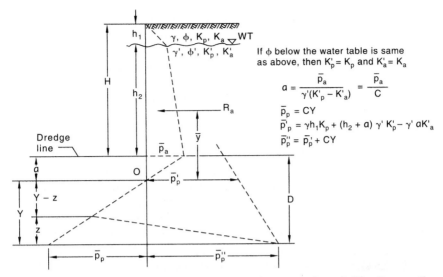

Figure 10-17 Cantilever support pressure diagram for a granular soil. The diagram illustrates the possibility of different soil properties below the water table. If other stratification exists, the pressure diagram should be appropriately modified. Assumptions shown are for "classifcal method" analysis.

where all symbols correspond to the notations of Fig. 10-17. Summing moments at a convenient point, a fourth-degree equation is derived for Y and is applicable with or without water or

$$Y^4 + Y^3 \frac{\bar{p}_p'}{C} - Y^2 \frac{8R_a}{C} - Y\left[\frac{6R_a}{C^2}(2\bar{y}C + \bar{p}_p')\right]$$
$$- \frac{6R_a\bar{y}\bar{p}_p' + 4R_a^2}{C^2} = 0 \quad (10\text{-}11)$$

where all terms are again as shown in Fig. 10-17. If water is present, R_a and $\bar{y}$ are adjusted accordingly.

With ASD an arbitrary increase in depth of 30 to 40 percent may be preferred in lieu of using a performance factor for K_p. If the water is at different elevations on each side of the wall, the effect of unbalanced pressure should be taken into account. The solution can be simplified if the following steps are used:

1. Prepare a diagram showing the geometry and load conditions.

2. Estimate active and passive earth pressure coefficients, and adjust if load factor design is used.

3. Compute the pressures $\bar{p}_p$, $\bar{p}_p'$, $\bar{p}_p''$, the distance a, and the resultant pressure R_a (resultant of all forces above point 0 in Fig. 10-17) with

its location $\bar{y}$. Note that $\gamma'(K_p' - K_a') = C$. If the pressure diagram is a regular triangle with base $(H + a)$ and height $\bar{p}_a$ the dimension $\bar{y}$ is

$$\bar{y} = \frac{H + 2a}{3} \tag{10-12}$$

4. Insert the values from step 3 into Eq. (10-11) and compute Y. This dimension may be obtained by trial and error, beginning with $0.75H$.

5. Compute total required embedment $D = Y + a$.

Structural capacity. With factored active pressures and factored passive resistance the cantilever bending moment is easily obtained (usually about point 0 in Fig. 10-17). The T-beam walls are analyzed in much the same way as rectangular beams and slabs. The same limitations should be placed on the tension steel, limiting the steel ratio to $0.75p_b$. This should not be a problem because the large flange area will keep compression on the concrete quite low. If the depth a of the stress block is less than the flange thickness (wall thickness), the analysis is identical to that of a very wide beam of width equal to the stem spacing.

The individual T sections must also be designed for horizontal bending. Referring to Fig. 1-36, the flange is a cantilever fixed at the junction with the stem, and subjected to the action of a uniform earth pressure. Sufficient reinforcement must be provided horizontally along the inside face to resist this moment.

10-9 Design Considerations of Arch (Quay) Walls

Arch walls are shown in Figs. 1-37 and 1-38, with a view of the Seaforth dock (Liverpool) shown in Fig. 1-39. This is essentially a gravity structure, but the long back fin provides considerable resistance to overturning, since before the wall could rotate the fin would have to be extracted like a tooth. Resistance to laminar displacement is provided by the stiff deck rigidly connected to the arches.

The design of these walls must consider the following:

1. Stability against overturning

2. Stability against sliding along the base of the wall

3. Ability to transfer the loads from the gravity action, and particularly at the front corners, without overloading the soil

4. Structural capacity of the wall and its members to resist moments, shears,and axial compression

Lateral earth pressure. Among the factors to be considered is the magnitude of earth pressure and the amount of wall friction and adhesion that may be relied upon after the excavation of the dock basin. In the past, it has been assumed that structures of this type are rigid and unable to yield sufficiently to mobilize the full shear resistance of the soil. For this condition, most standards recommend designing for at rest pressure.

However, results of tests reported by Uff (1970) on a prototype bay in conjunction with the Seaforth (Liverpool) dock (Fisher, 1974) showed this assumption to be invalid. This was confirmed by similar tests in the permanent wall of Fig. 1-37, after the removal of the earth from the front face of the structure (see also Fig. 1-39) that recorded a yield of 50 mm (2 in) on a height of 22.5 m (74 ft). This would suggest a rotation about the front toe.

Earth pressure readings on the test bay are shown in Fig. 10-18. As a result of this investigation the structure for the Seaforth dock was finally analyzed for an equivalent fluid of specific gravity 1.0.

Stability against overturning. Resistance to overturning is provided by (1) the weight of the structure that may include a heavy superstructure with artificial weights as shown in Fig. 1-37a; (2) by the rear wall (back fin) that inhibits overturning before the wall is distorted and extracted like a tooth; and (3) by anchors installed at the end of the back fin. For the Seaforth wall, anchors to tie down the structure were considered unnecessary as a result of tests on the prototype bay.

Stability against sliding. Resistance to sliding is important as a post-construction problem. Sliding can occur along the base of the wall. This condition is manifested in the absence of a base footing that normally supports a substantial earth column load, and then adds to the frictional resistance along a plane at this level. The possibility that this may happen warrants a complete analysis based on reliable soil data. Sliding is not a problem only at the wall base. If a thin seam of plastic clay exists below the base and remains undetected, it may lead to sliding, although tilting is not necessarily involved.

Thus the decision to rely on friction along the base, penetrate into rock, or provide embedment below excavation level to generate passive resistance must be made from a consideration of the lateral forces, wall geometry, and subsoil conditions.

Ability to transfer vertical loads. Increasing resistance to sliding by increasing the dead weight of the structure means more vertical pres-

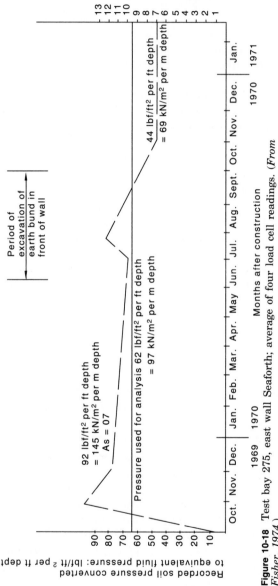

Figure 10-18 Test bay 275, east wall Seaforth; average of four load cell readings. (*From Fisher, 1974.*)

sure at the base of the wall. The combination of overturning forces and axial loads causes maximum pressure at the front face. Typically bored cylinders are incorporated at the front corners to increase the bearing area. In spite of the extra foundation area, walls of this type should not be considered unless there is a competent foundation stratum such as rock, weathered sandstone, or very dense incompressible material.

Structural capacity of wall. The arch configuration ensures that most of the forces on the structure, mainly lateral earth stresses, are carried in compression. This shape is developed to encourage progressive arching also in the ground behind the wall, expected to be effective in reducing the resultant pressure. With nominal wall dimensions, the vertical load capacity is considerable, so that the reinforcement requirements are minimal.

A further consideration is the extent to which frictional or adhesive forces are mobilized at the soil-structure interface. Analysis of these forces should involve the complex structure geometry, and the combined horizontal and vertical movement. Some theoretical work has been carried out but there is a paucity of such data; hence much reliance must be placed on experience and retrospective analysis.

10-10   Design considerations of Diaphragm Wall Cells

General principles

A description of these wall types with examples from applications is given in Sec. 1-10. A cellular wall is shown in Fig. 1-41 and an open cell in Fig. 1-42.

Cellular cofferdams are of three basic types: circular, diaphragm, and cloverleaf. Examples of the first two types are shown in Fig. 10-19. Of these, the types shown in Fig. 10-19b and d, straight and curved diaphragms, are suitable in conjunction with diaphragm wall construction because of the compatible geometry.

These structures are used primarily as retaining systems, with the retained material usually being water and earth. Their stability depends on the interaction of the soil used to fill the cell and the concrete wall. The massive work makes the final structure suitable for marine terminals and where a large dredged depth must be provided. As an example, the Redcar terminal shown in Fig. 1-41 has a maximum dredged depth of 28 m (92 ft) below core. Cellular cofferdams with a series of diaphragm wall panels are more likely to be used along the

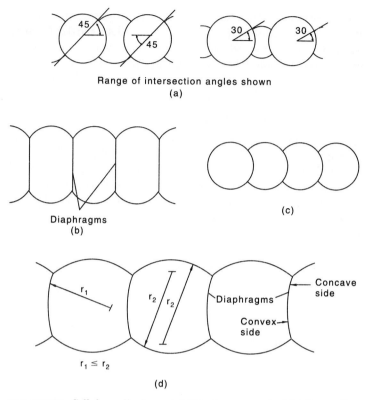

Figure 10-19 Cellular cofferdams: (*a*) Circular, economical for deep cells. (*b*) Diaphragm, may be economical in quiet water. (*c*) Modified circular (special case of *d*). (*d*) Diaphragm with circular cross walls.

waterfront, and less often out in the water to function as a pier-type structure.

Diaphragm cells are assembled from a series of circular arcs connected by cross walls. When made with sheet piles, the radius of the arc usually is selected to be equal to the cell width so that the interlock tension in the arcs and diaphragms may be equal. The first consideration, however, in adapting the cell design to concrete is to reverse the front arches as shown in Fig. 1-41 so that both front and back walls are in compression.

Curved diaphragm cells. These, shown in Fig. 10-19*d*, have curved cross walls. The introduction of curvature in these walls makes each cell a self-supporting unit, particularly for large heights. For the usual diaphragm lengths of 20 to 25 m (65 to 80 ft) the extra wall length resulting from the conversion of straight wall to a curved shape is minimal and may justify the increased stability. Individual cells may be filled to considerable depth with the adjacent cell empty, assuming suitable materials are available such as sand, gravel, or crushed stone.

The self-supporting characteristics of this type have been demonstrated in many applications (Cushing and Moline, 1975) as early as 1935.

Stability considerations, cellular cells

Where diaphragm wall construction is contemplated, the site of the cellular cofferdam is usually reclaimed. A working platform is formed by depositing earth and compacting accordingly. Alternatively a new water area is created by dredging (excavating) along the front of a wall cell. In either case the walls are in place prior to dredging or general excavation in front of the structure.

In these conditions the design of the walls must consider the following:

1. Stability against cell sliding
2. Stability against cell overturning
3. Structural capacity of cells and members therefrom such as restraint against laminar tilting, shear transfer between adjoining panels, and bending forces imposed by the contained soil in the cells after dredging in front of the wall

There are no precise theoretical solutions to these problems because of the complex interaction of the cell geometry, contained earth, and imposed loads from facility operations. The analysis and design is therefore carried out using semiempirical methods that have been applied to the design of steel sheet pile cellular cofferdams. The procedure presented here is a combined version of the Terzaghi (1945) and the Cummings (1960) method.

Stability against sliding. The wall cell must provide adequate resistance to sliding along the base caused by the unbalanced lateral forces, with dredging in front of the wall fully completed but without water.

Referring to Fig. 10-20a, the cell is on the verge of sliding if

$$P_a = P_f + P_p \qquad (10\text{-}13)$$

where P_a = lateral force acting on the back of the wall (usually effects of earth stress and water pressure); P_f = developed frictional resistance = fW (for soil- to-soil sliding f can be taken as tan ϕ; for soil on smooth rock $f = 0.5$, and on rough rock $f = $ tan ϕ is satisfactory); P_p = passive resistance if the front walls extend fairly below dredge

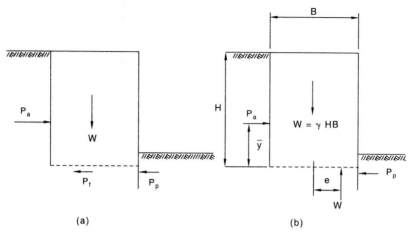

Figure 10-20 Stability of cell wall: (a) Sliding. (b) Overturning.

level (with no embedment, as in rock, this term is zero). From Eq. (10-13) the factor of safety against sliding is

$$SF = \frac{P_f + P_p}{P_a} \qquad (10\text{-}14)$$

This factor should be no less than 1.25 if the basin remains empty for a short time. If longer delays are anticipated, the factor of safety may be increased accordingly. The total weight W should include the weight of earth plus the weight of the structure. Whether the lateral force P_a should be computed for the active or the at rest condition is a decision to be based on expected lateral movement. This movement can be monitored as excavation is carried down in front of the wall.

Resistance to overturning. The wall cell must be stable against overturning with dredging completed but with basin empty. Referring to Fig. 10-20b where for simplicity the structure is assumed to have a plan close to a rectangle, overturning is avoided if there is no tension in the soil, or the resultant lies within the middle third of the base. This means that

$$e \leqslant B/6 \qquad \text{where} \qquad e = P_a y/\gamma HB \qquad (10\text{-}15)$$

For the configuration shown in Fig. 1-41, the location of the resultant weight should be determined accurately with respect to the front corner, since the balancing moment is taken about this point.

In most cases resistance to overturning will be improved considerably by soil friction or adhesion expected to be developed if laminar tilting at the cross walls is prevented.

Since sliding and overturning are two temporary conditions, the analysis of stability does not warrant load factor methods. Instead, the use of ASD using suitable factors of safety will be adequate.

Bearing capacity. With water in the basin, the lateral forces tend to compensate each other so that the soil pressure is merely the weight of overburden. With dredging at final level and no water in the basin, the front corners tend to overload the soil under the overturning effect. It is therefore essential to provide sufficient bearing capacity at these locations. Often the front arch and transverse walls penetrate into bedrock.

Laminar tilting. In some instances, heavy surcharge loading eccentrically placed on the cell can be combined with lateral forces to cause laminar tilting. This tendency is best resisted by the cross walls provided distortion along the joints is prevented. The usual means to ensure action as a unit is to provide panel connectors at the joints that can transfer tensile forces along the entire wall depth. A detail is shown in Fig. 1-41 and consists of straight-web piling extended into the adjoining panel.

Front arch. Reversing the arch shape of the front wall as shown in Fig. 1-41 ensures that the structural action under the interior lateral stresses will be compression. However, the base restraint by the wall embedment below dredge level will tend to induce vertical bending. The usual practice is to have the front arch stiffened vertically against flexural bending, imposed by the contained soil in the cells after dredging in front of the wall, by means of ribs extending out from the arch, as shown in Fig. 1-41.

Superstructure deck. The structural system is completed with a solid deck. The tops of all diaphragm walls are integrally connected to a superstructure framework that consists of reinforced beams, slabs, and the like. This deck stiffens the cells at the top, and supports the unloading facilities.

Stability considerations, open cells

An open cell is a free quay form of construction; examples are shown in Fig. 1-42. As mentioned in Sec. 1-10, the bents form the legs of a continuous portal frame that derives its stability from gravity action; hence undesirable effects are controlled if more weight is placed on the cells.

The structural characteristics of the open cell walls shown in Fig. 1-42 provide a strong resistance to transverse bending. For this example, the portal is capable of resisting the imposed bending intensity with bents spaced 10 m (33 ft) apart.

The structural deck is conveniently cast on the ground. Because of the considerable spans, this slab must be reinforced as a continuous beam and may have to carry considerable service loads.

Since the diaphragm wall panels are constructed from ground surface, with the top slab and sheet pile back wall in place before any excavation, provisions must be made for revetting the slope under the quay. The quay is designed to stand in the dry for many months, and also with the full surcharge loading to withstand rapid drawdown of the basin (or dock) water level in case of emergency.

With full dredged level and dry basin, the back sheet pile wall retains the soil. The sheet piles are laterally supported by embedment below the base and by the concrete deck at the top. The lateral reaction at top slab level is a force tending to overturn the cells. This overturning must be resisted by the quay acting as gravity structure. Under an overturning moment and vertical load there will be a differential bearing pressure exerted by the wall panels. Where conditions warrant, the transfer of vertical load may be assumed to occur both by side friction in the embedded wall portion and by base bearing.

10-11   Walls Built to Protect Dikes, Reservoirs, River Banks, and Dams

General features

The T walls, arches, and cells discussed in the foregoing sections have wide applications in marine installations. This section discusses the uses and design criteria of linear diaphragm walls, used singly or combined with other structure types, for waterfront facilities of both marine and nonmarine type.

The wall shown in Fig. 10-21a can be designed as a gravity structure and assumed to fail by overturning if the cap is fairly stiff, has rigid connection with the wall, and the front diaphragm rests on solid materials. This system is essentially a derivative of open cells shown in Fig. 1-42. With a thin cap slab the diaphragm wall has partial restraint at the top and is likely to deform as a cantilever. In this case the design should consider passive resistance mobilized in front of the interior fly or rear wall, equivalent to a deadman anchorage.

The wall shown in Fig. 10-21b is partly gravity type and partly free cantilever, and probably comes closer to a rigid frame. It should be considered where heavy service loads are imposed on the cap slab. The system is more stable if the rear diaphragm wall is built in firm ground. The lateral forces along the back are resisted by passive pres-

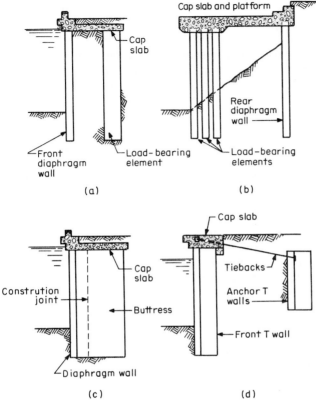

Figure 10-21 Schematic designs of waterfront facilities by diaphragm walls and related elements.

sure on the slope side and partly by the cap slab. The latter reaction is transmitted to the front group of vertical elements, and if the structure has high rigidity, the horizontal reaction is transferred as axial forces.

The wall shown in Fig. 10-21c is a T beam with long stems. With appropriate geometry and height-to-depth ratio it may be analyzed as a gravity structure. It must therefore satisfy the associated requirements, namely, stability against sliding and overturning with the basin dry.

The T wall shown in Fig. 10-21d is braced at the top by an anchorage that transfers the lateral force to a deadman, and by embedment at the bottom. The orientation of the wall as shown is not the most favorable because the T beam action is reversed. However, this scheme is functionally desirable because it gives a straight, smooth front. The stems serve also as support for the cap slab.

Construction through seawater. The construction of walls in seawater requires the use of steel casing, which is also necessary for tremie placement. The casing is driven to penetrate the bottom for some distance and seal the excavation. The seawater is then pumped out and replaced by bentonite slurry. Drilling for the round elements is started at sea bottom under slurry and is likely to encounter unusually large amount of salt, and hence a special slurry must be used.

Dikes, reservoirs, and river banks. Representative examples of protective works along the banks of rivers are the diaphragm walls along the Arno River in Florence constructed after the damaging floods of 1966. Besides protection against flooding and erosion, walls along river banks create new stable river beds, and important improvement where channel relocation is difficult. Another application is the protection of sections immediately upstream or downstream from hydraulic projects such as water intakes and basins.

For protection against erosion the walls are built parallel to the banks and keyed into the river bed. A top connecting beam ensures an integral structure. If the protection must be extended to adjoining areas, seepage and water infiltration are intercepted if the walls are seated in impervious formations. Whether the excavation is carried from existing ground level or from a specially prepared working platform depends on site topography and the groundwater table.

Special details. Figure 10-22 shows the quay wall for the Peterhead (England) harbor development. The diaphragm wall is 1 m (3.3 ft) thick and was constructed through sand fill. The wall is keyed into

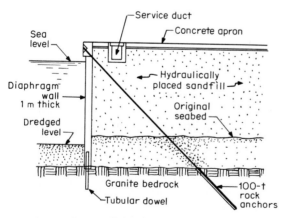

Figure 10-22 Quay wall for the Peterhead (England) harbor development.

bedrock by large-diameter steel dowels, placed by drilling holes into the bedrock through shafts left in the concrete panels. In certain locations the rock is softer so that the walls are braced by sockets. The concrete panels are capped by a continuous beam 2 m deep fitted with sleeves to install the top anchorage fixed into rock.

The protective walls on the Arno River were initially conceived as a watertight screen for the hydraulic works merely to protect the surroundings from rising water level in the river. Subsequently, the design was modified, and the walls were also used as foundation elements for the restoration of the bank and as lateral protection of adjacent buildings.

A special application is shown in Fig. 10-23 for the water supply of the industrial area of Nottingham (England) by creating an artificial accumulation basin. The top of the basin above existing ground was obtained by a concrete dam enforced on the outside by a clay embankment as shown. The stability of the dam, in either direction, is further secured by a system of bored piles and a diaphragm wall built from initial ground level. The diaphragm wall is extended into an impervious layer to serve as a cutoff for the basin. The walls and the piles are rigidly connected to the dam structure by special details. Inside the basin similar structures are used to divide the area into smaller sections, and are arranged to accommodate varying pond conditions such as one side full and the other empty.

Rigid cutoff walls, design considerations

The general principles of rigid cutoff walls are discussed in Sec. 1-11. Notable examples are found in conjunction with earth dams where the walls are used either as remedial work or as part of the initial design.

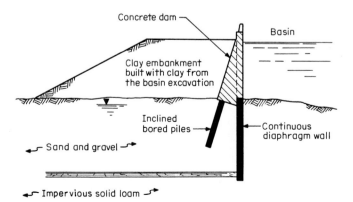

Figure 10-23 Concrete dam and diaphragm wall for Nottingham (England) water basin.

Typically these cutoffs are very deep, sometimes in excess of 50 m (165 ft), but alternate technologies have been developed to ensure the quality of the wall in terms of verticality and panel connection (see also Secs. 1-11 and 2-11). A recent example is the Fontenelle dam in Wyoming, constructed in the early 1960s as an earth embankment with clay core. The embankment rises 34 m (112 ft) above the local bedrock, interbedded with medium and hard horizontal sediments. Despite early rock grouting, monitoring showed that there was a strong possibility of structural failure as a result of water piping through and under the contact zone. The remedial design focused on a concrete diaphragm wall 0.8 m (32 in) thick, installed from the crest of the dam through the embankment, and penetrating 14 m (46 ft) into bedrock.

The structural requirements of concrete cutoff walls interrupting water flow are mainly resistance to deformation within an elastic medium and under the effect of differential pressures. Deformability without exceeding the structural capacity can be understood by reference to Fig. 10-24. For simplicity, full hydrostatic pressure and effective pressure is assumed on the upstream face, whereas the water level at the downstream face is drawn down to the base of the wall. Lateral wall movement at the base is prevented or inhibited by restraint such as friction or embedment.

The lateral force P is the sum of water pressure (static) and effective earth pressure that goes from the at rest condition to partial or full active state if enough movement occurs. The resisting force P_p is the soil pressure that may go from initial at rest to partial passive state if enough movement occurs to warrant this condition.

The deformation of the wall due to the unbalanced pressures (the different changes with movement) depends on the flexural rigidity of

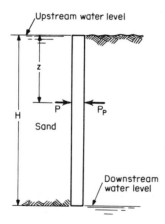

Figure 10-24 Impervious rigid diaphragm in cohesionless clean sand.

the wall, and on the coefficient of subgrade reaction k_h of the downstream soil. A crude conception of the factors that determine the subgrade reaction is given by Terzaghi (1955). As an initial approximation, the coefficient k_h may be computed from the expression (see also Sec. 9-9)

$$k_h = l_h \frac{z}{H} \tag{10-16}$$

where l_h = coefficient depending on the relative density of the sand in contact with the wall, and the other symbols correspond to Fig. 10-24. The contact pressure p_p on the downstream face at depth z is given as

$$p_p = K'_0 + y l_d \frac{z}{H} \tag{10-17}$$

where K'_0 = earth pressure coefficient corresponding to lateral wall
    displacement of wall height H over a distance y_0 =
    $0.0002H$
  y = displacement at depth z
  l_d = coefficient appropriate to cutoff, usually = l_h

Terzaghi (1955) gives the probable values of K'_0 and l_h for vertical walls such as anchored bulkheads and concrete diaphragms.

Equation (10-17) must be used in conjunction with flexural theory to obtain moments and shears, and this generally leads to a differential equation of the fourth order.

10-12 Special Uses

Humber bridge. An unusual application of diaphragm walls is shown in Fig. 10-25, in conjunction with the cable forces of the Humber suspension bridge. The 36,000-t pull from the suspension cables is transferred into a clay formation at the Barton side by an anchorage of composite construction. The high stress concentration from the cables is dissipated by terminating the cables in the upper half of the anchorage block. The lower part of the structure consists of five longitudinal sections 24.5 m (80 ft) deep excavated between diaphragm walls. The composite construction is over 70 m (240 ft) long and has an average width of 40 m (131 ft).

The intent of the composite construction was to penetrate the underlying clay in a controlled manner (Ground Eng., 1974) in order to prevent flooding of the excavation by groundwater that might have

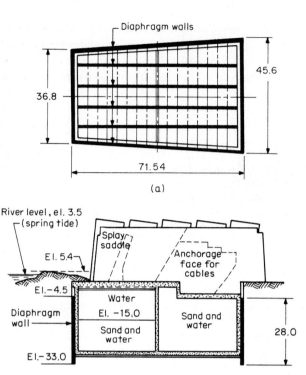

Figure 10-25 Foundation anchorage for the Humber suspension bridge at the Barton site: (a) Plan showing diaphragm wall block and anchorage. (b) Longitudinal section. All dimensions and elevations in meters.

softened the clay. Long-term effects were prevented by speeding up the construction.

The dead weight of the cell structure was increased by placing sand and water inside. This operation was introduced progressively to control the response of the large foundation. The horizontal bracing of the diaphragm walls across the five sections is provided by precast concrete struts placed in sets of two. This design is therefore considered a trend for the adaptation of precast members in underground construction.

Rupel Tunnel, Belgium. This project is located between Antwerp and Brussels, and carries an expressway under the Rupel River and a maritime canal. Figure 10-26 shows an aerial view of the project under construction. The two waterway crossings consist of sunken tubes of precast and partially prestressed concrete box sections. On the same site diaphragm walls provide protection of the dikes of the canal and

Figure 10-26 Aerial view of the Rupel Tunnel in Belgium (from bottom to top) showing the center portion, consisting of a cut-and-cover tunnel built with diaphragm walls; the river tunnel, consisting of two sunken tubes, and the canal tunnel, consisting of one sunken tube shown floating. (*Franki.*)

along the bank of the river where they retain access ramps. Diaphragm walls are also used as foundations for a bridge and two underground pumping stations (Barr, 1977).

The approaches to the tunnel consist of cut-and-cover construction 260 m (850 ft) long. Between the two waterways a multiple-level structure is used, as shown in Fig. 10-27, having diaphragm walls as permanent elements. These walls are 1 m thick (40 in) and 26 m deep (85 ft). They were braced temporarily and permanently with cast-in-place concrete ribs that also serve to support the floor slabs. A special chamber is provided at the center of the lower level to house utility lines.

As shown in Fig. 10-26, a drydock alongside the waterways was used as a casting yard for the sunken tubes. These docks were formed by steel sheet pile cofferdams and earth banks. With the sunken tubes completed and prestressed, the cofferdam was removed, the site was flooded, and the precast tubes were floated to the correct position. The sections were sunk and placed in specially prepared beds. More details on this project are given by Baar (1977).

10-13   Design Example 1, Quay Wall along River

The quay wall in this example was constructed close to the mouth of the river to create a parking lot along the river banks and also to provide temporary mooring for small fishing boats (Pfister et al., 1982). The total length of the wall is 192 m (629 ft) and required an excavation 7.5 m (25 ft) deep. The wall is laterally supported by ground anchors near the top, and by embedment below excavation level. Figure 10-28 shows a typical cross section, wall and anchor profile, and soil data.

Wall type. The wall structure consists of precast reinforced-concrete panels, with the following dimensions and weight:

- Thickness = 0.35 m (15 in), increased locally to 0.45 m (18 in) at the level of ground anchors.
- Height = 12.50 m (41 ft), that includes the exposed and embedded portion.
- Width = 1.90 or 2.60 m (6 or 8.5 ft).
- Average weight = 30 t (66 kips).

The panels were installed in preexcavated trenches using the single grout method discussed in Sec. 1-5. The precast sections were lowered into a trench excavated under a cement-bentonite slurry, functioning

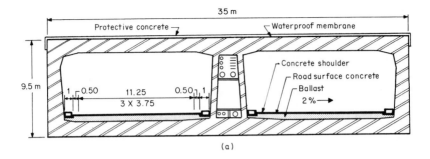

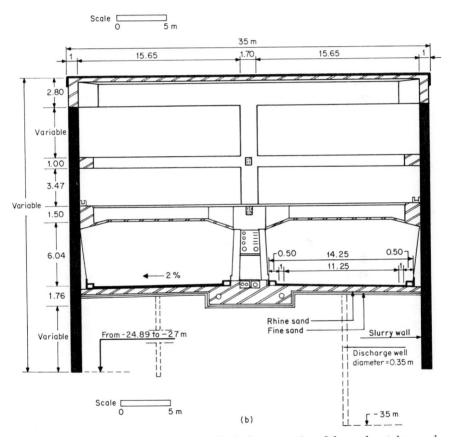

Figure 10-27 Rupel Tunnel, Belgium: (*a*) Typical cross section of the sunken tubes used in the Rupel River and the maritime canal. (*b*) Typical section of the cut-and-cover tunnel used in the land portion between the waterways. (*Franki.*)

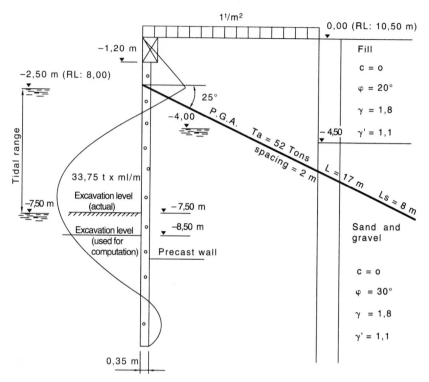

Figure 10-28 Wall profile, section and soil data; Design Example 10-1.

initially as stabilizing fluid and later setting to a specified strength. The trench was excavated with a kelly-mounted grab that gave a trench width of 0.62 m (24 in). On the river side, the ground was excavated after completion of the wall and the ground anchors, and after cleaning the slurry the front face emerged with the smooth surface inherent in precasting.

The panels are provided with a recess through which the ground anchors are inserted. The anchors are inclined at 25° with the horizontal and have a fixed length of 8 m (26 ft). The lateral stability and wall embedment were analyzed assuming an overexcavation 1 m (3 ft) below the proposed dredged level. The wall was designed using the fixed-earth support method, and the resulting moment diagram is shown in the wall profile of Fig. 10-28.

The ground anchors have permanent corrosion protection consisting of (1) protective plastic sheath along the free length; (2) annular space between the tendon and the sheath filled with an epoxy pitch; and (3) cement grout in the borehole around the plastic sheath.

The construction sequence of the quay is shown in Fig. 10-29. Stage I shows the site conditions and profile of the ground and the river. During this stage the panels were precast on a flat area near the site. In stage II, the construction area is excavated to give a flat platform as shown, and the excavated material is used to backfill the site with a stable slope. Trench stability had to be maintained with full water head. During the same stage the panels are inserted into the trench.

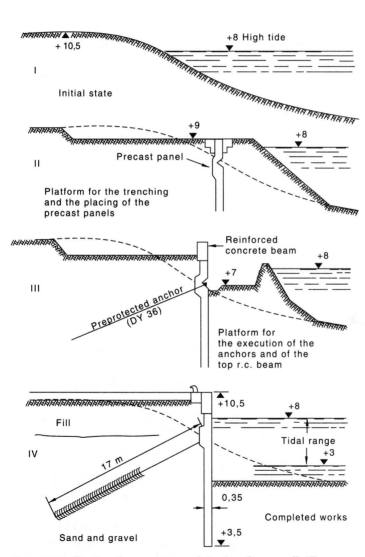

Figure 10-29 Construction sequence and staging of quay wall. (*From Pfister et al., 1982.*)

In stage III, a reinforced cast-in-place capping beam is placed on top of the panels, the front of the wall is excavated as shown, and the ground anchors are installed and prestressed. In stage IV the river is dredged to the specified level, and this completes the construction.

10-14   Design Example 2, Circular Enclosure

A circular enclosure with a mean radius of $r = 45$ ft and a depth of 60 ft provides access for the construction of a transportation tunnel. Because of the construction is extended over a period of several years, the design will use criteria applied to permanent structures, and since the structure will accommodate a transportation facility, we will apply AASHTO load factors.

The soil parameters are $\phi' = 30°$ and $\gamma = 120$ lb/ft³. Although the excavation inside the enclosure is dewatered, it is conceivable that the water table outside may rise to ground level. The wall will be designed, therefore, for effective earth stress based on $K_0 = 1 - \sin \phi' = 0.50$, and full water pressure. At a depth of 60 ft, the pressures are as follows:

Effective earth pressure $p_e = (58)(0.50)(60) = 1.74$ kips/ft²

Water pressure $\qquad p_w = (62)(60) = 3.72$ kips/ft²

The maximum permitted deviation from the true circular profile is 6 in, and may occur as shown in Fig. 10-13. The load factors are selected as follows: $\gamma = 1.3$, $\beta_e = 1.4$, and $\beta_w = 1.0$. The factored (design) pressure at the design depth is therefore

$$p = 1.3(1.4 \times 1.74 + 3.72) = 8.00 \text{ kips/ft}^2$$

At the maximum depth, the misaligned panel is subjected to an axial compressive (hoop) load

$$P_u = 45 \times 8 = 360 \text{ kips} \qquad \text{and a moment}$$

$$M_u = 360 \times 0.5 = 180 \text{ ft-kips}$$

The wall will be processed in 40 chord lengths, each chord approximately 7 ft long. Adjacent chords have a deflection angle $360/40 = 9°$. The design has two requirements: (1) select an effective circular ring thickness and then determine the actual chord panel thickness such that the ring fits within the area geometry provided by the two chord perimeters; and (2) analyze the reinforcement requirements when the panels are subjected to the P_u and M_u load effects.

In more general terms the panels are members subjected to combined axial load and bending. The question arises, therefore, whether they can be considered short columns. Referring to Fig. 10-13, the ends A and C of the misaligned panel AB'C are assumed restrained against lateral displacement. If the wall penetrates into rock, its bottom is fully restrained, and in this case vertical bending must be considered. Under these assumptions the analysis can be based on short-column theory (this covers strengths ranging from where moments are small to the other limiting condition of flexure alone, i.e., zero axial load). Note, however, that the problem at hand represents the combined action of these effects in a version where both axial load and moment are considerable.

The next step is to recognize that the wall, under horizontal compressions and bending, does not fit into the characteristics of tied or spiral columns. Although the panels have substantially lower ductility at failure than beams, they come closer to slab behavior where buckling is critical in one plane only. Because of these uncertainties, the strength reduction (performance) factor ϕ is lowered to 0.75.

As a first trial we select a 30-in-thick (effective) cylindrical ring. Evidently the eccentricity e is, by design criteria, $180/360 = 0.5$ ft $= 6$ in. Note that for a 30-in-thick member, the load P_u is only 1 in outside the middle third. A wall segment 1 ft deep has a section modulus $S = (12 \times 30^2)/6 = 1800$ in^3. The stresses in the concrete (plain) are therefore

$$f_c = \frac{360}{12 \times 30} \pm \frac{180}{1800} = 1.0 \pm 0.1 = 0.9 \text{ kip/in}^2 \qquad \text{or } 1.1 \text{ kips/in}^2$$

If the ultimate (nominal) strength of plain concrete is assumed to be $0.85f_c$, and a resistance factor $\phi = 0.75$ is used, the factored strength for $f_c' = 3000$ lb/in^2 is $\phi(0.85)f_c' = (0.75)(0.85)(3000) = 1900$ lb/in^2. Since the actual stress is far below this value and tension in the concrete is absent, theoretically reinforcement is not required. The nominal strength may be further restricted as follows:

$$f_{c(max)} = (0.80)(0.85)\phi f_c' = 1530 \text{ lb/in}^2$$

However, as a compression member the wall should contain horizontal bars sufficient to make the steel ratio at least 0.01.

In addition, the panels must be checked according to the requirements set forth in Sec. 10-4, assuming that the lateral earth stresses are not necessarily converted into hoop stresses. By applying Eq. (10-5) with $l = 14$ ft and $q = 8$ kips/ft, we obtain

$$M_u = -\frac{8 \times 14^2}{32} = -49 \text{ ft-kips}$$

so that sufficient horizontal steel must be provided to resist this moment acting with no axial load.

Where considerable eccentricity is permitted as misalignment, the stresses due to the resulting moment can be considerable. In this case a plot of the wall axial load capacity against the moment it can simultaneously carry may be constructed as an interaction diagram (see also Figs. 7-24 and 7-29). The axial load capacity decreases as moment is increased. Any loading that plots within the area of the diagram is a possible loading, whereas any combination outside the area represents a failure combination.

For this example, the initial selected effective thickness of 30 in can be possibly reduced to 24 in. However, judgment is necessary when attempting to bring the circular wall within provisions intended to apply to short columns.

10-15   Design Example 3, T-Quay Wall

A buttressed diaphragm T wall is to be built along a waterfront to retain the earth as shown in Fig. 10-30. The dredged area will have a final height 25 ft. Because the basin will remain empty for some time after the excavation is completed, we use the design criteria for permanent walls but with modifications in the load factors. The soil data are shown in Fig. 10-30a, and an important requirement is to provide a safe structure with the water table at ground surface. The wall will be designed as free cantilever, so that the design must address two parameters: wall embedment below excavation for lateral

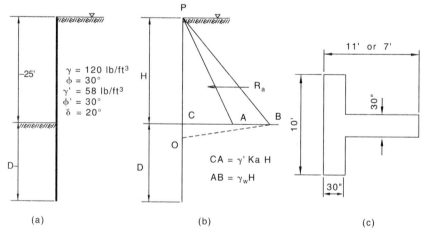

Figure 10-30 (*a*) Geometry and soil data. (*b*) Lateral pressure diagram. (*c*) Cross section of T unit.

stability, and structural capacity to resist bending moments. T walls have also been used in traffic underpasses, and an example is the structure shown in Fig. 1-11.

Wall embedment

Step 1. Prepare a diagram showing the geometry and load conditions. This diagram is shown in Fig. 10-30b. The wall is expected to yield sufficiently to mobilize active conditions on the retained side.

Step 2. For $\phi = \phi' = 30°$, we compute $K_a = K'_a = 0.33$. Likewise, for $\phi' = 30°$ and $\delta = 20°$, we compute $K_p = K'_p = 6.105$. Next, the load and resistance factors are selected on the basis of the expected worst credible conditions. Using judgment, we select load factors $\beta_e = 1.4$, $\beta_w = 1.0$, and performance factor for passive resistance $\phi_p = 0.75$. Also $\gamma = 1.0$.

The pressures CA and AB (earth and water pressure, respectively) are computed and factored as follows:

$$CA = (58)(0.33)(25)(1.4) = 665 \text{ lb/ft}^2$$

$$AB = (62.4)(25) = 1560 \text{ lb/ft}^2, \text{ and } \bar{p}_a = CB = 2.22 \text{ kips/ft}^2$$

Step 3. Compute R_a, a, $\bar{p}_p$, $\bar{p}'_p$ and $\bar{p}''_p$.

First, we compute $K' = K'_p - K'_a$, where both coefficients are factored, or $K' = (0.75)(6.105) - (0.33)(1.4) = 4.58 - 0.46 = 4.12$, and $C = 0.06(4.12) = 0.25$. Also $a = \bar{p}_a/C = 2.22/0.25 = 8.9 \text{ ft} = CO$.

The resultant R_a is computed from the pressure and force diagram POB, or $R_a = (25 + 8.9)(2.22)(0.5) = 37.6$ kips.

The dimension $\bar{y}$ is computed from Eq. (10-12) since the pressure diagram is a regular triangle, or

$$\bar{y} = \frac{25 + 2(8.9)}{3} = 14.3 \text{ ft}$$

Referring to Fig. 10-17, the parameter p'_p is computed as $p'_p = (0.06)(33.9)(4.58) - (0.06)(0.46)(8.9) = 9.32 - 0.25 = 9.07 \text{ kips/ft}^2$.

Step 4. Find coefficients and substitute into Eq. (10-11) to find Y.

$$\frac{\bar{p}_p}{C} = \frac{9.07}{0.25} = 36.3 \qquad \text{also} \qquad \frac{8R_a}{C} = \frac{8(37.6)}{0.25} = 1200$$

Likewise we compute

$$\frac{6R_a}{C^2} = \frac{6(37.6)}{0.25^2} = 3620$$

$$2\bar{y}C + \bar{p}'_p = 2(14.3)(0.25) + 9.07 = 16.22$$

So that the Y term is $(3620)(16.22) = 58{,}716$. The constant term is

$$\frac{6(37.6)(14.3)(9.07) + 4(37.6)^2}{0.25} = \frac{29{,}178 + 5656}{0.0625} = 557{,}340$$

Now inserting these coefficient in Eq. (10-11) we obtain $Y^4 + 36.3Y^3 - 1200Y^2 - 58{,}716Y = 557{,}340$, which is satisfied for $Y = 40$ ft.

Therefore, total embedment $D = Y + a = 40 + 8.9 = 49$ ft. It is obvious that, for stability, the ratio D/H is $^{49}/_{25} = 1.96$. Thus it may be more economical to consider complete dewatering of the retained area down to the dredged level until the basin is filled.

For comparison, we recompute the required embedment assuming only active pressure with no water. Then

$$\bar{p}_a = CA = CB = (120)(0.33)(25)(1.4) = 1390 \text{ lb/ft}^2$$

Likewise, $K = K' = 4.12$ (the same as before), and $C = 0.12(4.12) = 0.49$. Also $a = CO = 1.39/0.49 = 2.8$ ft.

The resultant R_a is computed again from the pressure and force diagram POB, or

$$R_a = (25 + 2.8)(1.39)(0.5) = 19.3 \text{ kips}$$

Also,

$$\bar{y} = \frac{25 + 2(2.8)}{3} = 10.2 \text{ ft}$$

From Fig. 10-17, we compute the parameter $\bar{p}_p'$ as

$$\bar{p}_p' = (0.12)(25.0)(4.58) = 13.74 \text{ kips/ft}^2$$

Next, we compute

$$\frac{\bar{p}_p}{C} = \frac{13.74}{0.49} = 28.0 \quad \text{and} \quad \frac{8R_a}{C} = \frac{8(19.3)}{0.49} = 315$$

Also, we compute

$$\frac{6R_a}{C^2} = \frac{6(19.3)}{0.49^2} = 483$$

$$2\bar{y}C + \bar{p}_p' = 2(10.2)(0.49) + 13.74 = 23.74$$

so that the Y term is $(483)(23.74) = 11,466$. The constant term is

$$\frac{6(19.3)(10.2)(13.74) + 4(19.3)^2}{0.49^2} = \frac{16,254 + 1490}{0.24} = 73,933$$

Now inserting these coefficients in Eq. (10-11) we obtain

$$Y^4 + 28Y^3 - 315Y^2 - 11,466Y = 73,933$$

which is satisfied for $Y = 20.7$ ft.

Therefore, total embedment $D = Y + a = 20.7 + 2.8 = 23.5$ ft, which is a substantial reduction from the embedment required with full hydrostatic pressure.

Structural capacity

Full hydrostatic pressure. The moment about point 0 is $R_a\bar{y}$, or $M_u = (37.6)(14.3) = 537.7$ ft-kips/ft of wall length. We select stem spacing of 10 ft and total wall depth of 11 ft as shown in Fig. 10-30c. Both flange and stem are 30 in thick. Assume that $a < 30$ in (see also Fig. 6-18) so that the section can be analyzed as a rectangular beam. We use $f_y = 40$ kips/in^2 and $f'_c = 3000$ lb/in^2.

From Eq. (6-12),

$$M_u = \phi M_n = \phi A_s f_y \left(d - \frac{a}{2}\right) \qquad \text{where} \qquad \phi = 0.9$$

For a 10-ft section $M_u = 537.7 \times 10 = 5377$ ft-kips, or $M_n/0.9 = 5930$ ft-kips. Next, we assume $d = 10.25$ ft and $a = 6$ in $= 0.5$ ft. Then $5930 = A_s(40)(10.25 - 0.5/2)$, or

$$A_s = 5930/400 = 14.8 \text{ in}^2$$

Check $a = A_s f_y/(0.85 f'_c b) = 2$ in, original assumption on the safe side. Provide 15 No. 9 bars, $A_s = 15$ in^2, arranged in three rows.

Complete dewatering. Likewise the moment about point O is $M_u = (19.3)(10.2) = 197$ ft-kips/ft of wall length. For a 10-ft section $M_u = 197 \times 10 = 1970$ ft-kips, or $M_n/\phi = 2189$ ft-kips. Then, approximately $A_s = 2189/(6 \times 40) = 9.12$ in^2 (based on total wall depth of 7 ft). This area is provided by 10 No. 9 bars arranged in two rows.

It appears from this preliminary analysis that the two schemes must be compared for total cost. The savings in the cost of the structure made possible with full dewatering must be compared with the cost of dewatering, which depends largely on how long the basin will be empty.

We should also note that the design should consider the lateral deflection of the wall as well as other serviceability requirements.

References

Abdelhamid, M. S., and R. J. Krizek, 1976: "At-Rest Lateral Earth Pressure of a Consolidating Clay," *J. Geot. Div., ASCE,* vol. 102, no. GT7, July, pp. 721–738.

Agar, M., and F. Irwin-Childs, 1973: Seaforth Dock, Liverpool, Planning and Design, *Proc. Inst. Civ. Eng.,* part 1, 54, May, pp. 255–274.

Barr, M., 1977: "The Rupel Tunnel," personal communication.

Bowles, J. E., 1988: "Foundation Analysis and Design," McGraw-Hill, New York.

Brooker, E. Q., and H. O. Ireland, 1965: "Earth Pressure At-Rest Related to Stress History," *Canadian Geot. J.,* vol. 2, no. 1, pp. 1–15.

Clough, G. W., and J. M. Duncan, 1991: "Earth Pressures," Chapter 6, *Foundation Engineering Handbook,* 2d ed., edited by H. Y. Fang, Van Nostrand Reinhold, New York.

Cummings, E. M., 1960: "Cellular Cofferdams and Docks," *Trans. ASCE,* vol. 125, pp. 13–45.

Cushing, J. J., and R. M. Moline, 1975: "Curved Diaphragm Cellular Cofferdams," *J. Geot. Div., ASCE,* vol. 101, no. GT10, October, pp. 1055–1059.

Evers, G., and C. Hovart, 1991: Diaphragm Wall Techniques for the Channel Tunnel Shaft-Sinking on the French Side, personal communication.

Fisher, F. A., 1974: "Diaphragm Wall Projects at Seaforth, Redcar, Bristol, and Harrow," *Proc. Diaphragm Walls Anchorages, Inst. Civ. Eng.,* London.

Ground Eng., 1974: "Humber Suspension Bridge," reprint.

Hvorsley, M. J., 1960: "Physical Components of the Shear Strength of Saturated Clays," *Proc.* Research Conf. Shear Strength of Cohesive Soils, ASCE, Boulder, Colo., pp. 169–273.

Mayne, P. W., and F. H. Kulhawy, 1982: "Ko-OCR Relationships in Soil," *J. Geot. Div., ASCE,* vol. 108, no. GT6, June, pp. 851–872.

Montgomery, C. T., R. Gerard, W. J. Huiskamp, and R. W. Korngisen, 1984: "Application of Ice Engineering to Bridge Design Standards," *Proc.* Cold Regions Engineering Spec. Conf., Canadian Society for Civ. Eng., Montreal, Quebec, Canada, pp. 795–810, Apr. 4–6.

Montgomery, C. J., R. Gerard, and A. W. Lipsett, 1980: "Dynamic Response of Bridge Piers to Ice Forces," *Canadian J. Civ. Eng.,* vol. 7, no. 2, Ottawa, Ontario, Canada, pp. 345–356.

Montgomery, C. J., and A. W. Lipsett, 1980: "Dynamic Tests and Analysis of a Massive Pier Subjected to Ice Forces," *Canadian J. Civ. Eng.,* vol. 7, no. 3, Ottawa, Ontario, Canada, pp. 432–441.

Neill, C. R., 1981: "Ice Effects on Bridges," Roads and Transp. Assoc. of Canada, Ottawa, Ontario, Canada.

Pfister, P., G. Evers, M. Guillaud, and R. Davidson, 1982: "Permanent Ground Anchors, Soletanche Design Criteria," Report FHWA/RD-81/150, Fed. Highway Admin., Washington, D.C.

Rigden, W. J., and P. W. Rowe, 1974: "Model Performance of Unreinforced Diaphragm Wall," *Proc. Diaphragm Walls Anchorages, Inst. Civ. Eng.,* London.

Rowe, P., 1957: "C = O Hypothesis for Normally Loaded Clays at Equilibrium," *Proc. 4th Int. Conf. Soil Mech. Found. Eng.,* London, England, vol. 1, pp. 189–192.

Terzaghi, K., 1945: "Stability and Stiffness of Cellular Cofferdams," *Trans. ASCE,* vol. 110, pp. 1083–1202.

Terzaghi, K., 1955: "Evaluation of Coefficients of Subgrade Reaction," *Geotechnique,* December, pp. 295–326.

Uff, J. F., 1970: Insitu Measurements of Earth Pressure for a Quay Wall at Seaforth, Liverpool. Insitu Investigations in Soils and Rocks, British Geotechnical Society, London, pp. 229–239.

11

Economic and
Legal Considerations

11-1 Factors Affecting Cost

This section deals briefly with the economic factors influencing slurry wall construction. In a broad sense slurry walls can be defined as tremied concrete walls built by the slurry trench method and consisting of elements whose depth far exceeds the dimensions in plan. The associated process and structural characteristics imply the use of specialized equipment and techniques, and require previous experience with this type of work.

Given the fact that slurry walls are built when particular site and ground conditions (usually difficult and often adverse) necessitate this solution, a second cost factor is identified and relates to the physical location and to the subsurface environment. The feasibility of integrating engineering features of the system into the overall design, considering the many structural and functional advantages of the walls, gives rise to another important economic factor that relates to proper planning.

From these brief remarks it appears that four main cost components in slurry wall construction are: (1) site conditions including the underground environment (physical and geotechnical); (2) the use of specialized equipment; (3) the need to assign the work to experienced personnel; and (4) the decision to expand the service functions of the walls as part of a general design. To these we should add incidental factors such as seasonal effects, availability of local labor and materials, owner-contractor relations, legal disputes, market conditions, and local labor practices.

Example of cost methodology. The interaction of these economic forces may be best understood by referring to the development of a diaphragm wall project from its initial conception to completion. This can be done by following relevant contracting practices and contract implementation procedures where the role of engineer, owner, and contractor may be played in full harmony or, occasionally, with some antagonistic attitude.

When a diaphragm wall is conceived as a viable solution to a particular problem, the first step is to compare it with other forms of construction; typically "ball park" prices are used to make cost comparisons, and initial decisions are based on "rule of thumb" estimates.

The first obvious consideration that will make a slurry wall concept competitive to other solutions is the possibility of utilizing three major performance components: watertightness, load-bearing ability, and use as ground support. If these characteristics are design requirements and can be integrated into one design scheme, the end result is reflected in cost savings and reduction of construction time. At best, this effort is pursued at a level of a comprehensive conceptual design supported by engineering data and input from a competent team of designers and specialist contractors familiar with the possibilities and limitations of this application.

Occasionally, the slurry wall construction is carried out as preparatory work at the beginning of a given project, and has only a minor relation to the subsequent phases. This drawback can be avoided if the slurry wall system has been integrated in the global design so that there will be technical continuity between this and subsequent stages. Some investigators contend, however, that it is reasonable to assume that if contractually the slurry work can be isolated and treated as a separate entity, the resulting advantage is a better pricing arrangement. The other philosophy is to have slurry wall construction under the general contractor's umbrella at a time when the latter has not even begun the work and thus cannot be of any service to the slurry wall contractor. In this case, the contention is that there will only be a markup to the price of the slurry wall segment. From these remarks it follows that engineers should always consider letting out the slurry work as a separate contract.

Important choices at design stage. Usually the first decision will influence subsequent choices. Thus it is important to understand that the choice of a construction procedure will influence cost as it does affect also wall quality and final performance. Equally essential is to realize that a slurry wall project is basically a process clearly related to a predominant operation, i.e., the successful excavation of wall panels. The choice of excavation technique and the associated equipment relates to the many factors discussed in the foregoing sections but mainly to (1) production rates and (2) permitted tolerances. Materials are substantially a fixed quantity, whereas other costs, equipment, labor, and supervision, are directly influenced by site and ground conditions.

Typical data on production rates have been included in other sections but should be interpreted and used with caution. Meaningful data on production capabilities of various systems can only be accumulated from continuous experience. In urban sites production rates will be affected by the following factors:

- Noise restrictions whereby the operation is limited to one shift or part of a shift.

- Traffic restrictions, depending on site and traffic maintenance.

- Labor and union regulations that may govern number of personnel assigned to equipment, construction stage and supervision, and regular or overtime work.

- Size of job (a small job carries substantial mobilization costs and inhibits the opportunity to develop skills necessary to overcome unexpected conditions).

- Wall depth (in general the greater the depth the greater the risk of encountering adverse conditions and the greater the difficulty of maintaining the wall verticality).

- Hard obstacles and boulders (these retard excavation and require conversion of equipment).

- Panel length (longer panels result in higher production rates, but this should be balanced against the more difficult trench stability, concrete placement, etc.).

It may appear that the choice of an appropriate excavation procedure is essential to a reasonable cost estimate and production rate given the site and ground conditions. An obvious question relates to the use of simple mechanical clamshells, complicated or kelly-mounted hydraulic clamshells, or boring machines with reverse circulation and other features for soil removal.

Materials constitute three main categories: excavated soil, bentonite, and ready-mixed concrete. Quantities therefrom remain essentially fixed except for some variation by the quantity of concrete and the amount of bentonite. The extent of overexcavation relates mainly to the type of soil (see also the foregoing sections). The amount of bentonite may vary somewhat according to the method of excavation and spoil removed.

Contingencies. Traditionally, contingency has been claimed to be a real site cost since it relates to a construction segment assumed to carry high risks. Because it is difficult to express in terms of a reasonable cost percentage, contractors tend to develop in-house policies that often tend to be unrealistic. Thus it usually is expedient on the part of the owner-engineer to address the amount of capital set aside by the contractor for contingencies by including clauses such as changed conditions and provisions for unanticipated ground conditions. Likewise, a history of fair contract administration diffuses the expectation of risk and may result in lesser contingency in the final bid price.

Overhead and profit. Overhead depends on company size, efficiency, work volume, etc. Usually it is computed on the actual job basis. In slurry wall construction, overhead covers also the cost of fees and royalties paid to licensers and organizations that provide special assistance to a contractor using patented or proprietary processes. These costs should not be considered an additional burden since they would not exist in a free market economy unless they enhance the specialized expertise in a given difficult job.

Profit must be accepted as the ultimate goal in the construction business. Since it is an economic reality in which contractors operate, profit may be the ultimate measure of success and competence.

Procurement practices. In this country the most common procurement method of slurry wall construction is competitive bidding. It is used almost exclusively by public agencies as well as by the private industry with a minor modification: while in a public bid the low bidder is awarded the contract, in private negotiations the process continues after the first bid and may even result in lower prices. While on the surface this approach seems fair and realistic, some contractors appear to question its advantage. These objections relate to possible failure to distinguish company reputation, history, and record, particularly past performance and technical competence. Although prequalification criteria or bid and performance bonds are intended to protect the owner from these shortcomings, many point to the fact that the construction industry is fraught with companies that were able to get a contract when in reality they could not perform.

A further comment is that the competitive bid format may deprive a public owner of the opportunity to realize the input of a specialized contractor during the design phase. Whereas we should not suggest abandoning the practice of competitive bidding, engineers should be cautious to recognize the need and usefulness of redefining the scope of work in the design phase by including as much construction input as possible.

Cost data. Generalization of cost data may be dangerous as well as misleading because of the many variables affecting cost. Thus cost figures and unit prices can provide only an index of how well slurry walls fit within the scope of underground construction.

An example of unit prices and costs for various wall depths and soil conditions is given in Table 11-1, referring to the 1979–1980 construction period. These can be used for comparison only and may be extrapolated to the current price system by adjustments to reflect inflation and the demand for underground construction.

Interestingly, on the Red Line Extension, 1980 unit price bids by successful contractors were as follows:
Harvard Square:

$$\text{Overburden} = \$50/\text{ft}^2 \ (54,000 \ \text{ft}^2)$$

$$\text{Rock} = \$150/\text{ft}^2 \ (2500 \ \text{ft}^2)$$

Davis Square:

$$\text{Overburden} = \$25/\text{ft}^2 \ (82,000 \ \text{ft}^2)$$

$$\text{Rock} = \$150/\text{ft}^2 \ (4000 \ \text{ft}^2)$$

A probable breakdown of this cost is as follows:

$$\text{Labor cost} = 20 \text{ percent}$$

$$\text{Material cost} = 35 \text{ percent}$$

$$\text{Equipment cost} = 45 \text{ percent}$$

11-2 Legal Considerations

Among the many legal aspects of slurry wall construction influencing the preparation of plans and contract documents are unique problems not usually encountered in other forms of construction work. Among the typical problems are:

- Bonding of all contractors and subcontractors, formulated by a bid and performance bond.

- Breach of contract vs. administrative remedies, related to the fact that there is an implied obligation on each party to a contract to do nothing to hinder or prevent performance by the other party.

- Various contract adjustment clauses, arising out of the determination that one party experiences costs exceeding revenues because of some action or inaction of the other party.

TABLE 11-1 Example of Unit Prices and Costs for Walls of Various Depths

	Slurry trench prices in 1979 dollars			Unreinforced slurry wall prices in 1979 dollars		
	Depth ≤30 ft	Depth 30–75 ft	Depth 75–120 ft	Depth ≤60 ft	Depth 60–150 ft	Depth >150 ft
Soft to medium soil, $N \leq 40$	2–4	4–8	8–10	15–20	20–30	30–75
Hard soil, N 40–200	4–7	5–10	10–20	25–30	30–40	40–95
Occasional boulders	4–8	5–8	8–25	20–30	30–40	40–85
Soft to medium rock, $N \geq 200$ sandstone, shale	6–12	10–20	20–50	50–60	60–85	85–175
Boulder strata	15–25	15–25	50–80	30–40	40–95	95–210
Hard rock, granite, gneiss, schist*	—	—	—	95–140	140–175	175–235

*Nominal penetration only.
For standard reinforcement in slurry walls add $8 per square foot. For construction in urban environment add 25 to 50 percent of price.

- Changed conditions article, the purpose of which is to prevent bidders from adding high-contingency factors as protection against unusual conditions during the work.

- Suspension of work article, probably found mostly in government contracts, with the intent to limit relief by excluding the application of other articles in the event construction is stopped.

- Variation in quantities article, usually found in unit-price-type contracts where the owner makes an estimate of quantities and the contractor bids a set of unit prices that collectively make up the total contract bid.

- Termination for default article, related to causes within the control of the contractor.

- Inspection and acceptance article, intended to rectify a difference of opinion as to whether some segments or components of the work comply with the plans and specifications.

- Escalation of labor and materials article that covers occasions where problems associated with an untested and unstable construction market must be recognized in a specified manner in order to make bids more competitive.

These considerations are covered in many legal documents and are beyond the scope of this text. Hence this brief review focuses on topics associated with slurry wall construction.

The principal problem is the design responsibility. The slurry wall serves the two distinct functions, first as the temporary ground support and then as an integral part of the permanent structure. Both the engineer and the contractor may contribute to the design or to modifications therefrom. Questions of legal responsibility for adequacy of design to fulfill both temporary and permanent wall functions will largely depend upon obligations assumed in the contract documents and the degree to which each party participates in the design process. Interestingly, however, the subject must be dealt with in a close territory. Initially, there is a general design and detailed specification which encompasses and overlaps a second specification that addresses limited results. Temporary support of the walls during excavation requires a performance criterion, and this responsibility is placed with the contractor. This covers the structural capacity of the wall but extends also to serviceability criteria such as ground movement and associated effects. If there is a general contractor who can select a slurry wall subcontractor, and the contracts stipulate that the design of the subcontractor is subject to approval by the engineer, then it may be argued that the general contractor has the right to rely on this approval as a matter of proper authority.

If the slurry wall contract is directly with the owner-engineer, the responsibility for the design and performance of the temporary support is directly administered through a proper contractual specification. This arrangement may also have intricate implications, so that the details should be addressed carefully and with explicit understanding of what approval means and who guarantees the work.

For the permanent phase, the slurry wall is integrated in the overall structure which is designed by the engineer. The wall may serve as a foundation element or as perimeter wall of the basement portion of the building. The general opinion is that structural failure or inability of the wall to satisfy serviceability criteria should be the responsibility of the engineer. There is an area of uncertainty, however, during the transition of the wall from the temporary to the permanent stage as the temporary bracing is removed and eventually replaced by the permanent structure. In this case ultimate liability may be dispersed in many ways and to many parties, and unless the contracts contain explicit stipulations the result may be serious legal complications.

A matter closely related to the question of design responsibility is the constructibility of the project. For example, subsurface conditions substantially different from those assumed in the design may result in extra costs or, at the extreme case, preclude the construction as a whole. In addition, slurry wall construction may have adverse effects on adjacent structures and buildings that may have to be supported or protected. The contracts should thus stipulate the associated responsibilities and explicitly define the varying levels of liability among the contractor, the owner, and the engineer.

When slurry walls are constructed along streets and public right-of-way, they may interfere with existing utilities. This raises the further issue as to respective rights and responsibilities of owner, contractor, and the utility companies for the protection and maintenance of all utility lines and services.

Technology, Preparation, and Control of Slurries

Control limits

Since the 1979 edition (*Slurry Walls*), the technology, preparation, and control of slurries in diaphragm wall construction has not changed, although several polymer stabilizers and alternate materials have appeared in local and foreign markets. Among the latter, the introduction of synthetic biodegradable polymers may remedy the problems associated with used slurry disposal in an environmentally satisfactory manner. In fact, in large projects the partial or total substitution of bentonite by these materials is becoming common practice, particularly in certain European countries. In technical terms, the common characteristics between a bentonite slurry and a synthetic biopolymer slurry is their ability to gel and form a filter cake. However, a polymer-based slurry may have a different thixotropic behavior, and thus a comparison between the two materials is mandatory and should be made under competent technical advice.

Thus the main problems associated with the application of slurries in structural diaphragm walls are: (1) deeper structural excavations where the cost of slurries represents an important cost component; (2) interrelated effect regarding temperature, pressure, stability requirements, and displacement by concrete; (3) additional phases, such as mud treatment and disposal; and (4) the effect of slurry on the appearance and strength of the finished structure. Accordingly, slurry systems continue to receive broad attention, and specifications for the preparation and control of slurries are normally drafted by geotechnical and structural engineers.

Xanthakos (1979) gives a review of the fundamentals of clay colloidal systems, proportion of slurries, materials used in slurries, and function of slurries. The associated control limits apply to face support during trenching, sealing process and slurry loss, suspension of excavated materials, displacement by concrete, separation of noncolloid fraction, and pumpability of slurries.

Control limits based on the foregoing functions and requirements are summarized in Table A-1. These are quite general, but the range can be further articulated or refined where the scope of the work is known more specifically. Some questions still remain whether and when the apparent viscosity, Marsh cone viscosity, plastic viscosity, yield strength, and 10-min gel strength are always relevant and must be specified in slurry controls.

The following comments are useful.

1. Reference to the flow curve of slurries shows that the apparent viscosity depends on the rate of shear of the measuring system. Plastic viscosity measures resistance to flow for ideal slurries or for slurries of very low initial shear strength. For the usual conditions the plastic viscosity must be combined with the 10-min gel strength to describe the flow behavior.

2. Although Marsh cone tests do not provide absolute viscosity measurements, they furnish useful data for routine site work. They are therefore simple and practical in relating the slurry properties to the soil conditions on a comparable basis.

3. The Bingham yield stress is important for the study of the flow curve and useful for a theoretical analysis of colloidal behavior. However, in practice it is seldom necessary to estimate this stress, and furthermore its correlation to the initial or 10-min gel strength is impractical.

Field controls and treatment

The field testing and controls specified in the 1979 edition (Xanthakos, 1979) reflected the FPS (1973) specifications. This program continues to represent a reasonable balance in the field requirements, and hence is still recommended.

Thus tests must be carried out before, during, and after certain operations. A routine procedure includes density (specific gravity), viscosity, filter-press, sand-content, and pH measurements. The slurry sample as well as the sampling point must be consistent with the purpose of the test and relate to the phase for which the property measurement is necessary. Thus sampling points are rotated to in-

TABLE A-1 Control Limits for the Properties of Slurries*

Function	Average bentonite concentration,† %	Density, lb/ft³	sp gr	Plastic viscosity, cP	Marsh cone viscosity	10-min gel strength (Fann), lb/100 ft²	pH	Sand content, %
					Property			
Face support	>3–4	>64.3	>1.03	.....	Limits established by soil type	‡	.....	>1§
Sealing process	>3–4	.....	.....	.....			.....	1
Suspension of detritus	>3–4	.....	.....	.....		>12–15		
Displacement by concrete	<15	<78	<1.25	<20			<12	<25
Separation of noncolloids	.....	.....	.....	.....		......	.....	<30
Physical cleaning	<15	<78	<1.25	.....			.....	<25
Pumping of slurry	.....	.....	.....	.....		Variable		
Limits	>3–4	>64.3	>1.03	<20		>12–15	<12	>1
	<15	<78	<1.25	.....				<25

*Controls are not considered necessary for apparent viscosity and yield stress. Whereas fluid loss commonly is judged by standard filtration test and a maximum film thickness of 2 mm, better control limits are established by stagnation-gradient tests.
†Should be expected to vary widely because of different bentonite brands.
‡The shear strength filter cake is more applicable to peel-off control (also the time required for its-formation).
§Optional.

clude the mixer, the trench, and the mud-treatment plant. A routine testing program includes the following:

1. After the slurry is fully mixed, measure the specific gravity, funnel viscosity, and filtration. Before use measure the 10-min gel strength.

2. As a daily routine check the specific gravity, funnel viscosity, and filtration.

3. Before concrete placement check the specific gravity, plastic viscosity, and pH.

4. Repeat the measurements listed in step 3 at the end of a pour (slurry in storage tanks).

5. Check the specific gravity, funnel viscosity, and filtration during excavation.

6. After a slurry is reconditioned for reuse, repeat the measurements listed in step 1.

7. Check the slurry upon the occurrence of certain events (rainfall, contamination with materials from the ground, trench left open for a long time, etc.).

During trenching bentonite slurries change color and overall appearance. They generally become denser and lose some of the thixotropic characteristics. Clay from natural formations usually raises the viscosity and may result in high gel strength. Sand causes viscosity humps and can give rise to low gels. Groundwater enters the slurry and lowers viscosity and gel strength.

Waste materials and sewage can adversely affect the flow properties if they are absorbed in large quantities. This problem becomes more severe if the slurry is prepared with treated (peptized) bentonite. There have been instances where the pressure of sewage resulted in complete loss of colloidal stability and caused trench collapse.

Recently, several alternate materials other than sodium bentonite have been tested to determine whether they may be suitable for containment structures but are not adversely affected by waste chemicals. These consisted of calcium bentonites from several sources (United States, Germany, and Greece) that received pretreatment with sodium carbonate. Different blends of cement, slag, and fly ash were used for preparing cement-bentonite mixes. The results show that calcium bentonite-cement-slag mixes provide more stable chemical barriers. In some instances, some types of fly ashes may replace part of the cement to yield less permeable mixes at greater cost savings. These findings have applications in soil-cement mixes used as cutoff walls.

TABLE A-2 Summary of Slurry Problems and Treatment

Problem	Control and treatment
To increase viscosity and gel in fresh water	Add bentonite, CMC, or both
To reduce viscosity and gel when slurry has adequate colloid material	Add water slowly or treat with thinners
To reduce viscosity and gel due to high noncolloid solid content	If solids are not completely dispersed, use mechanical separation; add water slowly and thinners
To reduce viscosity and gel when dilution is inadvisable because of inadequate colloid material or weight reduction	Add thinners; if viscosity drops appreciably and overtreatment occurs, adjust using CMC
To increase viscosity and gel due to high noncolloid solid content (sand)	Remove solids by mechanical separation; add bentonite or CMC
To decrease density	Recirculate fluid to remove solids by mechanical separation or by allowing them to settle; do not add water, but adjust flow properties if required after the density is decreased
To reduce filtration rate and thickness, i.e., reduce fluid loss	Add bentonite and CMC; if viscosity becomes too high, treat with FCL or other thinners
To handle large volumes of entrained sand and cuttings	Use mechanical dispersion; avoid adding water and chemicals
Salt flocculation from contamination by seawater	Add FCL but keep close control of slurry
Salt flocculation in offshore drilling and excavation in salt formations	Stabilize solution through the protective action of CMC or use thinners
Trench excavation in sand and gravel (sand will increase density, decrease viscosity, and aggravate tendency toward lost circulation)	Provide adequate initial gel strength to keep sand in suspension; build good filter cake and film to keep fluid loss low; use higher bentonite concentrations and add CMC
Trench excavation in clay	Keep viscosity and gel low; use thinnest suspension colloidally stable; use thinners
Trench excavation in shale	Reduce filtration rate to prevent hydrous disintegration or sloughing formation; add bentonite and CMC; monitor slurry level to control sudden loss of fluid
Excavation in erratic formations	Base selection of slurry on most critical formation; make periodic adjustments
Lost circulation	Use lost-circulation materials; maintain minimum safe slurry weight
Contamination with cement	Add FCL or other thinning agents; if restoration is not achieved, reject slurry; use pretreated bentonites
Contamination with organic matter and sewage	Avoid peptized brands; use natural bentonite and monitor slurry closely

Effect of cement.   Contamination of slurries with cement from fresh concrete is a typical problem in diaphragm wall construction. It occurs when calcium ions are exchanged for sodium ions. The result is a thick, permeable filter cake with subsequent high slurry loss. Calcium may also come from soil deposits such as gypsum, but the common source is the cement in the concrete.

Contamination effects are absent with certain polymer stabilizers. For example, in Japan the problem of contamination by cement has been remedied by the use of materials such as Telmarch (Xanthakos, 1979), which remains insensitive and free from change when admixed with cement.

Effect of salt.   Likewise, if a fresh-water-based slurry encounters sea-water or pore water containing NaCl, it will retain an amount of salt

TABLE A-3   Common Slurry Materials and Additives

Weight materials	Barite (barium sulfate) or soil (sand)
Colloid materials	Bentonite (Wyoming, Fulbent, Aquagel, Algerian, Japanese, etc.), basic fresh-water slurry constituent
	Attapulgite, for saltwater slurries
	Organic polymers and pretreated brands
Thinners and dispersing agents	Quebracho, organic dispersant mixture (tannin)
	Lignite, mineral lignin
	Sodium tetraphosphate
	Sodium humate (sodium humic acid)
	Ferrochrome lignosulfonate (FCL)
	Nitrophemin acid chloride
	Calcium lignosulfonate
	Reacted caustic, tannin (dry)
	Reacted caustic, lignite (dry)
	Sodium acid pyrophosphate
	Sodium hexametaphosphate
Intermediate-sized particles	Clay, silt, and sand
Flocculants and polyelectrolytes	Sodium carboxymethyl cellulose (CMC)
	Salts
	Starches
	Potassium aluminate
	Aluminum chloride
	Calcium
Fluid-loss-control agents	CMC or other flocculants
	Pregelatinized starch
	Sand in small proportions
Lost-circulation materials	Graded fibrous or flake materials; shredded cellophane flakes, shredded tree bark, plant fibers, glass, rayon, graded mica, ground walnut shells, rubber tires, perlite, time-setting cement, and many others

but at a lower ratio than in the original liquid. The result is (1) a decrease in viscosity and gel; (2) a sharp increase in viscosity and gel because of flocculation effects; and (3) a succession of both in that order. The usual salt effect, however, is tendency toward flocculation, and in some instances complete gelation.

Common problems and treatment. Most common problems arise in coastal areas, in soils contaminated with organics, and in excavation in erratic formations where the slurry requirements are conflicting. Tables A-2 and A-3 present a summary of these problems, suggesting also a practical treatment.

B

Specifications

Objectives and general principles

Specifications for construction under the slurry process usually must provide guidelines and data for (1) the design of the project, if the agreement is based on performance type of documents or it includes the clause of value engineering; and (2) the materials to be used, including testing and quality control programs. In addition, there must be instructions pertinent to the workmanship and the details of construction. Finally, the contents must reflect the possibility of field changes in the event of unforeseen conditions.

Most engineers insist that specifications for diaphragm wall construction should be a technical document. Contentious items occurring in specifications often are found to combine a technical matter with a condition of contract, and those opposing this combination suggest that is is far more advantageous to clearly separate the two matters and treat them in separate documents.

Specifications that are too broad and general or too extensive are likely to be ignored or waived. Likewise, obscure statements will create problems instead of solving them.

Several specifications published in the 1970s have been used as models for articulating the design and construction of diaphragm walls and related elements. Among those to be mentioned is the document prepared in Austria, England, and Japan.

Cast-in-place diaphragm walls

Design. If there is a design-construction contractural agreement, the guidelines should result in the same total safety factor for structural stability during and after construction irrespective of bid prices or alternate methods of construction.

The design criteria should articulate loads and load effects, stresses and load factors, safety factors and performance coefficients, and methods of analysis and design. Serviceability criteria should address lateral movement and settlement, the need for underpinning, and ground strengthening for global stability.

Consideration should be given to structural compatibility in order to produce uniformity in the manner in which the wall resists and transfers the loads, such as structural connections, panel length, wall thickness, and bracing systems in the temporary and permanent condition.

Materials. Although the applicable code of practice generally will cover this item, certain provisions must be stipulated because of the special requirements. Thus the specifications must cover maximum aggregate size, water-cement ratio, minimum concrete slump, and retarders such as air entraining to delay initial setting.

Reinforcement details should include splice lengths, bar spacing, spacer blocks, concrete cover, and details for reinforcement assemblies.

Suitable provisions should cover the type of bentonite, synthetic colloids, slurry control agents, slurry properties, tests, and adjustments.

Construction. Relevant considerations should address the excavation phase, stability requirements, guide walls, steps to avoid damage to panels already cast, construction tolerances (deviations from verticality and true horizontal alignments), bottom cleaning, handling of excavated materials, and compliance with environmental regulations, traffic maintenance, etc.

Tolerance. The usual minimum specified tolerance at the ends of panels is $1:100$. Additionally, a tolerance of 7.5 cm (3 in) is allowed for protrusions resulting from irregularities in the ground and beyond the general wall face. The specified vertical tolerance of $1:100$ may be increased to $1:80$ or reduced to $1:200$ or even less where necessary, and in this case it must be considered in relation to the wall thickness. Likewise, the 3-in tolerance normally will apply to homogeneous clays, and can be increased in sands, gravels, or loose and unstable ground. Appropriate tolerances must also be established for reinforcing steel bars.

Concrete placement. The specifications should address the method of concrete placement, size and number of tremie pipes, and routine guidelines to ensure the continuous and complete pouring until the panel is cast while the fresh mix remains workable and flowable. In general, provisions that pertain to concrete placement are intended to ensure upward flow of the fresh mix, prevent reentry of bentonite in the pipe, and confine contact between concrete and bentonite to the interface only.

Workmanship. Special care must be exercised in executing construction joints, and the construction should be completed to the end result that the wall is watertight (there may be a difference of opinion as to what constitutes a watertight wall: in many instances moisture may be permitted to ooze out slowly in small drops through fine pores or emerge like stains, and this can be used as a basis to define a watertight wall).

Cast-in-place bored pile walls

Bored pile walls may be formed with various configurations of piles, such as secant, contiguous, or intermittent, or used in conjunction with lagging.

The minimum clear spacing between vertical bars may be reduced to 4 in (10 cm). This is appropriate in view of the smaller confinement of the lateral flow but also serves the practical purpose of locating the main steel on one side of the wall. The minimum pile diameter should not be less than 24 in (60 cm).

Where bored pile walls must carry vertical loads, the method of load transfer must be clearly stated. Likewise, consideration should be given to anticipated ground movement and settlement resulting from construction operations and at service loads.

Special care will be necessary in lowering the reinforcing cage to prevent its disorientation, especially with small hole diameters and where the main steel is located on one side only. The method of excavation should be identified at the time of offer submission (in lieu of guide walls it may be necessary to use a protective collar near the top of the hole to prevent surface sloughing and to guide the equipment).

As in linear walls, the casting of any pile should be completed in such a manner and within such a time that the fresh mix remains flowable and workable until the entire pour is made. In determining the vertical tolerance, the interlocking of secant piles should be maintained throughout their length, and adjoining piles should not be allowed to become unlapped. A minimum overlapping should be set at 4 in (10 cm).

Load-bearing elements

Specifications for load-bearing elements may be based on items covering diaphragm walls and bored piles. In addition, provisions should be made to identify the method of load transfer and to establish procedures for load tests where these are indicated.

Where panel load tests are contemplated the specifications should include provisions for the loading system; procedures for load application, sequence, and duration; observations to be made and measurements to be taken; results to be achieved; and records to be kept. As part of a load testing program the operation may also include field instrumentation in proximity to the test panel to allow observation of effects caused by the construction and the load application.

Special wall systems

Prefabricated walls.   Specifications for precast panels normally should cover general items, materials, quality control programs, acceptance tests for special conditions, and guidelines for transportation and erection.

Special emphasis should be placed on the grout system. The choice of a single or displacement grout may be dictated by technical considerations, or it may be based on a series of tests carried out after the details and construction procedures are established. An item of particular importance is the development of grout strength with time, and this should be fully covered in the provisions.

Posttensioned diaphragm walls.   For design-construction contracts, the specifications should cover methods of analysis and design, but equally important are stipulations for construction procedures and the installation of posttensioning cages supporting the ducts.

Where the mobilization of partial passive resistance is expected to accompany the application of prestress with the panels buried in the ground, it may be necessary to introduce the posttensioning in stages in order to check the soil response and thus confirm the validity of design assumptions.

Index

Access shafts, 778
Active state, 264, 270, 271
Active wedge, 264
Adhesion factor, 335, 385
Admixtures, 79
Aggregate in concrete, grading of, 79
Air entraining, 437
Air lift, 97, 99
Akasaka subway station, Tokyo, 655
Allowable stress design, 326, 328, 329, 398
Angle of friction between wall and soil, 121, 272, 385
Angle of shear resistance, 124, 779
Anisotropy, 250
Apparent pressures, 245, 273, 276
Apparent viscocity, 836
Arched roof, 667, 673–678
Arched structures (walls):
    stability of, 800–803
    structured capacity, 803
    types, 49
Arching:
    effect on lateral loads, 274
    effect on trench stability, 135, 141

Barrettes, 116, 403, 404
BART (Bay Area Rapid Transit) San Francisco, 225, 650
Base bearing:
    estimation of, 373, 385, 386–387, 388, 389, 392, 395
    as function of allowable settlement, 385
    as function of vertical displacement, 368, 371, 392, 393, 395
Basements, deep, in buildings:
    assessment, 715, 756
    bracing, 10

Basements, deep, in buildings (*Cont.*):
    completion time, 723
    cost of expected use, 715
    dynamic effects, 741, 745, 752–754, 756–759
    function as supports, 716
    interaction with superstructure, 717
    loads and load groups, 751–755
    plan area and shape, 722
    requirements during construction, 10, 732–735
    underground parking, 711
    wall embedment, 726
Beam on elastic foundation, 736
Bearing capacity factor, 131, 147, 389, 401
Bearing capacity failure, 389
Bearing elements, load:
    advantages and disadvantages, 367
    bottom cleanliness, 365
    circular, 361
    deflection and repairs, 366
    design for axial load, 387
    diaphragm wall-panels, 381, 401
    effective perimeter, 372
    preparation of base, 364
    prismatic and linear, 363
    selection of, 384, 386
Benchmarks, 171
Bentonite, 1, 3, 20
Bentonite cake (*see* Filter cake)
Berms, earth (*see* bracing with)
Bingham yield stress, 836
Bloomsbury Square parking garage, London, 772
Bond strength, 459, 460, 461
Bond stress, 459, 464
Bored pile walls, 28, 652
    advantages and limitation, 31, 722
    classification of, 29, 30, 33

Bored pile walls (*Cont.*):
  construction and installation, 29, 30
  design of, 576–592
Boulders:
  effect on excavation, 84, 109
  method of removal, 84, 85, 110
Bourse station utility tunnel, Brussels,
    Belgium, 766
Brace stiffness, effect of, 209, 211
Bracing:
  center-core, 728, 729
  combined, 213, 236–244, 728
  counterforts, 729
  cross walls, 202, 221
  deep basements, 228, 727–729
  elastic shortening of, 211
  embedment, 215, 222, 248, 291, 324,
    349
  ground anchors, 215–217, 229–234,
    249, 300, 727
  long narrow cuts, 202, 205, 210, 221
  permanent floors with, 214, 222, 226,
    228, 291, 729
  rakers, 212, 728
  slopes and berms, 212, 248, 728
  struts, 204, 209, 224, 225–226, 293,
    296, 298
Bracing sequence, 201
Brackets, 514
Bridges, 402, 403, 404, 409, 412
Bristol Harbor, England, 404
Brittania House, London, 237
Brussels Metro, Belgium, 684
Bucket excavators, 85, 87
Buckling, load bearing elements, 388
Buildings, 404
Built-up walls, 596, 613
Buttressed walls (*see* T-shaped walls)
BW System, 94

Cadweld splices, 503
Caliper logging, 367
Cantilevered walls, 16, 234–236, 349,
    551, 808
Casing of holes, 361
Cement, 79
Center posts, 678–682
Central YMCA, London, 236
Chelsea Town Hall, Kensington, London,
    400
Chisels, 109, 110
Churchill Subway Station, Edmonton,
    Canada, 652

Circular cuts, 162
Circular drills, 105
Circular enclosures:
  construction of, 772, 775, 820
  polygonal shapes, 777
  stability of, 780, 784–790
Circular slides, 160
Civic Center Station, BART, San
    Francisco, 651
Clamshells:
  cable-suspended, 87, 88–90
  excavation with pilot holes, 112
  excavation rates, 88
  hydraulicly operated, 90
  power-operated, 89
Coefficient:
  of active earth stress (*see* Earth stress
    coefficient)
  of earth stress at rest (*see* Earth stress
    coefficient)
  of fluid concrete pressure (*see* Earth
    stress coefficient)
  of horizontal subgrade reaction (*see*
    Modulus of subgrade reaction)
  of passive earth stress (*see* Earth
    stress coefficient)
Cohesion, 124, 348
Collapsible soils, 254
Compacting factor test, 436
Compensated foundations, 718, 729–732
Composite sections, 596–597, 613
Composite walls:
  bored piles and concrete panels, 38,
    570
  examples of, 35, 36, 37
  soldier piles and plain concrete, 36
  soldier piles and reinforced concrete,
    35
  steel-and-concrete panels, 35, 570, 571
Compression:
  load bearing elements, 387
  resistance factors, 333
Concrete:
  aggregate of, 435, 436
  cement quantity, 436, 437
  compression tests on, 438
  compressive strength, 436, 438, 450–
    459, 539, 554, 561
  contaminated, 442, 443
  defective, 366, 434, 442
  elasticity of, 439
  flow motion of, 444–450
  hydrostatic thrust of, 443

Concrete (*Cont.*):
  intermixing with bentonite, 434, 449, 450
  modulus of rupture, 439
  placement of fresh, 4, 365, 433, 441–443
  plug motion of, 449
  proportioning of mixes, 433, 434
  setting time of fresh, 437, 450
  shear strength, 440
  tensile strength, 439
  ultimate strength of, 451, 468, 470
  water-cement ratio of, 436, 438, 450
  workability of, 435
  working stress of, 459
Connections, structural:
  column-foundation, 622
  moment transfer, 485, 487, 489, 502
  shear transfer, 53, 483
  tension transfer, 485
  vertical loads, 483
  (*See also* Joints, vertical construction)
Connections, structural capacity of:
  beam-to-wall, 501
  deck plate, 511
  moment, 502
  requirements, 495
  transfer of shear, 497
  wall-to-slab, 497–500, 513
Consolidation, 123
Construction at crossings, 639
Construction from a lower level, 637
Construction sequence, 1, 9, 69, 101, 114
Control limits of slurries, 835
Cost factors, 827–831
Coulis, 20, 25
Couplers, 502, 504
Crack control, 470, 571
Creep, 440, 503
Cross walls, 202
CWS Joint, 91, 482
Cyclones, 97, 101
Cylindrical method, 160, 257

Dams, 808
Deep beams, 572–576
Deep filtration, 179
Deep foundations, 719
Deep shafts:
  advantages, 777
  design considerations, 778–784
  polygonal configurations, 780

Deep shafts (*Cont.*):
  structural action, 780–784
  uses, 777–778
Deflection, 471
Density of slurries, 837
Desanding, 87, 101
Design methodologies, 324–329, 694–696
Detailing, 6
Development of bars (*see* Reinforcing steel)
Dewatering, 68, 69, 638
Dikes, 808, 810
Direct circulation, 94, 109
Docks (*see* Waterfront installations)
Dowels (*see* Reinforcing steel)
Downdrag, 330, 407
Downward construction method, 759–762
Ductility, 469, 744, 745, 747

Earth pressure cells, 174
Earth stress coefficient:
  active, 142, 270, 346
  passive, 270, 325
  at rest, 122, 134, 263, 265, 288, 346
Earth stresses lateral:
  active, 264, 270, 271
  factors affecting, 119
  as function of strains, 274, 277
  observed, 276, 291–303
  passive, 264, 270, 271
  predicted by refined analyses, 272, 274, 313
  recommended, 278, 279, 288, 324
  at rest, 263, 288, 778
Earthquakes, 730, 741–747, 750–751, 752
Effective overburden stress, 196, 719
Effective stress analysis, 326, 390
Elastic shortening:
  of bracing, 211
  of posttensioned walls, 548
Elastic theory, method of analysis, 265, 321, 469, 525, 562, 571
Elliptical enclosures, 774
Embarcadero Station, BART, San Francisco, 225
Embedment of wall, 205, 324, 613, 726, 798, 823
Equivalent beam method, 283
Equivalent tie support (method of), 288–291
Eurotunnel, English Channel, 790
Excavating equipment, 5, 85, 94, 103
Excavation in hard ground, boulders, 109

Excavation rates, 100, 103
Excavations, 195, 207
Extensometers:
    multipoint, 169, 170
    tapes, 170

Factor of safety, 262, 329, 398, 400, 414
    (*See also* Safety index)
Factored loads, 327
    (*See also* Load factor design)
Factored resistance, 327
    (*See also* Load factor design)
Failure surface of shafts, 409
Fatigue, 470
Filter cake, 175, 177, 178, 187
Filtration, 176, 178
Finite element analysis, 265, 272, 303,
    739
Fixed-earth support, method of, 280
Fixed-head bored piles, 580, 584
Flat plates, 523
Flexural stiffness (*see* Flexure)
Flexural stress (*see* Flexure)
Flexure:
    assumptions, 469
    balanced failure, 469, 471
    compression failure, 469
    equilibrium analysis, 471, 555, 556
    flexural behavior, 470
    resistance factors, 332
Flow curve of slurries, 836
Flow properties of slurries, 836–841
Folded plate roof, 667, 673–678
Free-earth support, method of, 285
Free-head bored piles, 581, 585
Friction angle, 123, 127, 137, 141, 150,
    263, 335, 346, 779

Gages:
    crack, 172
    for heave measurements, 170
    strain, 172
    for subsurface settlement, 169
    trench width, 171
Gel strength of slurry, effect of, 154, 158
Gravity-type walls, 792, 808
Ground anchor loads:
    distribution, 300
    effect of prestressing, 311
    effect of rigidity, 315
    single-tie response, 314–316
Ground anchors, 5
    (*See also* Walls, Anchored)

Groundwater, 63, 69, 120, 138, 145, 196,
    687
    lowering, 138
    protection of excavation from, 63, 724
Grout systems:
    cement-bentonite, 21
    displacement grout, 20
    single grout, 19
    (*See also* Coulis)
Grouting, 367, 542
Guide walls, 72, 73, 74
Guildhall Precincts Development,
    London, 229

Harrow-on-the Hill reservoir, England,
    48
Heat bents, 507
Heathrow Central Station, London, 649
Heave, base, 201, 204, 206, 730
Humber suspension bridge, England, 813
Hydraulic gradient, critical, 184
Hydrofraise system, 112–116
Hydrostatic thrust:
    of fresh concrete, 443
    of slurry, 126, 136
Hysteresis effects, 719

Ice load (forces), 794–795
Impact, 688
Inclinometers, 167–169
Industrial installations, 774–778
Integral structures, 690
Interaction diagrams, 562, 564, 570, 588
Interlocking elements, 56
Interlocking enclosures, 775
Irlams O' Th' Height underpass,
    Manchester, England, 16

Joint defects, 490
Joint, tests on:
    axial tension, 492–494
    shear transfer, 494
    vertical load, transfer of, 491
Joints, structural capacity of (*See also*
    Connections, Structural capacity of)
Joints, vertical construction:
    CWS joint, 91, 482
    Franki joint, 488
    I-beam joint, 480
    Locking box, 488
    modified round tube joint, 480
    requirements, 478
    round tube (interlocking pipe), 479

Joints, vertical construction (*Cont.*):
  RPT joint, 480
  Steel-plate-and-casing, 487
  TEBA joint, 483
  TECA joint, 483
  Watertight, 517
  (*See also* Connections, structural;
    Connections, structural capacity
    of)
Joints, wall-roof, 640

Kelly bar, 90
Keybridge House, London, 232
Kire Station, Osaka, Japan, 658
Kranz, method of analysis, 257

Laminar tilting, 51, 480
Lateral earth stresses (*see* Earth
  stresses, lateral)
Lateral loads:
  design for, 415–418
  deflection under, 579–586
Leakage (*see* Concrete, defective)
Legal considerations, 831–834
Limit theory, 326, 331, 337, 385
  code provisions, 332
  definitions, 326
  extreme event limit state, 331
  serviceability limit states, 327, 337,
    340, 373
  ultimate limit states, 327, 337, 373
Load, plunging, 385
Load, ultimate (failure), 384, 385
Load and resistance factor design
  (LRFD), 327
Load bearing elements, linear and
  prismatic, 363, 419
Load-distribution curves, 377, 385
Load factors, 327, 331, 374
Load-settlement curves, 378, 382
Load tests:
  on bored piles, 367, 376, 386
  on diaphragm wall panels, 381, 383,
    400
  load bearing elements, 367, 386
Load transfer curves, 378, 382, 386
Loads, nominal, 327
  dead, 322, 330, 688
  transient, 320, 330, 688
Loads, variability of, 331
Lower level, construction from, 637, 638,
  647

Maine-Montparnasse Tower, Paris, 404
Marsh cone, 836
Marsh cone viscosity, 836
Mat foundations, 626, 627
Mersey River underpass, Liverpool,
  England, 778
Mixing facilities, 71, 97
Modulus of subgrade reaction, 546, 736,
  737–738, 813
Mohr's circles, 263, 348
Moment releasing joints, 669
Movement, ground and wall:
  anchored walls, 10, 229–234, 249–250
  bracing with permanent floors, 222,
    228
  cantilevered walls, 234
  with combined bracing, 236–244
  control of, 217, 245–250
  detrimental, 218, 615
  due to excavation, 219–220
  finite-element analysis method of
    predicting, 272
  heave in narrow excavations, 201, 204,
    206
  observed with diaphragm walls, 220,
    221–226, 227–234
  prediction of, 217
  procedure for reducing, 244–250
  slurry trenches, 128, 136
  tolerable, 375, 615
  walls braced before excavation, 221
Moving loads, effect on trench stability,
  156
Multilevel sections, 635, 646

Neasden underpass, London, 229
Needle beams, 687
Negative skin friction, 405
Neutral plane, 407
New Palace Yard car park, London, 226–
  227
New York City Subway, 524
Noise, effect of, 630
Northumberland Park depot, London,
  648

Observation walls, 173
Optical survey, 166–167
Osaka Metro, Japan, 597–600
Osaka utility tunnel, Japan, 768
Oslo, Norway, tunnels, 131–133

Overconsolidation ratio (OCR), 263, 347, 779
Overturning (*see* Stability)

Panels, wall:
  depth, 6
  length, 4, 5
  sequence and arrangement, 7, 114
  width, 6
Parking, underground, 770–774
Passive state, resistance, 264, 270, 271, 279, 325
Peel-off, 182
Peel-off test, 183
Penetration of soil by slurry (*see* Filtration)
Percussive tools, 86, 87, 110
Performance factors (*see* Resistance factors)
Permeability:
  of concrete, 80
  of soil, 122
Pierre-Benite excavation, France, 139
Plane failure surface, 256
Plant facilities, 71, 114
Plastic analysis (nonlinear), 269, 564, 567
Plastic flow (*see* Creep)
Plastic viscosity, 836, 837
Poisson's ratio, 266, 390, 440
Pore-water pressure, 148, 159, 253
Post Office Square garage, Boston, 423
Posttensioned walls:
  advantages, 12, 553
  analysis, design of, 10, 545–551, 553–560
  construction and installation, 12
  field tests, 12, 17
  multibraced systems, 16
  posttensioning techniques, 14, 542–545
  prestress loss, 548–551
  stability of, 545
  wall types suitable for posttensioning, 551–553
Precast deck panels, 690, 693
Precast (prefabricated) wall uses, 19, 22, 23
  advantages and disadvantages, 27
  bearing capacity of, 418–419
  design of, 561–570
  installation, 20, 25
  waterproofing, 27, 28

Prefabricated elements, 690
Prefounded columns, 619–624
Preloading, 245–248, 288, 311
Prestressing steels:
  tendons, 14
  types, 539–542
  ultimate moment, bonded tendons, 555
  ultimate strength, 554
Probability density functions, 328

Quay walls (*see* Arched structures)

Rectangular stress distribution (block), 471
Redcar ore terminal, England, 53
Reinforcement ratio, 469
Reinforcing steel:
  allowable stress, 440
  assembly of cages, 5, 472, 477
  balanced reinforcement, 469, 471
  bar spacing, 473
  bending bars, 507–509
  boxes and inserts, 473–476
  cover, 473
  corrosion protection, 473
  deformed bars, 460
  development length, dowles, lap length, 467–468
  ductility, 469
  method of detailing, 477
  plain bars, 459
  splices, 467, 476, 503, 504
Reservoirs, 808, 810
Resistance:
  factored, 327, 374
  factors, 327, 332, 333, 336, 374, 393, 554, 555
  nominal, 327, 374
Retarders, 437
Reverse circulation, 86, 94, 97, 105
Reversibility, 182
Rheological blocking, 179
Rigid cutoff walls, 55, 811
Rio De Janeiro subway, Brazil, 600–612
River banks, 810
Rock Quality Designation (RQD), 122
Rock sockets, 395, 422, 425
Romill excavator, 103
Rotary drilling equipment, 86, 87, 94
RRC drill, 105
Rupel tunnel, Belgium, 814

Safety factors (*see* Factor of safety)

Schneebeli method in trench stability,
143, 144

Seaforth dock wall, Liverpool, England,
49, 50

Seal formation (*see* Filtration)

Secant piles, 33, 650, 722

Seismic analysis and design (*see*
Earthquakes)

Separate walls, 597

Service loads (*see* Loads)

Settlement:
control and estimation of, 399
correlation with side and base
resistance, 392, 408
detrimental, 218
due to excavation, 200, 219–220, 730
observed, with diaphragm walls, 223,
224–226
in slurry trenches, 146
tolerable, 385

Shafts (drilled), 361, 367

Shear connectors, 501, 510

Shear friction, 497

Shear in walls:
allowable, 534
critical sections, 532
design for shear, 531
failure modes, 531
lateral loads, 534
punching shear, 531, 532–534

Shear strength, resistance factors, 333

Shear walls, 747

Sheet pile walls, 721, 792

Shrinkage, 440

Single walls, 592–596, 612

Site inspection, 69

Slenderness, 562

Sloughing, 182

Slump of concrete, 435

Slurries, 1, 3, 20, 36, 71, 114, 177, 179,
190, 361, 363

Soil-cement mixes, 58

Soil-cement walls, 56, 711

Soldier piles, with lagging, 65, 637, 641,
646, 647, 720–721

Shaft resistance:
development of, 369, 372
effect of excavation on, 370
estimation of, 373, 385
as function of vertical displacement,
371
ultimate, 388, 389, 391

Southern Pacific Excavation, San
Francisco, 242

Splices (*see* Reinforcing steel)

Stability of ground-wall system:
with ground anchors, 254–256
multianchored walls, 256–263

Stability of trenches:
arching, effect on, 135, 141
circular excavations, 133, 162–165
during concreting, 148, 443
under dynamic loading, 155, 157
effect of construction equipment, 156
effect of panel length, 4, 135
under external concentrated loads, 156
without filter cake, 151
general, 126, 638
impermeable layer at interface, 149,
152–154
under moving loads, 156
unsupported trenches, 123–125

Stage construction, 696, 699

Stagnation gradient, 184–187

Stiffness:
effect on load distribution, 311, 545
effect on wall movement, 311, 545

Stirrups (*see* Reinforcing bars)

Strain, 198, 318, 325, 571

Strain compatibility, 566, 571

Strength analysis (*see* Load factor
design)

Stress-strain relationship of soil, 198,
199

Strip panels, 42, 624–626

Structural capacity of:
bored pile walls, 587–592
joints and connections (*see* Joints,
structural capacity of)
load bearing elements, 387
of T-shaped walls, 800, 825

Strut loads:
distribution, 273, 275
measured, 273, 275

Struts, 209, 211, 273

Subbasements, effect of, 83

Subway Stations, 643–648, 673–682,
699–703

Subways, 632–643

Suction pumps, 94, 97, 99

Surface finish of walls, 76–77

Tanks, also reservoirs, 776

TBW System, 103

Telltales, 171
Temporary decking, 634, 646, 647
Tendons, prestressing (*see* Prestressing
    steels)
Tensile strength, 332
Tension cracks in soil, 125
Thermal forces, 689
Thixotropy, 181
Tiltmeters, 172
Time dependent effects:
    deflections, 549
    movement, 251–253
    strength development, (*see* Creep and
        shrinkage)
Tolerances, of diaphragm walls:
    allowable on verticality, 74, 76, 114
    angular deviations in plan, 76
    control of, 76, 77
    in ground with boulders, 84
    irregularities and protrusions, 76, 77,
        78
    walls terminated below guide walls, 78
Top concrete layer, 77
Traffic, effect on construction, 69, 630,
    682
Traffic maintenance, 70
Traffic underpasses, 660–667, 704–711
    (*See also* Underground motorways)
Tremie pipes, 4, 433, 441, 442, 446
T-shaped walls, 17, 47, 66, 669, 797, 808,
    809, 822
Two-way wall systems, 523–538

Ultimate bearing capacity, 121, 388, 395
Ultimate load (*see* Load, ultimate)
Ultimate strength design (*see* Strength
    design)
Underground motorways:
    with cast-in-place walls, 660
    details, 662
    examples, 665
    with prefabricated panels, 661
    requirements, 660
Underpinning:
    with diaphragm walls, 68, 614–619,
        686
    as lateral protection, 615, 686
Under-the-roof construction method, 632,
    635, 644, 647
Undrained shear strength, 121, 129, 131,
    147, 335, 389
Unreinforced wall panels (*see* Wall
    systems)
Uplift, 63, 67, 406, 408, 708

Utilities, 10, 69, 70, 71, 73, 81–83, 686
Utility tunnels, 765–770

Ventilation, 642
Vertical loads, 67
Vessel collision forces, 785
Vibrating screen, 97, 101

Wall cells:
    cellular cofferdams, 803
    closed, 51
    curved diaphragm cells, 804
    laminar tilting, 807
    open, 54
    marine installations, 808
    stability:
        of cellular cells, 805–807
        of open cells, 807
Wall embedment, 215, 222, 248, 291,
    324, 349
Wall movement (*see* Movement)
Wall panels (*see* Panels)
Wall systems:
    anchored, 8
    arched, 49
    bored-pile, 28
    buttressed, 47
    cantilevered, 16
    circular, 43
    composite, 35, 510
    gravity type,
    guide, 49
    on piers, 39, 41
    polygonal, 43, 45
    posttensioned (*see* Posttensioned walls)
    precast (*see* Precast walls)
    quay, 49
    secant-pile, 33
    sheet pile, 65
    on stilts, 39, 40
    on subpiers, 39, 41
Wall thickness:
    actual, 76, 77
    effective, 7, 77
Water-cement ratio, 79
Waterproofing, 641, 664
Watertightness of diaphragm walls,
    general, 78
    concrete, 79
    construction joints, 80, 81, 517

Watertightness of diaphragm walls
    (*Cont.*):
  effect of curing, 80, 81
  precast panels, 517, 664
Waterfront installations, 47, 791
Watertops, 518
Wave action, 796
Welded splices, 504

Wind loads, 689, 730, 752
Winkler model, 738
Working stress method (*see* Allowable
    stress design)
World Trade Center, New York, 233

Yield strength, of slurries, 836

ABOUT THE AUTHOR

Petros P. Xanthakos heads his own structural engineering consulting business in Virginia. A Ph.D. in civil and structural engineering, Dr. Xanthakos is widely considered a top authority in the technology of underground construction. His professional experience has involved work on hundreds of engineering projects, including bridges, dams, foundations, tunnels, buildings, and retaining walls. An award-winning author, his previous books include the original edition of *Slurry Walls* and *Ground Anchors and Anchored Structures*.